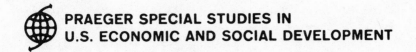

PRAEGER SPECIAL STUDIES IN
U.S. ECONOMIC AND SOCIAL DEVELOPMENT

Community Health Services for New York City

REPORT AND STAFF STUDIES OF THE COMMISSION ON THE DELIVERY OF PERSONAL HEALTH SERVICES

FREDERICK A. PRAEGER, Publishers
New York · Washington · London

The purpose of the Praeger Special Studies is to make specialized research monographs in U.S. and international economics and politics available to the academic, business, and government communities. For further information, write to the Special Projects Division, Frederick A. Praeger, Publishers, 111 Fourth Avenue, New York, N.Y. 10003.

FREDERICK A. PRAEGER, PUBLISHERS
111 Fourth Avenue, New York, N.Y. 10003, U.S.A.
5, Cromwell Place, London S.W.7, England

Published in the United States of America in 1969
by Frederick A. Praeger, Inc., Publishers

© 1969 by New York Foundation, Inc.

Library of Congress Catalog Card Number: 68-29784

Printed in the United States of America

FOREWORD

This volume presents the Report of the Commission on the Delivery of Personal Health Services together with other relevant documents, the major bulk of which is made up of the extensive staff studies prepared at the direction of the Commission.

The organization and work of the Commission, pursuant to its appointment by John V. Lindsay, Mayor of the City of New York, is described in the Appendix to the Commission Report. That Appendix also presents a note on alternative forms of organization and implementation, a statistical portrait of the city health services system and a background paper entitled "The Challenge and the Potential of the Future" contributed by Eveline M. Burns to the deliberations of the Commission.

This volume also presents the Mayor's charge to the Commission set forth in his letter of appointment (see page 80). Appendixes E and F constitute two reports to the Commission prepared by working parties from its Medical Advisory Committee (see pages 663 and 669).

The staff studies were conducted by a team of analysts supplied by TECHNOMICS, Inc., under the direction of Robert B. Parks, executive vice-president of that firm. Dr. Parks was well prepared for this assignment by his prior work on a preliminary study, "System Analysis and Planning for Public Health Care in the City of New York" (March 1966), sponsored by the Health Research Council of the City of New York, and by his work in support of Mayor Lindsay's Advisory Task Force on Medical Economics (February 1966). [See Bibliography.] The studies carried through at the direction of the Commission present a comprehensive picture of the health services systems of the City of New York, with special emphasis on the municipal facilities; they stand as a model of systems analysis applied to problems of health services in a contemporary U.S. metropolis. The studies played, of course, a

NOV 5 '69

HUNT LIBRARY
CARNEGIE-MELLON UNIVERSITY

central role in the work of the Commission; they do not, however, speak for the Commission.

The findings, conclusions, and recommendations of the Commission are set out in its Report entitled "Comprehensive Community Health Services for New York City" released to the public on December 19, 1967. The Report appears as Part One of this book.

The Commission herewith records its thanks to William H. Glazier, its staff director, Dr. Parks and his associates, to Peter Eccles of the firm of Cleary, Gottlieb, Steen & Hamilton for his counsel on matters of law, and to the many consultants, counsellors, public officials and health workers who appeared personally before the Commission or cooperated so generously with the work of its staff. The Commission also records herewith its indebtedness to the philanthropic foundations--The New York Foundation, the Commonwealth Fund, The Fairchild Foundation, Inc., The Grant Foundation, Josiah Macy, Jr., Foundation, Rockefeller Brothers Fund, Alfred P. Sloan Foundation, and Avalon Foundation--whose generous support made the Commission's work possible and secured its independence.

Gerard Piel
Chairman

ACKNOWLEDGMENTS

The staff studies prepared for the information of the members of the Commission on the Delivery of Personal Health Services are published here with the authorization of the Commission in order to make this assembly of data available to professionals and students of the health services. The opinions, findings and recommendations which appear in these studies speak for the staff member or members responsible in each case and do not speak for the Commission.

In preparation of the studies presented in this volume, the staff supplied to the Commission by Technomics, Inc., made site visits to each of the municipal hospitals of the City of New York. In the course of these visits, the staff interviewed the responsible officials, professional and non-professional staff members and patients. Similar visits were made to a representative sampling of the health centers of the Department of Health of the City of New York and to representative voluntary hospitals and proprietary hospitals. Accordingly, the staff accumulated obligations, hereby acknowledged, to several hundred persons who cooperated in furnishing information, insights, opinions and counsel. In addition, the staff wishes to acknowledge similar indebtedness to dozens of other persons. Those who participated in formal interviews are cited individually in Appendix A.

Other Technomics personnel provided valuable assistance to the staff. Serving as consultants were Norton F. Kristy, Ph.D., President; Warren J. Pelton, Ph.D., Vice-President; Burton R. Wolin, Ph.D., Vice-President; and Florence Segelman, R.N., Consultant to Technomics, Inc. Staff support was also provided by Linda Goffen, Technical Editor; Elaine J. DeVantier, Executive Secretary; and Eve Herrera, Executive Secretary.

For assistance in providing health care information and statistics, the staff wishes to acknowledge the cooperation and invaluable assistance provided by the many public and independent agencies dedicated to improved health care delivery, in particular these:

Health and Hospital Planning Council, Inc.
New York City Planning Commission
Urban Medical Economics Research Project
New York City Department of Hospitals
New York City Department of Health
New York City Community Mental Health Board
District Council 37, American Federation of
    State, County and Municipal Employees, AFL-CIO

Members of the Commission on the Delivery of Personal Health Services: Background

Eveline M. Burns

Professor Emeritus of Social Work, Columbia University School of Social Work

Member, Federal Advisory Council on Employment Security and National Public Advisory Committee on Regional Economic Development. Consultant to Federal and State Agencies

Past President, National Conference on Social Welfare

Benjamin J. Buttenwieser

Limited Partner, Kuhn, Loeb & Co.

United States Assistant High Commissioner to Germany (1949 to 1951)

Trustee, Columbia University, Fisk University, Lenox Hill Hospital, Federation of Jewish Philanthropic Societies, Foreign Policy Association

William T. Golden

Corporate Director and Trustee

Former Assistant to the Chairman, U.S. Atomic Energy Commission; Special Consultant to President Truman on military-scientific activities; Consultant to the Director, U.S. Bureau of the Budget;

Overseer, Harvard College; Trustee, Radcliffe
College, American Museum of Natural History

William Glazier, Staff Director

Assistant for Scientific and Academic Affairs to
the President of The Salk Institute for Biological
Studies

Members of Medical Advisory Committee of the
Commission on the Delivery of
Personal Health Services

Dr. George Baehr
Director Emeritus of Medicine
Mount Sinai Hospital

Dr. Henry L. Barnett
Professor of Pediatrics
Albert Einstein College of Medicine
Yeshiva University

Dr. Leona Baumgartner
Visiting Professor of Social Medicine
Harvard Medical School

Dr. Norton S. Brown
Chairman, Committee on Social Policy
    for Health Care of the New York
    Academy of Medicine

Dr. Howard Reid Craig, Chairman
Former Director
New York Academy of Medicine

Dr. Elizabeth B. Davis
Director of Psychiatry
Harlem Hospital

Dr. C. Joseph Delaney
Past President, Medical Society of the
    County of New York

Dr. Louis M. Hellman
Professor and Chairman
Department of Obstetrics & Gynecology
State University of New York
Downstate Medical Center

CONTENTS

Dr. E. Hugh Luckey, President
Cornell University
New York Hospital Medical Center

Dr. Edwin P. Maynard, Jr.
Senior Physician
Brooklyn Cumberland Medical Center

Dr. Eugene G. McCarthy, Jr.
Assistant Professor of Administrative
    Medicine
School of Public Health and Administrative
    Medicine
Columbia University

Dr. Peter Rogatz
Director
Long Island Jewish Hospital

Dr. Howard A. Rusk
Director
Institute of Rehabilitation Medicine

Dr. E. Richard Weinerman
Professor of Medicine and Public Health
Yale School of Medicine

CONTENTS

LIST OF TABLES

LIST OF FIGURES

PART ONE

Comprehensive Community Health Services
for New York City

CHAPTER 1
THE FINAL REPORT OF THE COMMISSION

Reflecting the recommendations of the
Commission members:

Eveline M. Burns

Benjamin J. Buttenwieser

William T. Golden

Leo Gottlieb

Francis Kernan

Thomas R. Wilcox

Gerard Piel, Chairman

Ex Officio: Howard Reid Craig, M.D.
             Peter Rogatz, M.D.

Staff Director: William H. Glazier

* *

TOWARD COMPREHENSIVE COMMUNITY HEALTH SERVICES

"The availability of health services, as a matter
of human right, should be based on health needs alone,
not on a test of ability to pay." This declaration by
the New York Academy of Medicine effectively states the
moral undertaking of the City of New York in the delivery of personal health services. As early as the beginning of the last century, the City Charter recognized
the condition of medical indigency, that is, the inability of otherwise self-supporting citizens to pay their

3

medical bills. The City has ever since assumed increasing obligations in the financing and delivery of
medical care. Over the past decade, City expenditures
have increased steeply as the costs of medical care
have gone up and as the City has taken on an increasing share of the burden. Personal health services
will this year absorb nearly $800 million, or approxi-
mately one-sixth of the total City budget, the largest
expenditure after education and welfare. Even in advance of anticipated large inflows of Federal funds
under the Medicare and Medicaid legislation of 1965,
40 per cent of all the hospital inpatient days and
25 per cent of all physician-patient contacts will be
paid for by public funds. All told, nearly half the
population--four-fifths of the aged as well as more
than one-third of the children--depend upon the City
to provide some or all of their medical care. No more
than 20 per cent of the City's medical dependents receive public assistance payments; the 80 per cent
majority are members of families that pay their other
bills. The City's annual per capita expenditure on
behalf of its medical dependents significantly exceeds
the national average.

        This humane concern of local government has helped
to concentrate in New York City a disproportionately
high percentage of the country's precious human and
physical assets in the science and technology of medicine. There is one physician for every 350 New Yorkers,
compared to a national ratio of 1 to 1,000. There are
seven medical schools in the City and more than a
score of teaching hospitals. The City itself owns and
operates twenty-one hospitals; four of these provide
the primary teaching centers for four of the seven
medical schools. All persons in the community thus
benefit from the City's outlays for its medical
dependents.

        The role of the City in the delivery of personal
health services has been brought forcibly to public
attention in recent months by two ongoing events, one
local and the other national. Here in the City, the
rising public expectation of medical care and increasing
discontent with existing arrangements for its delivery
have again focused public attention upon the inadequacy
of the facilities and services provided by the City.
No less than five formal investigations of the City
health services (including that of this Commission) have
been under way during the past twelve months. At the

same time, the implications of the Federal Medicare
and Medicaid legislation are being comprehended in
the deliberations of state and city legislatures and
in the Congress. After the example set by the City
of New York, public policy across the nation as a
whole is embracing the principle that needed medical
care should not be denied to any person because he,
individually, cannot pay the costs.

The resulting increase in the flow of Federal
and State funds now makes it possible for the City of
New York to find a new approach to its historic undertaking. The public interest makes the search for a
new approach imperative. Recognizing both the chronic
failings of the City's arrangements for the delivery
of personal health services and the new opportunities
presented by developments in public policy at the
Federal and State levels, Mayor John V. Lindsay, in
December of 1966, asked a group of private citizens
to organize the present Commission on the Delivery of
Personal Health Services. The Mayor charged this Commission "to make a thorough inquiry into the institutional, administrative, and fiscal aspects of the
system through which public funds now deliver personal
health services to one-third of the people of New York
City" and to make recommendations relative to the
"optimum employment of the magnificent resources available in the medical economy of the City for the delivery of personal health services to all the people of
the City."

In acquitting its charge, the Commission recruited
staff and secured financing independent of the City
Administration. At work over the past nine months,
the Commission has heard the testimony and opinion of
responsible officers of the City Administration and
of interested persons and organizations representing
the organizers, providers, and recipients of medical
care; it has had the counsel of qualified experts,
including administrators of health systems in other
communities; it has made site visits to the City hospitals and the neighborhoods they service; it has
met in numerous executive sessions. At the Commission's direction, its staff has made exhaustive
studies (to be published separately) of major elements
in the City's health-service delivery system.

Out of this inquiry, the Commission concludes that the fulfillment of New York City's commitment to provide medical care to all persons on the basis of their health needs calls for the redesign and systematic reconstruction of the relationship between public authority and community initiative in the delivery of health services. Its recommendations call, on the one hand, for the enlistment of private initiative from the diverse communities of the City to manage the ultimate delivery of personal health services and, on the other hand, for the exercise by the City of its ample powers to set community health goals and service standards and to secure fiscal and performance accountability of agencies receiving public funds. With responsibilities thus allocated, it should be the mission of public and private agencies to work together in the development of a system of comprehensive health services available and accessible to all on the basis of their health needs.

As to the results delivered by present arrangements, the Commission finds that the health services available to the City's medical dependents through public and private agencies fail to meet urgent needs for preventive, ambulatory, and long-term care. Consequently, these people and the City are burdened with high costs of excessive hospitalization. For episodes of acute illness, the City's expenditures do purchase treatment of high quality, especially where the care is administered in one of the score of large voluntary hospitals that carry approximately 40 per cent of the inpatient burden financed by public funds. But a person must be acutely ill or badly injured to qualify for such care. Inpatient care, moreover, is the most expensive mode of medical care. Existing facilities and institutions, in the private as well as the public sector, do not meet people's needs (1) for preventive services, particularly in the crises of maternity, infancy, and childhood; (2) for the long-term care of chronic illness, particularly among the aged; and (3) for care within the community of the mental and emotional disorders that so complicate other illness and intensify the social pathologies of alienation, vice, and crime.

These deficiencies--along with other deprivations of poverty--are reflected in the indices of mortality and morbidity by which New York compares unfavorably with other large cities in this country and abroad.

Each of these indices is depressed by the poor health
status of the low-income and otherwise disadvantaged
groups that are most dependent on the City for the
delivery of personal health services.

The deficiencies in facilities and services are
more grossly apparent in the conditions to be seen
in the City's own hospitals. While excellent medical
treatment is available in these hospitals, it is rendered principally by physicians provided through the
affiliation contracts that link all but two City hospitals to voluntary hospitals. These contracts stand
as evidence that the City has been unable to fulfill
the primary function of owner-manager: the professional staffing of its hospitals. What is more, the
City has been unable to meet its obligation under
these contracts to provide supporting personnel, supplies, equipment, and decently maintained plant.

This Commission concludes that conditions in the
City Hospitals are not only deplorable but, under existing arrangements, irremediable. The affiliation
contracts have fulfilled in large measure the limited
purposes for which they were executed. But they cannot be regarded as more than an interim measure; in
fact they originated as a crisis measure. These
contracts place the City hospitals under divided
management; so long as the hospitals continue under
such management, they are fated to remain second-rate
institutions. In providing inadequate and substandard health services and in serving only the indigent
population through its own clinics and hospitals,
the City is perpetuating a dual system of medical
care with a built-in invidious double standard of
private and welfare medicine. The system is demeaning to all concerned and wasteful of the community's
medical resources. Now that Medicare and Medicaid
funds give the City's medical dependents a choice,
the inpatient load of the City hospitals is declining
and the voluntary hospitals are overcrowded and over-
booked. The now idle portion of City plant represents
an equivalent of at least 2,000 beds and, at current
replacement cost, an investment on the order of $100
million.

The situation cannot be blamed on the responsible
officials of this or the preceding City administrations.

In recent years, the highest offices in the City
health agencies have been occupied by distinguished
men and women; they have brought valuable innovations
to the system and to their profession in exercising
the authority available to them. The health officials
of the present Administration have made considerable
progress toward the important goal of unifying and
coordinating the work of their agencies in a single
Health Services Administration. They have work
going forward in a number of significant problem
areas: planning for a city-wide program of ambulatory
care facilities; construction starts on mental health
centers; planning for the difficult redistricting
of health services over the City, and improvement
in administrative procedures by the Department of
Hospitals. Finally, a basis for comprehensive
health-care planning is being laid cooperatively by
the City Planning Commission and the Health Services
Administration.

These good efforts are thwarted, however, by the
intricate and archaic system of "checks and balances"
designed in another day to secure public accountability of elected and appointed officials. Responsibility for personal health services is fragmented among
the major health agencies and, within the agencies,
among numerous bureaus that represent the historical
accumulation of ad hoc programs. The limited authority that does repose in the agencies is concentrated
at headquarters, remote from sites of operating responsibility in the field. A district health officer
of the Department of Health thus finds that his presumed subordinates in his district report over his
head directly to their bureau chiefs at headquarters.
A hospital superintendent cannot order a minor repair without review and approval by an assortment of
officials in the Department of Hospitals and in the
overhead agencies. Above the level of Commissioner,
authority is dissipated in the web of rules and regulations administered by the overhead agencies and
mandated by State as well as City law.

The procedures set up to secure the desirable and
necessary end of public accountability thus function to
stifle initiative and paralyze decision. Other operating agencies of the City feel the same constraints.
In the health agencies these constraints impede the
performance of officials charged with life-and-death

responsibilities. As a result, the health services
paid for by the City are provided, whether by public
or voluntary agencies, without overall plan or coordination in response to haphazardly asserted and recognized needs. Because there is no established locus of
responsibility for program, the City health agencies
have been unable to exercise their considerable authority to promote innovation in the delivery of health
services and to secure accountability for performance
by the private agencies and institutions that are providing an increasing percentage of the services paid
for by public funds.

These findings have convinced the members of the
Commission that nothing short of a total reconstruction
of the City governmental machinery can capacitate the
City health agencies to manage the facilities and services for which they are now responsible. The prospect
of such action is neither early nor likely. Pressing
human need calls for alternative measures. The basic
changes under way in public policy with regard to medical care and its financing make it possible to put
such measures forward. Medicare and Medicaid funds,
plus the imminence of compulsory health insurance under
State and perhaps Federal law, promise to place the
delivery of health services on a nearly self-sustaining
basis. The City health agencies can now be relieved
of the task of attempting to fill gaps in the system
by providing services directly. Freed from operating
and administrative assignments that are impossible
within the present framework of the City government,
the officials of these agencies can devote their talents and energies to assessing the health needs of the
population and to securing performance in the public
interest by the health organizations and institutions
that receive public funds.

These considerations underlie the Commission's
first recommendation--that the City of New York should
employ the authority and resources at its disposal to
promote the integration of the present dual system of
health facilities and services into a single comprehensive system. With the wealth of resources available
in New York City, it should be feasible to organize
the delivery of health services in five or more regional systems, each centered in a major teaching hospital
or medical school and linking together the community
hospitals and ancillary facilities in a structured
network of referral and shared responsibility. In
response to the needs of their communities and to
economic compulsion, such systems can be expected to

reduce the burden of inpatient care in favor of preventive and ambulatory services and long-term services for chronic illness. The health services, public and voluntary, can thus be organized to fulfill their proper function--protecting and improving peoples' health--and should no longer be preoccupied with rendering care to health already damaged.

The Commission's second recommendation endorses the consolidation of the City health agencies in a single Health Services Administration as proposed in the Administration's Charter reforms. Unification of the agencies is essential to creating a clearly defined locus of public responsibility for the development and performance of the health service system. The functions of the unified agency should be the maintenance of the environmental defenses of public health; surveillance of the health status of the population and determination of unmet needs; long-range planning and the setting of objectives and standards for the personal health service delivery system; the inspection of health and hospital facilities; the accreditation of professional capacities as required; the securing of performance and fiscal accountability of all agencies receiving public funds; and the sponsorship of health research. To this end, the Health Services Administration should be designated by the State of New York to organize the comprehensive health planning agency for the five boroughs of New York City under the Federal comprehensive health planning law (PL 89-749). The State should, moreover, delegate or restore to the City health agencies the authority now vested in State agencies for the auditing and inspection of the vendors of health services in the City.

This recommendation is coupled to the Commission's third recommendation, which calls for the creation of a public non-profit corporation to take over the facilities and services through which City agencies now undertake the ultimate delivery of medical care. If the Health Services Administration is to discharge the vital accountability functions proposed here, it should not also be responsible for operations, lest its own performance compromise its authority as the judge of performance by others. The City retains, of course, the power to render services directly and the obligation to do so when necessary.

The public, non-profit Health Services Corporation, put forward in the Commission's third recommendation, would have these functions: (1) the

operation of the City hospitals and health centers
and the physical and administrative repair of these
facilities so that they may, in time, be integrated
into the health service system under appropriate
sponsorship as teaching centers and community hospitals;
(2) the construction of hospitals and such ancillary
facilities as neighborhood ambulatory care centers;
(3) the development and operation of system-wide services, including communication and referral, medical
information and data processing, personnel training
and career development, purchasing, and laboratory
services. The charter of this Corporation should be
drawn to place its operations outside the constraints
of the "checks and balances" system but to make it
fully accountable for its use of public funds and for
the fulfillment of its assigned mission. Procedures
should be established for review of its activities and
for program audit of its fiscal performance by the
Health Services Administration and the appropriate
fiscal agencies of the City.

The Commission believes that the creation of this
new agency is justified by long-term desirability as
well as by short-term necessity. On the one hand, it
is essential that the municipal hospitals and clinics
be put immediately into working order both for the
well-being of their patients and as a vital public
contribution to the development of a single health
service system. These hospitals and their ancillary
facilities should eventually--sooner in some cases
and later in others--take their place in the system
under appropriate sponsorship as community hospitals
and teaching centers on a par with the best voluntary
institutions. On the other hand, the system-wide
services projected for the Health Services Corporation
will give this agency a vital, continuing role in the
development of the comprehensive community health
service system.

In the past, unmet need has forced the City to
own and operate hospitals and clinics to the neglect
of the vital task of assuring the effective functioning
of the health care system, public and private. Dis-
appointment in the performance of the City has brought,
in recent years, loss of its authority to the State
and even to the Federal government as well as to nongovernmental agencies. The recommendations of this
Commission are intended to halt and reverse this trend.
In recommending that a public, non-profit corporation
take over the operation of the City health facilities,

this Commission recommends at the same time the strengthening of the powers of the Health Services Administration in order that it have the authority necessary to secure public accountability, both fiscal and performance, of all elements of the health system.

This responsibility belongs inescapably to local government. Crises in education, transportation, housing, environmental pollution, as well as in health services--in other cities as well as in New York-- show that progress in the art of local government has not kept pace with the growth of the modern city. The American preference for minimal government has created the weakest agencies in precisely those functions of government that bear most directly on the well-being of the individual. To meet urgent public need, local governments have often turned to the creation of "Authorities." That device is rejected by this Com- mission for its inherent denial of adequate fulfill- ment of public accountability. The Commission would also reject any arrangement, such as that between the Board of Education and the City, that would disengage vital public services from accountability to the pub- lic through the political process. The Health Services Corporation, in the design proposed here, is structured to enlist, on terms responsive to the public interest, the high quality of management required to fulfill its function. Correspondingly, the Health Services Admin- istration would be equipped with the authority and professional capacity to secure the accountability of the Corporation and other agencies engaged in the ultimate delivery of medical care. Together, the Health Services Administration and the Health Services Corporation should employ the City's capital and oper- ating expenditures to secure the rational organization of the health services available to the people.

The City is fortunate at this moment in its his- tory to have an Administration committed to fortifying the capacity of local government. With the advice and consent of a City legislature committed to these ob- jectives, the City of New York may set a significant example for other cities of the nation.

THE DELIVERY OF PERSONAL
HEALTH SERVICES BY THE CITY

Finding 1 Nearly half the population of New York City receive their medical care at public expense.

The health services available to them through
public and private institutions fail to meet
their urgent needs for preventive and ambulatory care, on the one hand, and for long-term
care, on the other. As a result, these people
and the City are burdened with costs of excessive hospitalization and other costs not so
easily measured.

The deficiencies of the health services available
to the people of this City are all too plainly evident
in the character of the facilities and services that
the City itself provides. Because municipal hospitals
are the site for most of the services offered at public expense, much attention in this report and in the
Staff Studies is focused on conditions in these hospitals. It must be emphasized, however, that those
conditions are symptomatic of a much larger problem.
Less plainly evident, but of equal importance, are
the deficiencies that persist because essential health
facilities and services are not provided by either the
public or the private agencies in the community. The
needs of the people that go unmet and unrecognized
ultimately add to the burden of costs carried by the
public treasury and waste the resources of the local
medical economy. Hospital inpatient care, as shown
in the Mayor's Executive Expense Budget, absorbs 58
per cent of the City's total outlay for personal health
services. The comparative figure in the country as
a whole is an estimated 40 per cent of the total outlay
for personal health services. The absolute cost of
inpatient service to the City is huge: $440 million
annually. Of the total funds, which pay for 6 million
"public charge days," 64 per cent are spent in the
City's twenty-one municipal hospitals and 36 per cent
in the voluntary hospitals.

The heavy burden of hospital inpatient care carried by the City reflects, in large measure, the
failure of the community to provide adequate preventive
and ambulatory services on the one hand and extended
and home care services on the other. With costs running upward from $80 per day in the municipal hospi-
tals and even higher in the voluntary hospitals, in-
patient care is the most expensive kind of care. In
a startling percentage of cases, hospitalization could
be reduced in duration or averted entirely by alternative modes of care, bringing greater benefit to the
individual and achieving economy of medical resources.

The existing system's real costs to the health of the population cannot be reckoned. Available statistics show that the City's medical dependents, despite a City expenditure per capita which exceeds the national average, suffer rates of morbidity and mortality well above those of the rest of the population. Maternal mortality, for example, reaches a rate of 55 per thousand among some low-income groups in this City, compared to rates of less than 15 per thousand among other inhabitants. This figure reflects the fact that 40 per cent or more of mothers in poor neighborhoods receive medical care for the first time during the last trimester of pregnancy. Infant mortality in all low-income groups runs at a high rate, and this is associated with high rates of prematurity, congenital defect, and other disability afflicting these children from birth. Well over a third of all children depend upon the City for their medical care; on first entering school half of the children must be given medical examinations by school physicians because they do not turn up with certifications from private physicians. Steep barriers of inconvenience and humiliation cause the City's medical dependents to seek medical care as a last resort and at the point in their health history when medicine can do them the least good--when, in Professor Nora Piore's words, "they are very sick and very broke." Dr. George James, former Health Commissioner of the City, estimates that the low-income population of the community suffers an annual excess of 13,000 deaths.

It is necessary, of course, to distinguish between medicine and health. Medicine cannot cure the ills of poverty. Ill health, however, is a part of the vicious circle in which the poor get sicker and the sick get poorer. The health service system fails to make its contribution to breaking this vicious circle.

(a) Treatment for episodes of acute illness or injury, by qualified physicians and surgeons in the voluntary hospitals and in most municipal hospitals, is available to the City's medical dependents. That treatment is typically compromised in the municipal hospitals because these institutions do not provide an adequate setting for modern medical care. The care is optimum in the best of the voluntary hospitals that are among the principal vendors of inpatient care to the City. In the municipal hospitals, medical treatment is rendered for the most part by physicians whose services are provided under affiliation contracts with

the major voluntary institutions. The effectiveness
of this service is compromised, however, by the divided
management inherent in this contractual arrangement
and by the City's inability to fulfill its side of
these contracts in the provision of supporting staff,
supplies, equipment, and decently maintained plant.

(b) Ambulatory care services, available principally in outpatient departments and emergency rooms
of hospitals, are grossly inadequate. Because low-
income neighborhoods are largely abandoned by practicing physicians, the hospital outpatient departments
and emergency rooms have become perforce the family
doctor of the poor. The number of patient visits to
the outpatient departments of the municipal hospitals
increased from 2.7 million in 1960 to nearly 3.5 million in 1966. Visits to the emergency rooms of municipal hospitals ascended even faster, from a little more
than one million in 1960 to nearly two million in 1966,
and continue to increase. At almost any hour of the
day, but especially after hours when the outpatient
departments are closed, the emergency rooms are populated by mothers and children, who make these facilities do service as walk-in ambulatory care centers.

In the outpatient departments, the interminable
waiting for appointments, the fragmentation of service
into specialty clinics requiring separate appointments
and waiting times for each, the abrupt, hurried, and
impersonal treatment by the overburdened staff, the
confusion of complicated regulations, the crowded
quarters and the lack of adequate medical records--all
subject the patient to inconvenience, discomfort, and
humiliation. No single physician assumes responsibility for any one case and there is no unit record to
relate the findings of the separate clinics. While
the emergency rooms provide service on equally depersonalized terms, they are open around the clock; a
working mother can bring her child there after hours
and not give up a day's pay as the price for seeking
medical care. Outpatient services, in general, have
low status in the hospital hierarchy and do not attract the best staff. The municipal hospitals are no
exception to this rule, and the staffing supplied by
the affiliated hospitals has not been able to match
the ascending demand under existing circumstances.

The crowding of the hospital outpatient facilities
is evidence of their inadequate capacity and anachro-
nistic geographical distribution. The health centers

and well-baby clinics operated by the Department of
Health, accounting for additional millions of patient
visits per year, do not relieve pressures on the hospitals, nor do they maintain systematic relations with
the hospitals in their communities. The services
available in these ancillary facilities are depersonalized, fragmented, and discontinuous, as in the out-
patient departments of the hospitals. There is, again,
unsatisfactory record-keeping and, with one or two
exceptions, little or no continuity of physician responsibility from clinic to clinic or from one patient-
visit to the next. In addition, the various specialty
clinics tend to be scattered geographically, adding
expense and hours of travel time to the already for-
bidding inconvenience confronting the patient.

The services offered by ambulatory care facilities, whether public or voluntary, are thus necessarily
episodic and discontinuous. They are correspondingly
unequal to delivery of the preventive and supportive
care required of them in particular by the mothers and
children who make up such a high percentage of their
clientele.

(c) Long-term care services--provided by extended-
care facilities, home-care programs, and nursing homes--
are too limited in availability and too uncertain in
quality to meet the increasing burden of chronic illness, especially among the aged 11 per cent of the
City's population. Every hospital census in recent
years has shown that at least 30 per cent of the City-
financed general care beds in the voluntary and municipal hospitals are occupied by patients suffering from
non-acute illness. These beds are not only costly;
they also provide a destructively inappropriate hospital setting for the care required by these, for the
most part, elderly patients. The City hospitals for
long-term care patients located on Welfare Island
cruelly isolate their patients from their families and
communities. The proprietary nursing homes licensed
by the City for care of its dependents provide uneven,
uncertain, or no systematic medical service. In the
absence of positive programs for development of non-
acute treatment facilities, the City's coding, licensing, and inspection powers, exercised by the
Departments of Health and of Hospitals, can secure no
amelioration of conditions in these institutions.

(d) Facilities and services available for ambulatory care of the mentally ill have not met the newly
recognized need and opportunity to provide therapy

for such illness in the supportive setting of the
community. Mental and emotional illness accounts for
the major portion of the nation's hospital inpatient
care burden. In New York State, patient days in State
mental hospitals per 1,000 population are nearly double
the national average, and more than half of these patients are City patients. This is a reflection, in
part, of the fact that the duration of stay for the
individual patient runs at about twice the national
average. The quality of care available to the patient
in State hospitals is suggested by the fact that they
are inadequately staffed, largely by foreign-trained
physicians. Under the Community Mental Health Act
of 1954, State funds are available to reduce this
burden and to improve prognosis for patients by providing ambulatory care services in the community.
Principally for lack of initiative and coordination
on the part of other agencies, the Community Mental
Health Board has been unable to put into operation a
single one of some fifty community mental health centers that are to be established in New York City.
Because the City does not match the State funds for
ambulatory psychiatric care provided by the voluntary
hospitals, efforts to develop programs in these institutions have been discouraged. Except in those few
cases where the affiliated medical school or teaching
hospital has instituted programs, the municipal hospitals continue to serve as staging centers for delivery of mental patients to long-term care in State
hospitals.

> Finding 2 In providing inadequate and substand-
> ard care and in serving only the indigent popu-
> lation in its own hospitals and clinics, the
> City is perpetuating a dual system of medical
> care with a built-in invidious double standard
> of private and welfare medicine. The system is
> demeaning to all concerned and wastes the re-
> sources of the local medical economy.

Hospitals were first opened for the poor; the
well-off could afford to be sick at home. In creating
the municipal hospital system more than 150 years ago
to take care of the "emergent and indigent sick," the
City made this service a function and obligation of
government. As voluntary hospitals grew up alongside
the municipal system, the City continued to carry the
main burden of care for the medically indigent. More
important, although the charters of the private, non-
profit voluntary hospitals require them to render care

to any person who comes to their doors, these hospitals exercise selectivity, to greater or lesser degree, in admitting patients. The City hospitals remain the sure, if last, resort. The City beds charged with this profound obligation make up 32 per cent of the total beds available in the City today.

Each generation of New Yorkers has had its hospital crisis, and successive waves of reform have ameliorated one or another set of faults in the system. With the present crisis, the time has come to acknowledge that it has now become impracticable, if not impossible, for the City with its present administrative structure and procedures to operate its municipal hospitals. Change and progress in medical science and technology over the past twenty-five years have radically altered the character of the hospital as an institution. A hospital is no longer a kind of hotel for the patient and workshop for the doctor. It is no longer feasible to staff a hospital, as the City's hospitals used to be staffed, by attending physicians whose eminence would attract the necessary house staff of interns and residents to provide most of the patient care. The modern hospital is an organization of highly trained specialists supported by a skilled staff and employing instrumentation and equipment of constantly greater capital cost. To keep such an organization functioning requires an ever larger nucleus of full-time staff.

The impact of these developments on the City hospital system is reviewed at length in discussion of the affiliation contract device which was invoked early in this decade to bring qualified medical staff back into the City hospitals. While there is much else to be said about the affiliation contracts, these contracts stand as persuasive evidence that the City has been unable to staff its hospitals through its own payroll. Under the affiliation contracts the City has contracted out its major responsibility as owner-manager of a hospital.

In meeting its undertaking to provide a hospital bed for each and every person who comes to its doors, the City contracts out 40 per cent of the burden to the voluntary hospitals that offer beds in their wards. Through the affiliation contracts, the voluntaries have assumed responsibility for most of the medical services required in the City hospitals. The City

has thus in total contracted more than half of its
historic undertaking to the voluntaries.

As set out below, this Commission finds conditions
in the City hospitals and clinics not only deplorable
but also, as a practical matter, irremediable under
existing circumstances. So long as present arrangements persist, they perpetuate a double standard of
medical care: a reasonably adequate standard for the
well-off and a desperately inadequate standard for the
poor. The elimination of this invidious discrepancy
is essential for the optimum utilization of the community's medical resources as well as for the well-
being of the people served.

(a) The affiliation contracts, which have brought
some measure of qualified professional service into the
City hospitals, place them under divided management;
these hospitals are fated to remain second-rate institutions so long as they remain under such management.
While some of the most distinguished voluntary hospitals in the City are operated by partnerships of medical schools and medical centers, the identity of their
interests and the interlocking of their boards and
professional staffs are such as to place these hospitals essentially under single management. This is not
the case in the relations between the City and the
affiliated hospitals and medical schools. Quite apart
from the adversary character of their economic relationship, there is a diversity of mission--between the
research and teaching mission of medical school and
teaching hospital on the one hand and the City's obligation to deliver care, even to the "uninteresting
case," on the other. Under authority thus divided the
City hospitals respond passively to the burdens that
are laid on them and take limited or no initiative in
the development of ambulatory and extended-care programs for their communities. They would be fated to
drift as second-class institutions even if it were
not necessary also to report that:

(b) The City has been unable to meet its commitment, under the affiliation contracts, to provide supporting personnel, medical records, supplies, instrumentation and equipment, and decently maintained hospital plant. Of greatest consequence is the City's
inability to provide supporting staff in its hospitals.
With budget provision for 5,721 registered nurses, the
City manages to employ 1,363. The skills of these
nurses are not efficiently used because of the shortage

of personnel to support them.   The empty positions are
filled from the ranks of licensed practical nurses,
nurse's aides, and others numbering 3,696 in 1966.
Physicians working in City hospitals cannot, accordingly, repose confidence in the bedside care available
to carry out their orders for medication, other treatment, and diet.   Frequently, these physicians are
compelled to do tasks that ought to be done by other
personnel.

In view of the enormity of the problems and the
remoteness of their solution, it is not surprising that
morale and discipline among the supporting staff are
low in almost all of the City hospitals.   In this connection District Council 37, American Federation of
State, County and Municipal Employees, AFL-CIO, is to
be commended for its initiative in the institution of
in-service training programs.   This is a significant
step toward the building of a career spirit in the
ranks of the supporting personnel.   Meanwhile, because
of the shortage of personnel and the low morale,
patients find themselves waiting for hours on litters
in the halls of these hospitals for diagnostic service,
or for other interminable periods of time in ward beds
for help that can be summoned only by the patient's
own voice.

Typically, medical records and record rooms are
in disarray.   In one municipal center, the affiliated
medical school must contend with the fact that records
are chronically eighteen months behind.   At Bellevue
Hospital this important responsibility had to be
contracted out to New York University Medical School
when that hospital was on the verge of losing its
accreditations.   Delay and discontinuity in record-
keeping contribute to the discontinuity of service
from episode to episode in a patient's history and
from clinic to clinic in the course of treatment.

The City-side management is chronically unable
to maintain dependable supplies of such essentials as
linens, towels, diapers, and sanitary napkins on the
hospital wards.   Inflexibility and undependability in
the City-wide purchasing system create even more
critical problems with respect to such items as drugs
and hypodermic needles.   Where City hospital administrators resort to overstocking of inventory in order
to avoid shortages, poor control of inventory and
pilferage waste City funds and exacerbate the crises
of supply.

With the institution of operations under the
affiliation contracts, City hospitals have been shown
to be furnished with instrumentation and equipment
obsolete by the standards of present hospital practice.
In anticipation of this situation, each affiliation
contract has provided a substantial emergency sum to
be expended at the discretion of the affiliating
institution. Because purchases on these funds have to
be made through regular City channels, interminable
delays in delivery have been encountered along with
error in fulfillment of specifications. In one hospital after another, equipment has waited in storage
after delivery, for rewiring or other renovation required for its installation. Some $12 million worth
of renovation projects are now backed up in the channels and bottlenecks in the City administrative
machinery.

The condition of the City hospital plant ranges
from that of old buildings that ought to have been
demolished to recently constructed buildings suffering
from archaic design and inadequate maintenance. All
of the hospitals have been made obsolete by the standards required by Medicare legislation, which call for
four-bed semi-private accommodations, as contrasted
to the open wards of nineteenth-century welfare standards to which the City hospitals were designed. Much
of the $12 million worth of renovation is occasioned
by inadequate provision for surgery and laboratory
facilities. These strictures apply as much to the new
Harlem and Bellevue Hospitals, still under construction, as to others because they are being built to
design concepts of twenty years ago.

The inadequate maintenance of almost all the
buildings contributes to the demoralization of staff
and patients. Peeling paint and decaying plaster,
filth and vermin-infestation blight these places as
settings for modern hospital therapy. The "crash
programs" of renovation now under way at Bellevue and
other hospitals promise to remedy some of the gross
deficiencies but will not cure the obsolescence of
the open ward.

(c) Waste of resources is evident in the declining occupancy of the City hospitals and overcrowding of voluntary hospitals, in the deterioration
of the City hospitals, and in the chronic underspend-
ing of the City's capital budget for construction of
health facilities. The decline in the occupancy of

City hospital beds has been hastened by the consumer-
choice open to the recipients of Medicare and Medicaid
funds. Now that they are able to, the City's medical
dependents are choosing semi-private and ward beds in
voluntary hospitals in preference to those available
in City hospitals. An additional unreckoned number
of these beneficiaries of the new Federal legislation
are seeking care in proprietary hospitals. Even before
Medicaid and Medicare, the "bed complement" of the
City system (that is, beds ready for occupancy) had
been reduced by 3,000 beds below its installed capacity
of 21,500 beds. The occupancy of the City hospitals
has now declined to well below 80 per cent of the
bed complement, while the occupancy of beds in voluntary hospitals has climbed to above 90 per cent.

The distribution of beds in the hospital plant
(both municipal and voluntary) of the City as a whole
has failed to keep up with the internal migration of
the City's population. The poor distribution of
facilities, taken together with the aging of the
plant, calls for new investment of at least $800 mil-
lion, according to the Health and Hospital Planning
Council. Meanwhile, the City hospital system, with
a five-year capital budget of $500 million, is attempt-
ing to put only about $50 million into construction
and repairs in fiscal year 1967-1968.

The significant number of proprietary hospitals
in the City, especially in such areas of rapid middle-
class population growth as the Borough of Queens, is
explained in large part by the failure of the public
and voluntary systems to expand in this and other
areas of the City. These hospitals, most of which are
small and too poorly staffed and equipped to provide
comprehensive hospital care, are outside the mainstream of developments in medicine. Nevertheless they
clearly fill a hospital need not otherwise met by
existing facilities, as indicated by their increased
use by Medicare and Medicaid patients.

The underutilization of City hospital beds has
created a virtual shortage of beds in the system as a
whole. The waiting lists for beds in desirable voluntary hospitals are lengthening all over the City, to
the jeopardy of the health and life of many individuals. At the same time, City facilities, representing
an asset of $100 million at current replacement value,
stand idle.

Finding 3 The City health agencies are impeded
in the performance of their functions by the
fragmentation of their assigned mission, by
their own archaic administrative structures, and
by dissipation of their authority in the system
of "checks and balances" administered by the
overhead agencies of the City and mandated by
both State and City law.

To a greater or less extent, all of the operational agencies of the City function under the same
handicaps. Authority tends to be centralized in headquarters remote from the point of active responsibility in the field. But that authority tends to be
dissipated in the headquarters bureaucracy just below
the level of the principal executive officer and is
dissipated equally above his level in the lines of
constraint that run to the "overhead agencies" of the
City--the agencies charged with regulating and providing services to the health and other operating agencies
of the City. This system of "checks and balances,"
designed to secure the accountability of public officials, dates from an era when public need and expectation placed lesser demands on the City government
and when suspicion of the probity of officials was
widespread. It now frustrates initiative and disrupts
efficiency in the operational agencies of the City.
In the health services, it impedes the performance of
officials charged with life-and-death responsibilities.

(a) The health services paid for by the City are
provided, whether by public, voluntary, or proprietary
agencies, without overall planning or coordination and
in response to haphazardly asserted and recognized
needs. Concentration and fragmentation of authority
at the headquarters of the health agencies, away from
responsibility in the field, obstruct remedial action
and systematic planning. Accidents of history rather
than current needs account for the present structure
of the health services. The Department of Health was
established a century ago to set up the classical
environmental defenses of public health. The Department acquired significant functions in the delivery
of personal health services in order to meet public
needs as such needs were recognized from time to time
over the past century and a half. The Department of
Hospitals was organized in 1929 to bring under single
management the three separate municipal hospital systems then being operated by the City. The Community
Mental Health Board, an agency financed entirely by

State funds and operating under the State Community
Health Act of 1954, was created to provide therapy
for mental and emotional illness on an ambulatory basis
in the community. This agency has not assumed operating functions and presently serves primarily as a
planning, program-initiating, and funding agency.

The diverse operating functions in the delivery
of personal health services are lodged haphazardly
in the Departments of Health and Hospitals. The district health centers and well-baby clinics of the
Department of Health are located without reference to
the availability of outpatient services of City (or
voluntary) hospitals. As a result, many needful
neighborhoods are left entirely uncovered. The maps
of the City on which the two departments district their
operations bear no logical relationship to one another.

The tendency for authority to concentrate in the
headquarters of City agencies, remote from operational
responsibility in the field, appears in pronounced
form in the health agencies. The Commissioners who
seek, from administration to administration, to exercise their authority find it blocked by inertia in the
top-heavy headquarters bureaucracy at 125 Worth Street.
The most successful Commissioners in recent years have
managed to accomplish their objectives principally by
ignoring or flanking their headquarters organization
or by adding their own bureaus to the existing ram-
shackle structure.

From headquarters in both departments authority
runs vertically from bureau chiefs to subordinates in
the field. As a result, a typical Health Department
district officer, supposedly responsible for all departmental operations in his district, finds he has
no real authority over the personnel of the various
bureaus at work in his district. Correspondingly, the
typical municipal hospital administrator finds he must
refer the most routine decisions for approval to one
or another of more than a dozen bureau chiefs at the
Department of Hospitals' headquarters. The internal
checks and balances system of the Department inter-
venes in the purchase of supplies or equipment, in
the hiring of employees, and in the execution of minor
repairs and renovations. Against this system, honorable and devoted officials at all levels have found it
necessary to breach regulations in order to get things
done; if they did not take such risks, the system
would not work at all.

(b)   The authority of the City health agencies
is circumscribed by a web of rules and regulations
administered by the City overhead agencies. The levels
of City salaries, for example, are established across
the board for all City agencies by the Civil Service
ladder. In consequence, the City is unable to enter
the market with salary offers to doctors of medicine
or to hospital administrators remotely competitive
with the incomes and salaries available to them in
voluntary institutions and in private practice. This
was the compelling consideration in the establishment
of the affiliation contracts. The Office of Personnel,
charged with responsibility for enforcing Civil Service regulations established under State law, rigidly
maintains promotion lists on which personnel are ranked
by their standing on competitive examinations. This
system as administered is so inflexible that ability
and initiative must be ignored or sacrificed in making
appointments or promotions.

The Purchasing Department, set up to give the City
the significant market power of centralized purchasing,
dissipates that power through the inflexibility of its
administration. The purchasing machinery, involving an
approved list of vendors, multiple reviews of specifications, and sealed bidding, does not dependably get
the best price or the optimal quality for the City.
These procedures and their results constitute a special affliction for the health services, whose purchases constitute a large portion of the total outlays
of the City made through the Department of Purchases.

An action flow chart devised to guide officials
in the health agencies shows that eighteen authori-
zations and clerical procedures, involving three different agencies with average total delay time of nine
months, are required to hire an x-ray technician.
Similarly, fifteen steps involving as many as four
different departments are required to make a routine
purchase. A study has shown that the average time
from the initiation of a requisition to delivery is
eighty-eight days; this compares to four days for a
similar routine in a well-managed voluntary hospital.

The Bureau of the Budget, despite the undertak-
ings of the previous and present City administrations,
continues to supervise departmental budgets and expenditures by the technique of "line-item" budget
control. Budget lines may bear some relationship to
program at the time of their initiation in the

department, approval by the Bureau of the Budget and authorization by the Board of Estimate. They persist, however, without relationship to changes in programs because they are the instrument of appropriation and central control. The administration of the line-item budget--with its self-defeating techniques of line-swapping and enforced savings after budgets have been approved--frustrates initiative in the operating agencies and submits routine executive decision to external review, delay, and veto. This constraining system functions under the ultimate sanction of the Office of the Comptroller, which may refuse to honor an expenditure without means for adequate consideration of the item's relationship to the success of a given program.

Construction of health facilities is hampered not only by the City's checks and balances system but also by State legislation requiring that New York City contract separately for each of the major construction elements of a given project rather than employing a general contractor. This formidable set of obstacles not only delays all City construction projects but places the City at a serious disadvantage when competing with private builders for the services of contractors. The City is chronically unable to spend appropriations from capital. To the delays imposed by the government on itself, the contractors add further delay out of their reluctance to take City business and their tendency to regard City contracts as fill-in work, with priority subordinate to opportunities offered by private builders.

Until recently the Department of Welfare engaged directly in the delivery of personal health services, hiring physicians and nurses on its own account. The Department now functions as an overhead agency with respect to a major percentage of the funds expended on health service programs. It disburses funds under the Charitable Institutions Budget, which purchases inpatient hospital services rendered to City dependents by the voluntary hospitals. Under mandate from the State, reflecting Federal requirements, the Department is charged with the validation of the Medicaid clients of the City; its clerks also conduct the sign-up of these patients when they appear seeking medical care at a municipal hospital. This fragmentation of authority between the agency responsible for the delivery of care and the agency charged with validating claims for reimbursement has resulted in the loss of millions of dollars of reimbursement properly owing to the City from the State and Federal Governments under Medicaid and other programs. The Medicaid situation is the subject of a separate finding and recommendation by this Commission.

The dissipation of the authority of the City government goes above even the office of the Mayor himself. The role of State regulations in the fragmentation of City construction contracts and in the division of authority between the Department of Welfare and the City health agencies has already been mentioned. Another formidable obstacle to the structuring of an effective health service system in the community is presented by the fact that the inspection and auditing of the municipal and voluntary hospitals in New York City are mandated by State law to the State Department of Health.

(c) The City health agencies have been unable to carry out their responsibility to secure performance and promote innovations in the delivery of health services by the private agencies and institutions that are providing an increasing percentage of the services paid for by public funds. Perhaps out of their preoccupation with the management of the huge medical plant of the City, the health agencies have been unable to carry out other critical functions with which they are charged and which are vital to the securing of public objectives in the delivery of personal health services. These functions are to set community health goals and service standards and to secure the fiscal and performance accountability of all health organizations and institutions receiving public funds. Ample power to carry on these functions is vested in the code-writing authority of the Board of Health, the Board of Hospitals, and the Community Mental Health Board, from which the several agencies derive their operating mandates. The City health agencies possess the further potentially fruitful power for the setting of standards and objectives that is inherent in the deployment of public operating and capital funds. These powers lie largely dormant. The Department of Health, for example, has not adequately employed its validation of expenditures under the Charitable Institutions Budget to encourage programs of community service by voluntary institutions receiving such funds. In writing the affiliation contracts, the Department of Hospitals set up inadequate fiscal review procedures and, perhaps even more unfortunately, failed to establish contractual program objectives.

The Affiliation Contracts

Affiliation contracts now link all but two of the City hospitals to a voluntary teaching hospital or medical school and bring into the City hospitals full-time senior and house staff recruited and supervised by the affiliated voluntary institution. With this device the Administration of Robert F. Wagner, Jr., undertook to meet the major crisis in the City health service system, which preceded the present situation.

By the mid-1950's, progress in the science and technology of medicine had radically changed the character of the hospital as an operating institution. It was no longer possible to depend upon the services of attending medical staff contributed in exchange for the privilege of admitting patients to the hospital (in the case of voluntary hospitals) and for the use of ward patients as teaching and research "material."

The high degree of specialization in medicine today requires the intimate collaboration of practitioners in diverse specialties. To make such group activity effective requires the presence in every general hospital of an increasing staff of full-time internists, surgeons, radiologists, anesthesiologists, and pathologists. The hospital must place at their disposal an ever larger capital investment in complex instrumentation and equipment. Taken as a whole, the modern hospital has become one of the most intricate organizations in our society, subject to increasing demands from the community, pressured by changes in technology, and sensitive to fluctuations in morale and in logistics support.

With the exception of those hospitals that had been affiliated with medical schools--to which the schools, at their own expense, supplied professional staff and much of the necessary supplies and equipment--the City hospitals ceased to attract attending physicians. They accordingly failed to attract the house staff of qualified residents and interns who traditionally render most of the care to ward patients in voluntary and public hospitals. Residents and interns with questionable qualifications from medical schools overseas came in to supply the overwhelming majority of house staffs in the City hospitals. In the absence of adequate supervision by qualified seniors, these residents and interns were grievously shortchanged for the services they rendered at

shamefully low compensation. Many of these house officers could not speak English and so worked in almost
total isolation from any meaningful contact with most
of their patients as well as from the local medical
community. City hospitals proceeded to lose what standing they had as teaching institutions, and patient care
in these hospitals depreciated correspondingly.

In 1960, the Mayor's Commission on Health Services headed by David M. Heyman, facing the fact that
the prevailing salaries for medical staff in the voluntary hospitals were twice to three times the top
salaries available in the City budget, concluded that
the City hospital system was patently unable to hire
competent staff on its own payroll. As a means of
curing this particular problem, the Commission recommended that the City extend the affiliation principle
and contract with voluntary teaching hospitals to
provide senior staff and house staff to the municipal
hospitals. This recommendation was, in due course,
put into effect by the City government. Under these
contracts, the voluntary hospitals were compensated
for their costs, including overhead for which a 10 per
cent allowance was granted. It should be noted that
the medical schools already affiliated to City hospitals were excluded from this initial round of contracting and continued to render the services of their
staffs without reimbursement of their costs although
compensated by the provision of space and facilities
in City hospitals and by access to City patients for
teaching and research.

A summary evaluation of the working of these
contracts must find that they have largely accomplished
the purpose for which they were designed: to raise the
professional standards of the City's hospitals through
the employment of competent full-time and part-time
professional personnel operating under the supervision
of chairmen of various clinical and laboratory
divisions of teaching hospitals. Where the strength
of the affiliating voluntary made it possible to place
other services under contract to it, those services
were correspondingly improved. The contracts have
served also to avoid some of the constraints described
in Commission Finding 3; to this end some of the affiliating institutions have spent portions of their overhead allowance under the contracts as well as the dis-
cretionary funds provided by the City.

The affiliation relationship has been most successful in those cases where the municipal hospital
was linked to a strong voluntary. Since the number
of strong voluntary hospitals is limited, some municipal hospitals were affiliated to weak contractual
partners. In these cases, the affiliation contracts
have yet to bring staff of the hoped-for quality into
the City hospitals.

In many of the City hospitals the initiation and
administration of the affiliation contract resulted
in the exclusion or alienation from the hospital of
the physicians who formerly attended the wards and
rounds, either as volunteers or on per-session payment. But the services of many of these physicians
are essential to the functioning of these institutions
as community hospitals as well as to the professional
development of the doctors themselves. The question
of how to restore relationships with them is the subject of a separate recommendation.

As instruments for administration, the affiliation contracts have had the prime virtue of effectively replacing the line-item budgeting, which otherwise
cripples the operation of the City health services,
with program budgeting of the vital services covered
by the contracts. The contracts, however, have never
specified objectives and programs or means to evaluate
performance. Moreover, in the present round of negotiation of contracts that have expired and of new contracts with the medical schools for services rendered
by them to the City medical centers, there has been an
unfortunate return to line-item budgeting and less
than satisfactory progress toward performance specification. The present status of the affiliation contracts was studied by a special subcommittee of the
Medical Advisory Committee of this Commission and is
the subject of a separate recommendation.

In conclusion, the Commission finds that the affiliation contracts have substantially accomplished
the particular purpose for which they were written.
In the light of conditions described in Finding 2,
however, the Commission regards the affiliation contract as no more than an interim step toward the objective of making City hospitals into first-class
community hospitals and teaching centers. The affiliation procedure commits the City hospital to second-
class status because it places the hospital under
divided management. Quite apart from the City's

failure to deliver on its commitments under the affiliation contracts, the divided management and dispar-
ities in staff salaries and other benefits between the
"affiliated staff" and the City staff tend to inhibit
and stifle initiative on both sides. The intricate
nature of the modern hospital as an organization is
such that it requires the devoted leadership of a
unitary trusteeship and management and the support of
a staff with high morale.

Under the best of circumstances, some hospitals
will always be better than others. There is no justification, however, for using public authority to
preserve a system of second-class hospitals and thereby perpetuate a double standard of health service in
this community.

The Proposed Charter Reform

The Lindsay Administration's charter reform creating a Health Services Administration has been strongly
endorsed by this Commission. A single City health
agency, comprehensive in its authority and responsibility, is essential to the restructuring of the relationship between public authority and the evolving
community health service systems. The Commission's
recommendations in this regard are set forth at length
in Recommendation 2.

The Health Services Administration, in fact, began operations eighteen months ago under Executive
Order. Pending enactment of the charter reform embodying the sense of this Executive Order, the officials of the City's health agencies made significant
progress toward accomplishing its purposes.

Measures must be taken, however, to ensure that
the unified City health agency is not impeded in carrying out its vital functions by the constraints and
inhibitions to executive initiative which are imposed
by the City's overhead agencies on the operating agencies. A significant forward step toward the reduction
of these constraints is promised by the Administration's commitment to program budgeting in place of
line budgeting.

The defects in the City administrative machinery
are inherited from earlier days in the City's history.
They hamper performance in other operating agencies

as well as in health services. The Commission's Recommendations have the effect of removing the ultimate
delivery of health services from the reach of these
constraints. These Recommendations reserve to the
Health Services Administration the critical functions
of monitoring, planning, evaluating, and securing public accountability. To make the Health Services Administration fully effective in these functions will
require continued effort to restructure the apparatus
of the City government as a whole along the lines
pointed by the Lindsay Administration's reorganization
proposals.

PUBLIC AUTHORITY AND COMMUNITY
INITIATIVE

Recommendation 1 The City of New York should employ the authority and resources at its disposal
to promote the coordination and integration of
public and private resources in the development
of comprehensive community health services offering medical care to all persons on the basis of
their health needs.

Progress in the science and technology of medicine
over the past thirty years has made medical care more
effective. At the same time, progress has placed barriers between the consumer and needed care. The barriers are not only financial--medicine costs more--but
physical and institutional as well.

With the expansion of knowledge there has come,
of necessity, the fragmentation of medical practice
into a constantly larger number of relatively narrower
specialties. Thirty years ago, 70 per cent of U.S.
physicians were engaged in general practice; today
that same percentage are engaged in full-time practice
of a specialty. Because the rendering of care so often
requires the collaboration of two or more specialists
and access to expensive equipment, physicians are increasingly dependent on the hospital. Employment of
physicians in hospitals has increased from 10 per cent
of the profession thirty years ago to 25 per cent today. In New York City, 40 per cent of all physicians
have full-time salaried appointments.

Patients, of course, have had to follow physicians
into the hospitals; the rate of hospitalization has
doubled in this thirty-year period. The soaring of

this index, along with other indices of utilization of medical resources, reflects the public's rising expectation of medical care and the economic pressures in favor of hospital treatment set up by available insurance coverage. Increased hospitalization also accounts for a major portion of the increase in the costs of medical care. These costs have increased faster than family incomes. Between 1948 and 1962, private consumers increased their annual per capita expenditures on medical care from $86 to $120, in constant (1962) dollars. This required an increase in outlay from 4 per cent of disposable (after tax) personal income in 1948 to nearly 6 per cent in 1962. For a family of four the disposable income required to finance such an outlay is $8,000. This is $2,000 above the median family income. In New York City, per capita expenditures from all sources for medical care came to $227 in 1965 (compared to a national average per capita expenditure of $145 in that year). A demonstration program now under way in this City indicates that this expenditure is almost adequate to purchase complete coverage of all medical needs at an optimum level of care, provided the human and physical resources are organized for high efficiency. At 6 per cent of disposable income, however, the purchase of such service for a family of four would require an income of $15,000. Only 5 per cent of the families in the country have incomes that big.

Most families experience the implications of this arithmetic in acute fashion. Medical insurance, or "prepaid medical care," was counted on years ago to alleviate such problems for the vast majority of the population. Today more than 75 per cent of the people have such insurance. Typically, however, it covers less than a third of the total cost of their medical bills. Because of the uneven incidence of illness and disability and the very high costs of some types of care, many families are either unable to meet the costs of needed care or can do so only by exhausting their savings and going into debt. Many other families in New York City are unable to purchase needed care from their own resources at any time. The migration of practicing physicians from low-income neighborhoods and the concentration of medical resources in hospitals have placed additional obstacles--physical and institutional--between many people and the health services they need.

Summarily stated, these are the considerations
that underlie the new commitment by the Federal and
State governments to the underwriting of the costs of
medical care. The arithmetic also explains why the
index family income for entitlement to Medicaid was
set in New York State legislation at $6,000 per annum
after taxes. This was the income at which the City
of New York was already providing medical assistance.
The recognition of the condition of medical indigency
that has made the City atypical in the past now makes
this City the model toward which other communities are
evolving.

With funds available from State and Federal
sources to reduce the financial barrier to needed
care, it becomes the obligation of the community to
reduce the remaining barriers by seeking a more rational and effective organization of its wealth of
resources. This Commission proposes a systematic re-
constitution of the relations between public authority
and the medical economy of the City. It calls, in
this Recommendation 1, for (1) a single standard of
medical care in place of the invidious double standard
that now distinguishes the City hospitals and clinics
from the voluntary; (2) vesting the City health-
delivery facilities in a public, non-profit corporation
charged with the mission of rehabilitating these resources and integrating them into the community health
service system; and (3) the employment of City authority to encourage and secure from all institutions--
public, voluntary, and proprietary--adherence to the
public policy of this community as set forth in the
declaration of the New York Academy of Medicine: "The
availability of health services, as a matter of human
right, should be based on health needs alone, not on
a test of ability to pay."

(a) The delivery of personal health services
should be so organized as to be accessible and available to all from the point of primary service or care
through the community hospital to the well-spring of
medical science represented in the teaching hospital
and medical school. A fully comprehensive system of
health services places the individual, from the moment
he enters a physician's office or other place of primary service or care, within the reach of any service
he may need. This requires the systematic structuring
of institutional relationships in accord with the
community of needs and resources. It has been reckoned that a population of 500 to 1,000 people will

keep a physician busy; 30,000 to 50,000 people will
fully engage the talents of 30 to 50 physicians representative of the major specialties in a well-staffed
ambulatory care center or group practice unit; 200,000
to 300,000 people will keep the standard facilities of
a 300- to 400-bed general hospital occupied; while a
population of 1.5 to 2 million people must have available the full range of facilities and services to be
found in a major teaching hospital or medical school.
Each ambulatory care center, group practice unit, or
individual physician in such a system has ties to the
local community hospital, and the community hospitals
have ties in turn to the medical center of their region. Regional hierarchies of this kind have served
as the model in the planning of health services ever
since the Congressional deliberations over the Hill-
Burton hospital construction act in the 1940's. Informal channels of communication and referral thus
link many institutions in this and other cities and,
indeed, link the major medical centers in this City
to hospitals throughout the metropolitan region.

     For the purpose of securing the objectives of
public policy the Health Services Administration should
encourage the organization of such communities of affiliation on a formal and systematic basis. With seven
medical schools in the City and a score of teaching
hospitals, it should be possible to organize a "regional" system for each borough--or, perhaps, to let the
communities of resources and needs dictate the layout
of a larger number of regional systems (see Figure 1).

     One important objective to be achieved is the
resolution of the clash of mission--between service on
the one hand and teaching and research on the other--
that now complicates the relationship of the sponsoring
voluntary teaching hospitals and their affiliated municipal hospitals. The community hospital should be
obliged to receive and care for anyone in the community
who requires its service. The medical school and medical center on the other hand, must be permitted reasonable selectivity in the admission of patients. This
requirement is satisfied when the medical school and
its hospital, with command of the rarer specialties
and more exotic instrumentation and equipment, serve
as a regional medical center and backstop the community
hospitals in the region. Given the rising interest in
"community medicine" in the medical schools, however,
it is likely that the regional medical center will

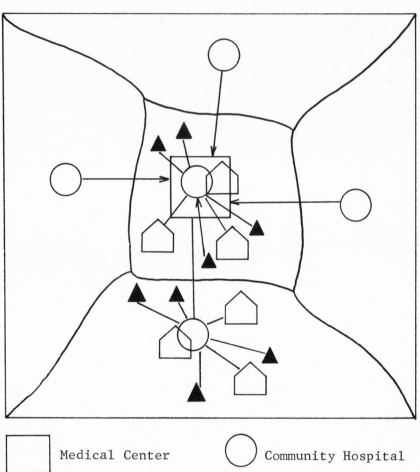

	Medical Center		Community Hospital
	Extended and Chronic Care Facilities	▲	Ambulatory Care Facilities

Figure 1.   Integrated Health Services Delivery

Health service facilities in a borough or "region" should be linked by rational allocation of responsibility to form a comprehensive delivery system. Sites of primary care in each community are related to the community hospital. Each community hospital is tied, in turn, to the teaching hospital or medical school that serves as the regional medical center. The medical center, in this model system, also serves as a community hospital backing up the primary care facilities of its immediate community.

want to serve also as a community hospital for its immediate community of 200,000 people.

A fully comprehensive system of health services
lays as much emphasis upon preventive, supportive, and
positive health measures as upon treatment for illness
and injury. Rationalization of community resources
makes it possible by these measures to "narrow the
front door and widen the back door of the hospital."

Preventive or sufficiently early ambulatory care
may avert hospitalization. Extended-care facilities
can reduce the length of stay in the costly general
hospital bed. A "day hospital" service can keep an
emotionally ill person ambulatory and on the way to re-
covery instead of occupying a bed in a State hospital.
Affiliation of nursing homes to a community hospital
can ensure high-grade care in a setting more supportive of an elderly person's health needs and morale.

The rising costs of medical care require every
community to promote such structuring of its resources
on a formal basis. Some portion of the current increase in costs is attributable to the redress of inequities in wage scales that have made non-professional
hospital employees serve as involuntary philanthro-
pists. Some cost increases are attributable, however,
to inappropriate use of resources encouraged by present
modes of compensating and reimbursing physicians and
institutions. With institutions linked in logical
relationships to one another, it will be possible to
establish financial incentives for more effective and
economical utilization of resources.

For the low-income neighborhoods of New York City,
the presence of the private primary physician available on call must be regarded as a remote prospect.
To bring physician services into these communities
will require the establishment of ambulatory care centers, such as that successfully demonstrated in the
Gouverneur Ambulatory Care District. The need for a
network of these centers is urgent, as the crowded and
demeaning conditions of the hospital outpatient departments and emergency rooms make plain. These centers will, in all likelihood, be staffed by physicians
from associated community hospitals and by neighborhood physicians on a part-time basis. To achieve the
necessary continuity of care under these circumstances
will require devoted supervision and the development
of painstaking unit-record procedures. If such

centers are to provide adequate primary care they must
be firmly linked to the community hospital, and ways
must be found to give recognition and prestige to this
much-needed service (see Figure 2).

(b) Community initiative should be enlisted to
manage the ultimate delivery of personal health services by arrangements that assure responsiveness to the
needs of the community and accountability for the use
of public funds provided for this purpose. The City
of New York has had to build and operate hospitals in
the past in order to fulfill the public commitment to
provide care to those who could not secure it elsewhere. Many of the voluntary hospitals in the City
were built by religious, cultural, and ethnic communities to serve members of those communities more or less
exclusively. The great teaching hospitals had to reserve the right to turn patients away in order to have
beds available for their teaching and research missions. So long as these institutions had to depend
upon philanthropy to make ends meet, they were short
of facilities, beds, and funds. The City filled the
gap.

In recent years, as the burden of medical depend-
ency on the City has grown, the City has found it possible to contract out an increasing part of its burden
to the voluntary hospitals.

A City hospital serving the medically indigent is
not providing the quality, scope, flexibility, and
economy of services of which medicine is capable. With
public funds now available to ensure the reimbursement
of hospital costs, there is no longer any reason for
the City to continue its attempt to operate hospitals
exclusively for the indigent. The segregation of hospital and other health facilities in the present dual
system not only perpetuates an invidious double standard of care but also results in uneconomical multiplication and inflexible use of facilities and personnel.

There are also strong, affirmative reasons why
the City might better serve its responsibility for the
community's health by disengaging itself from its
direct role in the operation of hospitals and health
facilities. The proposed transfer of the operation of
the City hospitals and health facilities to the public
non-profit Health Services Corporation, described in
Recommendation 3, would be a long step toward the
fusion of the present dual system into a single

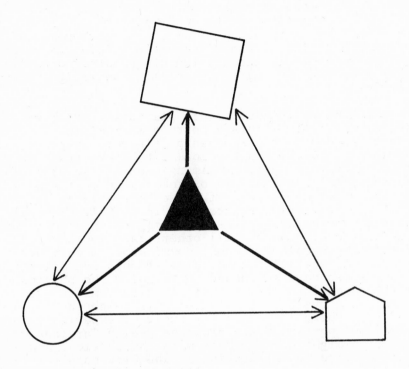

Figure 2.   The Individual in the
       Health Services System

The model comprehensive health service system is shown here as it appears from the
point of view of the individual consumer.
From the site of primary care, at the center
of the diagram, the system places him within reach of any resource he may need,
whether it be the services of the community
hospital or medical center or ancillary
facilities for chronic and extended care.
(See key to symbols in Figure 1.)

39

hospital system. All of the voluntary hospitals are now, or shortly will be, dependent upon public funds for half or more of their operating income. Thus, along with the former City hospitals, they will owe much the same accounting of costs and performance to public authority. It now becomes possible, therefore, to bring about the integration of private and public resources into a single high-quality community health service.

Voluntary initiative has played a central role in the development of this country's medical institutions, providing dedicated leadership, financial support, and personal service. In New York City there are eighty-two voluntary hospitals. Among them are several of the greatest institutions of their kind in the world. On the other hand, some of these hospitals are too small to be viable, others have lost their original constituencies as the result of migration within and out of the City, and still others face increasing difficulty because of their commitment to outmoded service as specialty hospitals. Though not all boards of trustees have succeeded in building the physical and financial assets of their institutions to adequate size, many oversee institutions with high quality and morale. There is here a reservoir of experience and devotion upon which the proposed Health Services Corporation might draw to help with the physical and administrative rehabilitation of the City hospitals and their integration into a unified health delivery system.

This development could also provide an important link between the City hospitals and the communities they serve. Other equally important channels of communication to the community must also be developed. Between the people of middle-class background who operate the medical institutions and the low-income and otherwise disadvantaged groups of the City there is a significant "culture gap." It is important that this gap be bridged in order to ensure that the health services are responsive to needs. A "feedback loop" is a recognized essential linkage in all institutions. These considerations lead the Commission to recommend the incorporation of community advisory boards in the structure of the proposed Health Services Corporation. Similar considerations urge the desirability of adopting the same policy for the voluntary hospitals that undertake service as community hospitals.

(c) The role of the Health Services Administration in the delivery of personal health services should be to plan, monitor, coordinate, and evaluate health care in the community. These responsibilities, along with the necessary authority, should be vested in the elected and appointed City officials because they are most immediately accountable to the public and are called upon to deliver services when others fail. The separation of the responsibility for operating health facilities from the planning and regulation of them is a desirable end in itself. In its management of hospitals, the City has set a poor example of the standards it is charged with maintaining. Freed of the task of operations, the Health Services Administration should be able to acquit its regulatory responsibilities in better fashion. The Commission's Recommendation 2 sets out proposals for the creation of a model service that would have the mission of assuring that optimum health care is available and accessible to all.

The Commission here urges that these responsibilities and the powers necessary to fulfill them be vested in the Health Services Administration. Among the ruling considerations is the fact that New York City is perhaps the foremost medical center in the nation. The standards of excellence toward which it can aspire are unique. This community has an obligation to the country as a whole to realize the potentials of its disproportionate wealth of medical resources.

In recent years, the City has been losing authority to the State. Inspection and auditing of the voluntary hospitals in the City, for example, are now vested in the State Department of Health. Continued transfer of the City's health responsibilities to the State does not of itself solve problems and brings further fragmentation of services. The Commission urges that full authority be restored to the City. The City must continue to carry a significant percentage of the cost of the health services out of its own tax levies; indirectly, its citizens, as State and Federal taxpayers, carry the full burden. Whether the City has authority or not, its officials are held responsible by the community for the performance of its health services. If the reconstituted health agency of the City is to function effectively, its authority must be as comprehensive as its responsibility.

The Commission believes that long-range comprehensive health facility planning for New York City
constitutes a primary assignment of the Health Services Administration. In particular, this will involve
guiding the evolution of smaller voluntary hospitals
toward fulfillment of one of these roles in the comprehensive system:

- Expansion to a 300- to 400-bed community
  general hospital;

- By conversion, a major community-oriented
  ambulatory care center, satellite to a general
  hospital;

- Relocation to be physically adjacent to a
  large general hospital, serving its community
  as an extended care or "self care" center;

- Conversion to an appropriate form of long-
  term nursing home and rehabilitation center.

In any event, all medium- and small-size voluntary hospitals should be in active affiliation with
large general hospitals, should serve as a focus of
working relationship with community physicians, and
should evolve according to comprehensive planning
for the City as a whole.

The Commission has not made a detailed study of
the proprietary hospitals. It recommends that an
objective study be made by a competent disinterested
group, looking to proposals for legislative, regulatory, and functional changes.

A similar foundation should be laid for the development of a comprehensive program for improvement
of nursing home facilities. In the process, the
entire system of regulation, inspection, and licensing
should be examined objectively and appropriately
revised. Deficient nursing homes should not be allowed to continue as they are. Renovation programs
should be instituted (this need not mean expansion in
bed count) in accord with a City-wide scheme for
meeting this crucial need. All long-term-care beds
should be located either adjacent to general-care
hospitals or have the in-house advantage of medical
staff specializing in geriatrics. All nursing homes
should be affiliated with strong general hospitals;
all should have strong rehabilitation services.

Recommendation 2 The City health agencies should
be consolidated in a single Health Services Administration charged with monitoring the health
status and determining the health needs of the
population, long-range planning and the setting
of standards and broad objectives of the health
services system, the coordination of the use of
health resources, the maintenance of the environmental defenses, the inspection of health and
hospital facilities, the securing of performance
and fiscal accountability of agencies receiving
public funds, and the sponsorship of health
research (see Figure 3).

The Commission's recommendation to consolidate
the City health agencies in a single Health Services
Administration is coupled with its recommendation that
the City create the public, non-profit corporation,
the Health Services Corporation, described in Recommendation 3. The effect of these recommendations will
be to transform the historic health-care delivery
activity of the City.

The Health Services Administration will continue
its responsibility for environmental defenses and
strengthen its traditional public health activities.
With regard to personal health services, its role
will be to assure satisfactory delivery through planning, financing, and regulating.

The Commission, in its Interim Report to the Mayor
on May 4, 1967, strongly supported the creation of a
single Health Services Administration. This is an
indispensable first step in ending the fragmentation
of responsibility for the health of the people of the
City. Such fragmentation would be especially inimical
to the effective exercise of the vital functions envisioned by this Commission for the unified City health
agency. Relieved of its present onerous burden of
operating hospitals and clinics, the Health Services
Administration will be free to pioneer the extension
of the disciplines of public health for the improvement of the delivery of personal health services. In
this work it must provide leadership to the other
elements in the health services system. As Dr.
Richard Weinerman of the Yale Medical School has
emphasized: "The needed balance of interests depends
upon the conscious and systematic cooperation of the
four groups concerned with the giving and getting

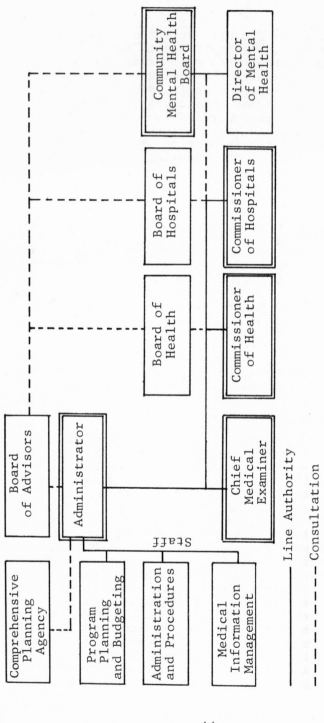

Figure 3.   Health Services Administration

Health Services Administration brings together in a single agency all of the City's
health services. Loci of line authority are indicated by double boxes. The Community
Mental Health Board, appointed by the Mayor, derives its authority from state legislation. Other Boards, under City Charter, have considerable code-writing and standard-
setting authority and bring expert counsel from the community into policy-making.

of medical care: consumers, arrangers, providers, and payers."

The statutory Boards of Health and Hospitals will play integral roles in the policy-making of the unified City health agency: the Board of Health as promulgator of the City Health Code and the Board of Hospitals in the establishment of the hospital and other health facility codes. The Community Mental Health Board, created to carry out the provisions of the State Community Mental Health Services Act, will continue to promote the development of mental health services and facilities through the Health Services Administration.

From the authority of these Boards, the Health Services Administration derives ample powers to carry out the functions envisioned for it in this recommendation. The Board of Health is authorized: "to enforce all provisions of law ... for the care, promotion, and protection of health"; the Board of Hospitals: "to establish and promote the highest possible standards for the care of sick, injured, aged, and infirm persons."

These Boards bring highly qualified professional skills and experience from the community into the highest policy-making level of the Health Services Administration. Each Board should have representation, through appointment by the Mayor, on the Health Services Administration Board of Advisors.

The Administrator of the Health Services Administration may be a layman or a Doctor of Medicine experienced in urban health affairs. The headquarters organization should be a small elite staff, headed by three deputy administrators responsible for (1) program planning and budgeting, (2) management information systems, and (3) administration and procedure. From the Administrator, line authority should run directly to four principal executive officers, corresponding to the present Commissioner of Health, the Commissioner of Hospitals, the Director of the Community Mental Health Board, and the Chief Medical Examiner.

The Commissioner of Health, as chief health officer of the City, should be a qualified Doctor of Medicine; he should serve as chairman of the Board of Health. He will have responsibility for the professional medical input to the planning function of the

Health Services Administration and for the supervision
of medical standards. The Health Department will
evolve into the Administration's agency for monitoring
the health status and determining the health needs of
the population, for the formulation of health program
objectives, for the design of programs, and for the
evaluation of the performance of the personal health
services system as a whole.

It must also be emphasized that a prime duty of
the chief health officer will be to maintain the environmental defenses of public health. The City's
responsibility for environmental defenses, epidemiology, and preventive medicine will continue. Efforts
must be made to repair the staff erosion of recent
years in order to fortify the City's strength in these
functions. Where public health programs involve routine personal health services, these services should
be conducted by the proposed Health Services Corporation and voluntary agencies under suitable arrangements for performance and fiscal audit.

The Health Services Administration public health
activities have a central place in this agency's prospective contribution to the delivery of personal
health services. Out of community-wide health intel-
ligence gained from these operating responsibilities,
the Health Services Administration will be able to set
health goals and evaluate program performance, to help
design new health-care delivery systems and programs
aimed at specific health objectives, to evaluate the
effectiveness of these new systems and programs in
achieving these objectives, and to plan the development of resources, both human and physical, necessary
to support the plans and programs formulated.

The director of the Community Mental Health Board,
in carrying out the programs of this Board, will be
one of the principal line officers of the Health Services Administration. It is necessary, for the present,
to maintain this degree of fragmentation--between
somatic and mental health--in order to give impetus
to the evolving programs for ambulatory care to the
emotionally and mentally ill. The chief of this
agency should be a suitably qualified Doctor of
Medicine.

The Commissioner of Hospitals will be the chief
fiscal and facilities officer of the Health Services
Administration. He may be a layman, experienced in

health administration. He should have responsibility
for the City's contribution to the forward planning
of the facilities of the health-services delivery system, for the validation of the outlay of public funds
to capital users, and for the administration of the
flow of the public funds that reimburse the providers
of health services. The agency under his direction
will develop techniques of program budgeting in place
of line-item budgeting. These techniques are essential to effective and constructive exercise of a
primary power vested in the Health Services Adminis-
tration--the power of the purse.

While funds from sources other than the City's
own tax levies are becoming available in increasing
amounts, it is anticipated that the City will continue
to bear a residual--and substantial--share of the cost
of personal health services. City funds will be needed
for operating as well as capital purposes. Wise administration can give City expenditures the decisive
power of the marginal input with the leverage to make
the total flow of funds serve the public interest.
Through its contractual relations with the Health
Services Corporation in particular, the Health Services Administration can use City operating and capital
funds to promote the development of the single, comprehensive health-services system out of the present
fragmented dual system.

The close connections already established, through
the support of medical research, between the City
health agencies and the medical schools and universities of the City can help significantly to enhance the
community leadership supplied by the Health Services
Administration. In the creation and support of the
Public Health Research Institute--a free-standing,
non-profit corporation supported by public funds--the
City has sponsored a now world-renowned laboratory
devoted to fundamental research on intractable problems of public health. Through the agency of the
Health Research Council, an advisory body of professional and lay citizens, the Department of Health has
provided "seed money" grants to the local medical
schools, research institutions, and museums. These
funds have powerfully strengthened the full-time faculties of the medical schools and have been multiplied
by an average factor of six in the inflow of project-
support funds from Federal agencies. The Health Services Administration should continue to back these two
agencies with City funds. In particular, it should

encourage the new initiative of the Health Research
Council in the development of research enterprises
in the delivery of health services.

In view of the intensely personal and individual
character of the services placed under its jurisdiction, the Health Services Administration should go
further than most governmental agencies to inform the
community of its programs and policies and to enlist
responsible community leadership in their formulation.
A major public health function of the Administration
is education of the public in matters of health and
hygiene. Such understanding on the part of the individual is the first step in effective preventive
medicine.

It is the aim of these Recommendations to vest in
a single governmental agency, directly in touch with
and responsive to local needs, the entire range of
responsibility and authority required to assure that
personal health services are available and accessible
to all. The New York Academy of Medicine, addressing
itself to the role of government tax funds in health
care, had this to say in 1965:

> When federal, state, or local tax funds are
> allocated for health-care purposes, an ap-
> propriate governmental agency must be fully
> accountable for achievement of the purposes
> for which the funds were made available--
> including the establishment of standards of
> performance and administrative procedures
> required for economical use of funds.

(a) The Health Services Administration should
be designated by the State of New York to organize the
comprehensive health planning agency for the health
services of the five boroughs of New York City under
the Federal comprehensive health planning law (PL 89-
749). The planning power is central to the fruitful
exercise of public authority in the development of
comprehensive community health services. That power
will have at its command increasing flows of capital
funds from Federal and State governments, as well as
City sources, for the construction of health service
facilities. The public interest--and every principle
of good government--argue that this power should be
exercised by a government agency. It is so designated
for the level of State government by Federal legislation. For the State of New York the planning power

under Public Law 89-749 is vested in the State Health
Planning Commission, with the State Commissioner of
Health as its chairman and nine other appropriate
State officials as members. It is here recommended
that a complementary New York City Comprehensive Health
Planning Agency be established for the five boroughs
of the City. The comprehensive health planning agency
for the City of New York should be chaired by the
Health Services Administrator, with the chairman of
the City Planning Commission, the Administrators of,
the Human Resources Administration and the Environmental Protection Administration, the Chancellor of
the City University of New York, and the President of
the Health and Hospital Planning Council designated
as members of its governing board. In the person of
the last-mentioned member, the chief executive officer
of a quasi-public agency set up under State law, both
the State and the voluntary institutions of the City
would have direct representation on the local comprehensive health planning agency. The directorate of
the agency should have the counsel of an advisory
board broadly representative of responsible agencies
and persons representing the "consumers, arrangers,
providers, and payers," with representatives of the
consumers in the majority as provided in the Federal
law.

The evolution of a comprehensive community health
service in New York City requires the rapid renovation
and rebuilding of existing health care facilities and
the funding of the construction of new hospitals,
neighborhood ambulatory-care centers, extended-care
facilities, and other ancillary and satellite facilities. The capital funds required for this program,
estimated on the order of one billion dollars for both
the public and the non-profit voluntary sector, must
originate primarily in government sources. Through
the local comprehensive health planning agency, the
Health Services Administration should have a major
voice in assuring that the disbursement of these
funds--whether originating in the City's Capital Budget or drawn from City, State, or Federal funds under
Medicaid or Medicare programs--accords with the goals
and objectives of the community.

To insure that the health planning process is
responsive to community needs and opinions it is essential that public hearings and public reporting be
an integral part of the operation of the agency.

(b) The City Administration should take measures to relieve the Health Services Administration of inappropriate constraints imposed by the overhead agencies of the City government; in particular, the archaic procedures of line-item budgeting should be replaced by program budgeting. The legislation of the Health Services Administration will not of itself cure what has been repeatedly found to be the central flaw that runs from top to bottom in health services in New York City--the absence of authority to carry out responsibility. The authority of the Health Services Administration and its constituent agencies to act is inhibited and frustrated by the procedures and regulations administered by the "overhead" agencies of the City government (see Finding 3). In order to secure for the Health Services Administration the authority and flexibility it requires, the City Administration must continue its efforts to restructure the City's governmental machinery; in particular, to install the techniques of program budgeting in the City's budgeting and accounting system.

(c) To ensure that these necessary powers not be fragmented, the State of New York should delegate to the Health Services Administration the authority for standard setting, inspection, and audit of voluntary and proprietary hospitals and other health facilities. Compliance with the standards established by the Health Services Administration should be a condition of compliance with State Law. The power to inspect, audit, and set reimbursement rates is essential to the fruitful exercise of the power to secure fiscal and performance responsibility and accountability which must be vested in the unified City health agency. The City health agencies now have licensing control over proprietary hospitals and nursing homes. To strengthen this power further and to end the newly developing fragmentation between State and City, the Commission strongly recommends that the power to inspect, audit, and set reimbursement rates for all classes of service rendered by all health facilities in the City be delegated to the Health Services Administration. If the State health agency were to acquit this responsibility adequately, it would have to duplicate here in the City a substantial part of the machinery of the City health agencies. The State can delegate these powers to the unified City health agency under suitable arrangements for review, accountability, and conformance to Federal requirements.

(d) A revised salary schedule must be established for the Health Services Administration to recruit the talented officials and staff necessary to operate the central agency of the City's health services. This recommendation is critical to carry out the enumerated responsibilities of the Health Services Administration. It will not be enough to give the reorganized Health Services Administration a clear-cut and manageable mission. It must be provided with the kind of staff that can carry out such a mission. The salary scale of the agency must be as competitive for the talent it requires as, say, the City University.

Recommendation 3 The City should initiate the creation of a non-profit Health Services Corporation chartered to carry out these functions:

(a) Operate the City hospitals and health centers and undertake the physical and administrative repair of these institutions.

(b) Repair, renovate, and construct health facilities.

(c) Develop and operate system-wide data processing, communication and referral, transportation, personnel training and career development, purchasing, and laboratory services.

(d) Promote decentralized regional community health services throughout the City in cooperative planning with the Health Services Administration.

If the foregoing Recommendations are adopted, the City should at once take steps to establish the Health Services Corporation as a vehicle for early remedial action (see Figure 4).

As proposed in this Recommendation it will be the mission of the Health Services Corporation to facilitate the transformation of the present dual system of private and public hospitals into a single, regionalized, and decentralized comprehensive health-care system. For the system, the Corporation will perform system-wide services.

The Corporation will take over the operation of the City hospitals and other health facilities now

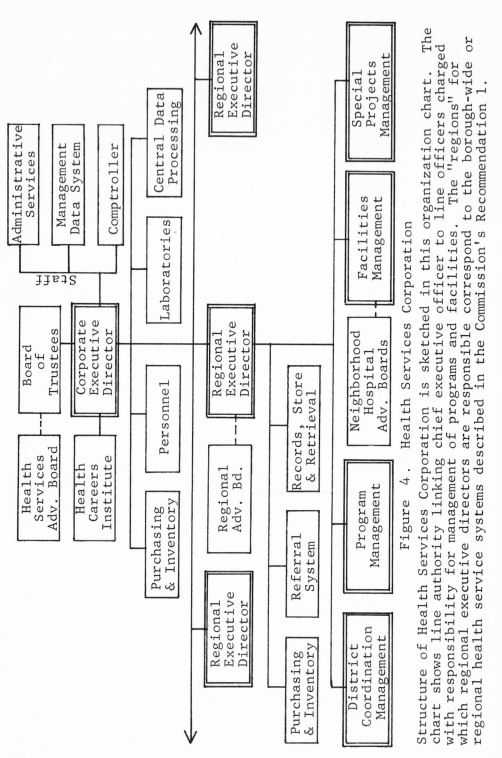

Figure 4. Health Services Corporation

Structure of Health Services Corporation is sketched in this organization chart. The chart shows line authority linking chief executive officer to line officers charged with responsibility for management of programs and facilities. The "regions" for which regional executive directors are responsible correspond to the borough-wide or regional health service systems described in the Commission's Recommendation 1.

52

operated by the Departments of Hospitals and Health;
it will thus assume the City's present obligations in
the ultimate delivery of personal health services.
By this arrangement, these facilities and services
will be placed outside the constraints of the "checks
and balances" system administered by the overhead
agencies of the City. Decentralization and delegation
of authority down to the place of primary responsibility for medical care will become possible at the outset. As the Corporation proceeds to the physical and
administrative repair of these assets of the health
services system, it will seek to place their operations under sponsorships appropriate in each case to
the character of the facility and the resources and
needs of the community. The task of rehabilitating
the City hospitals cannot be delayed, both for the
sake of the patients they must continue to serve and
for the important role they have to play in promoting
the development of comprehensive health services
throughout the City.

In the renovation and construction of health
facilities the Corporation should be chartered to
operate outside the constraints imposed on the City's
construction operations by State law as well as by
City overhead procedures.

The Corporation has a further major assignment
in the creation and operation of certain system-wide
services which are now lacking but which are essential
to the functioning of a truly comprehensive community
health service system. Principal among these is the
design, installation, and operation of a central data-
processing system. This will not only serve the facilities operated by the Corporation; it will also provide
the communication and referral services necessary to
link together the facilities in each of the regional
systems in the City (see Recommendation 1) and it will
provide the Health Services Administration with a data
bank to support its planning and monitoring functions.

While freed to meet its important responsibilities
outside the constraints that impede the City operating
agencies, the Corporation must he held fully accountable to the public and responsive to the goals and
policies set by the Health Services Administration.
The Commission has given careful consideration to
measures to secure this end and makes the following
recommendations with respect to the drafting of the
charter and by-laws of the Corporation:

(1) The Corporation will be governed by a board
of outstanding, independent citizens, not more than
nine in number, appointed by the Mayor. The terms of
office shall be such that the appointments of one-
third of the membership of the board expire every two
years.

(2) The trustees will appoint the chief executive officer of the Corporation with the concurrence
of the Mayor.

(3) The Corporation will operate under an annual
program budget concurred in by the Health Services
Administration.

(4) The performance of the Corporation in the
execution of planned programs and attainment of stated
objectives will be publicly reviewed by the Health
Services Administration.

(5) The fiscal operations of the Corporation will
be subject to public post-audit by the appropriate
fiscal agencies of the City.

The Corporation will thus be held responsive to
the public, through the elected and appointed officials of the City, by the power of appointment and of
the purse, implemented by the techniques of program
budgeting and benefit-cost analysis.

The Health Services Corporation will necessarily
assume all existing obligations of the City with regard to the personnel now employed in the facilities
and services to be placed under its management, including pension rights and collective-bargaining agreements. The Corporation will be relieved of the Civil
Service System requirements so far as new employees
are concerned and will establish its own merit system.

A Corporation Advisory Board, to be described
below, will enlist the participation of community
representatives in the planning and review processes
of the trustees of the Corporation.

(a) Upon formation, the Health Services Corporation will take over operation of the municipal hospitals and health centers. It will assume the City's
obligations under the outstanding affiliation contracts
and will review, negotiate, let, monitor, and evaluate

performance under such additional affiliation contracts
as may be required to staff hospitals and other health
facilities under its management. With the affiliating
institutions it will arrange to open the City hospitals
to the paying patients of private physicians whose
privileges will be granted according to sound procedures and practices of staff affiliation. The Commission recognizes that if private paying patients are to
utilize these facilities they must be improved to the
point where they become comparable--in physical plant,
staffing, and amenities--to the best in the voluntary
system.

In the operation of the City hospitals, it will
be the Corporation's mission to rehabilitate each of
them physically and administratively. In the case of
the medical centers, it may be possible and desirable
to transfer their operation to the medical schools
affiliated with them at an early date. For other hospitals, especially those in the disadvantaged neighborhoods, it will be necessary to encourage the organization of new community sponsoring arrangements. While
these hospitals remain under its own direct management,
the Corporation will seek to operate them as model
community hospitals. To this end, it will establish
and operate such needed ancillary facilities as ambulatory-care centers, extended-care units, and long-term-
care facilities. The Corporation should phase out the
City's chronic-care facilities, especially those in
isolated locations. The elderly are too easily forgotten at best; their isolation should not be geographically emphasized. Chronic-care beds should be established in connection with community hospitals serving
their neighborhoods. The operation, change, or disposal of existing facilities and the development of new
facilities will be carried through in accordance with
the overall City plan for an integrated comprehensive
health system.

The Corporation will, subject to State and Federal approval, be classified as a provider of health
services for the purpose of collecting Medicare,
Medicaid, and other third-party reimbursements; it
will be reimbursed by private patients, public agencies, and other third-party payers for the services
it performs.

Despite substantial reimbursement from State and
Federal sources that will come to the Corporation,
the City must expect to bear a part of the cost of

operations. In the first place, the City may expect
to carry a continuing obligation to contribute 25 per
cent or more in Medicaid reimbursement and to make
similar contributions to other medical assistance
programs. The fiscal officers of the City and the
Corporation will also have to reckon with the inevitable lag between the increase in costs and the increase in reimbursements and with attrition in the
flows from Federal and State sources. On the positive
side, additional inputs of City operating funds can
start new programs initiated by the Health Services
Administration or by the Health Services Corporation
and concurred in by both.

Each year, upon review by the Health Services
Administration of the entire program and budget of
the Corporation, the City will make its commitment on
a lump-sum basis to the Corporation's budget, with
lump-sum payments to be made quarterly in advance of
expenditure. These funds and the contractual terms on
which they are advanced will help to secure the Corporation's performance in the public interest.

The Health Services Administration will maintain
a continuing program and fiscal surveillance of the
Corporation. The Corporation will also be subject
to standard setting and inspection by the Departments
of Health and Hospitals. In addition, the Office of
the Comptroller will be responsible for a post-audit
with regard to the City funds involved in the Corporation's operations.

In order to increase Medicaid income the Commission strongly recommends that the Corporation be
responsible for Medicaid sign-ups in its own facilities under the policy guidance of the Department of
Welfare.

(b) The Health Services Corporation, with the
authorization of the Health Services Administration,
will be empowered to undertake the construction of
health facilities for operation by itself or by voluntary institutions. With the Health Services Administration, the City Planning Commission, the Comprehensive Health Planning Agency, and the Health and
Hospital Planning Council, the Corporation will develop short- and long-range capital construction and
renovation requirements for (1) new hospital structures or for renovation of existing structures, (2)
extended-care units, (3) ambulatory-care centers and

related facilities, and (4) chronic-care facilities.
The Corporation will be responsible for the design
criteria for all of these and for the specification
and purchase of equipment. The Corporation will let
appropriate planning and construction contracts,
manage the contracts, and see to their successful
completion. With appropriate State legislation, the
Corporation will be freed of the regulations requiring
multiple contractors on all public construction in
New York City and will be able to select a single
acceptable contractor after competitive bidding. As
the trustee of the City's capital assets in personal
health services, the Corporation will also see to the
disposal and demolition of outmoded structures.

     The Commission recommends that the Health Serv-
ices Corporation not be vested with the power to
finance its capital and operating requirements auto-
nomously and independent of the City. Several considerations prompt this negative recommendation. First,
the funds allocated for construction of health facilities in the published capital budget of the City
appear to be sufficient to get a substantial program
of construction under way; these funds are presently
under-spent because of constraints imposed by the
checks-and-balances system. Second, the power of the
purse gives the City a significant mode of control
over the performance of the health services system.
Third, if the Health Services Corporation were to
enter the capital market, it would probably incur
higher financing costs on its borrowing than the City
does. Fourth, the establishment of yet another autonomous Authority within the City, with power to create
its own tax-exempt debt, would, the Commission believes,
have an unfavorable effect on the City's credit. For
the future relief of the City capital budget, the
provision for depreciation in the cost-reimbursement
formulas of the government and other third-party payers provides a return of capital, which could be seg-
regated in a revolving construction fund. In addition,
there is the prospect that substantial Federal funds
will be available for the construction of health facilities in the near future. The Corporation might nonetheless be empowered to issue its own notes and bonds
with the consent of the City, should such additional
funds be deemed necessary to support the health facilities construction program and this method of obtaining such funds then be deemed advisable. This and
related questions are discussed at greater length in

A Note on Alternative Forms of Organization and
Implementation, page 70.

(c) The Corporation will design, develop, and
manage a city-wide medical information and data-
processing system. This system will support the management and operations of the health services system
and the monitoring, planning, and evaluating functions
of the Health Services Administration. The Health
Services Corporation should undertake this assignment
on behalf of the City because the Corporation will
have the necessary flexibility in administration,
personnel acquisition, and equipment purchase to carry
out timely efforts in designing, installing, manning,
and operating the system.

Integral with the design task would be specification of operational procedures for the management
activities of the Corporation as a whole, and for
determination of the role computers would play in
their implementation. Long-range planning for an
efficient, evolutionary data-processing system can be
fulfilled best when based on a whole-system concept.
Premature or unrelated projects in the automation of
information handling should be avoided. Existing
projects and capabilities must be evaluated and incorporated appropriately. Lack of compatibility in
programming and equipment can disrupt system efficiency as the larger system evolves.

This system development will be an ambitious
undertaking; in fact without precedent in this field.
Its full development would have to take place over a
number of years. As elements become operational, the
system will begin to emerge as the most consequential
operating tie between the Health Services Administration and the Health Services Corporation and, indeed,
the entire health services system.

A centralized laboratory service, equipped with
automatic instrumentation, could increase efficiency
and lower costs for the entire health services system.
The Corporation should therefore study the feasibility
of establishing such a centralized service on a city-
wide and borough-wide basis.

To build morale and relieve personnel shortage,
the Health Services Corporation should institute
training programs for bedside-care, technical, and
plant-support personnel. Initially, this effort will

be required for the staffing of the City hospitals
under the management of the Corporation. To the extent necessary and appropriate, the Corporation would
also provide central personnel recruiting and training
support for the entire health services system.

The Corporation should provide centralized purchasing, inventory, and delivery of drugs, equipment,
supplies, and all other commodities needed by its hospitals and other facilities. For each kind of item,
it should be determined whether or not "central purchasing" should be city-wide, at borough level, or at
an institutional level. As procedures are perfected
and economies demonstrated, the Health Services Corporation should make this service available to voluntary institutions on a suitable reimbursement basis.

A coordinated ambulance system, integrated with
a referral procedure, is essential to ending the trag-
ically recurring situation in which seriously ill or
injured persons are turned away from hospital doors.
Here, again, the automatic data-processing system has
a central role to play.

(d) The Health Services Corporation will employ
its substantial assets to promote the creation of the
regionalized community health service system described
in Recommendation 1. Toward this end the Corporation
will decentralize its own organizational structure,
with major operating divisions corresponding to each
borough or other smaller health services region.
Within each borough or region, the Corporation will
encourage the formal link-up of community hospitals
and their ancillary facilities with the central regional teaching hospital or medical school--in the
first instance by linking the institutions under its
management to the regional medical centers. The Corporation will also encourage the evolution of these
regional health service systems by providing data-
processing, referral, purchasing, and other services,
and by the construction of new facilities, in accord
with the long-range planning of the Health Services
Administration.

In structuring its own organization the Health
Services Corporation will decentralize authority to
the loci of responsibility for the delivery of health
services. The central staff, in keeping with this
principle, will be held to minimum size and charged
only with city-wide functions. It will carry out

operational planning in concert with the long-range
planning undertaken by the Health Services Administration. The staff will specify and fulfill manpower
requirements for health-care delivery, provide internal support services for top management, and undertake
appropriate central laboratory and related computer-
based services.

Each regional executive director will have a
minimal support staff. In addition, his office will
require a modest regional computer capability which
will be tied to the central data system in corporate
headquarters and to operating data centers at hospitals and other facilities. The regional executive
director will have four major responsibilities:

(a) Supervising hospital and other health care
facilities. Each facility manager will be given relatively complete autonomy in administration with the
annual budget of his facility underwritten on a lump-
sum basis.

(b) Management of district coordination programs designed to maintain liaison between health
agencies, organizations, and projects.

(c) Program management of contract relationships
between the Corporation and other institutions and the
coordination and delivery of borough-wide services
rendered by the Corporation.

(d) Management of special or temporary projects
in the field of health delivery. Projects might be
initiated, developed, and budgeted by the Health Services Administration, then contracted for execution to
the Health Services Corporation. They might involve
demonstration programs, mobile programs (having to do,
for example, with the feasibility of diagnostic
screening), or programs of health-need assessment.

For each hospital or other facility under its
management the Corporation will initiate the organization of a Community Advisory Board made up of representatives of the local community to assure expression
of community needs. Each local advisory board would
delegate a member to serve on the regional advisory
board, and each regional advisory board of the City
would be represented on the city-wide Corporation
Advisory Board functioning in relation to the board
of trustees of the Corporation as a whole. Thus, the

Health Services Corporation would have not only the normal and necessary line of management passing from trustees, to president, to regional executive director, to facility administrator, but "back-up" from the local community level, through the region, and finally to the level of the City as a whole. This separate line of advisory bodies would assure appropriate and timely consideration of actions and forces that arise from the community and that must be taken into account by all levels of management and delivery.

Implementation: A first necessary action will be the drawing up of enabling legislation for submission, as appropriate, to the City Council and to the State Legislature. Detailed by-laws of the Health Services Corporation should be prepared. As these efforts achieve essential completion, the legal formation of the Health Services Corporation may be carried out. Accordingly, if the Commission Recommendations are approved, the Mayor should appoint a task force to prepare for his review and endorsement the necessary legislation, proposed corporate by-laws, and the proposed corporate form, with attending selection of incorporators, initial trustees, and officers.

In all of these actions the members of the Commission on the Delivery of Personal Health Services tender their continuing assistance to the City Administration.

It is the anticipation of this Commission that the principal transition steps, as cited, can be accomplished in the very near term and that, upon formation of the corporate shell, immediate action can be taken with respect to many of the problems besetting the delivery of personal health services at public expense in this City.

RECOMMENDATIONS FOR THE INTERIM

The Commission recognizes that time must pass before the City's health services are reorganized and restructured and before the Health Services Corporation becomes fully operational. Meanwhile, people will be forced to use the City's health facilities, staffed and operated as they are now.

There are some actions which can be taken at once to begin improving the situation. The recommendations which follow include several which were proposed by the Commission in its Interim Report to the Mayor on May 4, 1967.

Shortage of Nurses

The critical shortage of nurses urgently requires immediate action. Of 5,721 positions authorized in 1966 for professional nurses in the City hospitals (to serve as staff nurses) only 1,363 are filled by registered nurses, while 3,696 are filled by practical nurses, nurse's aides, and other personnel. This already critical shortage of nursing personnel in the hospitals will be further intensified by the expansion of home-care services under Medicaid.

The Commission urges that all of the following steps be taken at once to arrest this deteriorating situation which jeopardizes the lives of patients:

(1) The City and the voluntary hospitals should establish a uniform nursing salary schedule for the entire community. Evening and night duty should be paid for at substantially increased rates. Nurses newly recruited to the City payroll should be paid at a rate warranted by their previous experience and training and should not, as now, be compelled to start at the bottom of the Civil Service ladder.

(2) The City should provide subsidized apartments for nurses convenient to all City hospitals. For security and economy purposes, the City can lease accommodations and sublease to nurses.

(3) Many of the City hospitals are located in run-down and unfavorable neighborhoods. Hazards to person and property make employment there unattractive to nurses. The Police Department should be enlisted to reinforce protections provided by the Hospital Department's own security forces.

(4) An experimental program at Bellevue has shown that retired nurses can be brought back into service by the offer of part-time employment on a per-diem basis. This arrangement should be extended to other hospitals at once and, if results warrant, should be made city-wide.

(5)   The training of practical nurses and nursing
aides to undertake an increased responsibility for
bedside care should be conducted in the City hospitals.
A major program can be mounted in a short time, with
recruitment from among lower ranks on the City hospital payroll and of young men and women from disadvantaged areas.   Recruits to such a program should be
paid while being trained.   In addition, career advancement programs for other positions should be established
for practical nurses, nursing aides, and other support
personnel.

(6)   The Health Services Administration should
enlist the City University, the Board of Education,
and the local community colleges to implement the
longer-range recommendations on nursing education of
the Mayor's Task Force on Hospitals (June 10, 1966).

Outpatient Departments

For the vast majority of the City's underprivi-
leged, the hospital outpatient department and emergency room are the "family doctor."   These services, as
the Commission report and staff studies make clear,
have been highly unsatisfactory to everyone concerned--
the patient, the doctor, and the hospital.

With Medicaid funds available to reimburse the
cost of outpatient care, the financial obstacles to
the creation of the necessary physical facilities, to
staffing, to proper record-keeping, and to other minimal necessities of adequate medical care are being
removed.   The major obstacle to making the out-patient
department a fit place to practice medicine and receive medical care continues to be the administrative
machinery through which the City must work to get
things done.   In order to eliminate this obstacle,
the Health Services Administration should invoke the
Mayor's emergency powers to seek immediate improvement
in the outpatient departments in the City hospitals.
Emphasis should be on the following high-priority
problems:

(1)   Space shortages.   Outpatient departments and
emergency rooms are short of space and in need of
emergency renovations.   Even temporary structures would
be of great help.   Until there is more space, little
can be done to meet other urgent problems.

(2) Nursing and support personnel. Most outpatient departments and emergency rooms are short of nurses and clerical support personnel. The Commission's recommendations on this matter appear as a separate statement.

(3) Medical records. For the most part, the vital function of medical record-keeping is in chaos. In view of the fact that services in the outpatient departments are so highly fragmented by specialty and so often rendered by part-time physicians, the medical record provides the only thread of continuity for the individual case. An expert task force should be set up to install a sound record-keeping procedure in the outpatient departments of the City hospitals at the earliest possible date. And means should be explored to bring about the same improvement in the voluntary hospitals.

(4) Recruitment of community physicians. Assuming adequate space, staff, and records support, the Department of Hospitals and the affiliating institution in the case of each municipal hospital should immediately develop programs to recruit otherwise unaffiliated community physicians for outpatient department service. This can be done as part of a general program to bring unaffiliated physicians back into the hospital system as recommended by the Commission.

Affiliation Contracts

Affiliation contracts, under which voluntary hospitals supply medical staff to the City hospitals, have been the subject of highly publicized controversy in recent months. The focus has been on alleged fiscal abuses by the affiliating hospitals and poor fiscal administration by the City agencies. This has had two unfortunate consequences. In the first place, the new contracts reflect a regrettable regression toward line budgeting, as against the lump-sum arrangements that permitted the voluntary hospitals to deliver services with necessary flexibility. The controversy over fiscal matters has further preempted attention from other significant matters: for example, that affiliation contracts can and should be used to develop programs of community health service. So long as the Health Services Administration continues to write affiliation contracts, it should observe the following guidelines:

(1) Program budgeting, as distinguished from
line-item budgeting, should be established by these
contracts. One of the great values of the affiliation
contract has been to cut some of the red tape that
impedes the City's contribution to the operation of
municipal hospitals. Program budgeting techniques
will help shape and extend the authority of the Health
Services Administration through these contracts.

(2) Fiscal accountability should be ensured by
provision for review of program and fiscal performance
at stated intervals, during the life of the contract,
with annual post-audit.

(3) Program specification should be employed in
the affiliation contract to encourage the development
of community services and to attain specific programs
for improvement of the services provided in the
hospitals.

(4) Program accountability can be attained by
provision for review of progress on specified programs
at stated intervals.

(5) Incentives for economy and superior performance can be provided in the contracts by provision for
sharing any savings on the program budget and application of such savings to the funding of innovative programs of interest to the affiliate institution as well
as to the City. Investigation should also be made of
cost-control programs already successful in other
parts of the country in which staff doctors, as a
group, and the hospital share in savings.

(6) Provision for new programs should be built
into the affiliation contracts by permitting either
side to reopen a contract for this purpose.

Private Patients, Physicians, and City Hospitals

It is a matter of urgency to open the City hospitals to private paying patients and private practitioners. This would not only relieve the present
waiting period for beds in the voluntary hospitals,
but also create an articulate demand for improvement
in the City system. Inevitably the City hospitals
would have to improve their nursing, technical, and
para-medical support, their record-keeping and

accounting capability, and their amenities. At the same time many of the presently unaffiliated doctors would thereby begin to be brought back into the mainstream of medical practice.

Subcommittees of the Medical Advisory Committee of this Commission have prepared special reports on this question and submitted the following proposals which the Commission recommends for study by the Health Services Administration:

Licensed physicians who do not hold appointments in voluntary hospitals should be invited to become attending staff members of an affiliated municipal hospital, provided they are qualified and agree to the following requirements:

(1) Restrict in-hospital practice to their training and experience as recorded in the directory of the State Medical Society, and according to the regulations of the Departments of Health and Hospitals.

(2) Abide by the regulations of the hospital's medical board and accept supervision of in-hospital practice by the chairman of the respective clinical department or his designated representative.

(3) Attend at least 50 per cent of the teaching rounds, clinical pathology conferences, and other educational programs of the department.

(4) Because in-hospital practice differs from private practice in that it involves the collaboration of many staff physicians and hospital services, inpatient income from private paying patients will be pooled in some appropriate way with all other professional income of the medical staff of each department (except official salaries). Each participating physician will receive a monthly payment from his department based on rank, hours of attendance, and other regulations of the medical board.

Opening the City hospitals in this way will speed the day of a single hospital system.

Compulsory Insurance and Comprehensive Coverage

On the assumption that the State legislature will reopen the matter of compulsory health insurance, the

Commission urges that any State program be made as
comprehensive as possible. It is especially important
that out-of-hospital care, including preventive care,
ambulatory services, and psychiatric needs be covered.
In anticipation of an expanding capacity to deliver
health care, the program should provide means to widen
the coverage from time to time.

Comprehensiveness of insurance coverage is essential to promote economy in the use of medical resources and to dampen the current inflation in the
cost of medical care. The rapid increase in hospital
utilization and the cost of health services is due in
good part to the absence of coverage by Blue Cross-
Blue Shield and commercial insurers of out-of-hospital
coverage at a price the public will pay. Expanded
and coordinated ambulatory care, home care, and nursing
home care, all hospital-connected, are needed to brake
the spiraling increase in medical care costs. In
further conformance with this objective, provision
should be made for compensating physicians and hospitals on a capitation and prepayment as well as fee-
for-service and straight cost reimbursement basis.

City Funds for Community
Mental Health Activities

The Community Mental Health Act, passed by the
State legislature in 1954, had the valuable purpose
of promoting ambulatory care in the community for
emotional and mental illness. Such care can be rendered at lower cost and with a more hopeful prognosis
than commitment of the patient to long-term and often
merely custodial care in a State mental hospital.

The Community Mental Health Board of New York
City, set up under this legislation, has State funds
available to support local programs on a 50-50 matching
basis. Expenditures under its program now run at
about $80 million annually, with funds matched, pro-
gram by program, by the City or by the voluntary agencies rendering care. In the case of inpatient care
rendered in voluntary hospitals to patients eligible
for medical assistance from the City, it is the City
that matches the State funds supplied by the Community
Mental Health Board. The City does not, however,
offer such matching funds for services rendered by the
ambulatory-care programs of voluntary hospitals. In
the funding of these programs, the voluntary hospitals

have been providing the funds to match those available from the State. The development of ambulatory-care programs in this City, in line with a primary objective of the Community Mental Health Act, thus depends upon the limited resources of the voluntary institutions, without encouragement by the City.

The Commission strongly urges that the City immediately institute a program of support for the development of ambulatory mental health care programs in the voluntary hospitals and undertake to supply half or all of the funds required to match the funds supplied by the State.

Medicaid Program

In its examination of the flow and impact of public funds, the Commission has given particular attention to the Medicaid program. The provisions of this program are of far greater scope and consequence than have generally been appreciated. Valid criticism continues to be directed to its administration, primarily by the vendors and providers of care. It is a fact that unfortunate delays in reimbursement payment continue; these delays obscure the fact that progress has been made in coping with the deluge of claims.

With approximately half of the estimated eligible population now signed up for Medicaid, there is prospect that the reimbursement cycle will be reduced to sixty days by the end of the year and the present backlog of early claims substantially reduced. A target date of June 1968 has been set for achieving a thirty day reimbursement cycle.

So heavy have been the demands for processing of reimbursement claims that little has been accomplished in the important area of monitoring and improving standards of care under Medicaid. For the same reason, administration is hampered by absence of effective management information and controls.

In response to a request from the Mayor, the Commission has prepared a separate, supplemental report dealing with Medicaid. That report calls for the creation of a single agency to administer the program, that agency to be vested with the now separate Medicaid responsibilities of the Departments of Welfare and Health. The Commission believes that this may be accomplished by Executive Order of the Mayor, after certain necessary agreements have been reached cooperatively by local, state and federal officials.

In making this recommendation, the Commission observes that the administration of Medicaid at the local level is complicated by forces beyond the control of local authorities and that a full clean-up of present difficulties simply cannot be anticipated for the near future. Resolution of certain basic difficulties must be sought at the Federal level; to clear other obstacles, action must be taken at the State level. Profound complications are introduced by the apparently inextricable involvement of Medicaid with traditional welfare procedures and practices.

A case in point is the applicant registration form MA-11, Application for Medical Assistance. By its complex nature, this form presents, on the one hand, a major obstacle to securing maximum reimbursement for the city and, on the other, an instrument of dehumanization for the applicant. The Commission strongly urges that this onerous form of means test be simplified, perhaps to a simple affidavit, at the earliest possible date. A successful demonstration here in New York City of the feasibility and desirability of employing a simple affidavit could help to promote the success of the Medicaid program for the country as a whole.

For the long run, the Commission urges that public financing of personal health services be clearly established as a health rather than a welfare function. Federal legislation presently places the determination of entitlement to medical assistance in the Welfare Department. Welfare agencies, imbued with means test psychology, tend to be exclusive and set up barriers to the potential beneficiaries. A comprehensive health care program demands an "inclusive" policy that carries preventive and early diagnostic services to people and does not require them to be sick enough to submit to the humiliation of a searching and exhaustive means test.

APPENDIX

A Note on Alternative Forms of
Organization and Implementation

In the course of its investigations the Commission
examined with great care a number of alternative forms
of organization to secure the delivery of personal
health services financed by public funds in New York
City.

The first alternative, of course, was the possibility of capacitating the present governmental apparatus
to improve its performance of this task by restructuring
the relationship between the operating agencies and the
overhead agencies. An important step in this direction,
for example, is the present Administration's determination to place the City fiscal management on a program
budget as distinguished from a "line-item" budget basis.
When the Commission completed its review of the required
reforms, however, it concluded that the "treatment"
would necessarily be as chronic as the ills that afflict
the governmental machinery of the City. Nothing short
of a total reorganization of the system would do the
job, and this would require months and years of careful
study and drafting of legislation. Many of these reforms lie beyond the reach of the City government, because the constraining regulations and procedures are
mandated by State and even Federal law. Nonetheless,
the Commission supports wholeheartedly the Charter Reform placed before the City Council by the present Administration. The creation of the Health Services Administration under this legislation is integral to the
redesign of the health-service delivery system proposed
by the Commission.

A second alternative considered by the Commission
was the possibility that the City might turn over the
responsibility for delivering publicly financed personal health services to the "private sector"--in effect,
transforming the City hospitals into free-standing
voluntary hospitals. While this approach might improve
the situation in those City hospitals for which responsible sponsorships could be found or organized, it
would contribute little to the system-wide objectives
set forth in the Commission's Recommendation 1. Moreover, the Commission doubts that the City could find
responsible and competent "takers" for all of its facilities, in particular those facilities located in

low-income neighborhoods whose populations are most
in need of improved health services.

A third alternative considered by the Commission
was to seek improvement in services through extension
of the affiliation contract device. The affiliation
contracts, however, in no way improve the City's ability to fulfill its part of these contractual arrange-
ments--the provision of adequate supporting staff,
supplies, equipment, and necessary renovations. There
is no question that affiliation contracting has improved
the quality of medical services in the City's hospitals.
But the divided management of the hospitals, under
existing conditions, is an awkward expedient and an
inefficient coupling of capability, authority, and public accountability.

The Commission also considered "total affiliation,"
i.e., contracting out to the voluntary hospitals or
medical centers all of the services and the complete
administration of the City facilities. While this
measure would in theory solve the problem of divided
management, it would not in practice automatically
provide sound management for all of the City hospitals.
Moreover, this alternative offers no significant contribution toward attainment of the system-wide objectives envisioned in the Commission's Recommendation 1.

The Commission also considered a variety of
"Authority" alternatives. The Committee on Public
Health of The New York Academy of Medicine has proposed, for example, that the municipal hospitals be
converted to open, autonomous community hospitals under
an independent Hospital Authority. The Committee later
recommended that in order to meet the need for an over-
all City-wide organization of personal health services,
the Hospital Authority be expanded into a Health Services Authority (see Bulletin of the New York Academy
of Medicine, September 1967, Vol. 43, No. 9, pages
843-849). There is no provision in this proposal for
a competent City agency, such as the Health Services
Administration projected in the Commission's Recommendation 2, charged with responsibility to determine
community health needs and to plan, monitor, coordinate,
and evaluate the delivery of personal health services.

Another proposal has been put forward by the
Institute for Policy Studies, Washington, D.C. This
agency made a detailed study of the origins and development of the City's affiliation contract system

(see New York City's Municipal Hospitals: A Policy
Review, Robb K. Burlage, Study Director, Institute
for Policy Studies, Washington, D.C., May 1967). Out
of this study came a recommendation for the creation
of a consolidated city-wide, extra-governmental Health
Care Commission to develop comprehensive public policy
for all tax-supported health services and activities
and for an independent Authority, separate from existing City agencies, to implement the Commission's
policies. In this Commission's view this proposal
makes inadequate provision for public accountability
and for effective performance of the vital public
functions assigned to the Health Services Administration in the Commission's Recommendation 2.

From somewhat different considerations District
Council 37, American Federation of State, County and
Municipal Employees, AFL-CIO, also proposed a Hospital
and Health Care Authority to assure equality of care
and equality of access to care through a single hospital system and, among other things, to stimulate training, upgrading, and promotional opportunities at all
levels of hospital employment.

Also helpful to the Commission in its final determinations on this matter was the study prepared in the
office of the Deputy Mayor-City Administrator. This
provided background information and discussion concerning various alternative organizational frameworks for
the delivery of personal health services (see Alternative Organizational Frameworks for the Delivery of
Health Services in New York City, Research and Planning
Unit, Sigmund G. Ginsburg, Director, September 1, 1967).
With respect to all proposed "Authorities" reviewed
here, the Commission shares the misgiving expressed in
this study that an Authority "may be responsive only
to its own needs and constituencies and not to the
needs of the community at large or to its elected
representatives."

The Commission concluded that the creation of a
Health Services Corporation closely coupled to the
Health Services Administration provides the way to
secure the best management under maximum accountability
and to create a health services system that would be
most responsive to changing needs and changing medical
opportunities (as illustrated in Figure 20, page 513).

The Mayor, in his Capital Budget Message, declared
that his Administration had under study the creation

of a Hospital Construction Authority. Draft legislation embodying this idea contemplates the establishment of a Health Facilities Construction Fund that
would finance the construction, renovation, and modernization of hospitals and other health facilities through
the sale of bonds on the open market. Such financing
would be available to non-profit voluntary hospitals
as well as to the City's own Department of Hospitals.
Return of capital would be secured from reimbursement
payments under Medicare, Medicaid, and other insurance
programs that provide for a depreciation allowance
large enough to amortize the capital investment. Such
a Construction Fund would help meet the urgent need of
the non-profit voluntary hospitals as well as of the
public sector for capital construction funds. It would
expand the pool of capital beyond that available in
the City's own capital budget--providing the proposed
Fund could market its notes and bonds--and would allow
the City government to enlist the voluntary non-profit
hospitals in the expansion of health facilities in the
areas of most urgent need. As now contemplated, the
Fund would be a "policy neutral" agency, with a directorate composed of City health, fiscal, and planning
officers, operating in accord with policies determined
by the Health Services Administration and the comprehensive health planning agency to be set up under
Public Law 89-749.

        The Commission finds no conflict between the de-
sign of the contemplated Fund and its own Recommendation 3 calling for the creation of a Health Services
Corporation. The Corporation, as proposed by this
Commission, would be chartered to carry out all of the
functions proposed for the Fund. Alternatively, the
Health Services Corporation could have its construction financed by the Fund. Whether the flow of capital funds is channeled through the Health Services
Corporation or through a Health Facilities Construction Fund, the facilities and programs served must
be defined by public policy expressing the needs of
the community.

        To implement the proposed reorganization of the
Health Services Administration and to establish a
Health Services Corporation, extensive further planning
and detailing of the table of organization in line
with the new functions will be required. New job descriptions will have to be written. Enabling legislation will have to be enacted. The Corporate by-laws
and the Corporate form will need careful specification.

Qualifications of present personnel will have to be
searched and decisions made as to new assignments
(including personnel in present City overhead and support agencies who will be transferred to comparable
or new functions in the Corporation).

Career ladders for health services personnel will
have to be devised, training programs created, and
training staff selected. Management support and
patient-data information needs will have to be specified and computer system needs determined. Finally,
the fiscal operations of the Corporation will have to
be established and appropriate enabling authority for
such functions provided.

Meanwhile, the Health Services Administration
would reorganize itself around its responsibility to
issue guidelines and goals for community health services, to plan comprehensive health care for all, and
to arrange the mechanisms for the disbursement of
funds and to conduct the audit of the Corporation's
operations. The transfer of line operations from the
Health Services Administration, and from other City
agencies, to the Health Services Corporation must be
an orderly step-by-step process beginning early in the
first year of corporate life and concluding by the end
of the second; several subsequent years would see full
corporate development.

The simplified operating flow chart shows the
working relationships between the reconstituted Health
Services Administration, other City agencies, and the
Health Services Corporation. From step to step, as
numbered, this chart may be interpreted as follows:

(1) The Mayor, acting for the people, sets the
executive policy for the operation of the Health Services Administration.

(2) The Health Services Administration assesses
the. . .

(3) health needs of the community, and
establishes. . .

(4) broad program goals for the delivery of
health care.

(5) Once established, these goals are entrusted to the Health Services Corporation, which then devises. . .

(6) a program plan to meet each established goal and prepares operating budgets accordingly.

(7) The Health Services Administration reviews program plans and budgets and thereupon issues. . .

(8) authorization to proceed. (Note: all of the above steps precede the applicable budget period.)

(9) The Health Services Corporation thereupon initiates its operations according to plan. (With approved budgets in hand, it would enjoy a high degree of autonomous annual operation; the line-item accrual system would have no place in this procedure.)

(10) During the course of operations, the Corporation incurs expenditures, and. . .

(11) produces results.

(12) The Health Services Administration then assesses results against plans in order to produce a continuing progress audit. (Such audit might well lead to modifications of program goals and changes in the terms of contractual agreements.)

(13) Because the results of operations are being carefully observed, it is possible to compare results with expenditures and thus make cost-effectiveness analyses.

(14) The results of program execution change the requirements to meet the health needs of the communities and therefore modify program planning for the next cycle of community effort.

(15) The overhead agencies audit expenditures on a post-annual basis and participate in original budget formulations and projections.

The City Health Services System

In New York City, as the Commission Staff Studies confirm, one-third of all the medical care and half the cost of institutional care received by City residents have long been paid for out of public funds. (See Tables 1 and 2.)

Total expenditures for health services from all sources amount to nearly $2 billion, of which more than a third, or nearly $800 million, comes from government funds. The provision or purchase of health and medical care accounted for 15.8 per cent of the Mayor's 1967-68 Executive Expense Budget of $5.18 billion.

New York City has the largest public financial commitment to medical care in the nation. In 1965 the per capita expenditure for personal care was 65 per cent greater than the U.S. average ($227 as compared to $146) and the one-third provided from tax funds compares to a national average of less than 20 per cent.

Despite a widespread belief that these public expenditures go for the care of the destitute portion of the population, the facts are otherwise. Almost 80 per cent of the patients in the municipal hospitals are people who manage to cover their ordinary living expenses but who lack the necessary margin of income, savings, or health insurance to pay their hospital and doctor bills when they are sick.

For every three days of care provided by the City in its own hospitals, two days of care are purchased from the voluntary hospitals. On an average day there are 5,000 such City charges in the voluntary hospitals; the City is thereby the source of more than half the income derived by voluntary hospitals for ward care.

Of the more than 8.5 million annual visits to various clinics in the city, over 3 million are to municipal hospitals; just short of 3 million are to voluntary hospitals; a little under 2 million are to clinics operated by the Health Department; and the remaining approximately one million are to thirty-six independent dispensaries. In addition, ambulatory care is given in the 3 million visits made to the emergency rooms of the municipal and voluntary hospitals.

The clinics and the emergency rooms are the "family doctor" for most of the Negro and Puerto Rican population. Outpatient departments are used per capita 3.5

Table 1. Application of Health Services Funds,
New York City Executive Expense Budget 1967/68

(millions of dollars)

Spending Agency	In-pat. Care	Amb. Care	Home Care	Mental Health	Death Investigation	Environmental Health	Research	Total
Dept. of Hospitals	305.1	52.0	4.6		.1	.4	.8	363.0
Dept. of Health		24.3	.3			7.3	6.0	37.9
Construction of Research Facilities							1.1	1.1
Chief Med. Examiner					1.2			1.2
Community Mental Health Board				73.8				73.8
Construction of Facilities in Voluntary Institutions				7.3				7.3
Dept. of Welfare	8.5	140.7						149.2
Charitable Institutions Budget	88.6							88.6
Fringe Benefits	37.8	31.4		.3	.2	1.9		71.6
	440.0	248.4	4.9	81.4	1.5	9.6	7.9	793.7

Table 2. Source of Health Services Funds,
New York City Expense Budget 1967/68

(millions of dollars)

Spending Agency	City Share	State Share	Federal Share	Other[e]	Error	Total
Department of Hospitals	182.6	45.4	133.0	2.0		363.0[a]
Department of Health	20.2	17.4		.3		37.9[a]
Construction of Research Facilities				1.1		1.1[a]
Chief Medical Examiner	1.2					1.2[a]
Community Mental Health Board	29.3	36.3	1.7	6.5		73.8[a,b]
Construction of Facilities in Voluntary Institutions		2.4		4.9		7.3[a]
Department of Welfare	44.9	44.9	59.4			149.2[c]
Charitable Institutions Budget	26.4	26.4	35.8			88.6[c]
Fringe Benefits						
Hospitals	21.9	5.5	16.5			⎫
Health	3.1	2.8				⎬ 71.6[d]
Welfare	.9	.9	1.3		18.2	⎭
Other	.2	.3				
	330.7	182.3	247.7	14.8	18.2	793.7

[a]Taken directly from department budget, intact or with only minor change.
[b]Drug addiction expenditure ($3.6 mill.) assumed to be split 50/50, City and State.
[c]Primarily for Medicaid, assigned 30/30/40 basis.
[d]Calculated on basis of percentages used in allocating department expenditures.
[e]Third-party collections and input from voluntary institutions mental health program.

78

times more in New York City than the national average;
emergency departments are used 2.3 times more.

Some twenty-five City agencies administer health
services to individuals in the City. They derive their
charters from statutes enacted over the years for a
variety of public purposes by the City, State, and
Federal governments. The twenty-five agencies constitute a patchwork array of services, with different
criteria of eligibility, separate medical as well as
administrative records, and different methods of providing as well as purchasing care.

In fulfilling its commitment on personal health   .
services, the City relies on the Department of Hospitals
to provide physical facilities, supplies, and equipment
and to arrange for the necessary physicians and supporting personnel. The Department of Hospitals, organized
in 1929, now operates twenty-one hospitals and medical
centers with nearly 18,000 beds. The Department of
Hospitals also supports and supervises, on behalf of
the Community Mental Health Board, in-patient and out-
patient mental health services in municipal and voluntary institutions and agencies throughout the City.
The Department of Hospitals, additionally, is responsible for licensing and inspecting more than 125 proprietary hospitals and nursing homes. In all of these
manifold activities the Department employs approximately
40,000 persons, manages a series of central bureaus,
and negotiates and supervises the affiliation contracts
through which voluntary hospitals supply physicians to
City hospitals.

The Department of Health has jurisdiction over all
matters affecting health in the City. These activities
are carried forward primarily through the promulgation
of the City Health Code by the Board of Health and its
implementation by the department. Among the major responsibilities of the department are protection of the
environment, disease prevention and epidemiology, maternal and child care services, public health nursing, and
health education.

There are some 6,000 employees in the Department
of Health who are located in the twenty-two central
bureaus and offices and in the hundreds of community
facilities, clinics, and projects. The latter are
customarily operating in or satellite to the District
Health Offices distributed through the five boroughs
of the City.

The New York City Community Mental Health Board was created as an independent agency of the City in 1954, in response to the enactment of the State Community Mental Health Services Act which, among other things, provides matching funds for a variety of outpatient and inpatient psychiatric services. The Board is responsible for the provision of adequate mental health services to the residents of New York City through municipal and voluntary organization and facilities.

The Board does not participate in the direct provision of psychiatric or other mental health services. It serves in a management, advisory, and support capacity Programs are carried out through contracting, affiliation contracts, and through the City's Charitable Institutions Budget. The Community Mental Health Board supervises and monitors these contracts and evaluates programs.

The Office of Chief Medical Examiner is charged with the duty of investigating deaths not attended by a physician or occurring "in any suspicious or unusual manner."

In May 1966 the Health Services Administration was established by executive order of the Mayor. The Health Services Administration, part of the Mayor's reorganization of New York City government, consolidates the Departments of Health and Hospitals, the Community Mental Health Board, and the Office of the Chief Medical Examiner. The Administration has the power and duty "to review, evaluate, initiate, conduct, and coordinate all programs and activites of these agencies."

The Commission on the Delivery of Personal Health Services

The appointment of the Commission on the Delivery of Personal Health Services was announced by Mayor John V. Lindsay on December 22, 1966. The Mayor, in his charge to this commission of private citizens, directed them:

> ...to make a thorough inquiry into the institutional administrative and fiscal aspects of the system through which public funds now deliver personal health services to one-third of the people of New York City.

> The inquiry shall consider the services rendered

directly by public agencies, the services delivered
through voluntary and other private institutions,
and it shall review the existing modes of delivery
in the light of opportunities presented by new
sources of public funds and by innovations in medical and management technology.

The Commission should set as its objective the
optimum employment of the magnificent resources
available in the medical economy of the City for
the delivery of personal health services to all the
people of the City. It shall recommend to the Mayor
specific institutional, administrative and fiscal
measures for implementation by the Health Services
Administration.

On the professional and medical aspects of its
investigations the Commission had the counsel of a Medical Advisory Committee. Co-chairmen of this Committee
were Doctors Howard Reid Craig and Peter Rogatz. Its
other members were Doctors George Baehr, Henry L. Barnett,
Leona Baumgartner, Norman S. Brown, Elizabeth B. Davis,
C. Joseph Delaney, Louis M. Hellman, E. Hugh Luckey,
Edwin P Maynard, Jr., Eugene G. McCarthy, Jr., Howard
A. Rusk, and E. Richard Weinerman.

The Commission meetings, at approximately two-week
intervals, got under way in January 1967 and continued
for nine months. Testimony and opinion were received
from responsible officers of the City Administration and
of the City's health and hospital system. Other interested
persons representing the organizers, planners, financers,
providers and recipients of medical care appeared at
Commission meetings. Included were spokesmen for non-
profit voluntary hospitals, organizations of private
physicians, academic medicine, and trade union organizations. Qualified experts, including administrators of
health systems in other communities, were invited to
share their experiences and knowledge with the Commission.
The Commission members made site visits to City hospitals
and to neighborhood clinics and services.

In addition some seventy-five of the City's major
community organizations were solicited for their suggestions on the Commission's task.

The Commission's field staff made exhaustive studies
(to be published separately) of major elements in the
health delivery system of the City.

A profile of each borough was prepared and its
health care needs and resources were analyzed. Every
City hospital was visited and studied from the point
of view of current operations and the fulfillment of
its role in meeting neighborhood and community medical
needs. A sampling was similarly made of non-municipal
hospitals and nursing homes. Studies were made of
medical manpower, the flow and impact of public funds
for health care, and the status and role of the City's
health agencies. The staff analyzed the operation of
the present health system as a whole, developed guidelines for community-wide comprehensive health care,
and made recommendations to the Commission for organizational changes to improve the availability and assessi-
bility of care. Some 500 persons were interviewed in
the course of Commission meetings, site visits, and
staff studies.

William H. Glazier, staff director, was responsible to the Chairman for organizing the work of the
Commission and its consultants, for planning Commission
meetings and site visits, and for general supervision
of the staff studies. Mr. Glazier is on leave for this
undertaking from his post as Assistant to the President
of the Salk Insitute for Biological Studies, La Jolla,
California. A team of analysts from Technomics, Inc.,
under the direction of Dr. Robert B. Parks, supplied
the supporting staff for the extensive field studies
and interviews.

The Commission's work was budgeted at $200,000.
This budget was funded entirely from private sources,
by major contributions from the New York Foundation
and The Commonwealth Fund and by supplemental grants
from The Fairchild Foundation, Inc., The Grant Foundation, Josiah Macy, Jr. Foundation, Rockefeller Brothers
Fund, Alfred P. Sloan Foundation, and Avalon Foundation.

Beyond the preparation of this report the Commission
members are committed to rendering whatever assistance
they can toward implementing their recommendations.

THE CHALLENGE AND THE POTENTIAL OF THE FUTURE
(by Eveline M. Burns)

The account in the Commission's Report of the inadequacies of the present system for the delivery of personal health services in New York City suggests that change is long overdue. In fact, change is likely to be hastened, and in some respects facilitated, by developments in three areas, whose impact on social policy for health services in the nation as a whole is likely to be so profound as to deserve the epithet "revolutionary." These are the revolutions that have occurred in the realms of social attitudes and values, scientific and technical advances in medicine, and arrangements for the financing of medical care.

The Revolution in Social Attitudes and Values

It is evident that in recent years the public has come to attach an increased value to health as such. By 1966, the Congress, in passing PL 89-749 (the Comprehensive Health Planning and Public Health Services Amendment Act) could declare: "...the fulfillment of our national purpose depends on promoting and assuring the highest level of health attainable for every person, in an environment which contributes positively to healthful individual and family living...." This is no mere rhetorical declaration. For it is obvious that the public's expectations in the field of health and its demands on medicine have become increasingly articulate, specific, and insistent.

There is now wide support for the belief that everyone should have access to the benefits of modern medicine, and Title XIX of the Social Security Act now gives effect to the view that medical care shall not be denied any person merely because he cannot afford to pay for it.

The public demand is also increasingly for continuous and comprehensive care in contrast to the present fragmentation. It follows that future arrangements must assure the availability of primary physician services to all residents and that the primary physician in turn (whether working in solo practice or as a member of a private group or neighborhood health center) must be related to the full spectrum of health resources and in particular to a teaching hospital or medical school, so that his patients may have available

to them the full reach of medical knowledge and
resources.

The public attitude toward the receipt of health
care appears, however, to go farther than this, and
to concern itself with the circumstances under which
this care is available. The demand now is for access
to health services to be prompt, convenient, comfortable, and free of offensive or discriminatory
conditions.

Satisfaction of these demands will require many
changes. It will involve the abandonment of the dual
system of personal health services whereby there was
one system of care for the comfortable or rich and
one, less desirable, for the poor. This change will
be hastened by the new financing under Titles XVIII
and XIX of the Social Security Act which, by making
public funds available to pay the reasonable costs of
care of the eligible population (both Medicare and
Medicaid) has at a stroke abolished whatever justification there might previously have been for treating
the "charity patient" as a second-class patient who
was expected to be grateful for whatever treatment he
received because much of it was rendered at zero or
submarket rates of remuneration by institutional or
professional providers. Today there are fewer and
fewer "charity patients."

But fragmented, inconvenient, and inconsiderate
treatment has not in the past been confined to the
poorer patients, and satisfaction of the demand for
access for all to needed health services that is prompt,
convenient, comfortable, and free of offensive conditions will involve a restructuring of the health services to provide that the point of entry to the total
system be geographically convenient and continuously
available to all the City's residents. It means transferring the functions of the often inconveniently
placed and overloaded hospital Outpatient Department
(and of the Emergency Room when used as a substitute
for more appropriate points of entry to the system)
to a series of neighborhood health centers or groups
of primary physicians. It calls for an expansion of
community-based services and facilities, many of a
paramedical nature. It is essentially a demand that
the interests and convenience of the patient, rather
than of the profession or the institution, shall be
decisive.

On the other hand there is a growing public restiveness about the mounting costs of health care and a demand for accountability on the part of the providers of medical goods and services, both in the narrower fiscal sense and in terms of performance, quality, and responsible use of scarce resources. The mystique that hitherto surrounded medicine is decaying, and there will be growing public support for public evaluation of the functioning of the system as a whole, as well as its individual parts, and for the use of controls and sanctions. This attitude will favor the adoption of changes aiming at a more effective structuring of the entire system.

The Technical and Scientific Revolution

The impact of modern science and technology on the practice of medicine has been spectacular. Refinements of techniques and almost incredible human skill, coupled with the availability of specialized and intricate equipment and the application of new knowledge from the physical as well as the biological and behavioristic sciences, have vastly increased the potential capacity of medicine as a whole.

But remarkable as have been its achievements in regard to specific procedures and the treatment of the individual patient, the application of modern science and technology to the organization and administration of the health services, either as a whole or in various subsystems, has so far lagged behind. From now on, one can expect a more general adoption of modern techniques for storing and retrieving information, for transmitting information, and for imaginative use of the newer methods of communication to facilitate consultation among geographically separated specialists. Automatic devices to facilitate follow-up of patients or identification of needs for further intensive service which so far have been little developed can be expected to become of general use. Automation of diagnostic procedures and laboratory tests is only now beginning to make an impact. Even the computerizing of appropriate aspects of hospital management and administration has not yet been fully exploited.

These developments in information and communication technology, and in automation, and their application to the operation of the health services make available powerful new administrative tools for grappling with some of the problems to which the practice

of scientific medicine has given rise. But they are
only tools and must be utilized in the framework of
specific social policy objectives if the potentialities
of modern science and technology are to be realized
and if the problems which they have created are to be
solved. These problems are numerous and stubborn.

(1) The rapid advances in knowledge and skills
make it impossible for any one individual doctor to
provide the whole span of modern medicine.

In consequence, there has been a vast growth of
specialization with a resultant fragmentation of care,
which has been the more pronounced and serious because
of the decline in the absolute and relative number of
physicians in general practice. This decline, in turn,
has been in part due to the fact that general practice
has not been generally regarded as a specialty commensurate in status and prestige with other recognized
specialties and, until the coming of Medicare and
Medicaid, has not offered financial rewards, especially
in the poorer neighborhoods, that compare with those
reaped by the specialist.

The resulting increase in the use of hospital
Outpatient Departments and even Emergency Rooms as the
point of entry to health services has proved to be no
adequate substitute for the family-centered primary
physician. This is partly because the hospitals have
not been located by reference to the convenience of
the populations who need service and partly because
these departments too are overly oriented to a concern
with specialized and episodic care. What happens to
the patient before and after his contact with the hospital appears to be nobody's business.

Nor has this hit-and-miss episodic method of finding entry to the health system solved the problem of
redundancy of patient history-taking and the storage
and retrieval of essential medical data about patients.

(2) The rapid advances in medical science and
technology lead to a rapid obsolescence of the average
practitioner.

The old policy of licensing for practice once and
for all fails to meet the requirements of the present
scientific age. In its own defense the community must
require additional study or qualifications of those
who have been in practice for some specified period and

must use its influence and powers to help the practitioner attain acceptable competence. It appears to be
generally agreed that a minimum step in this direction
would be the requirement of a hospital connection whereby the practitioner would be brought in contact with
modern developments of practice and subject to the
abrasive stimulus of staff meetings and contact with
his peers.

(3) The necessity to bring together highly skilled
professionals, expensive and intricate equipment, and
pure and applied scientists, and also to provide appropriate patient diagnosis and care has led to an
enhancement of the importance and prestige of the
hospital.

But while the hospital has become increasingly
attractive to practitioners as the center for research
and training and to patients as the locus for the
giving and receipt of certain kinds of care, and has
tended to become a focal point for the provision of
health services as they are currently delivered, it is
far from certain that the hospital serves, or perhaps
even could serve, in this role for the provision of
health services as they should be delivered. For the
voluntary hospitals, answerable to none but their own
boards of governors or directors (frequently self-
perpetuating and unrepresentative of many of the population groups served) have been in the happy position
of being largely free to determine their own role. In
particular they have been able to control intake and
have tended to concentrate on those episodic complaints
that have been the subject of the more spectacular
advances in knowledge or skill or which appear to present challenging research or practice opportunities,
especially those useful for teaching purposes. They
have in large measure refrained from involvement in
the total spectrum of community health services, which,
it must be emphasized, comprise a range that is far
broader than those offered by even the most socially
oriented contemporary hospitals. Even in their role
as teachers of medical professionals the hospitals have
placed emphasis upon the production of specialists in
the types of care that are typically provided in a
hospital setting. Only recently have there been signs
of a revival of interest in community medicine and
general practice as areas worthy of specialized study.
Perhaps most notable of all has been the relatively
slight involvement of the hospital in programs and
techniques of prevention.

From this analysis it follows that proposals for reform in the delivery of health services that focus upon the hospital as the vital center around which everything else must be organized and to the needs of which other structures must be adapted, in effect put the cart before the horse. The problem today is to reassess and reformulate the role of the hospital as an institution, and of different types or categories of hospitals in the total spectrum of an adequate comprehensive system for the delivery of personal health services.

(4) The present arrangements governing the distribution of responsibilities for the performance of various functions among agencies and within geographical areas impede the most effective and economical delivery of services.

For technical reasons some of the new services and techniques call for centralized performance serving a very large geographical and population area. Among these are the operation of a central referral system and of a data bank, the running of a laboratory service for all except the most routine and simple tests, the operation of a city-wide ambulance service or other appropriate forms of transportation and the like. Again, for technical reasons there are differences in the size of the area that can be efficiently and economically served by certain types of skill and equipment. Thus, the service area for open heart surgery, kidney transplants, or cobalt treatments may be very large. On the other hand, the geographical unit for the rendering of primary physicians' services is necessarily quite small. The catchment area of the community hospital is larger, but it is still smaller than the area that can be effectively served by the medical center or teaching hospital.

An orderly system for the delivery of personal health services would be characterized by adjustment of the location of areas of services and of the siting of institutions to the varying market or catchment areas that are indicated by the nature of the service performed. Some central agency, representative of the public interest, must be charged with the responsibility of formulating plans, and suggesting ways and means whereby the rational distribution of institutions and units of service organization might be approximated.

(5) Effective utilization of the new knowledge, skills, and technical equipment clearly calls for teamwork and a high degree of coordination.

Among the more obvious of the changes satisfying these requirements are the following:

(a) Recognition of the fact that solo practice is today outmoded. Group or team practice under public or private auspices is clearly indicated.

(b) The primary physician who serves as the point of entry to the entire system must be related to the hospital or medical center.

(c) Isolation of the hospital from the community can no longer be tolerated. Among the more obvious of the areas where the hospital in future should exercise greater or more effective responsibilities are the tasks of assisting practitioners within its catchment area to keep abreast of modern knowledge and practice methodologies, helping in the professional staffing of other local medical institutions such as ambulatory care centers, nursing homes, chronic care facilities and the like, and above all functioning as a service resource for the variety of primary practitioners and their patients in its area.

(d) There is urgent need for the assignment, to some central authority representative of the public interest, of responsibility for assessing the effective-ness of the system as a whole in providing appropriate personal health services. No one part of the present complex of health agencies, institutions, and profes-sional practitioners can be entrusted with this task. All would bring to it bureaucratic rigidities, profes-sional myopias, and vested interests. Such an organi-zation might or might not be charged with the duty of setting objectives (especially if the City were to create an area-wide health planning agency under PL 89-749 with its heavy representation of consumers on its advisory board) but it would have the duty of periodically reporting on the extent to which goals were attained and on the existence of gaps and inade-quacies, and with making proposals for the remedying of observed inadequacies or inefficiencies. Of neces-sity it would have to be equipped with a research staff of high caliber and creativity.

(6) Modern scientific medicine is very costly.

The period of training for professional personnel is lengthening. The supporting equipment that is
regarded as minimal is very costly. The volume of
tests called for in a complete diagnosis appears to
be growing. Public opinion no longer tolerates the
staffing of hospitals with non-professional personnel
receiving sweated wages.

In consequence the proportion of gross national
product devoted to the health services is steadily
rising. Attention must increasingly be directed to
ensuring that there is economy in the use of all
resources devoted to the provision of health services.
This means:

(a) Assurance that no unnecessary institutional
facilities shall be created or, if existing, be allowed
to continue. A major step in this direction has been
taken in New York State by the passage of the so-called
Folsom Act.

(b) The extent and location of highly specialized
equipment and specialized procedures must be determined
by the size of the service area which can effectively
utilize them rather than by the desires of any given
institution to be in a position to supply them.

(c) Expensively trained personnel should be utilized only for procedures necessitating this degree of
training and experience. In particular, much more use
must be made of the allied health professionals and of
non-professional workers (in the latter case under
professional supervision) and efforts must be directed
to training and utilizing available health personnel
whose potential now too often goes to waste because of
the lack of any effective ladder for advancement. It
is obvious, too, that the potentials of automation
should be exploited to the full.

(d) Greater attention must be paid to prevention
and to the better health education of the people of
New York. Desirable in themselves, these objectives
will become ever more appealing as the costs of treatment and care continue to rise.

The Financial Revolution

It is stating a truism to observe that the use of
private (commercial and non-profit) and public

(Medicare) insurance, together with Medicaid, have
revolutionized the financing of personal health services. Not all of the features of this revolution,
however, will necessarily ease the task of the City in
developing a more rational and effective health system, even though the new financial arrangements make
certain kinds of organizational and structural changes
even more imperative.

The implication to which most prominence is given
is the expectation that vast new moneys will be available which will enable the City to improve the quality
of care and to provide more adequately for meeting
health needs. Admittedly both Medicare and Medicaid
will make a larger total of funds available to the
health system as a whole. This is not merely because
the Federal government will be paying for, or sharing
in the costs of certain types of care which were previously a personal, a state, or state and city responsibility, but also because the Federal government has
adopted a policy of reimbursing for the "customary and
usual charges" of practitioners and for the "reasonable
costs," including an allowance for depreciation and
obsolescence, in the case of institutions.

But these very policies limit the extent to which
the City can use these funds to purchase more or better
care. A sizable fraction of the new money must go to
increasing the incomes of the providers of care who
are now no longer expected to subsidize the City by
rendering services below market cost. Only to the
extent that higher payments automatically improve the
quality of service or to the extent that with more
generous "bait" the City can bargain for higher standards of care or greater conformity with policies in
the public interest, will these new funds prove to be
an additional weapon in the hands of the City for the
improvement of the delivery of health services.

Even the use of the new funds as a bargaining
weapon to secure certain ends is limited by the fact
that their administration is subject to standards and
controls laid down by the Federal and State governments. Thus, efforts of the New York City Administrator to require certain standards of physicians desiring
to participate in the program were nullified by action
on the part of the State Health Department (often more
sensitive to the views of the organized medical establishment than is the City).

There are also real limits to the extent to which the City can, without securing the approval of the State, use Medicaid money to influence the organization and delivery of health services. Federal law requires that there be a single state agency responsible to it for the expenditure of funds under Title XIX and for the administration of the program, though the latter may be delegated to subordinate political subdivisions operating under state supervision. And it is the Federal government which requires that the determination of financial eligibility for Medicaid shall be carried out by the Welfare Department.

Nor must the possibility be overlooked that should the provisions of Title XIX relating to the financial responsibilities of the states become effective in 1970, and should New York State decide to assume the entire non-Federal cost, it might also decide to operate and administer the program as a wholly State undertaking.

It must also be recalled that some part of the "new money" will be utilized to reimburse the City for its expenditures on behalf of eligible people who have been given claims to free or partly free medical service under the definition of financial eligibility adopted by the State.

That substantial additional funds will flow into the health services system of the City is, however, undeniable. This, plus the fact that the funds come from public sources, will intensify the necessity for policy and organizational changes.

(a) The new financial situation involves the providers of care in negotiations with large-scale purchasers both private (Blue Cross and Blue Shield as well as commercial insurance companies) and public (the administrators of Medicare and Medicaid). Prices paid will no longer be determined by a largely uncontrolled competitive market, but increasingly by a collective bargaining process in which a variety of interests, considerations, and pressures will play a role. Because of the enhanced visibility of the health bill in which rising prices charged by suppliers will be reflected in higher premiums or taxes, there will be renewed pressure on those who represent the interests of the consumer and purchaser to pay diligent attention to the appropriateness of the prices charged and the reasonableness of the operational costs on which they are allegedly based and to assure that the public is

getting value for money. Accountability, both fiscal
and performance, will assume new importance and much
new research will be called for to develop policies
and techniques for testing performance, quality, and
benefit in an area where definition and measurement of
"product" are notoriously difficult. Inevitably, in
this context, those who administer the growing public
share of the medical bill will find themselves forced
to consider the effect on costs of the way in which
health services are organized and administered. To the
extent that the present disorderly fragmentation and
multiple sponsorship (public, voluntary, and proprietary hospitals and private practitioners) lead to
wasteful use of resources both institutional and professional, the new financial arrangements are likely
to strengthen the forces working for a more rational
organization of personal health services.

Even here, however, the fact that the City shares
responsibility with the Federal and State governments,
whose policies prevail, will limit the use which the
City might otherwise make of its bargaining power with
the providers of service to influence the way in which
health services are rendered and remunerated. Levels
of remuneration will inevitably be influenced, if not
effectively determined, by the prices paid by the
Federal government in connection with the Medicare
program.

Use of the Medicaid funds to encourage group
practice or prepayment for the purchase of comprehensive care is rendered more difficult by the Federal
policies adopted under Medicare which in effect leave
it to the medical practitioner to decide how he is to
be paid. These policies have effectively perpetuated
the fee-for-service system, on an item-by-item basis,
as the normal method of paying for medical care. It
seems likely that systems of prepaid comprehensive
care undertaken by groups of physicians will have to be
introduced by the City through the public financing of
demonstration projects which will presumably "sell"
themselves by superior performance in competition with
solo practice on an item-by-item, fee-for-service
basis.

(b) A second consequence of the new financial
arrangements is that henceforth an ever larger proportion of the recipients of health care will be persons for whom the whole "reasonable" costs of care
will be paid for by third parties, and increasingly
by government agencies. This will sharply reduce

the supply of "charity patients" and thus of the human
teaching material so necessary for the training of
medical personnel and for research. Two solutions
would seem to be indicated. On the one hand, efforts
should be made to increase the supply of other teaching
"bodies" such as dogs and monkeys, which, while expensive to produce and utilize, might effectively fill
part of the gap. The other is to press for a policy
of utilizing all patients, both public and private,
for research and teaching purposes. This would undoubtedly be as shocking to some as the present policy
of reliance upon charity patients has been to others.
But it could at least be defended on the grounds of
democratic treatment and by the consideration that today only relatively few patients pay anything like
100 per cent of the costs of medical care in hospitals
from their own pockets.

(c) A third consequence of the new financial
arrangements will be of profound consequence to New
York City with its existing systems of voluntary and
municipal control and operation of hospitals. For the
fact that an increasing number of patients treated in
voluntary hospitals will be paid for by public funds
will further blur the distinction between what is
"voluntary" and what is "public."

In fact, of course, for many years, the so-called
"voluntary hospital" has not been purely, or even
predominantly, "voluntary," if by this is meant supported by philanthropic contributions and fees from
private patients. The voluntary hospital of today
would be incapable of operating without support from
the public sector. This support is not merely financial, although this is highly important, taking the
form of tax privileges allowed taxpayers' contributions
to the support of the hospital, tax freedom for property owned or occupied by the hospital, financial aid
for construction costs and capital needs as well as
the ever-growing grants for research, mainly from the
Federal government. Equally important is the symbiot-
ic relationship of the voluntary hospitals to the public system. On the one hand the City, by financing
the supply of charity patients and by operating public hospitals for the poor, has provided the medical
schools and voluntary teaching hospitals with badly
needed teaching and research material. On the other
hand, the existence of the public system has served
as a screen to protect the voluntary hospital system
as a whole (there are obvious exceptions) from the
public criticism that would otherwise have been

directed at (1) its operation of a highly selective
admission system which reflects neither any rational
division of labor among the various hospitals nor
concern for the patient group as a whole but is determined primarily by the institutions' needs as research
and teaching agencies, (2) its lack of concern with
what happens to the patient once he leaves the hospital premises, i.e., an indifference to, or lack of
involvement with, the community's health infrastructure,
and (3) the failure of the voluntary system to give
leadership in the realm of prevention.

In some respects the public and the voluntary
hospital systems are in a competitive relationship.
In the present state of shortage of trained personnel
and of competing demands on limited resources for
buildings, equipment, and the like, the voluntary system, answerable only to its own trustees and governed
primarily by what is best for the individual hospital
as a research and teaching institution, can outcompete
the public sector for manpower and can divert resources
to the construction of unnecessary facilities.

Some control over construction of buildings and
installation of expensive equipment can be expected
from the "Folsom Law" and the powers given to the
Health and Hospital Planning Council. But the former
does not deal with personnel and the latter is overly
representative of the voluntary hospital establishment
while there is still some doubt as to the extent of
its coercive powers.

In view of all these circumstances, the fact that
the taxpayer will be financing a growing volume of
health service (in some cases over half the income of
the "voluntary" institution may be tax money) is perhaps only the final evidence needed to demonstrate
that there can no longer be such an entity as a purely
"voluntary" hospital system. The voluntary hospital
today is a public, or more accurately, a social utility. As such, it must be more responsive to the coordinated health needs of the City as a whole and held
accountable for performance as part of an integrated
system for the delivery of health services.

Determination of the appropriate role of the
existing voluntary hospitals in the complex of health
services and assurance that they do indeed undertake,
in partnership with the public authorities, the responsibilities indicated by the wider public interest,
will be no simple task. For the more important

hospitals today have dual responsibilities. On the
one hand, the hospital performs the vital function of
a research and teaching agency with all that this
implies for the raising of standards and dissemination
of advances in medical science and technology. On the
other hand, it is also a provider of personal health
services, and an appropriate compromise between the
two roles will not be easy to find. Furthermore, it
should be noted that should some of the existing
municipal hospitals be improved and equipped to perform research and teaching roles (as would seem inevitable if the health needs of some sections of the City
are to be effectively met) they, too, will face the
same dilemma. It is the function, not the sponsorship,
that creates the problem.

It is also important to note that the requirement
that the hospital of tomorrow be more responsive to
the coordinated health needs of the City as a whole
does not necessarily imply that all aspects of the
functioning of the institution should be subject to
governmental fiat and control. The task of the future
is to determine which functions in relation to the
delivery of personal health services must necessarily
be undertaken by a major teaching and research institution and are of such vital importance that their
performance cannot be left solely to the decision of
the individual institution.

Assurance that the hospitals perform the roles
indicated by the public interest can be obtained in a
variety of ways. In some cases financial incentives
will be sufficient. In others, discussion and negotiation between the leadership of the hospitals and the
representatives of the City will lead to changes in
policy as dictated by the public interest. In yet
others, regulation and compulsion may be essential.
It has, for example, long been accepted that the public interest demands that government have the power to
license hospitals. More recently, governmental controls have been invoked to regulate the investment of
capital resources in hospital construction and costly
equipment.

But whatever the specific functions of the hospital deemed to be charged with a public interest, and
whatever the mechanisms adopted to assure their performance, the fact remains that the modern hospital
is a social utility and is accountable to the community for the use it makes of the resources that the
community entrusts to it.

There are some members of the Commission who have
the following view concerning one aspect of Dr. Burns'
paper:

The Commission has centered its recommendations
involving the delivery of health services and curing
the present fragmented method of delivering such services toward the integration thereof around major
teaching or medical school hospitals. We heartily
endorse the Commission's conclusion that this is basic,
and one of the important reasons for the failure of much
of the municipal hospital system in New York City to
provide the same care as the best voluntary hospitals
is attributable to the fact that their teaching for
the most part was sub-standard. Until the promulgation
of the affiliation program, much of the municipal hospital teaching was of such a low order that these hospitals could not attract interns and residents in the
proper number or caliber. A hospital cannot be first
class without an adequate number of first-class interns
and residents.

Dr. Burns lays much stress on the fact that the
teaching and medical school hospitals must be made more
responsive to the coordinated health needs of the City
as a whole. She does not limit her reference to scrutiny by the government as to standards of care and
costs of delivering care, where of course government
must be concerned. She has reference to first per-
suading such a hospital to take certain action, and if
persuasion is not successful, compulsion, even against
what might be the judgment of the teaching hospital on
what course of action it considers most consistent
with its teaching function.

We submit that such a point of view can have serious consequences for the best long-term public interest. There is nothing in the past administration
of municipal hospitals either in New York City or in
the other cities of the United States operating municipal hospitals which would lead to the conclusion
that municipal governments in general are qualified
wisely to assume such power.

PART TWO

Symptoms of a Failing System

CHAPTER **2** SUMMATION
AND A
GLANCE AHEAD

A shortage of surveys is <u>not</u> one of the problems
faced by New York City's system for the delivery of
personal health services. In this decade of crisis
and concern--but nearly as frequently in decades past--
various Teams and Committees and Task Forces have
walked the corridors of New York's hospitals, following the nurses and doctors on their rounds, transcribing
the comments of hospital administrators, and compiling
statistics from hospital records, reports, and budgets.
Some surveys have been conducted with an Olympian
detachment; some have been done because there was an
axe to grind. Some have been coolly focused on the
abstractions of budgets and funds; some have expressed
with a passionate vividness the concrete details of
human waste and pain. Some have studied the problem
from the top down--standing, as it were, on the steps
of 125 Worth Street and scanning the vista of the city;
others have looked upward from the OPD's and wards.

Though their individual premises may have been
quite different, these disparate investigations have
produced a common body of evidence for certain facts
and truths about New York's health-delivery system.
Each survey found:

- the hospital buildings old and ill-
  maintained

- the nursing staffs short-handed

- the burden of paperwork insupportable

- the administrators harried.

In short, they found the system as ailing as its
patients.

Why, then, another survey? Because the problems
persist, and each year they grow worse. Though previous studies found and reported the same characteristics in the domain surveyed, they were as disparate

101

as their premises in the solutions they proposed.
Some of those solutions were tried, either system-
wide or on a demonstration basis. Most of these attempted solutions failed. Those that succeeded had so
little effect on the whole system that their beneficial results, from any distance, were lost to view.

And so another study of health-services delivery
in New York was engaged, under the aegis of the Commission on the Delivery of Personal Health Services.

The Commission wanted to look at the city's
health-delivery problem through a wide-angle lens.
Health and Hospital Departments, hospitals of all
classes, medical and nursing staffs, patients, the
families of patients, the communities in which the
patients live--all the pieces and parts of a city
form an interlocking chain of cause and effect; short
lengths of that chain cannot be examined and understood in vacuo. Therefore, the Commission assigned
its support staff the task of a broad system analysis,
not only of the processes of health delivery in New
York City, but of other characteristics and components
that impinge on those processes. Wisely, the Commission wished to avoid intensive, precise study of
limited problems (such as flow of in-patient load) and
the subtle entrapment of limited specialty approaches
(such as operations research)--thus foreseeing the
need for a balanced consideration of all the major
factors operating in the system of health care delivery.

The many relevant factors had to be considered in
the very brief period of a few months. Each topic
could be addressed only for a few weeks. All had to
be integrated and tailored to the schedule of inquiry,
and the dialogue, of the Commission.

This volume presents the findings of the staff's
system investigation. At exhaustive length, it covers
health services in New York City--the communities
served, the hospitals and their personnel, the management levels from bottom to top, affiliation contracts,
financing, information systems, out-patient care, in-
patient care, mental health, maintenance and support
facilities, and other things ad infinitum.

For nearly five months, the project staff pursued
a variety of specific substudies, among which was that
directed to the status and role of the municipal hospitals. For weeks, the staff walked the corridors of
New York's hospitals, following nurses and doctors,

transcribing comments, compiling statistics. They
found (to no one's surprise):

- crowded wards

- nursing staffs desperately short-handed

- buildings dirty, crumbling, and dreary

- sullen, dispirited people, waiting by the
  hundreds in the ill-lit, noisy corridors
  of the OPD's

- administrators--disgruntled and dejected--
  fighting piles of paperwork and warring with
  their opposite numbers (equally dejected) in
  the central offices and the affiliate
  voluntaries.

For each such problem area exposed and expounded,
this volume also suggests a set of programs or recommendations that might serve to correct, or minimize,
or at least diminish, that problem. If these recommendations were followed, and if the Health Services
Administration (HSA) were established under a reorganized city charter, in the form specified by
Mayor Lindsay, the existing system for the delivery
of personal health services in New York City could be
somewhat revived and refreshed, with remarkably little
dislocation of present structures and procedures.
(Recommendations concerning HSA, although they are
part of the complete package of recommendations assembled in Part Two, are presented in full in Part
Three. Reasons for this arrangement will become evident as the reader follows the chain of argument
adduced in this report.)

Rather quickly, the staff believes, the health-
services system would become more pleasant and rewarding both for those who receive the services and those
who dispense them. Repairs and renovations would be
in evidence. Some new and improved equipment would be
purchased and installed. Procedures would be improved.
The whole vast apparatus would begin to operate "just
a little bit better."

A praiseworthy achievement, surely (and one for
which the city may choose to settle!). But suppose
that in ten years, or five, or perhaps only three,
another Task Force or ad hoc Commission were to send
its team of surveyors into the city hospitals. What

would they find? Ruefully, the staff predicts that
there would be:

- more crowded wards

- more short-handed nursing staffs

- more dirty, crumbling, dreary buildings

- more dejected administrators, fighting more
  paperwork, with more frustration and acrimony

- more patients waiting in OPD's and emergency
  rooms, untreated and unhappy.

Why? Because the existing system for health-
services delivery is not viable; there is failure
inherent in the ingredients of which it is compounded,
and all the work, talent, and benevolence in the world
will not make it function well. The recommendations
given in Part Two are good recommendations; they
are the right suggestions for the specific problems
they tackle. But they can only work when they are
joined to actions more fundamental, more penetrating,
and more pervasive than any suggested so far.

As this report points out, at great pains, current trends in the population, the economy, and the
practice of medicine are at odds with the existing
system. Patient loads have been increasing steadily,
and the rate of this increase is itself increasing.
Costs of medical care are skyrocketing--projections
of the current rate of increase would be literally
terrifying (though possibly misleading, since the
current accelerated rate of increase, induced by the
advent of Medicare/Medicaid, may not continue).
Patients' expectations about medical care are also
rising, due to advances in medical science itself and
general dispersion of the idea that full medical care
is a right. Government actions at both the state and
local level ensure that the expectation of full medical service will soon become universal.

Therefore, recommendations at the level of those
given in Part Two can only produce short-term remis-
sions of the cancerous degeneration of the health-
services system--none of them strikes at the real
problem. In a short time, as entropy and the shadow
of time steal over the "refurbished" system, the thin
gloss of improvement will dim, and all the problems
that presently exist will recur--probably in a more
virulent form.

A leader in the trend toward universal medical
service, New York City has committed itself, by its
own charter, to "care for the emergent and indigent
sick." Those words were not put in the charter in ill
faith, or to express a wishful thought. They were put
there because the city feels responsible for, and
truthfully intends to succor, its ailing poor. But
the garments in which the city has clothed this inten-
tion are threadbare. They can no longer be mended and
patched and darned and held together.

This discussion has reached a discouraging junc-
ture. Are there no answers to the problems that Part
Two describes at such length? Is every beginning its
own end? Every advance, a retreat? There are answers,
but to see them, one has to view the problem from a
new standpoint. The answers depend on perceiving not
just the symptoms of the city's disease, but the
disease itself.

The present survey and investigation--a brief
but comprehensive study of the system, whose scope
can be roughly judged by the size of its documenta-
tion--concludes that the real disease lies in four
factors, deceptively simple in their statement, but
complex and striking in their implications:

- existing health resources are being wasted

- new health resources are needed

- health services goals are ill-defined

- essentially, the whole health care "system"
  operates as a complex, mindless body, the
  responses of which are largely reflexive.

Part Three amplifies these observations and describes a health-services delivery plan that the staff
believes will cure all four problems. The keystone of
the plan is a new organizational structure capable
of releasing the bonds that currently paralyze the
exercise of authority in the health-services system.
The system could begin to respond intelligently to
its own needs, to plan and act with rational purpose,
to modify its behavior, to evolve in the directions
in which medicine and the economy and the population
have been evolving, to become more efficient, to become more economical. Most important, the proposed
organizational structure would make the health-
services system truly accountable to the people it
serves; its duties would be clear, and clearly

understood; its performance of those duties would be measurable.

Additionally, the proposed organizational structure has been shown by experience in other fields and other places to be of a sort calculated to produce advantageous partnership and cooperation with the federal government. This is an important consideration in the present social and governmental environment, which is characterized by an intermingling of the functions of private, local, regional, and federal authority. It represents a positive, exciting innovation for urban government. Finally, the structure proposed would include and permit all the specific recommendations covered in Part Two, but it would provide a framework within which those solutions could sustain themselves and survive.

The recommendations in Part Two do possess one virtue that has been only casually mentioned so far: They can be brought about with the least change in current practice. Fewer jobs need to be restructured or realigned. Fewer old habits have to be broken, or new habits learned. Simpler legislative measures are needed. Fewer toes may be trodden. But the problem is too serious (and the time before disaster strikes too short) to settle for a solution merely because it leaves much as it is, because it saves routines, because it is politically safer. The recommendations proposed in Part Two are, in a sense, inevitable; every survey propounds them, or something very like them. The recommendations that will be given in Part Three are not inevitable. In deference to current pressures, in recognition of the inertia of a large unwieldly system, this report could have avoided tackling the bigger issues. The staff has elected not to avoid them, for it is believed that solutions on the order of those in Part Three are workable, possible, and absolutely necessary. If such solutions are adopted, and if--in five years, or ten years--a Task Force or ad hoc Commission were to conduct a survey of New York City's health services, the staff believes they would find:

- a working system

- a viable system

- a system with the will and the capacity to grow.

CHAPTER **3** COMMUNITY
AND
INSTITUTIONAL NEEDS

FACTS AND PROBLEMS

Within the $5.18 billion city expense budget
for 1967-1968, 15.5% will be spent on medical care
delivery and costly associated programs and efforts.
These funds will help to support the world's largest
municipal hospital system, as well as huge programs
in public health, mental health, and medical welfare.
In the future the burdens of need and cost will
continue to rise. Hospital costs are rising dra-
matically, at an annual rate in excess of increases
in revenue. Medicare and Medicaid are helping, but
they came late to New York City.

New York is by far the most advanced of the
nation's cities in its evolution toward a working
responsibility for the well-being of its citizens.
As the first of our large cities to assume the profound responsibility of "providing aid for all those
having need," New York is pioneering--setting pre-
cedents and directions for city evolution for decades
to come. Of its nearly 8 million people, almost
one-half are direct beneficiaries of city aid
programs--more than the entire population of Los
Angeles--and all of the remaining population benefits
indirectly.

Through many years of neglect, the physical
facilities for health care in New York have suffered
severe decline and obsolescence. Through administrative neglect and an accretion of crippling bureaucratic procedures, there has occurred a substantial
decline in personnel capability. Today, the health
system as a whole operates far less efficiently than
required by the load placed upon it in spite of
great professional dedication and of drastic--sometimes
heroic--measures to achieve reform and to blunt

107

deterioration. But too often the response to "Byzantine bureaucracy" has been an expedient Potemkin village--a desperate demonstration of the will to improve.

If the combined hospitals, clinics, and programs of the health care system were to be completely modernized and properly implemented, the cost might well exceed $1 billion.

New York has groped through many decades for the achievement of a coherent system of personal health delivery that offers an equitable and workable balance between private interest, professional interest, and public interest on the one hand, and education, research and service, on the other. It is the only major city in this nation still extensively engaged in the administration of numerous, large municipal hospitals while, among its other hospital systems, problems of multiplicity of services and maldistribution of facilities have built up over the years. Thanks to a heritage of private philanthropy, New York City has been blessed with an abundance of voluntary hospitals. Unfortunately, what has resulted over-all is a profusion and conglomeration of hospitals and centers all performing similar functions for widely overlapping groups.

From this situation has evolved a hodgepodge of organizations and services with no over-all coordination, with less than adequate regulation, and with competition for funds and domain. No fewer than 25 separate agencies of government (6 federal, 5 state, and 14 municipal) are involved in the distribution of money for medical care in New York City. These agencies, plus all of the other medical agencies and facilities in the city, constitute a staggering problem of systematization. It is clear that investment in plant, personnel, and practices over the entire health delivery system is so great that planning toward coherent ends will require a great deal of "unplanning." That is, much must be done to dispose of outmoded plants and practices to provide reasonable assurance of realizing desirable objectives.

Population Factors

Replanning is also required to accommo[
changing patterns of health and medical car[
caused by dramatic shifts in the population[
city. The following table summarizes popul___⌐_ __
changes, by borough, that have occurred between 1940
and 1960 and that have been projected through 1985:

	1940	1950	(000) 1960	1970	1985
New York City	7,455	7,893	7,782	7,694	7,625
Bronx	1,395	1,451	1,425	1,375	1,350
Brooklyn	2,698	2,739	2,627	2,549	2,450
Manhattan	1,890	1,960	1,698	1,575	1,475
Queens	1,298	1,551	1,810	1,900	1,925
Richmond	174	192	222	295	425

Changes are also occurring in the distribution
of age and ethnic groups. In 1960 about 24% of the
city's population was under 15, representing a 13%
increase for this age bracket between 1950 and 1960.
During the same period, the proportion of people
over 65 in New York City increased 35%, bringing
this group up to 10% of the city's population in
1960. That decade's picture of the middle groups
was quite different. The 15- to 44-year-olds declined
by 16% and the 45- to 64-year-old group increased
only 3%. The pattern of increasing proportions of
very young and very old is expected to continue for
some time. These movements are placing a great
strain on the financial and manpower resources of
the community. The older and younger segments of
the population are requiring increased services at
a time when, relatively speaking, the city has less
money to spend on such services.

The movement of ethnic groups within the city
is best viewed on a borough basis. Important information is obscured, for example, if one only notes
that between 1950 and 1960 the Puerto Rican population of New York City increased by 149%, the nonwhite
by 48%, and the white population declined by 12%.
Focusing on the separate boroughs, one sees that the
relatively insignificant changes within Manhattan

stand in sharp contrast to the dramatic ethnic movements in the other boroughs; the gradual decline of
the white population in the entire city is emphasized by the dynamic changes in the other two ethnic
categories. Following are statistics from the
Research and Planning Division of the New York City
Community Mental Health Board that indicate the
specific movements within the five boroughs:

In Manhattan
    26% decline in white population
    6.2% gain in nonwhite population
    63% gain in Puerto Rican population

In the Bronx
    17% decline in white population
    68% gain in nonwhite population
    202% gain in Puerto Rican population

In Queens
    10% gain in white population
    188% gain in nonwhite population
    261% gain in Puerto Rican population

In Brooklyn
    17% decline in white population
    79% gain in nonwhite population
    347% gain in Puerto Rican population

In Richmond
    13% gain in white population
    83% gain in nonwhite population
    238% gain in Puerto Rican population

Clearly, poverty is becoming more evenly distributed among the boroughs. Unless serious consideration is given to meeting the special needs these
people are taking with them to their new communities,
infant mortality rates, rates of communicable diseases, and crime and death rates can be expected to
rise rapidly. As the former New York City Health
Commissioner, Dr. George James, once commented,
"Poverty is the city's third leading cause of death."

The shifting proportions of age groups are
making other demands on health facilities and services. This has been evidenced by the special attention focused lately on the increasing problems of

the aged in New York City. Planning for the future
will call for a similar emphasis on caring for the
rising numbers of young people. This will include
not only pediatric services but also prenatal,
maternity, and mental health and related services
necessary to control and combat the soaring juvenile
delinquency rates correlated with low income and poor
health.

Environmental Factors

The movement of poverty from borough to borough
calls attention to the emergent needs in environmental health throughout the city. Here are some
indicative statistics:

An average of 700 rat-bite cases a year are
reported among the city's residents. That represents
only the officially reported cases; the true figure is
doubtless much higher.

New York City has 400 miles of bathing beaches;
only 40 are being used. In areas such Rockaway,
which the District Health Officer asserts has unfortunately "been allowed to become a slum," a beautiful
surf is obscured by boarded, deteriorating houses,
devastated property, and other manifestations of
poverty.

Approximately 40,000 buildings--housing about
1 million New York City residents--have been condemned as unfit.

There are over 100,000 retail food establishments in the city of New York. Only a fraction can
be inspected by the city due to limitations in manpower. Quality maintenance of the rest must rely on
an "honor" system of self-inspection. Reportedly,
there are 22,000 restaurants requiring inspection.

The city has approximately 200 accidental bar-
biturate poisonings each year and approximately the
same number of deaths from liver disease that are
believed to be associated with the illegal use of
drugs. There are an estimated 200 food poisoning
outbreaks annually.

New York City has several hundred hospitals, some of them in such poor and unsanitary condition that it has been said they are "no place to go when you're sick."

The Health Department now has special control programs in effect, inadequate in some cases, over hospitals and special institutions, nursing homes, schools, day-care facilities, swimming pools and bathing beaches, rodent extermination, mosquitoes, pigeons, carbon monoxide poisoning, lead poisoning, and food-borne diseases. Such control programs are urgently in need of re-evaluation, not only in the light of changing technology but also to consider redeployment of personnel and funds to anticipate future needs in environmental health.

The Pervasive Problems

Although far greater in scale, New York City's problems are the same in kind as those of most other urban communities:

- poverty

- changes in character of the population

- changes in the requirements for preventive services

- requirements for financial expansion of funds allocated to health and medical care services in the face of possible reductions in revenues

- proliferation and fragmentation of services

- complex financial distribution and accounting

- lack of required communication and coordination among agencies

- increased public demand for total or comprehensive health care services

- emergent needs in environmental health

- obsolescent facilities and methods of administration and distribution of health services

- scarce professional personnel, the scarcity
  becoming more pronounced with growing demands

- wide variation in the quality of medical care
  and related services

- a history of poor planning

- fractionation of authority.

The unique thing about New York City's health
problems, then, is their enormity.

Attempts To Improve

Despite the frustrations in trying to achieve
improvements in the whole system, New York continues
to be a city of <u>doing</u>. For example, while it may
currently present a confused picture insofar as coordination among agencies is concerned, a number of
developments over the last few years in the public
health and medical care agencies reflect its "natural
tendency to do something."

1) Health Services Administration. This agency
would include the Departments of Health and Hospitals,
the Community Mental Health Board, medical welfare,
and the Office of the Medical Examiner. As an amal-
gamation of executive health agencies, HSA represents
a positive step in the direction of integration of
health delivery activities.

2) Gouverneur Project. This aims at combining,
at the delivery level of district health, the operational capabilities of the Health, Hospital and
Mental Health service organizations (and hopefully
of the Welfare Department). This combination leads
to correlated planning, and toward comprehensive
care. The concept of joint action at the delivery
level plus improved services resulting from this
joint action may set the pattern for other health
districts within New York City, and in other metropolitan centers.

3) Affiliation contracting of municipal
hospitals to voluntary, teaching or medical college
hospitals. In effect, two positive benefits have
resulted from this practice. In the first, the
superior talents and abilities of the voluntary and
other hospitals are brought to bear on the problems
inherent in the municipal hospitals. In the second,
a high degree of joint action develops between the
voluntary and other participating hospitals and the
municipal hospital system. In a sense, more of a
system approach to planning and coordination can
emerge from this development than has been possible
in the past.

4) Queensbridge Health Maintenance Project.
This is aimed at providing health and medical care
services to 1,000 elderly residents of Queensbridge
Houses. These people are cared for in their homes
in a program pointing a way toward partial solution
to the vexing, pervasive problem of chronic-disease
treatment for the aged. It is interesting to note
further that five public and three voluntary agencies
are involved in this joint undertaking.

5) Development of a master plan for comprehensive mental health and mental retardation services.
In reorienting the mental health field to a comprehensive approach to control and treatment of mental
disorders, related fields of psychiatric and physical
medicine are brought together and assigned the responsibility of mental health service to the general
population. The plan incorporates the principles of
geographical regionalization and administrative
decentralization.

6) Plan for neighborhood ambulatory health
centers. This plan is aimed at providing a comprehensive health service on a community basis. Preventive and treatment medicine will be coordinated,
as will the various facilities and services within
the geographic region of a back-up hospital. Although critical problems still remain to be solved,
this innovation in the delivery of health services
in New York is progressing. The 1967-1968 budget
has provided for initial planning and development of
approximately half of the proposed free-standing
satellite clinics as well as renovation of certain of
the hospitals.

Focus Upon Boroughs

The health system survey reported herein has been guided by the belief that understanding of the health problems of the city requires understanding of the health problems of the separate boroughs, the communities within them, and key health care plants. As the bibliography of this report indicates (Appendix B), an abundant store of information exists on health facilities, services, and problems in New York City. Relevant data have been drawn from these related studies and, together with other statistical compilations, have been analyzed to provide a comprehensive, borough-by-borough report on health needs. Descriptive characterizations are also based upon interviews with key medical, social, and political leaders in each of the boroughs.

It will be noted that included in each of the borough reports are priority recommendations made by the City Hospital Visiting Committee and published by the United Hospital Fund of New York. Later in Part Two, there will be special reports of staff visits to each of these hospitals within the context of this study. Care was taken that these reports would not merely duplicate findings presented by the Visiting Committee. Although many observations were similar, the staff findings place primary emphasis on aspects other than those discussed by the Committee.

To close this introductory discussion, some statistical facts and problems have been abstracted to emphasize, in brief form, the magnitude of the whole health establishment that has evolved over the years and the vital role that local government plays in meeting the health needs of its residents. The listing that follows is by no means exhaustive. Its purpose is to highlight the over-all problems that will be examined in more specific detail.

- Approximately one-half of New York City's population is fully or partially "medically indigent" as defined by the provisions of new state and federal medical legislation.

- Three years ago, about 30% of the $2 billion spent annually for all personal medical

services provided to the city's citizens
derived from state, federal, and local
tax funds. Today, following the advent of
Medicaid and Medicare, the total sum spent
and the tax-defrayed portion are much higher.

- In 1966, for reimbursable public charge expenses, approximately 40% came from federal
sources, with 30% each from state and city
funding.

- Approximately 15.5% of the city's 1967-68
expense budget of $5.18 billion is for health
and medical services.

- The City of New York operates (through its
Department of Hospitals) 21 hospitals and
medical centers with nearly 18,000 beds, a
variety of specialty clinics emanating from
26 health centers of the Department of Health,
and numerous Department of Welfare clinics,
which, in addition to Hospital and Health
Department clinics, service public assistance
recipients. The city also supports and supervises (through its Community Mental Health
Board) mental health in-patient and out-
patient services in municipal and voluntary
institutions and agencies throughout the city.

- Over 40,000 city employees--about 17% of all
city employees--are in the Health and Hospital
Departments.

- The bed facilities operated by the city are
part of a much larger system: Of the approximately 39,000 short-term acute hospital beds
in the city, an estimated one-quarter are in
city-owned facilities, with the majority
(over 60%) in voluntary nonprofit hospitals
and the remainder in proprietary hospitals.

- Of the approximately 18,000 general care
ward beds, which serve the indigent and medically indigent of the city, over 8,000 are in
voluntary, and nonprofit hospitals Municipal
hospitals have been operating at close to 75%
bed capacity (and declining),while the service
wards of voluntary hospitals have been operating at about 80% bed capacity (and rising).

- New York City purchases two days of short-term patient care from the 79 voluntary hospitals in the city for every three days of care it provides in its own hospitals. On an average day there are some 5000 such city-charge patients in voluntary hospitals; hence, the city is the source of more than half the income derived by voluntary hospitals for ward services.

- Of the more than 8.5 million visits to various OPD clinics in the city in 1966, slightly over 3 million were to municipal hospitals, just short of 3 million to voluntary hospitals, a little under 2 million to clinics operated by the Health Department, and the remaining 1 million to 36 independent dispensaries.

- Close to 3 million visits were made in 1966 to emergency departments of hospitals, with over half of them to municipal facilities.

- While 6 of the 18 in-patient units of general hospitals caring for the mentally ill are in municipal hospitals, these units account for 52% of the 2,666 beds allocated for this function. In addition, there are 13,000 psychiatric beds in state hospitals in the city.

- There are nearly 1 million "person interviews" in psychiatric clinics throughout the city. Three-quarters of these visits are to clinics either operated by New York City or supported with city funds.

- Of the approximately 20,000 long-term beds in the city, about 25% are in municipally operated hospitals and public home infirmaries; 45% are in proprietary nursing homes; 30% are in voluntary institutions.

- The Department of Hospitals is responsible for licensing 33 proprietary hospitals and 125 nursing homes. The Department of Welfare

purchases services from the nursing homes,
which, on the average day, care for about
6000 elderly patients.

- Fourteen of the 24 hospitals in New York City
with active home care programs are municipal
institutions. On the average day there are
about 2000 patients in the home care programs.
This is about 80% of the total census in all
such programs.

MANHATTAN

Population Dynamics

Several million people crowd daily into Manhattan
from other boroughs and other states, but the health
needs of this visiting/working population become the
concern of the city only on an emergency basis. Private corporations provide facilities and services
for their employees and, to some extent, Manhattan's
private physicians and other services are used.
Approximately 10% of patients in a one-day census of
city hospitals were nonresidents of the city. The
city's primary responsibility for health care is to
the approximately 1.7 million people who live in
Manhattan. This population is 63% white, 24% nonwhite,
and 13% Puerto Rican. More people over 65 years of
age live in this borough than in any of the other four
and, in 1960, Manhattan had the highest percentage
of families with incomes under $4,000 and the lowest
median income of the city's boroughs.

When the five counties first merged early in
the century to form the City of New York, Manhattan
was the most heavily populated. Between 1920 and
1930, when the rest of the city was entering a period
of explosive growth, Manhattan's population decreased
by 417,790. During the succeeding 20 years, the
in-migration of Puerto Ricans and nonwhites gradually
increased the population until 1960, when another
decline commenced. The whites were the first to move
out, 26% of their numbers leaving between 1950 and
1960. Following this initial large exodus, less than
1% left between 1960 and 1965, whereas approximately
5% of the Puerto Ricans and 4% of the nonwhites
moved out.

The large increases in numbers of Puerto Ricans
and nonwhites and the decreases or relatively small
changes in the white populations in the other boroughs
between 1950 and 1965 indicate that the movement of
the Puerto Rican and nonwhite has been largely from
borough to borough within the city, whereas many of
the whites left the city altogether. There has been
movement within Manhattan, too. Those residents who
have been forced out of their neighborhoods because
of new building, renovation, or expansion of business
and cultural affairs, have moved into tighter clusters
in the borough if not out into other boroughs.

For example, the area selected for the first
community mental health center (bounded by 125th and
181st Streets on the west side of Manhattan) is undergoing rapid social and economic transformation because
of the increasing number of nonwhite and Puerto Rican
citizens entering that community. Unlike the city
as a whole, or even certain other areas of Manhattan,
this community of some 170,000 people is characterized by a "lower median income, a higher proportion
of unemployed, a high percentage of substandard
housing, a high number of dependent children, and a
disproportionate number of juvenile arrests and juvenile offenders," (quotation from "The Architectural
Program for the Manhattan Community Mental Health
Center," see Appendix B).

The Gouverneur district could be described similarly. However, more Puerto Ricans than Negroes
have moved into this area. A 1961 neighborhood study
by the Urban Medical Economics Research Center reported 82% of the population to be white, 23% Puerto
Rican, 8% Negro, and 10% other nonwhite, of which
over half were of Chinese origin.

The composition of Manhattan's over-all population has changed in age of residents as well as ethnic
group distribution over the past several years. Between 1960 and 1965, increases occurred in the age
groups under 30 and over 65, while a slight decrease
was observed within the middle group. The proportion
of elderly persons in Manhattan is the highest of all
the boroughs. In 1965 the percentage was 16.4, whereas in Brooklyn it was 13.5, in the Bronx 12.8, in
Queens 12.2, and in Richmond 10.0.

The aged population is predominantly white. Although the most recent statistics for age by ethnic
group were for 1960, the proportions have probably
not changed substantially. At that time the number
of whites over 65 was more than double that of nonwhites in this age group and was nearly ten times
that of Puerto Ricans over 65.

Most indices of poverty place Manhattan at
either the lowest or the second-to-lowest economic
level in the city. Infant mortality per thousand
births is a highly sensitive index of economic level;
in 1965, Manhattan's average of 28.2 and Brooklyn's
average of 28.5 were the highest, followed by an
average of 25.7 for the Bronx, 21.7 for Richmond and
20.0 for Queens. With respect to income, the 1960
census figures showed that 34.4% of Manhattan families
earned less than $4,000, the highest percentage for
the boroughs. The Bronx was second with 26.2% of the
families in this lower income bracket. Manhattan's
median income, $5,338, was the lowest for the city.

A closer examination of the infant mortality
rate reveals that Harlem and the Lower West Side
are largely responsible for the lower rates. In
Harlem, the average for nonwhites was 38.9 in 1965;
for Puerto Ricans it was 35.3. In the Lower West
Side, the average for nonwhites was 40.8 and for
Puerto Ricans, 37.8. In contrast were the averages
for whites in these areas: Harlem, 23.9; the Lower
West Side, 19.8.

Within Manhattan are distinctly defined areas
representing a wide variance in most of the standard
measures. From the viewpoint of health needs,
Manhattan cannot be described as homogeneous. Consider
the economic and cultural differences between the
residential area of the East Side north of 59th street,
and the slums of Harlem, Gouverneur, and the Bellevue
district. Most apparent are the variances of health
needs in these areas.

A number of studies have attempted to characterize the individual areas and to determine their
special needs and problems. One such investigation
is that of Elison and Lowenstein on the Washington
Heights area, 1960-1961 (School of Public Health and
Administrative Medicine, Columbia). From this work

emerged a "Community Fact Book" that defines
Washington Heights statistically with respect to over
100 significant parameters. The study is now in process of being updated through 1970.

This same research group has designed a study
of Harlem to determine health characteristics and
habits of the area. (The purposes of this study are
cited, in part, to illustrate the surprising lack
of community health information characteristic of
the city.) Planned as an on-going effort to be conducted within Harlem itself, the study's essential
objective is to assess the impact of Harlem Hospital
Center's program and patient care services on the
health of the population it purports to serve. Within the general framework, four substudies will be
conducted:

1) A discharged-patient study to investigate
the care currently provided by Harlem Hospital and
the effects of this care upon the subsequent health
and social functioning of a sample of discharged
patients;

2) A community process analysis to analyze the
effect of sociopolitical forces on Harlem Hospital
and other health resources in, or available to, the
community of Harlem;

3) A master sample survey of the Harlem Hospital community in order to aid in (a) characterizing
qualitatively and quantitatively the changing patterns
of use of health care services, (b) assessing priorities of health care needs, and (c) evaluating the
effect of programs designed to provide better health
care services;

4) A computer-based community health inventory
to (a) explore the feasibility of establishing a
community health information system that would draw
upon all available sources of data concerning the
health conditions of the population, including hospital medical records, and (b) provide a continuing
health inventory capable of serving the purpose of
evaluation of health care services and medical and
public health research.

Findings, then, will define the health status
and habits of the individuals in the community.
Other areas that may be pursued are knowledge of (and
attitudes toward) health, disease symptoms, medical
and dental care, financing of medical care, and epidemiological factors. The investigators believe that
the systematic information obtained should facilitate
planning to meet demands for care; the survey data
can serve as a base line, and comparisons of findings
for various periods of time will make possible assess-
ments of the impact that hospital and medical programs
have on the health and medical care practices in the
community.

The Gouverneur district has also been the focus
of a number of special studies. A 1961 study by the
Urban Medical Economics Research Center compared
Gouverneur with Manhattan as a whole and with the
larger area represented by the city. Gouverneur
proved to be well below the borough and city averages
in income and health indices. For example, data indicated that 30% of Gouverneur families had incomes
under $3,000 and 61% of single individuals had incomes
under $2,000, as against Manhattan's 22% and 29%, and
the city's 15% and 44% for these measures. Median
incomes for all ethnic groups in Gouverneur were
lower than in either Manhattan or the city. In the
Gouverneur district (uniquely), males outnumber fe-
males in both the white and nonwhite populations.
This is largely because of the Bowery, where 99% of
the population consists of males.

Existing Facilities and Services

In spite of Manhattan's declining population,
this borough remains "the city" in the minds of people
both inside and outside New York. Not only are the
cultural, financial, government, and other major centers located in Manhattan, but in most cases the provision of facilities in a given service category is
greater than in the other boroughs. This, however,
is a gradually changing pattern. As the lower income
groups spread out into other parts of the city, they
take their particular needs with them and these are
showing up as new problems for the four other boroughs.

Currently, Manhattan is served by 54 hospitals, of which 33 are voluntary institutions, 9 are municipal, 11 are proprietary, 2 are state, and 1 is federal. The highest concentration of these hospitals is in east mid-Manhattan, between 42nd and 110th Streets. There are more welfare centers in Manhattan than in any other borough; 4 of these are general services (veterans, nonresidents, etc.). In Manhattan there is a greater number of laboratory facilities, of rehabilitation centers, of narcotics addiction service agencies, and of most kinds of health and welfare services than elsewhere in the city.

For some time Manhattan has provided special training centers for the 17- to 21-year-old mentally retarded, a service that has been lacking in other boroughs. In limited instances, the most advanced cases of this group in all boroughs have been put into special classrooms in the regular high schools, but the majority have been sent to the Manhattan schools if room permitted. For lack of room they have sometimes had to lose out altogether on special training past the age of 17. In 1966 a special training center was opened in Queens. This fall Brooklyn will have its own school for the first time; and, if not this fall then in the very near future, the Bronx hopes to be able to take care of its own mentally retarded in this age group. In the meantime, Manhattan continues to take care of the overload.

The first community mental health center will be built in Manhattan in the Washington Heights District. The initial area selection was made because of the need, but the concept of comprehensive psychiatric services within a community setting will eventually be developed throughout all boroughs in carefully defined catchment areas that correspond to health areas. (The problems and proposed plans for the community mental health centers are discussed in some detail elsewhere in Part Two.)

Discussion

Of the seven municipal hospitals in Manhattan County, four are responsible for the low average occupancy rate of

74.5% in 1965. These are the Bellevue Hospital Center, with an occupancy rate of 68.3%; Francis Delafield Hospital, 57.7%; James Ewing Hospital, 72.4%; and Sydenham Hospital, 72.5%. In view of the declining use of in-patient services at Bellevue, the new center has been designed with a smaller general care bed complement than the present center's 1,523. The under-utilization of the other three hospitals represents a priority consideration in planning.

At the same time that use of in-patient services is decreasing for these hospitals, the out-patient services in Harlem, Bellevue, and Metropolitan Hospitals are becoming increasingly overburdened. Although this, of course, is the situation in all municipal hospitals, and the problems should be alleviated ultimately through implementation of the neighborhood ambulatory health services plan, the intensity of the problem at Metropolitan's OPD is too critical to wait for long-range solutions. Nearly a half-million people visited its clinics last year, and the census is increasing annually. By accepted measurement criteria, the 30,000-square-foot area in which this OPD operates is barely one-third the size it should be.

In light of contemporary professional opinion regarding needless institutionalization of the aged, the isolation of Coler and Goldwater Hospitals is a major issue. As discussed elsewhere herein, many chronic medical problems can now be prevented or at least arrested; too many of the aged are placed in long-term institutions when, with home-health aid, they could remain in their own homes. Further, in those cases where hospitalization is required, it is believed desirable that patients be near their families and friends so that contact within the community can be maintained. Clearly, the locations of Coler and Goldwater Hospitals are not compatible with this philosophy.

The problem of staffing is also critical for these isolated hospitals. In an ideal situation, provision of optimal patient care is difficult enough. The additional problems of transportation, housing, etc., make the burden of administration even greater.

Special studies, cited briefly above, have brought to light the extreme conditions of poverty in Manhattan. In both the Gouverneur and Washington Heights districts, the high infant mortality rates, high unemployment, high rates of crime and juvenile delinquency, high incidence of disease, and low income levels present multiple and critical health problems that need both immediate and long-range attention. Consider, for example, the infant mortality rates for the Washington Heights, Bellevue, Lower East Side and Lower West Side health areas. In 1964, Health Area 15 in Harlem had 63.4 infant deaths per 1000 births; two areas in Washington Heights also had rates over 60--Health Area 7.10 had 60.2, and Health Area 7.20 had 63.7; Health Area 41 (near Bellevue) had an infant mortality rate of 54.5; Health Area 85.10 (Harlem) had 55.6; four areas in the Lower West Side registered rates over 40, as did Health Area 63 in the Lower East Side, and three additional areas in Harlem. Many of these areas are in close proximity to health services.

These conditions might be expected in obviously poor areas, but to find a relatively high infant mortality rate in a higher income area, which is presumably covered adequately with health facilities and services, is rather a surprise. Such is the case in the Kips Bay-Yorkville district where the median income in some areas exceeds $10,000 and where the greatest concentration of hospitals is found in Manhattan. The number of births to nonwhites and Puerto Ricans in this area is too small to show in department of health records (no annual rates are computed when the base is less than 200), but the rate of 23.5 for white infant mortality is higher than Manhattan's average for this classification (21.9) and far exceeds the city's average of 19.4 infant deaths per 1,000 white births. Among the seven districts of Manhattan, the Kips Bay-Yorkville infant mortality rate for whites is third highest, with the Lower East Side at the top with a rate of 24.0, and East Harlem next with 23.9.

Various studies and recommendations have been made regarding the major public hospital plants of the borough. Some findings are these:

1) Under-utilization of Sydenham, Ewing, and Delafield Hospitals;

2) Over-utilization of Metropolitan's Out Patient Department;

3) Inadequate hospital coverage in the Lower West Side and the upper Harlem areas;

4) Isolation of Coler and Goldwater Hospitals;

5) The high infant mortality rate for white births in the Kips Bay-Yorkville district, the area most abundantly supplied with hospitals in Manhattan;

6) The many health needs of Gouverneur and Harlem districts where the highest infant mortality rates in Manhattan indicate concentrated poverty and consequent health problems.

Regarding hospital problems, the following priority recommendations were made by the City Hospital Visiting Committee following its visit to the Bellevue Hospital Center:

● Considering the desperate and urgent need for new facilities, they urge that the target date of January 1969 be brought forward.

● An autonomy plan was proposed for this hospital; i.e., an executive order, signed by the Mayor, would grant administrative autonomy to the municipal hospitals and health centers, thereby cutting red tape, and encouraging efficiency. It was thought that personnel could be hired and equipment purchased without prior approval of the hospital department or health department. Administrators could draw on the resources provided by department specialists, but the decisions would be their own, reviewed by the department. It was noted by the committee that this plan would involve "many millions of dollars, much thought, and care. It would involve strict controls and a proper system of accountability to the city." However, they feel that the sentiment "expressed by Dr. Howard J. Brown,

Health Services Administrator, of Bellevue
and Metropolitan Hospitals as 'heart-breaking,
depressing, and disgraceful' will be drasti-
cally changed with autonomy."

- More security officers are essential to maintain "on the beat" programs as pilferage
continues to be a problem.

- The visitors supported Dr. Richard Karl's
comprehensive plan for the emergency services
of the hospital and pushed immediate implementation. Specifically:

    Experienced physicians on duty, three
    from 8:00 to 4:00 and four from 4:00
    to 12:00

    Regularized schedule

    Distribution of patients is a very im-
    portant question

    Additional messengers and clerks are
    necessary; also more nursing discipline

    A chart for each patient as well as book
    entry

    Improved administrative surveillance

    X-ray results expedited.

- Linen shortage is a problem. Further, linen
should be marked by the supplier (at present
six employees work at marking linen). The
three washing machines need to be replaced.

- Laboratory housekeeping personnel should be
provided by the universities that build the
research laboratories.

- Plans for renovation of the garbage disposal
(which is in "atrocious condition") should
go forward immediately.

- The L & M Pavilion is badly in need of painting with permanent repair of the roof before

the painting. Further, completion of painting of the C & D Pavilion was only half finished last year.

- Cushions need to be provided for wheelchairs.

- Maintenance is almost an "impossible task"
  in the old pavilions. The staff should be
  brought up to normal working strength with
  the addition of skilled maintenance help.

- Window washing is recommended at a rate of
  two to three times per year.

- Ice-making machines should be installed where
  block ice is still being used.

- Only proven suppliers should be accepted.

The City Hospital Visiting Committee made the
following priority recommendations for the Harlem
Hospital Center:

- Establish the earliest possible completion
  date.

- More assistant hospital administrators are
  needed, particularly in planning the move to
  the new building and in providing around-the-
  clock administrative coverage throughout the
  year. Administrative assistants are needed
  also.

- House staff positions are open and need to
  be filled as soon as possible.

- The need for parking space near the hospital
  is "desperate" and available housing in the
  area is "essential in order to attract house
  staff to this hospital."

- Additional personnel and tools are needed to
  accomplish the essential work of maintaining
  the plant.

- Replacement of worn-out plumbing, steam lines,
  and fixtures is urgently needed (and has been
  requested since 1960).

- An increase in security staff is essential.

- For safety, and for proper working conditions, utmost speed is recommended in acquiring and installing the following major equipment items for the record room: a sprinkler system, proper lighting, and air-conditioning.

The City Hospital Visiting Committee made the following priority recommendations for the Metropolitan Hospital Center:

- Completion of negotiations for a contract with the New York College of Medicine to improve four major professional services: anaesthesia, laboratories, medical records, and X-ray.

- Reduce the census on critically over-crowded medical wards by transferring patients within the hospital to less crowded specialty wards and by making more consistent efforts to arrange patient transfers to other hospitals in the area; also by making every effort to have geriatric and chronically ill patients sent to more appropriate hospitals or nursing homes.

- Obtain the property on 99th Street for future development of this hospital center, including parking garage and residents' quarters.

- Staff and supervisory nurses are urgently needed.

- Improved maintenance is needed.

- Expedite construction of a new building for the mental health center.

The City Hospital Visiting Committee made the following priority recommendations for the James Ewing Hospital:

- Complete reconstruction of the X-ray department (new equipment, new X-omat, and new hand-processing tank). The city has promised this for a year. To this time, nothing has been done. The developing tank has been leaking through the ceiling of an operating room.

- Appoint a qualified plumber to the staff. (There are constant stoppages of the waste lines--equipment is far from new and there are many plumbing emergencies.)

- Appoint two additional employees for telephone and information service. (There is no replacement if anyone is ill.)

- The administrator has requested a ramp to the solarium on the 11th floor.

- Continue to explore with Memorial Hospital possible ways of improving nursing service at Ewing.

The City Hospital Visiting Committee made the following priority recommendations for the Bird S. Color Memorial Hospital and Home:

- A major staffing need is the provision of better nurse coverage on the wards.

- Six new lines in housekeeping are necessary for afternoon and evening tours.

- A page system is needed in B Building and C Building.

- More maintenance men are needed.

- There is need for more security men.

- There is need for more messengers and ward clerks.

- Linen is in short supply.

- Bath slabs in A Building need replacement.

The City Hospital Visiting Committee made the following priority recommendations for Goldwater Memorial Hospital:

- Modernize elevators for safety and for self-service at night.

- Connect the 3rd and 4th floors and expand to the same size as the lower floors. The buildings should be connected on all levels to save time and to improve services.

- Realistic increase of food budget is essential for patients and for staff.

- Improve use of space by modernizing and equipping one kitchen to serve two wards. Modern dishwashing facilities should be provided.

THE BRONX

Population Dynamics

During the first decade of this century, the population of Bronx County rose 115%. Then followed 40 years of a slowly decreasing rise that leveled off in the 1950's. By 1960 the population had decreased about 1.8%. An offsetting increase was estimated for the 1965 population.

Recent significant dynamics of the Bronx population have not, then, been explosive growth, but rather, movement within the borough and changes in the distribution of ethnic groups. In 1950, 89.0% of the total population was white, 6.7% nonwhite, and 4.3% Puerto Rican; by 1965, only 66.7% was white, 16.6% nonwhite, and 16.7% Puerto Rican. With the exception of some of the older, more stable neighborhoods, communities have shifted in composition throughout the years, with groups moving in and out, sometimes integrating, sometimes not.

The health needs of the different groups have accounted for varied demands on the community's health

facilities. At one time, the community served by
Lincoln Hospital had a large proportion of older
people. The hospital was then oriented to cardiacs,
strokes, chronic illnesses, and other characteristic
health problems of the "aged." Today, only about 10%
of the people Lincoln serves are over 65 years of age.
The community is largely made up of younger Puerto
Ricans and Negroes. Puerto Ricans are traditionally
hospital users. Within a given neighborhood, the
proportion of Puerto Ricans in the hospital and
clinic census will be higher than the proportion of
Puerto Ricans in the community as a whole. Further,
the Lincoln neighborhood is defined as "migratory"
as well as "young": its hospital needs tend to be
acute. When members of this population are sick,
they are very sick; their problems are not likely to
be circulatory or chronic. The hospital has had to
change its orientation.

Other Bronx communities have followed a similar
pattern. The younger population is migrant, and the
older residents remain as the last vestige of the
communities they once represented. Much of the Bronx
is transforming from one-family housing to apartment
buildings, a change that is disturbing the elderly
who enjoyed suburban, family-style living. Further,
in neighborhoods that are experiencing growth, fundamental facilities such as health and education are
lagging behind needs for them.

While a majority of Bronx citizens still travel
to other boroughs to work, a new movement has begun
to create jobs for people in their own communities.
This is an effect of antipoverty programs that have
encouraged community responsibility among those who
live in the community. One example of the measures
taken to provide more employment is the move of a
large fruit and vegetable market from Manhattan to
Hunts Point. This will provide a broad range of jobs
for residents.

As in each of the boroughs, the proportion of
the aged in the Bronx population as a whole has been
steadily increasing throughout the past quarter-
century. Constituting only 3.4% of the total in 1930,
those aged 65 years old and over rose to 5.0% in 1940,

to 7.3% a decade later, to 10.7% in 1960, and in 1965
to 12.8%. The elderly are concentrated in certain
areas and their needs are high on the list of health
problems in the borough.

Economically, the Bronx is neither the richest
nor the poorest borough. According to the 1960 census (which registered 1959 income data), the Bronx
was second highest in percentage of families with
incomes under $4,000; the highest being Manhattan
with 34.4%. In the Bronx the percentage was 26.2,
and this was closely matched by Brooklyn (26.1% of
whose families are in the lower income group). The
median family income in the Bronx in 1959 was $5,830.
With respect to education, the Bronx and Brooklyn
each had a per capita average educational level of
9.5 years of schooling, the lowest figures in the
city.

A study of infant mortality rates in 1965 also
indicates a fairly low average living standard for
the Bronx. The average rate for nonwhites (39.3 per
1000 births) matched the city average and was second
only to Brooklyn, where the average rate for nonwhite
infant mortality was 41.6. Indicating the range in
living standards in the Bronx, however, was the low
infant mortality rate for whites--18.0--second only
to Queens, which averaged 16.4. Within the borough,
the highest rate in 1965 was for Puerto Rican infant
deaths in the Fordham-Riverdale area. The rate was
55.0, exceeded in the city only by Richmonds' 58.2
average rate for nonwhites. Three areas in the
borough had a higher rate than 40.0: nonwhites in
Morrisania, Mott Haven, and Tremont.

Some of the aged are also among the physically
handicapped group of close to 400 who utilize the
rehabilitation center at Jacobi Hospital. However,
no special compensations are made for these handicapped. A hydraulically controlled bus was requested
in February 1967, but as of June 1967 no response had
been made. Housing is a particular problem for these
people. Many would not have to be institutionalized
if special conveniences were built into the homes for
the handicapped. But these architectural barriers
are keeping them from returning home from the hospital,

as well as contributing to the overcrowding of the
hospitals. Further, the older people are lumped with
the physically handicapped at the hospital, a feature
that causes social problems.

Existing Facilities and Services

Unfortunately, a description of "existing" health
facilities in the Bronx can only reflect the scarcity
of those facilities, and must dwell on future plans
rather than on present conditions. Of four requests
in the 1967-1968 capital budget for facilities for
the aged in the Bronx, one was granted (according to
the borough president's final report to community
organizations). Specifically, the amount of $100,000
was provided for planning a neighborhood family care
center in the Mott Haven health district, through
which the elderly would get special service. However,
regarding the request for a Golden Age center in the
Pelham Bay-Throgs Neck area, "beyond the provision
for such facilities in the proposed scope of the
Northeast Bronx High School Community Center, no
other funds were provided for such an activity."
Also, funds were requested for a study to determine
the feasibility of building a Golden Age center in
the vicinity of White Plains Road and Pelham Parkway,
the center of a community containing a very large
percentage of elderly people. A similar request was
made in the Woodlawn district for funds to study the
feasibility of using the existing Forty-seventh
Precinct building (which was to be replaced shortly)
for a community center to include senior citizen
facilities. No funds were provided for either study.

Some areas of the borough are completely without medical facilities. The most critical example
of this situation is the Bruckner-Soundview area, one
of the worst poverty pockets of the Bronx. In this
rapidly growing community of 35,000 there are, reportedly, no health stations of any kind. Jacobi
Hospital is the closest facility, and this is three
bus rides away. The borough president stated in his
final report on the 1967-1968 capital budget, "The
Department of Health agreed, in connection with the
approval of the current budget, to conduct a study as

to the need of a health center and clinic for this
area, which is a growing community in desperate need
of health facilities. Funds were requested for site
acquisition and planning so that we may be ready to
proceed quickly when the study is received. No funds
were provided for this purpose."

Nor does a hospital appear to be likely for the
Bruckner-Soundview area. The borough president
stated in his report, ". . .this is a growing community and residents of the area are presently using
Jacobi Hospital and in many cases require a triple
fare. In view of the increase in population in the
last few years and the additional projects proposed
for the future, funds were requested for a study to
determine the feasibility of building a hospital
facility of approximately 250 beds. No funds were
provided for this purpose."

One serious health hazard was considered in the
capital budget, however. To quote the borough president again: "The entire district lacks adequate
sewer facilities. This is particularly unfortunate
because the area has been growing at a rapid pace with
considerable construction of new housing. Funds were
requested for a study and for preliminary plans to determine additional sewer needs within the area.
$88,000.00 was provided to do the study that had been
promised last year but not done by the Department of
Public Works."

Several other areas of low- to middle-income population are also without health facilities. These
are Community Planning Districts 8 and 9, which also
represent growing communities. Reportedly, in-
migrants from Manhattan are moving into these districts, where Mitchel-Lama homes (state-sponsored,
privately constructed buildings for middle-income
people), cooperative housing projects, and private
homes are being built. Bronx leadership is concerned
about these areas because there are not sufficient
health facilities, schools, etc., to serve the rapid
influx of new residents.

It was reported that the transportation element
of the home care service at Morrisania Hospital will
be cut back. Apparently, ambulance service is going

to be cut back at the same facility so that these
vehicles will not be able to make up for the loss of
transportation to home care patients.

Medicaid was found to have created problems for
both beneficiaries and physicians, with the core of
the problem being delay in reimbursement. One community leader suggested that the entire Medicaid
program be evaluated. Further, there is the difficulty of reaching people to tell them they must sign
up or pay $8.23 for each clinic visit. This latter
problem was approached in Hunts Point by the Community Progress Center (a part of the antipoverty program), which has set up a special program to "push"
Medicaid. Along with other forms of publicity, talks
are given before community groups to explain the benefits of Medicaid and to encourage registration.

It was reported that two of the state's narcotic
centers were to be opened in the Bronx. According to
the State Narcotic Control Commission's literature,
however, only one is planned for that borough,
specifically at 581 - 163rd Street. Apparently, the
communities that anticipate the opening of these
centers look toward the event with mixed feelings.
One district, Community Planning District 2, is a
narcotics problem area, so the state center will be
welcomed there. On the other hand, in Community
Planning District 12, the residents are fearful of the
threat addicts may pose to their neighborhood. This
has been observed to be a common reaction to the
state's placement of narcotic centers throughout the
city. According to the State Narcotic Control Commission, the people have nothing to fear as the addicts
will be, in a sense, institutionalized in the centers,
i.e., not permitted to roam around the neighborhood.
Further, they will presumably be within a rehabilitation stage and therefore not in search of narcotics
or under their influence. From the point of view of
the communities, however, the people have not been
advised as to the purpose of the centers or to the
disassociated role in the community that they will
play.

Mental health needs are great in the Bronx.
According to reports, the mentally retarded, for
example, do not get much attention. For more than a
decade, concerned professionals have sought a much-
needed occupational training center for the 17- to
21-year-old mentally retarded. Apparently, staff would
be no problem, as the activity would constitute another

school and the board of education was prepared to
provide adequate and qualified staff. All that was
needed was a building, but it was not obtained.   It
was reported that the proper steps are now being
taken; hopefully, all approvals will be met so that
the city will lease space in a building beginning in
September or October 1967. This will serve approximately 150 children, which represents two-thirds of
the need. Ultimate expansion could meet the total
need.

Another action taken to make both the public as
a whole and public officials more aware of the mental
health needs in the borough was to set up a conference
for November 1967. The central focus will be on
brain-damaged people who need rehabilitation. This
conference is being sponsored by the borough president's advisory committee on mental retardation.

Recognition of needs in the Bronx by the Community Mental Health Board was evidenced by allocation
of funds for three community mental health centers,
though neither was requested by the community planning board involved. These included $1,085,333.33
and $542,666.67 of city and state funds, respectively,
for a Lincoln Hospital Community Mental Health Center;
$666,666.67 and $333,333.33 of city and state funds,
respectively, for a Crotona Park Community Mental
Health Center, including the site; and $32,000 and
$16,000 of city and state funds, respectively, for a
Morrisania Hospital Community Mental Health Center
adjacent to Montefiore Hospital.

Two health programs were reported as currently
operating in the Bronx. Both are federally funded,
with the grant having been applied for by the
Morrisania-Montefiore affiliation. One of these
projects is a neighborhood medical care demonstration,
which is designed to demonstrate a new approach to
comprehensive medical care. Developed in the division
of social medicine of Montefiore Hospital, it was
funded in July 1966 by the Office of Economic Opportunity. The neighborhood chosen for the project is
one of the worst poverty areas in the borough.
Located in the East Bronx, it comprises approximately
11,000 families, or 45,000 people, of whom about 45%
are Puerto Rican, 45% Negro, and 10% white. A high
infant mortality rate, a high incidence of tuberculosis, and high drug use and crime rates characterize
the neighborhood.

This neighborhood medical care demonstration. will be organized around a health center and smaller "satellite" centers and will provide a four-component program: (1) Family-oriented medical services, with each family having its own team of physician, public health nurse, and a "family health worker." The health center will provide a focus for comprehensive medical service including therapeutic and preventive ambulatory medical and dental services, as well as social services and community activities. The satellites, run by public health nurses aided by family health workers and health technicians, will provide referral service, well-baby care, the bulk of the prenatal and postnatal care, immunizations, baby-sitting and transportation. Major medical and surgical procedures will be provided at Montefiore and Morrisania Hospitals, which will also provide in-patient care. (2) A training program for health personnel, with the dual purpose of providing good jobs in a community where there is high unemployment and well-trained personnel for the neighborhood medical care demonstration facilities and other health agencies in the neighborhood. (3) Community development. A principal objective is to involve neighborhood residents in the organization, policy planning, operation, and provision of services. (4) Research and evaluation. Analytic description and critical assessment of each stage of the neighborhood demonstration program and its impact on the community will be provided.

The second pilot program now in operation in the Bronx has its funding channeled through the neighborhood demonstration program. With the objective of developing new concepts for preparing health students to work in hospitals by introducing them to realistic situations, this student health project involves more than 250 medical students, student nurses, and other professionals in training from all over the nation. They are spending this summer in the Bronx, where they are assigned to clinics in the capacity of "patient advocates." That is, a given student interviews a patient, screens him, helps him through the maze of the clinic, and follows through on the case after the patient's visit to the clinic. This constitutes field training in the education of the student.

Also educationally directed is the borough's
plan for a new medical career institute, which is
proposed to be set up near the new Lincoln Hospital
to take advantage of the resources that will be
available under the affiliated auspices of the
Albert Einstein College of Medicine. Plans are still
tentative because of the uncertainty of timing on
availability of the new Lincoln Hospital.

Discussion

Various studies provide common views of city
problems and recommendations regarding hospital plants
and health services of the borough:

1) The aged population has many needs that are
not being met. In some cases home care is being cut
back and extended care facilities are in short supply.
Some believe that unmet social problems are of greater
significance than the health problems for this older
age group.

2) Transportation poses a serious problem in
the Bronx. The difficulties are inhibiting enough
for those who own cars, but problems are multiplied
for the indigent and the physically handicapped when
they are confronted with transportation obstacles.
This is particularly critical in transferring from
subway to bus and/or from bus to bus several times
to reach the health services needed. Reportedly,
there is a need for more buses and bus routes throughout the borough.

3) Architectural barriers exist that prevent
the physically rehabilitated and elderly from going
home from hospitals.

4) Some areas are completely without medical
facilities; unfortunately, these are predominantly
low-income communities. The area of greatest concern
with respect to this lack of health services is
Bruckner-Soundview, with its mushrooming population.

5) Ambulance service is commonly thought to be
slower than it should be.

6) Medicaid has posed problems for both its users
and the physicians. The major complaint is that
reimbursements are slow.

7) Mental health is a problem in the borough, particularly because the public does not appear to be concerned about it. Too little is being done.

8) The City Hospital Visiting Committee, 1965-1966, made the following priority recommendations for the Bronx Municipal Hospital Center, following their inspection of its facilities:

- Increase the hospital census to relieve the burden on obsolete Bronx hospitals.

- Provide more assistant hospital administrators.

- Provide more professional nurses and better nursing supervision of aides.

- Expedite construction of the Public Home Infirmary Building.

- Provide more clerks and messengers, especially in the out-patient area and the record room.

- Enlarge the maintenance staff; provide essential equipment and supplies.

- Provide more ambulance drivers.

- Provide more security officers.

- Improve linen and laundry service and distribution.

- Appoint a qualified director of social service to administer the department rather than a committee of four workers. Improve the stenographic and telephone services of this department.

9) The City Hospital Visiting Committee, 1965-1966, made the following priority recommendations for Fordham Hospital following their visit:

- Make a firm decision about continuing or closing all or part of this facility.

- Continue to expedite the physical plant improvements and installation of modern equipment now under way as essential to safe

operation of this facility until a new
hospital building can be completed.

- Provide additional space and expedite facilities planned for the Out Patient Department.

10) Following their visit to Lincoln Hospital,
the Visiting Committee made the following priority
recommendations:

- Expedite construction of the new hospital
and health center to replace the present
obsolete plant.

- Rush the long overdue repairs and renovation
of the main kitchen, and provide additional
personnel and a more realistic food budget
for the dietary department.

- Maintain a sufficient supply of linens.

- Provide personnel to improve the elevator
service at all times.

11) The City Hospital Visiting Committee made
the following priority recommendations regarding
Morrisania Hospital:

- Establish a demonstration project at Morrisania: either Montefiore would assume complete responsibility for operation of the
hospital, or the city's hospital administrator should have substantial additional
funds, more authority, flexibility, and
responsibility in his efforts to improve the
hospital.

- More space must be found so that ambulatory
care can be "decently provided for this
community."

- Enlarge the X-ray department and the
laboratories.

- Need for additional personnel was noted,
especially nurses, security officers (in
uniform), ward clerks, messengers, and dietary
aides.

- Additional supplies were needed, as well as a
more efficient supply system.

QUEENS

Population Dynamics

One of the more rapidly growing boroughs of the
city, Queens has passed the 2 million mark, making
it--as expressed by the community leaders--"one of
the largest cities in the country." Queens is unique,
it was pointed out, in that it represents a borough
of towns, rather than townships. Each area has a
town name and each has a civic organization fighting
for its individuality and identification. In a very
real sense, Queens is a collective suburb of the
"city," which, to the people of this borough, is
Manhattan.

According to the 1960 census, Queens has the
lowest percentage of families with incomes under
$4,000 and the highest median family income of all
five boroughs, as well as the highest number of school
years completed. Figures released in 1965 by the
bureau of records and statistics of the Department
of Health indicated that Queens has the lowest infant
mortality rate for white and Puerto Rican births, and
the second lowest for nonwhite births. In spite of
this preponderance of higher income families in Queens,
there are several poverty pockets which, in the
opinion of some community leaders, represent areas
that have "unfortunately been allowed to become slums."
Examples cited are Rockaway Beach and Jamaica.

In some places the dwellings of the well-to-do
are mixed closely with those of the less fortunate.
Homes costing $40,000 surround Kennedy Airport, yet
approximately 40% of the community members earn less
than $6,000 a year and the infant mortality rate (a
sensitive measure of poverty) is a high 39.8. The
greatest density of poverty, however, is found in
Jamaica; reportedly, the infant mortality rate in
this area is over 40 per 1,000 live births.

The aged constitute a fairly high proportion of
the total population of Queens. According to the
City Planning Commission's estimates for 1965, 12.2%
of the population are over 65 years of age as against
9.5% in 1960 and 7.1% in 1950. Although this follows
a rather standard pattern for all of New York City
during that period, it was reported that this segment
of the population is concentrated in particular areas

of the borough and their special problems are of great
concern to community leaders and planners.

Existing Facilities and Services

There are 26 hospitals in Queens County: 12
voluntary institutions, 2 municipal, 11 proprietary,
and 1 state-owned. Included in this count is the
Howard Park Hospital, formerly a privately owned
institution, which ceased operating in January 1965
and was bought by the state late in 1966 to be used
as a center for its narcotic program. The area in
which this hospital is located--southern Queens--
contains approximately 140,000 people for whom no
health facilities are easily available. Queens
General is ten miles away, two to three bus rides.

Although there is only one welfare center in
Queens, there is the Queensboro Council for Social
Welfare, an active organization with the primary purpose of "providing a means for individuals and representatives from organizations and agencies, both
public and private, to plan for and to promote the
general health and welfare of the Borough of Queens..."
(from the bylaws of the council). In effect a referral agency, this council coordinates and helps to
promote the health and welfare services of the borough.

One of the newest services in Queens, a diagnostic clinic for retardation, has been termed by the
leaders "a classic in community organization." For
this development, the Queensboro Council for Social
Welfare brought together all agencies interested in
retardation. Together these concerned parties planned
an institute for the major purposes of mobilizing the
community and of helping professionals learn about the
newest methods, but it was also hoped that the activity
would lead to a coordinated effort that would serve on
a continuing basis.

The institute, held in October 1964, provided
"some very exciting recommendations." Several weeks
after the institute, Mt. Sinai Hospital advised the
council that it wished to develop the first diagnostic
clinic in Queens. The clinic is now in operation in
Elmhurst Hospital with services for the very young to
the mature integrated in a junior high school building
contributed by the board of education. It also combines an occupational training day center, a sheltered
workshop, and a preschool educational program.

Another example of pioneering health service in
Queens is the Queensbridge Health Maintenance Program
for the Elderly, a project that had a modest beginning in a 1955 study conducted in response to the
New York City Housing Authority's expressed concern
to the Mayor's Advisory Committee for the Aged about
older persons with physical, emotional, social, financial, and other needs residing in public housing
projects. Findings from this study contributed to an
innovative development in comprehensive health services
incorporated within the Queensbridge housing project
where 13,000 people resided, 1,400 of whom were past
60, and more than 700 past 70. Early in 1961, the New
York City Housing Authority proposed that the Department of Health take the leadership in developing a
comprehensive health, medical, and social program in
this federally aided housing project.

According to a Public Health Report (Vol. 77,
No. 12, December 1962), "Queensbridge housing project
is located in an industrial area, isolated from any
other residential area. The nearest medical facility,
Elmhurst City Hospital, is about 4 miles from the
project, a short drive, but more than 1 hour away by
public bus transportation. This was a major reason
why Queensbridge's predominantly indigent residents,
the aged in particular, were not receiving sufficient
health and medical services. In addition, this older
age group, like their peers in projects in other parts
of the city, suffered from fragmented, poorly coordinated health and social care."

On November 3, 1961, the Departments of Health,
Hospitals, and Welfare, the Community Mental Health
Board, the city housing authority, and a group of
voluntary agencies (the Visiting Nurse Service of
New York, Jewish Community Service of Queens, and
the Jacob Riis Neighborhood Settlement House) established the now well-known Queensbridge Health Maintenance Program for the Elderly. Prior to the program's beginning, the commissioner of hospitals had
designated the new service as a branch clinic of the
Out Patient Department of Elmhurst City Hospital.
The program at Queensbridge includes preventive health
examination, public health nursing service, certain
simple and routine therapeutic services, podiatry,
physiotherapy, counseling and referral services, vocational guidance service, friendly visiting, mental
health services, and (with the cooperation of Elmhurst
City Hospital) specialized diagnostic, outpatient

and inpatient services, rehabilitation, and home
care service.

The organization of the Queensboro Council for
Social Welfare, Inc., is in itself a story of community
mobilization. Queens has had a coordinating council
for over 40 years, having first set one up in 1922.
Believing that higher income people as well as the
indigent "follow the gamut of social and health
problems," and that all should be the concern of the
community, a group of civic leaders, assisted by the
borough president, organized a $21,000-a-year budget
for the council, which was planned to serve as a
coordinating agency. Through the cooperation of the
Red Cross, office space was donated. The council has
apparently operated successfully for many years.
They never perform a direct service. Rather, the
community has learned to call for help with problems
and the function of this office is to refer the requests to one of their wide and growing variety of
resources.

It was reported that the Home and Hospital of
the Daughters of Israel, Inc., is coming to Queens
from Manhattan to set up a geriatrics center.

Discussion

A primary problem in the Queens health-services
domain turns on the disposition of the Howard Park
Hospital. As noted above, this institution was originally established as a privately owned and operated
hospital, ceased operation early in 1965 for
reasons not clearly defined, and was purchased by
the state as a center for its narcotics program. For
numerous reasons, this action disturbed the community.
Some leaders suggested that education of the community
by the state regarding the precise nature of its in-
tentions before the actual fact of purchase might have
made the idea more acceptable. As it was, the mixed
versions of the purpose of the center, hence the im-
agined potential harm its presence might cause the
community, drew active protest. Other protests masked
the fears in terms of specific community needs. Still
a third objection was expressed through a carefully
prepared report on the genuine need for a general
health facility in the neighborhoods surrounding the
Howard Park Hospital. This report said, "It seems
inconsistent for a health facility which is greatly

needed by a collection of neighborhoods to be limited
in its use as a specialty treatment center tying up
200 hospital beds. The general population of about
140,000 in its vicinity has no resources for general
personal care, ambulatory medical care, in-patient
care, mental health, and various ancillary and extended health facilities."

Statistics from a Queens Chamber of Commerce
survey in 1966 showed that 32 to 45 per cent of the
families of the six local health areas had incomes
under $6,000--near the ceiling for Medicaid reimburse-
ment. Statistics were also presented showing that
Health Area 36.12 had suffered an increase in infant
mortality rate from 20.4 (1964) to 39.8 (1965).

This report also pointed out other serious
problems in the area. For example, it stated that
within a period of seven months, 16 cases of infectious
hepatitis were reported in Broad Channel--out of the
total 63 cases reported in Jamaica West for 1966--
suggested as "unusual for a population of approximately 3000 people." It was also noted that Health
Area 36.11 had the second highest incidence of venereal disease in 1965 in the Jamaica West area; that
Health Area 36.12 "again tops Health Areas 36.11,
32.20, 32.10, 31.00, and 30.00 with seven newly reported cases of tuberculosis for 1965"; and, due to
the absence of a sewage system, cesspool problems
are present in the area. "The whole area of Broad
Channel has had a very high water table whereby, in
cases of rainstorms, flooding results because of poor
drainage. Cesspools, as a result, are not able to
take the load resulting in overflow."

The report, prepared by Nicetas H. Kuo, M.D.,
Director of Borough Health Services, Queens (February
14, 1967) concluded:

> The record of illness, disease and
> infant deaths in the low socioeconomic
> areas described indicates the need to
> revitalize them, to combat disease
> and ill health. The continuing rapid
> growth of these areas makes it essen-
> tial to carry out comprehensive plans
> and progress for their development
> with a view to meeting adequately and
> efficiently the people's medical and
> social needs.

This report was taken to Governor Rockefeller by a group of citizens; his response was reported to be that the community could have the hospital if they could raise the money to operate it. They were given a stated amount of time to accomplish this and, even though this period has passed, the situation still hangs in abeyance.

An alternative solution has been proposed--that the Jamaica Hospital take Howard Park on as a satellite since the latter is not complete enough to serve as a total hospital. Jamaica is said to be willing to do this, providing funds are made available to them for the project. It has been further suggested that the city take over the responsibility by supporting an affiliation agreement between Jamaica and Howard Park.

Still another alternative of merit is that of creating adequate ambulatory care and additional inpatient facilities at Jamaica Hospital, thus meeting local need and freeing the potential of Howard Park for state use.

A subject of similar controversy has been the problem of providing health services to the Negro ghetto in Jamaica. An integrated, though predominantly white, cooperative housing project has been built in the center of this poverty pocket and, according to the community leaders, one can find "every problem in the book there." With the advent of Medicaid and Medicare, Jamaica and Mary Immaculate Hospitals developed an interest in serving this community, but the Negroes strongly rejected the offers, pointing out that neither of these hospitals had ever accepted Negro physicians on their staffs or offered to help them before third-party payments were available. Instead, the Negroes simple took over an empty hospital, Interfaith. This, of course, raised financial problems that were solved with the allocation of federal funds to the Negroes to build up Interfaith. Though it would appear that the issue is settled. the situation reportedly has not yet reached equilibrium.

The third area of particular concern is that around Rockaway Beach. Though served by several voluntary hospitals, a branch of the health center, a well-baby clinic, and a branch of PRYME (a pediatrics group that provides total services for children up to 17 years of age, federally funded, affiliated with the Health Department, and cosponsored by Long Island Jewish and Hillside Hospitals), this area is approximately a three-bus-ride trip to Queens General, the nearest municipal hospital. Further, the area is geographically separated from the rest of Queens. The section of Brooklyn to which it is adjacent exhibits the same dearth of provisions for general medical care of the indigent. Suggestion has been made that a satellite clinic is needed in this isolated community.

Two additional locations were indicated as in need of ambulatory services. These are Bayside (Health Area 21)--specifically at 211th Street and Northern Boulevard--and the Ridgewood-Maspeth area. It was pointed out that both communities have high infant mortality rates and manifest additional serious health needs.

The other problems, though more general, were considered no less intense by community leaders interviewed. Particularly troublesome is the problem of the aged, solved only in part by the Queensbridge service. The opinion was expressed that should the neighborhood clinic concept be implemented, the "lumping" of geriatrics with pediatrics may cause problems. From the very beginning, it was suggested, these services should be planned for opposite ends of the clinics. Further, it was proposed that the home aid program be revived and extended to permit the elderly to remain for a longer time in their own homes, and that other special services be developed for the older people of the community.

Since this discussion of Queens health problems has been lengthy, it may be well to summarize the points covered:

1)   The one problem alluded to by everyone interviewed was the disposition of the Howard Park Hospital.

2)   Concern was expressed by both welfare and health workers in the borough that the health needs of Queens inhabitants on welfare are not being adequately met. Attributed in part to the failure of the old system to assign welfare clients to panel doctors, the general problem was described as being further complicated by the added burden of Medicaid and Medicare red tape that have made it "really a jungle for the indigent."

3) Concern was expressed for the health needs of the elderly who are not on welfare, but who are in need of financial assistance due to mounting chronic illnesses.

4) The problem regarding the aged was defined not so much as one of inadequacy in meeting their health needs, but inadequacy in meeting their social and emotional needs, which are believed to be of an urgency at least equal to that of their health problems.

5) While alcoholism apparently has been recognized in Queens as a serious problem, and a private grant has made it possible to give it particular attention, the opinion is shared by several medical leaders that specialized training is needed for those who wish to work in this area.

6) Another problem emphasized is the provision of health care for the poverty pocket in Jamaica (which includes a Negro ghetto) and the integrated though predominantly white cooperative housing project in the center of this ghetto. Of particular concern has been the assignment to a hospital of area responsibility.

7) The small community of Rockaway Beach is cited as a problem. Geographically separated from municipal hospitals, this area is populated predominantly by low-income people whose health care needs are not being met.

8) Apparently no health officer is assigned to either South Jamaica or Flushing-Corona, yet both of these areas reportedly manifest serious and unique health needs. South Jamaica, for example, is reputedly the poorest area of Queens (as indicated by its infant mortality rate). Flushing-Corona is the largest area, comprising three-fourths of Queens.

The City Hospital Visiting Committee made the following priority recommendations for the City Hospital Center at Elmhurst:

> Additional personnel: The nursing division is understaffed in proportion to the increased medical staff. Clerks, messengers, and switchboard operators are needed, as are more dietary aides and housekeeping aides.

- More funds are needed for equipment and supplies.

- Air-conditioning is needed for the speech and hearing clinic and the nursery.

- A conveyor belt is needed to handle medical records.

The Visiting Committee made the following priority recommendations for the Queens Hospital Center:

- Police protection needs much improvement (insufficient security guards and insufficient police protection in case of emergency).

- More space is needed for the Out Patient Department, which is becoming increasingly crowded.

- Locker space is needed on each floor of the hospital for staff and volunteer personal belongings.

- Pointing out that research facilities and laboratories were observed to be taking more and more space, thereby curtailing space formerly used for ancillary patient and staff purposes, the committee asked if this is "a necessary and proportionately worthwhile sacrifice."

- Better lighting is needed on the grounds.

- A better system is needed for classifying TB patients so that staff may know positive from negative patients.

- Better pediatric medical care is needed for TB nursery patients. Apparently the pediatric nursery in Triboro has had a 50% reduction in space. While only a few babies are there, they are very confined and have no place to play. A pediatric resident is assigned to the nursery, but nurses report that it is difficult to get a doctor when they need one for other than TB ailment. Also, this room is "dingy and dirty and needs painting."

BROOKLYN

Population Dynamics

Background information on this topic is presented
in the Health and Hospital Planning Council's report,
"The General Hospital Needs of Brooklyn." (This excellent borough-level, borough-wide health needs study
was the only one of its kind encountered in this survey.) The Council's report first notes that Brooklyn
was an independent city until 1898 when, along with
the other counties adjacent to Manhattan, it became
one of the five boroughs of the City of New York. It
observes that at that time the population was approximately one million, but the "next three decades saw a
rapid growth. By 1930 the population had more than
doubled--to 2,560,000--making Brooklyn the most popu-
lous of the city's boroughs. Growth continued, but
at a slower pace during the '30's and '40's, and by
1950 the population reached its highest point,
2,738,000. During the past 15 years the population
has declined to an estimated 2,600,000 (1965). It is
anticipated that the loss of population will continue
for the next 15 years, so that it is estimated that
by 1980 the population will number approximately
2,435,000 persons."

This report also explains that while the early
growth of population in Brooklyn took place in the
northern and central sections of the borough and
constituted, in fact, "suburbia for the middle-income
person moving from the crowded areas of Manhattan,"
the more recently developed parts of Brooklyn are in
the southern section. Growth since World War I--and
particularly since World War II--has left little
undeveloped land in the borough. The Health and
Hospital Planning Council's report describes the
changing character of Brooklyn with respect to distribution of age, ethnic, and economic groups within
the population:

> These changes involved shifts in the com-
> position and geographic concentration of
> the population compounded by sizeable out-
> migration of former residents and in-
> migration of new groups. In addition
> there was considerable movement within the
> Borough from the older north central sec-
> tions to the newly developed southern

section. This void left in the older sections was filled by an influx of economically disadvantaged groups. By 1960, there
were 376,000 nonwhites residing in Brooklyn--
five times the number in 1930. During the
same period, persons of Puerto Rican birth
or parentage had risen to 186,000 from an
estimated 15,000 in 1930.

Coincident with the population shift
in the Borough, and the change in ethnic
distribution of the population, Brooklyn
has, as have all other areas of the city,
experienced an increase in the number of
aged in its population. In 1960, there
were 259,000 persons aged 65 and over
residing in Brooklyn. This represented
nearly 10 per cent of the population. In
1930 this age group accounted for only
3.7 per cent of the population.

The more newly developed areas in the
south are less densely populated middle-
income or lower-middle-income communities.
Between these two extremes are other sections of the Borough which can be characterized as changing. Such a section would
be the Bushwick-Ridgewood area. In such
areas, out-migration of the middle income
group has occurred or is now occurring,
but the influx of the economically disadvantaged has not yet started.

For the immediate future it can be anticipated that the demographic trends which
have been evidenced over the past 35 years
will continue, although probably at a
slower rate. Note must be taken of various
urban renewal and redevelopment programs
which will, in the long run, tend to
counterbalance the deterioration of neighborhoods which has been the major problem
of recent years. For planning purposes,
however, the essential feature to be recognized is that the character of the Borough
has changed and is changing.

Other forces are currently at work in
Brooklyn which directly affect the health
needs of its heterogeneous population.

The low income groups in the older sections
of the Borough have a high birth rate, high
tuberculosis rate and high infant mortality
rate.   There is heavy dependence for medical care on out-patient clinics and emergency
rooms.   Hospitalization is generally in municipal
hospitals or in the service wards of voluntary
hospitals.

The higher income groups in the newer areas
have lower birth, tuberculosis, and infant
mortality rates; rely primarily on private
physicians for their medical needs; and
utilize private and semiprivate accommodations in voluntary and proprietary hospitals.

The large aged population presents a pressing need, not only for nursing home and
other extended care services, but also for a
whole array of sociomedical services, such
as home care, rehabilitation, and ambulatory care.

The other forces at work are economic and
legislative.   Notwithstanding the large
proportion of the population which is now
in the lower economic groups, income
levels and the general standard of living
are rising.   An ever increasing proportion
of the population--including those in the
lower economic groups--is being covered by
third-party payers.

Recent legislation will have a profound
effect.   By making all persons over 65
years of age eligible for private care,
both in hospitals and for physician's
services, Title 18 of the 1965 Amendments
to the Social Security Law will require
a complete reappraisal of hospital and
health needs in all areas.   Title 19 of
the same amendment will remove many of the
existing financial barriers to in-patient
and out-patient care for public assistance patients and will make available to
them a broader range of hospital services.

In addition, Article 28 of the New York
State Public Health Law will facilitate
the provision of these services by in-
suring to the providers reimbursement
which is reasonably related to costs.

In the heart of central Brooklyn is the Bedford-
Stuyvesant community--reportedly the second largest
urban poverty area in the nation. Encompassing
eleven health areas, the community of 288,000 is
crowded into a 500-block area. It is estimated that
there are approximately 260 people per net residential acre. Though the population has increased by
less than 2000 within the past six years, the proportion of ethnic groups, particularly of Negroes,
has changed significantly. In 1960, 58.6% of the
population was Negro and 4.5% Puerto Rican. Today
it is estimated there are 83.1% Negro and 4.1% Puerto
Rican--which, it was reported, is one of the largest
Negro concentrations in the country.

Uniformity in the type of housing also character-
izes the Bedford-Stuyvesant community. It is a predominantly residential community (65% of the total
net acres being devoted to housing), but unlike
Central Harlem and other low-income communities of
the city, Bedford-Stuyvesant has relatively few old-
and new-law tenements and only a minor scattering
of multidwelling-law buildings. Brownstones, white-
stones, and similar types of buildings make up the
largest proportion of housing units, and for the most
part, they are old and deteriorating structures.
Only 8.8% of all the buildings have been erected since
1939 (as against 19.7% for city-wide, 14.4% for
Brooklyn as a whole, and 10.1% for Harlem). Hence,
as Shiffman expressed it, "The age of the structures,
coupled with a generally tight and expensive mortgage
market in the area, and a low-income population with
proportionately less to invest in physical surround-
ings, has led to a rapid decline in the condition of
housing in the area."

Existing Facilities and Services

Of the 40 hospitals serving Brooklyn, 27 are
voluntary institutions, 4 are owned by the local
government, and 9 are privately owned and operated.
In addition, 30 or more distinct kinds of agencies,
most of which have multiple service centers, provide

various health and welfare assistance to the borough.
Listed for the convenience of Brooklyn citizens in a
"Community Information Manual" (published by the Pratt
Center for Community Improvement in cooperation with
the Central Brooklyn Coordinating Council, Inc.,
December 1966), these facilities provide services for
mental health, the aged, addictions such as alcoholism,
drugs and smoking, special diseases such as amoebic
dysentery, cancer, diabetes, leukemia, polio, T.B.,
and V.D., emergency situations such as ambulance
service, artificial respiration, poison, medical and
dental emergency services, birth control and maternity
care, special services for the blind, the deaf, and
the hard of hearing, child health, including dental
care, physical examinations, innoculation and immunization, parent education, problems of the handicapped,
and child health stations, dental services, Medicaid
and Medicare offices, counseling services, nutrition,
and a listing of all hospitals, health department,
nursing services and nursing homes.

Discussion

According to the 1966-1967 Annual Report of the
Office of the Borough President, a very serious problem
is the high infant mortality rate in more than one-half
of Brooklyn's ten health center districts, considerably
exceeding the city-wide rate.

An almost equally serious concern is "the fright-
ening problem of unabated crime."

Contributing to these two problems are the critical poverty areas of Brooklyn, in particular Bedford-
Stuyvesant and Brownsville, and for each of these
communities there are long lists of problems that are
correlated with poverty.

Specific problems confront hospitals in Brooklyn;
according to "The General Hospital Needs of Brooklyn,"
these can be attributed to four fundamental factors:
multiplicity of facilities and services, maldistribution
of facilities and services, fragmentation of services,
and obsolescence of facilities.

The two problems cited by the Office of the Borough
President are only the leaders in a long list of serious
situations. Regarding the whole list, the "board
members have expressed a sense of concern to the
Borough President over the backlog of unresolved social

and economic problems in most of the districts they
represent. These problems cast their long and ugly
shadows over the community. They include conditions
which must undoubtedly be considered serious if not
critical."

     With respect to the high infant mortality rate,
the Department of Health's 1965 statistics indicated
that Brooklyn's rate of 28.5 is higher than the rate
for any of the separate boroughs or for the city itself. Brooklyn's infant mortality rate of 20.7 for
white births was exceeded in New York City only by
the borough of Manhattan, which had a rate of 21.9.
The average for the city was 19.4; for the Bronx,
18.0; for Queens, 16.4; and for Richmond, 18.7.
Brooklyn's rate of 41.6 for nonwhite births was second
only to Richmond. For Puerto Rican births, Brooklyn
was exceeded again only by Manhattan, but the difference was negligible; Brooklyn's rate was 27.6;
Manhattan's, 27.8.

     It would appear that the infant mortality rate
for Brooklyn is raised primarily by the high rates
for Bedford-Stuyvesant, Brownsville, and Ft. Greene,
three of the ten health districts. Bedford's rate
of 41.9 is higher than that for any other health
district in New York City, and Brownsville's 35.4 and
Ft. Greene's 35.5 are exceeded only by Central Harlem's
37.2. The root of the problem can be pin-pointed by
observing the variance among the health areas within
the Bedford district. This ranges from a "low" 30.6
for Health Area 49 (considering the average city rate
is 25.7, this figure is low only in a relative sense)
to a high of 54.4 for Health Area 21. Further, 6
out of the 11 health areas of the Bedford district
have infant mortality rates exceeding 40.0. Clearly,
the priority problem areas of Brooklyn, are Bedford,
Brownsville, Ft. Greene, Bushwick, and Williamsburg-
Greenpoint.

     The Bedford district health education director
stated that the pressing needs are for alcoholic, eye,
and dental clinics. Also, she reported that the aged--
particularly those suffering from the "less interesting kinds of chronic illnesses"--need more help in
the Bedford community. They need more visiting nurses,
more aides, and more home care assistance. Among the
chronic illnesses is a high incidence of strokes, which
require special therapy of various kinds, and there
is neither professional nor volunteer help to offer.

So far as alcoholism is concerned, it was reported that the only clinics in the area are at St. John's Hospital, Brooklyn Jewish, and Kings County. There is a waiting line at each of these facilities, just as there is everywhere. Those who need help in the Bedford district have two choices. They may take a long bus trip, then wait a long time or be transferred from one facility to another. Or they may pay for treatment that is more accessible. It was pointed out that neither of these alternatives is satisfactory for an alcoholic who has made up his mind to do something about his problem. That is, the cost of the bus trips or the price of service at a nearer location would pay for more liquor, and the temptation at a moment of decision might be greater than the motivation to avoid drinking. One woman who approached the Bedford health center recently for help provides a significant anecdote. She pleaded desperately, "I'm tired of looking for help, tired of being sent all over, and tired of drinking. I want help now... do you understand?" They did understand, but there was no local place to refer her.

Regarding the problem of crime, the borough president emphasized the severity of the situation with the statement, "Business has suffered throughout the borough. Religious institutions have felt the effects of existing conditions. Attendance has fallen at meetings of all kinds. People have stopped socializing. We want our streets to be safe now. We want our homes and places of business to be secure now. We want to be able to visit our parks without fear now." To meet the rising problem of crime, the borough president listed three proposals for prompt action: (1) an increase of at least 3000 foot patrolmen in the ranks of the police department; (2) immediate activation and implementation of the police department auxiliary forces, at least for the period it will take to recruit and train new patrolmen; (3) mobilization of the services of recently retired officers of the police department to assist in the recruitment and training of auxiliary forces.

Spelling out the hospital problems, the Health and Hospital Planning Council pointed out (in "The General Hospital Needs of Brooklyn") the poor distribution of the hospitals within the borough of Brooklyn. Because most of the hospitals were founded between 1880 and 1920, it is explained, they were built in the areas of population concentration for

that period. Following the shift of population to
the south, no hospitals have been built, so this
area is without hospital services. As the report
concludes, "Any realistic and logical plan for the
improvement of the over-all hospital situation in
Brooklyn must therefore encourage the redistribution
of facilities. The north-central section simply has
more hospital facilities than it needs and the larger
southern area has not enough."

Regarding the fundamental problem of fragmentation
of services, the council's report points out, "In
addition to the 40 hospitals...there is a large variety
of other organizations and agencies in the Borough
providing some aspects of health services...These
facilities are under a variety of auspices, and, although there are affiliations of one sort or another
between and among some of them and some of the general
care hospitals, the over-all situation is characterized by lack of organization, problems of communication, and an absence of continuity of care for the
patient. This situation is also compounded by the
poor geographic distribution of Brooklyn's hospitals.
Orderly planning and provision of services are precluded by uncoordinated districting and overlapping
lines of authority. Patients often receive ambulatory
medical care from more than one institution. This
may occur at the will of the patient or because of
multiple referrals by several different agencies whose
efforts on behalf of the patient are uncoordinated.
Similarly, continuity of patient care is often lacking
as care shifts between ambulatory and in-patient
services."

The fourth major problem confronting hospitals
in Brooklyn, according to the council, is obsolescence
(attention is called to their recently published
Special Report 4, "Appraisal of Hospital Obsolescence").
(Since Special Report 4 was released, one proprietary
hospital has closed.) The Report states that in the
borough of Brooklyn, the total estimated cost for
correcting present plant deficiencies is $217,127,000,
which includes an estimated $78,361,000 for the reno-
vation of 25 hospitals and $138,766,000 for the re-
placement of 16 hospitals. The total estimate for
Brooklyn, including site acquisition and essential
expansion of services will probably exceed $300 million.

"Equally as startling as the total dollar figure,"
the Report points out, "was the finding that 16, or

nearly 40 percent, of the borough's 41 hospitals studied are completely obsolete. This group of obsolete hospitals includes 13 voluntary institutions and two of the four municipal hospitals. One proprietary hospital also needs replacement."

Seven specific problems are noted for Brooklyn in the report of The Mayor's Advisory Task Force on Medical Economics (February 1966):

1) Though there is a sufficient total number of general care beds in Brooklyn, these beds are poorly distributed. This is attributed, in part, to inflexibilities resulting from the existence of three separate systems of hospitals, and in part from the large number of small institutions that provide only limited services to specific groups within the population.

2) Present organizational patterns and methods of administering and distributing services result in fragmentation of patient care and inefficient use of resources.

3) There is wide variation in the ability of hospitals to deliver high-quality medical care and related services. Defining high-quality medical care as that which provides professional competency, comprehensiveness, and continuity, the Planning Council believes that "too often one or more of these elements is lacking."

4) There are serious deficiencies in facilities and services for the care of long-term patients, including a lack of home care programs. Further, it was pointed out, the "introduction of Medicare will merely accentuate these problems unless remedial action is forthcoming."

5) There is a lack of suitable organized ambulatory medical care programs.

6) The inability or unwillingness of many institutions in Brooklyn to provide a broad range of community-oriented health services constitutes a major problem. This problem is spelled out with the statement, "The relatively large number of small voluntary hospitals and proprietary hospitals in Brooklyn, which serve only a limited segment of the population and whose services are confined almost exclusively to the care of inpatients, places an

undue burden on the voluntary and municipal hospitals. The geographic maldistribution of hospital facilities compounds this problem."

7) The program for the care of the mentally ill residents of Brooklyn is seriously inadequate. Specifically, "there is a tragic shortage throughout the Borough of mental health facilities which are capable of providing comprehensive services, including inpatient care (both short-term and intermediate-term) and ambulatory care at a local community level."

To meet the problems discussed, "It is the conclusion of the Hospital Review and Planning Council of Southern New York, Inc., that the enormity of the problem forces the community to seek an overall remedy and not merely the piecemeal approach which has been attempted so often in the past." They propose, then:

1) That the future planning for the health facilities of Brooklyn center on the development of medical service centers that would concentrate many of the community's health functions in one complex;

2) That only those hospitals having the proven potential and the demonstrated desire to become medical service centers be encouraged to expand;

3) That hospitals not demonstrating the capability for developing into medical service centers merge either with existing strong institutions or with one or more smaller institutions so that together they can form the nucleus of a medical service center;

4) That institutions relocate from the north-central section, which has a high concentration of beds, to other parts of the borough where there is a low concentration of beds;

5) That certain highly specialized services such as neurosurgery, burn treatment facilities, and hyperbaric surgical facilities be centralized in a limited number of the larger medical service centers;

6) That every medical service center be designed and administered to insure maximum flexibility in the use of its facilities.

Supplementing the summary report of the Health and Planning Council are specific comments and recommendations made by the City Hospital Visiting Committee:

Regarding Coney Island Hospital:

- The most glaring deficiency is the lack of nurses, particularly at night. To relieve this highly critical nursing situation, the committee proposes that "salary increases alone are not enough." Better working conditions and more supplies and equipment are necessary.

- The position is available, but unfilled, for assistant director at night.

- The surgical supply room needs to be air-conditioned.

- A conveyor belt or dumb-waiter is needed to transport records.

Regarding the Brooklyn-Cumberland Medical Center:

- The building on the old Raymond Street Jail site must be constructed as soon as possible to provide adequate public home infirmary care and additional services in the areas of psychiatry and rehabilitation. This new service would also release beds at the hospital for acute care cases.

- The department of radiology is under-equipped and lacks sufficient working space for accomplishing its work. The equipment now in use has been obsolete for ten years. New equipment was promised by the city during the first year of Cumberland's affiliation (1963).

- Additional space is desperately needed in the Out Patient Department and new floors are recommended. Money has been appropriated by the Board of Estimate for this purpose and expansion should be begun. Adequate research space must be provided, either in this building or in a separate new building.

- Storage space is inadequate. There is no safe place to store combustible liquids necessary for laboratory usage.

- A properly designed permanent hemodialysis unit is needed, as the temporary facility established two years ago cannot handle the increased demand. Individuals desperately in need of the service are being turned away.

- Children's cribs need replacement.

- The working force of the hospital is overtaxed--especially in the nursing, clerical, and security areas. Request has been made for $916,000 to cover these additions to the staff. The lack of R.N.'s is the primary problem; 74 nurses are "totally inadequate for a hospital of this size and activity."

Regarding Greenpoint Hospital:

- A major need is for more professional nurses.

- Of equal importance is the construction of the new building.

- During the interim period, a ramp should be provided for the front entrance of the clinic building for wheelchair patients and for moving oxygen tanks.

- Drinking fountains should be provided for the clinic building.

- The porch area of the east building needs to be expanded.

- Installation of an information desk in the basement of the clinic building needs to be completed.

Regarding Kings County Hospital Center:

- Two assistant hospital administrator positions have been vacant for over a year and should be filled as soon as possible.

- A new and better designed emergency admitting unit is urgently needed.

- The third elevator in the vacant shaft in the
  Out Patient Department still has not been
  installed and should be immediately.

- More clerks, aides, and security guards should
  be provided for the Out-Patient Department,
  especially during peak registration periods.

- An adequate, competent, well-trained security
  force should be provided for the protection of
  patients, personnel, and property.

RICHMOND

Population Dynamics

The population of Richmond County has increased
from 221,988 in 1960 to approximately 302,000 today.
This accelerating growth, reportedly more rapid in
1966 than in 1967 because of the recent tightness of
money, is expected to continue at a rapid rate.

In land size, Richmond is the second largest of
the city's five boroughs. According to public leaders
interviewed, there is a closer relationship among the
people here than within the other boroughs.

By ethnic distribution, Staten Island is predominantly white (92%), with approximately 7% nonwhite
and 1% Puerto Rican. The white population is increasing at a faster rate than are the others. It is
asserted that at this time there is no serious racial
problem except, perhaps, on weekends when "outsiders"
visit the Island. No school on Staten Island is over
50% Negro, and the nonwhites and Puerto Ricans are
middle to lower class, with a number of them well-
educated. Hence, though there is some resistance to
integrated housing, a large number of the minority are
well accepted. Though heterogeneous in interest and
profession and, to a small degree, ethnically, the
general feeling is that the Islanders mix well and work
together with a good community spirit. It is considered advantageous that there are four community
planning boards in Richmond. (In other boroughs, one
community planning area might be of the same population as Richmond's total.) The idea was proposed
that if minority groups can be assimilated slowly,
as has been the case on Staten Island, there should
be only a minimum of problems.

Existing Facilities and Services

There are three voluntary hospitals, one proprietary hospital, one local government institution,
and one federal hospital on Staten Island. These
facilities offer a total of 2,720 beds, the majority
of which are not actually available to Island residents;
738 are in the voluntaries (Richmond Memorial, 160;
St. Vincent's, 310; and Staten Island, 268); 116 in the
proprietary hospital, Doctors' of Staten Island; 796
in the federal Public Health Service Hospital for
Seamen; and the remaining beds in the Municipal Sea
View Hospital and Home (including Richmond Boro Hospital):   244 general in-patient, 34 geriatric, 558
nursing (the Home), and 228 custodial beds for homeless old men and women, for a total of 1,064 beds.
(Sea View consists of 92 separate buildings, on 100
acres of land, served by eight miles of concrete
roads.)

Richmond Memorial Hospital is in a vitally
growing area of small homes that has been developing
over the past few years as a result of the construction
of the Outerbridge Crossing. The in-migrants have
been primarily middle-class, economically growing
families, many from Brooklyn.

St. Vincent's Hospital, located in the northern
section of Staten Island, is in a well-established
community; it has been concentrating during the past
several years on the improvement of both its plant
and its staff. There is ample room for expansion.

Staten Island Hospital, approximately a mile
east of St. Vincent's, was reported as in desperate
need of physical expansion, yet there is no physical
area for such growth. A bid has been made to move
this hospital to a more central point in the borough,
namely, to the site of Sea View in the center of the
Island, five miles south of St. Vincent's and Staten
Island Hospitals, and in an area that is in great need
of an acute-care hospital.

Staten Island and St. Vincent's, along with the
U.S. Public Health Service Hospital for Seamen, serve
a community of approximately 100,000. This district
along with the community of about 88,000 served by
Sea View and the Doctors' Hospital contain the major
slum areas of the Island.

Other facilities--which do not exhaust the list of health facilities that exist on Staten Island-- are:

1) Mt. Loreta, a home for children (orphans and children from broken homes) serving approximately 800 children. This is sponsored by the Roman Catholic Church.

2) A privately funded hospital for narcotic addicts containing approximately 200 patients who are, in fact, from other boroughs.

3) A mental health child guidance clinic for the 16- to 21-year age group.

Discussion

The four key hospitals were reported as over-taxed, with frequent times when no facilities are available for acute care. Contrary to the rather common characteristic shared by the other four boroughs, Richmond does not appear to be suffering an overcrowd-ing of out-patient clinics and emergency services. In fact, it was stated that should Staten Island Hospital be moved to Sea View as is contemplated, the ambulatory unity of St. Vincent's would be quite sufficient to serve the needs of that health district.

Apparently the greatest need, with respect to hospital services, is for additional bed space. A re-port issued by the Health and Hospital Planning Council (November 1964) stated that the need then was for an additional 50 to 70 medical-surgical beds, with 100 additional medical-surgical beds needed by 1970. A later report indicated the Island had suffi-cient maternity beds (106) to meet current needs.

In September 1966, administrators of the various hospitals were interviewed and the Planning Council was consulted for the purpose of updating these 1964 estimates to determine whether or not the advent of Medicare and the population boom on the Island were responsible for any significant changes. The general conclusion was that the needs described in 1964 were becoming "more acute and serious every day." It was said that the primary need in all Staten Island Hospitals is the upgrading of present obsolescent facilities. The planning council staff gave the

current figure (i.e., for September 1966) of better
than 95% as the rate of occupancy for all medical-
surgical beds on Staten Island, and now advise that
"a total of between 175 to 200 more beds will be
needed by 1970," with an immediate need for 75 to 100
additional beds.

Reports from the individual hospitals also substantiated the earlier projections. At Richmond Memorial,
for example, it was estimated that $3.5 million will
be needed for the first phase of a plan to upgrade
present facilities. This would not include the building of a nursing home, which had been considered
several years ago--a plan that apparently has been
postponed into the "far future."

St. Vincent's reported that there is a wait for
beds most of the time at their hospital; the wait is
often very long. Presently, they are engaged in a
program of upgrading ancillary services (specifically,
X-ray, emergency, and boiler plant) with the funding
coming from a federal grant (Hill-Burton). With the
consent of the city, St. Vincent's has applied for
state funds for the purpose of taking over Sea View
Hospital & Home as a nursing home and geriatrics center.
St. Vincent's has no other nursing home plans at this
time and no capital expansion is planned.

In November 1966, Staten Island Hospital reported
that there is always a waiting list for surgery and
the occupancy rate was running "very tight"--over 90%.
Apparently, their home care program has been successful
both in operation and in the freeing of 40 beds for
medical-surgical use. They are developing a long-
range plan for improvement and expansion and have
engaged an architect to begin formalizing these plans.
The initial phase is estimated as costing about $9
million, a sum they say will have to be obtained from
the federal government. Plans call for Staten Island
Hospital ultimately to become a 400- to 500-bed
teaching hospital, a plan that would involve relocation.

At Doctors' Hospital, occupancy rate was also
reported as running very high, approximately 92%. It
was estimated that 50% of the patients are on Medicare
funds, and a rise is expected because of the requirement that a Medicare patient must be in the hospital
for three days before he can be admitted to a nursing
home. In 1964, Doctors' Hospital applied for and
was granted permission to add 30 beds; construction is
under way.

Regarding the possibility of federal funding, it was reported that "there is, at present, a bill which we (the hospital administrators) feel has some chance of passing in the 90th Congress." (This legislation would provide for low-interest government loans for capital expansion of voluntary hospitals. This, the Hill-Staggers Bill, was referred to the Committee on Labor and Public Welfare, and hearings have been held on it. In the House it was referred to the Committee on Interstate and Foreign Commerce where no hearings had been held at the time of this writing.)

The problem of insufficiency of nursing home facilities was discussed only briefly. Apparently facilities do exist on Staten Island, but they are expensive (averaging between $100 and $125 per person per week) and they are inadequate. The two active homes are filled to capacity. Two new homes are under construction (with one of these planned for 120- to 150-bed capacity); another home is closer to completion.

The relation between Medicare and hospital bed utilization was suggested as a subject for research. The consensus of the group interviewed was that Medicare has not increased the number of admissions so much as it has increased the length of stay. This, it was explained, is because the patient--or more often his family--does not want him to be released. Since someone else is paying the bill, opportunity is taken to remain in the hospital until nursing home accommodations can be found for the patient or until he is better able to take care of himself before returning home.

Another problem discussed briefly was the pressing need for accredited teaching hospitals on Staten Island. It was pointed out that the Public Health Service Hospital for Seamen is now being placed in the position of having to help in general community care because of the insufficiency of good clinical facilities within the other hospitals. If available federal funds were used for building clinics, the clinics could then be staffed through the affiliation of good teaching hospitals and with the help of Medicaid funds. However, it was argued, this arrangement could force people into using clinics, and it is believed that the public should have the choice of going to a private physician. No physicians have been paid by Medicaid, it was asserted, except of course for those doctors who were on welfare panels.

Regarding the possibility of supplementing the hospital services with satellite clinics, the consensus was that this plan offers only an interim solution to the problem of meeting the rising medical needs of an exploding population. The opinion was expressed that hospitals will have to be built in the selected locations eventually, so why not plan for them in the beginning? Further, it was pointed out, there is no problem at present in Richmond County so far as space for clinics is concerned, nor has there been an appreciable increase in the indigent population.

Countering this argument, however, was the question that was raised regarding the possible influence, on the indigent population, of two proposed housing projects in the Fox Hills area. Presently there is a high mobility rate in the low-cost housing units because of employment problems, but the employment situation could be improved with a desirable hospital center building program at the Sea View site. This would create a need for many categories of both low- and high-skilled jobs. The conclusion was that although an actual "pocket of poverty" cannot be defined, there is potential developing for a rising number of indigent and that this trend could be relieved.

A major problem discussed was the lack of dental teaching units. There are none in the hospitals on the Island. There are dental chairs in the schools (through Department of Welfare programs) and dental care is offered in health centers, but there is no teaching unit in the hospitals. It was proposed that should the concept of comprehensive care be implemented, dental chairs will then be put in the clinics and ultimately the plan will be enlarged to include teaching institutions and dental internships.

From these discussions rose mention of problems caused by the advent of Medicaid. For example, regarding dental chairs in hospital clinics, will the hospital be paid a per patient rate for each visit? The general opinion expressed was that "hospitals should not go into business at the expense of the voluntary physician (as it is the hospital, not the physician, who collects Medicaid payments), nor should hospitals go into business to make money."

Regarding Medicaid problems, it was pointed out that 40% of the Richmond population are eligible for Medicaid, but many people are not signed up because of the complexity of the forms. Further, it was reported that Staten Island Hospital has not been reimbursed for almost a year for drugs dispensed to the clinic, nor have they received any Medicaid payments for patients who have registered. Another problem raised was the possibility that Medicaid will eliminate teaching cases as patients may elect to go to private physicians, thereby minimizing clinic services.

Two problems that Staten Island has not yet experienced are those of a serious infant mortality rate and high incidence of narcotic addiction. Regarding the former, those interviewed cited a good educational approach as responsible for alleviating a possible problem. Regarding narcotics, opinions were varied, the general conclusion being that Staten Island has been fortunate so far but that the potential is threatening.

The director of the Staten Island Mental Health Society summarized the problems in the mental health area as follows:

1) Richmond is the only county in the state that does not have a single psychiatric bed. Hence, any patient in need of in-patient care must now be transported to another area, which is "a painful matter" because the rapid admission and processing that should be given these patients cannot be offered. Further, because of the relatively small number of psychiatrists on the Island, the patients cannot be escorted by a physician. If the patient is indigent, he is transported in a Sea View ambulance; if he is not eligible to be a city patient, he is transported in a private ambulance. It was reported that in 1952 there were no full-time psychiatrists on Staten Island. Today there are 18. This number, however, is still grossly inadequate considering that a community of 300,000 people must be served. Until a mental health center is built, it will be difficult to increase the number of psychiatrists substantially. The work of doctors is limited without a hospital.

2) A second problem affects the 16- to 21-year age group. One of the largest child guidance clinics

is on Staten Island, yet this facility is overwhelmed
by patients from other counties. There is currently
a waiting list of 140. The problem is not a matter
of funds alone, it was reported, as the mental health
board has been "wise in distributing money," but there
is insufficient space to accommodate the staff that is
provided by the funding. The clinic expanded in 1960
to try to meet rising need, then doubled in size in
1964. However, the need for space remains acute.
There were 30 patients in 1952; in 1966, this number
had increased to 1,500.

This problem is being approached by plans for a
North Richmond Mental Health Center. Development of
this facility is in the capital budget for 1967-1968;
the center should be constructed by 1970. It will
provide bed space (24-hour beds, day beds, and night
beds), vocational rehabilitation, and a children's
day care center.

Actual physical space for expansion of facilities
is not a problem, apparently, as the Staten Island
Mental Health Society owns 6 acres next to St. Vincent's
Hospital, and the hospital owns 13 acres. These two
institutions have been pooling forces for a number
of years, and they plan to continue to pool both land
and staff to build the new center. There are hitches
in the actual means by which the center will be constructed, however, which will take time to straighten
out. The most probable solution involves a proposal
regarding the modification of the state constitution
that would enable the city to construct the center.
It was pointed out that on Staten Island the hospitals
tend to work together in the mental health field. It
is a shared staff; that is, one doctor may serve on the
staff of each of three hospitals. Apparently, this is
a much more flexible staff relationship than is commonly found, and should work to the advantage of the future
of mental health efforts on the Island. Most important,
it will ultimately enable each patient to have the same
psychiatrist on each visit, an arrangement particularly
desirable in this field.

3) It is considered unfortunate that Staten
Island is segmented with health districts that do not
coincide with natural population distribution, thereby
creating large differences from one area to another in
the numbers to be served.

Richmond includes the biggest land fill area in New York City, resulting in pollution of estuaries and the air. The air pollution problem is amplified by factories and manufacturing plants in New Jersey and in the industrial sections of the Island (north and west shores). Reportedly this condition kills vegetation and the incidence of cancer is heightened in these areas.

Apparently there is insufficient water pressure on Staten Island, a situation that can cause temporary periods of rationing.

It was also reported that there are no sewers on 75% of Staten Island. There has been some development of private sewerage systems, but for the most part, the problem is controlled with large septic tanks. It was estimated that there will be five to ten years of abatement planning before positive action will be enabled. Further, there is a drainage problem during the rainy seasons on the south shore and parts of the north shore. It was pointed out that Richmond hospitals treat their sewerage before disposing of it in the bay.

SUMMARY OF BOROUGH SURVEYS

A common set of health problems has been observed to characterize all the boroughs of the city. Occurring in varying degrees of intensity both from borough to borough and from one area to another within a borough, these problems manifest fundamental needs of the total system of health service delivery in the City of New York. The preceding analyses of the separate boroughs have defined these problems in relation to the specific environments in which they are found. It is equally essential to view these underlying health problems within the framework of the system which has been established to serve the needs they manifest.

Probably the most persistent of these common problems is infant mortality, continuing to plague certain sections of the city at appalling rates. Deaths per 1000 births among the nonwhite population appear to have no borough limits. Rates are abnormally high all over. Among the white and the Puerto Rican populations, however, infant deaths occur at a higher rate in Manhattan, the Bronx, and Brooklyn, than in Queens or Richmond. Specifically, the city infant

mortality rate of 26.7 for Puerto Rican births is
more than half again the rate in Queens, as compared
to Manhattan, the Bronx, and Brooklyn where the city
rate is exceeded in more than half of the health areas.
(The Health Department has not computed the rate for
Richmond because the base in that borough is below
200.) While the variation among boroughs is not so
great for white infant deaths, the city rate is exceeded in only one of Queens' six health areas whereas,
again, in the other four boroughs, the city rate is
exceeded in more than half of the health areas. On
the other hand, deaths among Negro and other nonwhite
infants occur at a rate higher than the city rate in
three of Brooklyn's health areas, three health areas
of the Bronx, two of Manhattan, two of Queens, and in
Richmond as whole (rates are not computed for separate
health areas because of the low base).

High infant mortality rates indicate not only low
income, but all the depressing correlates of poverty:
high incidence of tuberculosis and venereal diseases,
low level of education and income, high crime rates
and juvenile delinquency, crowded and deteriorating
housing. For example, the incidence of venereal
diseases and of tuberculosis (in terms of reported
cases and actual census) is higher in Manhattan,
Brooklyn, and the Bronx (in that order) than in Queens
and Richmond. Even when the venereal disease rates
are computed per 100,000 estimated population, the
incidence of VD (reported cases) in general, as well
as of each subclass, is higher in those boroughs with
high infant mortality rates and, with rare exceptions,
the same correlation is implied between these variables
in each of the health areas within the boroughs.

Further, just as Manhattan has the highest infant
mortality rate, so does it have the lowest median
family income. Bronx and Brooklyn can barely be distinguished in either of these terms and run close behind
Manhattan. Queens, on the other hand, has the highest
median family income, and Richmond the lowest infant
mortality rate. So far as education is concerned,
the 1960 census shows that the median number of school
years completed for Queens was 10.9; for Richmond, 10.7;
for Manhattan, 10.6; and for both the Bronx and for
Brooklyn, 9.5.

When juvenile delinquency is considered by borough,
Brooklyn and Manhattan are found to have the highest
total offense rate per 1000 youths 7 to 20 years of age.

Bronx has the next highest offense rate, and (typically) Queens and Richmond have lower rates.

Even in total death rate per 1000 population for
diseases of the heart, malignant neoplasms, vascular
lesions affecting the central nervous system, pneumonia
and influenza, and diabetes, Manhattan, the Bronx and
Brooklyn rank the highest.

Dental care and dental problems are also correlated with level of poverty. In the City of New York,
approximately 44% of elementary and junior high school
children are believed to have had no dental care (at
least until Medicaid). The borough with the highest
percentage of children for whom no care was reported
in 1966 was the Bronx. Manhattan had the second highest percentage, Brooklyn the third, Richmond the
fourth, and Queens the lowest. As could be expected,
in Queens 94% of the children who were treated in
1965-1966 received their care from a private dentist
or an agency other than the Health Department or
Guggenheim Clinic. By the same token, more children
in Manhattan were treated by the Health Department
(27.7%) or by the Guggenheim Clinic (15.9%) than in
any of the other boroughs. Children of the Bronx
came next by this count, then Brooklyn. The same
percentage (10%) of Richmond children as of Brooklyn
children received dental care through the Health
Department.

Translated into health needs, the general problems
that have been discussed call for an increasing effort
to provide more adequate facilities and services (or
more effective distribution) within the depressed
areas and a greater emphasis on health education and
communication between the health authorities and the
people in the community.

Consider, for example, the observation made in
the earlier borough discussions regarding the preponderance of health facilities in Manhattan. In spite
of that preponderance, Manhattan's population--in all
ethnic groups--ranks consistently high in disease and
other health problems. The quantity and/or quality
of facilities clearly are still not adequate (or
appropriately distributed or applied) to meet the
need in that borough, and/or the communities do not
know these services are available to them, or do not
have adequate access to them. These are basic system

problems that need investigation and solution in order
for any facilities or services to operate efficiently
and effectively in the community.

Common to all the boroughs, also, are the problems
of maintaining the quantity and quality of their hospitals and other instruments of health delivery.
These problems include multiplicity and/or poor
distribution of facilities and services, dearth of
vital facilities, shortage of personnel, critical
difficulties in procurement of equipment, fragmentation
of services, and obsolescence of facilities. Specific
needs can be determined only by studies of individual
problems of each borough and of the health districts
and areas within each borough. Overall, there exists
the need for periodic evaluation of not only the
adequacy of the facilities, but also the status of the
needs for which these facilities have been created.
Systematic renovation of facilities is contingent
upon the relationship between the available facilities
and the changing needs of the particular community
which they serve.

Disease and death related to poverty, maintenance
and administration of health facilities and services,
and associated social lags and disintegration of
property, can be classified as problems that underlie
community health for all age levels over the decades.
In addition to these, there are problems that are
unique for this point in history. Frequently these
evolve slowly at first, manifesting symptoms that do
not always indicate the magnitude of their potential.
Suddenly, at an exponential rate, these problems
spread at what appears to be an uncontrollable rate,
demanding special focus and immediate action. Unfortunately, immediate action often must be tentative
or partial because the problems are new and not easily
defined. They require long experimentation and study
before optimal solutions can be found.

At least four such problems characterize the
present era: (1) the need for a better understanding
of the health care needs of the aged and for new approaches to meeting them; (2) the need to replace
fragmentation and gaps in mental health care with a
system comprising the capabilities of modern comprehensive psychiatry; (3) the need for a feasible plan
for approaching the formidable problems of addiction;
and, (4) the need for taking the hospital into the
community by offering ambulatory care--both preventive
and curative--on a neighborhood basis.

The Aged Population

In 1930 there were 270,489 persons 65 years or over in New York City; in 1960 there were 813,802. This population is expected to increase by 25% and to total over 1 million by 1970. The expansion of life expectancy has caused much more than an increase in numbers of people. A completely new population is being formed. It is a population that could not be studied well until recently, and one that is still only partially understood because it is still in process of evolution. New diseases and extensions of chronic illnesses are posing new challenges to the medical field. Equally challenging, however, are the social problems for which solutions are lagging far behind.

For one thing, there is the unfortunate coincidence of a decreased and/or fixed income with the onset of chronic illnesses characterized by continuous and increasing medical costs. Although Medicare has helped this imbalance, there is still a long adjustment period ahead before this tremendously complex system will be working at optimal efficiency. During the interim there will be inevitable confusion for both the older people and those who administer the system.

The problems of greatest concern to medical leaders are what they consider unnecessary health deterioration of older people. Contemporary professional belief argues that aging people should be kept mobile and in their own homes as long as possible. Generally, some form of home health care can postpone institutionalization. However, the problem of case-finding complicates the situation. Too many of the aged do not know where to go for help, or do not know that help is available to them. Therefore, it is too often too late for them to benefit by new medical techniques that have made possible the prevention or arrest of many chronic physical problems. There is no choice but to yield to long-term bed care which must often be given far away from families and friends.

An overview prepared by the Citizens' Committee on Aging, in March 1964, spoke to this point: "Because of the staggering dimensions of the city's older population and the obvious social and economic urgency of preventing needless health deterioration and institutionalizing," a variety of approaches toward comprehensive home health care have been pursued. "The

majority of today's older people function surprisingly
well despite multiple problems, resist using available
but inadequate community resources, and struggle to
maintain an independent way of life. Their evident
demand for service is but a fraction of the estimated
real need, and often comes only when the situation
is deteriorated to a point of crisis, if not
catastrophe."

Two vulnerable groups have been defined by the
Committee on Aging: the elderly who live alone (one-
third of the half-million households in New York City
in 1960 headed by a person 65 years or older were
one-person households--in all, 295,975 "unrelated
individuals"); and the elderly who are 75 years of
age. Each of these vulnerable groups poses unique
needs that generally require more than extension of
existing services; in most cases, alternatives must
be considered or new services created with respect to
present practices.

It would appear that the two greatest needs of
the elderly are home-care kinds of services and long-
term care facilities. Both are in short supply. The
sooner the first need is met more adequately, the
less will be the demand for the second. In the meantime, both are desperately needed. The Community
Council of Greater New York has been studying the
home care and housing needs of the aged. In a first-
draft report promoting homemaker/home-health services
for New York City (May 1967), they pointed out, "Only
high-income persons can afford the $1.50 to $3.50
hourly fee for such service. It is even expensive for
a voluntary agency to place more than a limited number
of such personnel on their staff. The Department of
Welfare is rapidly enlarging its services, but it
still is unable to meet the existing need. Only a
small percentage of the elderly receiving public
assistance are eligible for Department of Welfare
services. Therefore, home health services are not
available to the majority of the aging."

How much help is the Department of Hospital's
home care program? Essentially, this service is quite
limited in the number it can serve. A special study
conducted early in 1966 (Health and Hospital Planning
Council: Report of the Special Committee on Home Care
and Extended Care Services) stated that several years
after the inauguration of this service in 1948, the
average census stabilized at about 2000 cases. This

was explained as probably resulting from budgetary
restrictions, shortages of staff, and variations
among hospitals in the activity of case review of
patients.

Another source of home care service, also limited,
is the Associated Hospital Service. In 1960, home care
was offered as a benefit in all participating hospitals
that would meet the standards that had been adopted.
The program was based on a demonstration and study
of the feasibility of providing visiting nurse services
following hospitalization for Blue Cross subscribers.

Still another agency that has approached the
problem is the Visiting Nurse Service of New York.
Prior to initiating a program, this organization
conducted a pilot study (Community Health Project,
Grant No. Ch 34-21 C-65 on Home Aides for the Sick
and Aged in Queens). This was completed in September
1966, and as a result, effective June 1967, there were
approximately 80 Home Aides serving Manhattan, Queens,
and the Bronx. A similar project is under way in
Brooklyn.

Measuring the need for either home care or for
long-term bed care is difficult. As with so many
problems involving the medically indigent, the need
is a product of the provision. Further, it is impossible to get even an accurate count of the aged who
are sick. They are almost literally hidden in their
homes, well enough only to survive in some minimum
fashion, but uninformed as to help that can be given
for their multiple physical and emotional problems
(of which even they are often unaware). The only
estimate that can be made of need is that the majority
of the aging are not able to get the help they need.

Some attempt has been made at measuring the need
for long-term bed care of the chronically ill. In
1960 it was estimated that 10,000 new beds would be
needed by 1970. This projection lost its validity five
years later with the advent of Medicare. The need
has doubtless multiplied now that beds are financially
available to all old people. Further, between 1960
and 1965 new construction of long-term care facilities
failed to compensate for the loss of beds when many
"small and marginal" facilities did not survive the
elevation of standards in the Proprietary Nursing
Home Code of the Department of Hospitals. There was,
in fact, a slight decrease in the numbers of beds
during that period.

A more recent study of this problem (by the Ad
Hoc Committee on Nursing Home Bed Needs, Health and
Hospital Planning Council, April 1967) determined
that the lag had not yet been made up. They estimated
that the unmet need was for 294 beds, a figure less
than half that quoted by the Department of Welfare on
June 14, 1967, as the number of city patients awaiting
placement in proprietary nursing homes at the close
of that day (716). On the same day there were two
vacancies in proprietary nursing homes.

The Department of Welfare statistics vary little
from day to day. Those quoted are not atypical.
However, the Department of Welfare figures deal with
city patients only, and the numbers refer to applications made. In other words, it is highly probable
that there were many more city patients who needed
hospitalization for chronic illnesses, but they had
not applied for beds. Further, there is still another
large group that did not know they could apply.
Lastly, if those aged who do not qualify for welfare
were counted, the number found in need would be great.

It bears mentioning that of the 20,000 long-term
care beds operating in the city at the time of the Ad
Hoc Committee's report, 3,000 were not considered as
conforming to standards. Though 10,000 new beds had
been approved for construction, the report was not very
optimistic. Not all approved projects are necessarily
carried through to construction.

In summary, the population of the aged is multi-
plying rapidly in New York City. By 1970 they will
number 1 million, and more than a quarter-million will
be over 75 years old. Modern medicine is meeting the
challenge of physical needs far faster than the community is meeting social needs. The underlying problems are that it is a new population that has to be
understood, but it needs definition; case-finding is
a fundamental obstacle; and the two kinds of service
that are clearly in desperate need are both in short
supply: homemaker/home-health services and extended
care for the chronically ill who can no longer remain
in their homes.

Comprehensive Mental Health Care

Traditionally, mental health facilities and services in the City of New York have been planned without consideration of regional, county, city-wide or national objectives. Consequent fragmentation, gaps in service, and duplication of services have been recognized as critical problems, but little success has been met in efforts to solve them. However, the city-wide planning process of 1962-1964, along with federal and state community mental health center legislation of 1963-1965, have stirred movement toward revolutionary change in the field.

Essentially, a totally new orientation has been forced upon the system. New requirements in systemactic planning have been placed on psychiatry, not only in terms of delivery and coordination of service within the field, but as it relates to other mental health professions and other fields of medicine. Most significant is that "responsibility may be now assigned for the control of mental disorders in the general population employing the principles of geographical regionalization and administrative decentralization." (Perkins, M. W. and Padilla, E., Area Planning for Comprehensive Mental Health Care in New York City.)

Though the new philosophy of approach to mental care is generally supported by medical authority, plans are being formulated and implemented on a long-term methodical basis. In particular, care has been taken not simply to thrust the new system on the public; rather, the public has been significantly involved in the planning. Mental Health Commissioner Perkins states "Contemporary mental health action programs are dominated by the concept that treatment of mental and emotional disorders is optimally based in the community of residence of the patient. Clearly, for a system of care so conceived to be feasible, appropriate public attitudes toward the mentally ill, as well as public acceptance of the services, are requisite."

The planning study cited surveyed the adult populations of all five boroughs to determine how New Yorkers go about seeking help, how aware they are of available help, and how they would respond to community-based mental health services. Accordingly, areas of particular interest included public knowledge and opinion about mental health care, appraisals of mental health facilities and professionals, attitudes toward

the mentally ill, public perceptions and conceptions
of mental illness, experience with professional mental
health help, and the sources and recognition of
personal problems.

"Chinks in the traditional public armor of rejection of the mentally ill" were indicated by the
results of this survey, as well as "widespread support
for a variety of ideas for community-based services
currently being suggested by mental health professionals for the care of mentally ill people, and especially
for those services offering quick assistance, such
as a telephone information service and walk-in clinics."
It was determined that the views now quite prevalent
are that mental illness is an illness like any other
and, like most other illnesses, treatable.

Developments indicate that from the very beginning
it was generally recognized that the full cooperation
of all levels of government with the relevant voluntary
and professional organizations would be necessary.
The area planning paper notes that "the Community
Mental Health Centers program has been planned as a
concerted approach toward the wide range of problem
areas directly relevant to the mentally ill and the
mentally retarded. Development and specific implementation has required continuous collaboration
between the New York City Community Mental Health Board,
other City and voluntary agencies, the New York State
Department of Mental Hygiene and the National Institute
of Mental Health. The NYCCMHB has been responsible for
the coordination of the planning and for the development activities of the program. These working relationships have underscored the interdependence of different
levels of government and of the private sector in
mental health and mental retardation."

Specific goals have been established toward the
development of a program of comprehensive mental health
care for New York City. Essentially, these are three:
(1) to construct community mental health centers and
mental retardation facilities for the primary purpose
of controlling mental disorders in the population;
(2) to provide decentralized services to achieve this
primary goal; thus, (3) to plan facilities and services
on an area basis, "both to make coverage possible and
to aid in the difficult process of making decisions
concerning priorities on a city-wide basis." (A Master
Plan for Comprehensive Mental Health and Mental Retardation Services in New York City.)

As the first step toward achieving these objectives, the Research and Planning Division of the Community Mental Health Board developed a Master Plan for coverage of New York City with networks of comprehensive community mental health centers and mental retardation facilities. Fundamentally, this is a flexible, long-range plan taking account of the possibilities of frequent alteration by providing for shorter time-span planning of objectives and redefinition of priorities within the framework of the long-range plan, which was designed as a guideline for achievement within a time span of 20 years.

The basic concept of the Master Plan for regionalization of service delivery is the "catchment area" organization. Though termed "areas," these are conceived not so much as places or districts, but as networks of comprehensive services. Delineation of these catchment areas by the physical boundaries of health areas (each catchment area contains a set of health areas) was a technical solution to the problem of characterization of the community which a particular center would serve. Both demographic and health data are available within these geographically identifiable sections of the boroughs.

The groupings of health areas to form catchment areas were formed not through sociopolitical, sociocultural, or professional criteria, but with respect to at least five factors: (1) networks of transportation available; (2) location of general hospital facilities (by definition, a CMHC is located near a general hospital); (3) districting systems relevant to mental health care whenever possible, (crosscutting of other service districts was avoided); (4) diversity of ethnic and socioeconomic groups (segrated facilities were avoided and a wide range of approaches to the problems of the population was encouraged); and (5) existence of large parks, cemeteries, or other physical barriers to reduce access to the CMHC that would have to be avoided in planning.

The plan has divided the city into catchment areas containing between 75,000 and 200,000 people (a range specified by federal legislation). Care was taken in defining the catchment areas to "strike a balance between requirements to provide comprehensive care to the city as a whole and specific needs and interests at each potential CMHC." Development of these centers is expected to raise more problems.

Some difficulty is anticipated, for example, in the changing working relationships that will be required both within and among disciplines in the new system. Adjustment to disturbances to long-cherished traditions is anticipated as a need. It is believed, however, that the program will be flexible enough to respond to these problems while achieving the desired objectives.

Somewhat larger difficulties anticipated are changes that will have to be considered in long-range planning. These may occur in the sociopolitical context, in public policy, in the size and scope of public need, in the kinds and organization of available resources, or in psychiatry, medicine and technological developments.

Defining the need which the CMHC program has been conceived to meet is difficult. A numerical measure in terms of deficiency in bed capacity might be the same measure used for physical health needs. Even the problem of case-finding describes only a small part of the need. "Our need is a function of the lack of services," one researcher said. Further, she added, with an increase in services, need then becomes a function of controlling the numbers.

In summary, the major need has been for a comprehensive plan for delivering mental health care in New York City. Such a plan would have to provide both preventive care and treatment; it would have to seek to overcome the case-finding problem; it would have to bring together related fields and make their resources readily available to the community; and it would have to coordinate this field of care with physical health services to provide both continuous and comprehensive care. Further, a comprehensive mental health program would emphasize environmental control. Behavior is a response to environment, and mental health deficiencies, in particular, are a function of the environment to a significant degree.

The new plan for comprehensive mental health and mental retardation services in the city is believed to have taken into account all these requirements. However, the designers are aware that no plan can anticipate all the needs the future may hold. The past ten years have witnessed a revolution in the field of mental health control and treatment. The speed and direction of new progress is unpredictable. No projection of numbers based on past or present resources and knowledge could possibly give accurate measure of the need for

mental health facilities and services of tomorrow.
Facilitating research in the field and providing mechanisms through which needs can be expressed and assistance most easily offered appear to provide the
most feasible approach to understanding, preventing,
and treating mental health problems.

The real challenge is to guarantee an over-all
system of total health care in which this plan can
function effectively.

Addiction Problems

Addiction, i.e., physical or psychological dependence upon a chemical substance, is an ancient
problem. The use of habit-forming substances for
psychological effect has characterized every society
in every age. In some cases, as with most drugs,
distribution to the general public has been prohibited by law, whereas, with rare exception, the sale
and consumption of alcohol has been legal. The many
differences among addictive substances--in acceptability of use, acceptability of production and distribution, availability of supply, withdrawal reactions,
types of antisocial behavior characterizing users,
capability for rehabilitating users--have always been
recognized and emphasized. What is new today is the
awakening to similarities among the widening continuum
of addictions and the gradual realization that the
total problem of addiction needs re-evaluation and a
coordinated comprehensive approach for solution.

Despite this growing concern, prompted by increasing numbers of addicts and the mounting problems
generated by them for self and society, the problem
of addiction has remained low on the "list of priorities" for medical challenge. In calling attention
to this fact, New York's Task Force on Addictions
emphasized, "Refusal to accept the problem through
resignation, oversimplification, overcomplication,
blame-assigning, buck-passing, etc., does not solve a
major complex of problems that should be everyone's
concern. Regardless of one's point of view with respect to etiology, complexity, prognosis, or whatever,
it nevertheless remains that we are confronted with
one of the largest and most troublesome social and
health problems of our times and it will not go away
by pretending it isn't there." (Report to the New
York State Planning Committee on Mental Health, 1965.)

This Task Force's conclusion was that all hopes to counter the explosive character of the addiction problem are contingent upon getting all addictions not only "intellectually and schematically recognized, but actually accepted as within the purview of the medical profession and its correlated institutions." Until now, responsibility for care of the addict has been assumed by default by the police. The new approach of the community mental health center, the report pointed out, will have "little impact on the problems of drug dependence unless the medical share of responsibility is honestly and wholeheartedly accepted, and programs commensurate with the magnitude of the problem are instituted."

One such program has been instituted since the release of the referenced report. In a special message to the legislature in 1966 Governor Rockefeller stated, "The problem of addiction to narcotics is at the heart of the crime problem in New York State. Narcotics addicts are responsible for one-half of the crimes committed in New York City alone--and their evil contagion is spreading into the suburbs." Pointing out the futility of approaching this formidable problem through public and private agencies (in spite of the efforts of "dedicated men and women who have devoted their time, energy and resources" through these programs), the Governor proposed a four-point modification of the state-sponsored program that had been evolving over the preceding seven years.

The new legislation motivated by the governor's appeal effected major and revolutionary (as well as controversial) steps in the control and treatment of narcotic addiction. Essentially, the goal of the program is to eliminate this prime cause of crime by "preventing those who have not resorted to crime from doing so, and those engaged in crime from repeating their acts; and to eradicate the fear and anxiety created by this problem." Achievement of the goal is approached through two central objectives:

● Removing the pushers of narcotics from the streets, parks, and schoolyards of our cities and suburbs to prevent these evil carriers from spreading their contagion.

● Providing up to three years of intensive treatment, rehabilitation, and aftercare designed to restore the addict to a useful, drug-free life.

Legislation has been passed that increases sen-
tences for pushers and that establishes three methods
by which narcotics addicts may be committed to the
control program: (a) civil certification of addicts
not accused or convicted of a crime, (b) commitment
of convicted narcotic addicts, and (c) opportunity of
civil certification for the defendant. A New York
State Narcotic Addiction Control Commission was established to enforce the new legislation and to operate
the program.

In urging this action, the governor emphasized
that the narcotics addiction problem is fundamentally
a federal responsibility--morally, financially, and
legally--primarily because most of the illegal drug
traffic originates abroad. Because the federal government has neither been able to stop the dope traffic
nor provided enough help to meet the cost of repairing
the social damage inflicted on communities, and because New York State has more than half the addicts in
the nation (and 90% of the addicts of tne state are in
New York City), the Governor believes that the state
and the city "must take the leadership in initiating
a major war on the problem of narcotics addiction--
with every right under the circumstances to expect
the federal government to shoulder a major portion of
the cost."

The program--totally supported by the state--is
barely underway, so it is impossible to judge its
potential for success. As bold as it is, however, it
is an approach to only a fraction of the addiction
problems in the city and state. So far as effects on
society can be measured, however, the fraction of the
problem represented by narcotics carries significant
weight. For example, the New York City police reported
that from 1963 to 1964:

- a 75% increase was observed in the number of
  children under 16 years of age taken into
  custody for criminal offenses who were
  admitted narcotics users;

- a 95% increase was recorded in arrests for
  murders by addicts;

- 80% of all women arrested for prostitution were
  narcotics addicts;

- almost half of all the persons arrested for
  serious misdemeanors and offenses in the city
  were admitted narcotics users.

A very large part of the addiction problem remains
to be approached. While narcotics users are estimated
at 200,000 to 300,000 in the United States, alcoholics
number 4.5 to 5.0 million. In New York City, narcotics
addicts are estimated to number 30,000, and alcoholics
to number from 200,000 to 300,000. Accurate counts of
any type of addict are impossible to get and, according
to field workers engaged in assisting the alcoholic,
a census of addicts in that classification is more
difficult to obtain than that for narcotic users.
(State legislation and special programs for narcotic
addicts are designed to obtain their registration.)

The addiction problem encompasses more than narcotics and alcohol. More than 20 different drugs have
been listed for various classifications of addictive
and nonaddictive drugs. The President's Advisory
Commission on Narcotic and Drug Abuse names 19 drugs
(see Table 3). Another classification of drugs
(S. J. Holmes, M. D., Alcoholism & Drug Addiction
Research Foundation of Ontario) includes 23 in four
categories found to be most commonly encountered in
the United States and Canada (see Table 4).

Regarding this large variety (not commonly identified with the total problem of addiction), the Task
Force recommended that an addiction program must not
allow itself to be trapped into over-concentration on
one or a limited number of addicting substances, "nor
must the necessary control of new drugs hamper useful
developments of these substances." The point was also
made that a number of substances now recognized as
"dangerous" or as "problem producing" drugs were hailed
at the time of their discovery as safe substitutes,
or even as treatment medication for other addictions.

In spite of the differences among addictions--
and therefore logical differences in the nature of the
institutions and programs that should be recommended
for each--increasing insight gained over the years has
led to the philosophy that similarities, rather than
differences, provide the guideposts to means of approaching the complex of problems involved. The philosophy of an over-all approach is becoming more and
more generally accepted. In the City of New York, the
Coordinator of Addiction Programs has developed a

Table 3. Addictive and Non-Addictive Drugs
as Listed by the President's
Advisory Commission on
Narcotic and Drug Abuse

Drugs associated with physical dependence:

A.   The opiate type

    1.   Morphine group: opium and its
preparations (laudanum, paregoric,
morphine, heroin, codeine, dihydro-
morphinone, dihydrocodeine, di-
hydrocodeinone, dihydrohydroxy-
codeinone, dihydrohydroxymorphinone)

    2.   Morphinan group (racemorphan, levor-
phan)

    3.   Benzmorphans (phenazocine)

    4.   Meperidine group ("demorol," alpha-
prodine, anileridine)

    5.   Methadone group (methadone, propox-
phene, diphenoxylate)

    6.   Dithienylbutenylamines

    7.   Hexamethyleneimines

    8.   Benzimidazoles

B.   The barbiturate-alcohol type

    9.   Barbiturates

   10.   Ethyl alcohol

   11.   Chloral hydrate

   12.   Paraldehyde

   13.   Meprobamate

   14.   Glutethimide

   15.   Methaminodiazepoxide

Drugs not associated with physical dependence:

   16.   Marijuana

   17.   Cocaine

   18.   Amphetamines

   19.   Hypnotics, sedatives and certain
"tranquilizers" (bromides, reserpine
and related alkaloids, chlorpromazine).

Table 4.   Four Classifications of Drugs
           Commonly Encountered in U.S.
           and Canada

A.   Non-narcotic depressive drugs

     1.   Tobacco
     2.   Ethyl alcohol
     3.   Barbiturates
     4.   Tranquilizers
     5.   Chloral hydrate
     6.   Paraldehyde
     7.   Bromides
     8.   Doriden
     9.   Methyl parafynol
    10.   Ureides

B.   Narcotic drugs

    11.   Morphine
    12.   Heroin
    13.   Codeine
    14.   Demorol
    15.   Methadone
    16.   Nalline
    17.   Marijuana

C.   Hallucinogenic drugs

    18.   Peyote or mescaline
    19.   LSD 25

D.   Stimulant drugs

    20.   Caffeine
    21.   Amphetamine
    22.   Psychic energizers
    23.   Cocaine

comprehensive plan for the management of the problem.
Although his plan focuses on the treatment of narcotics users, he advocates the system for all addictions.

It would appear that the primary tasks of the
immediate future in the control and treatment of addictions is to identify them in terms of responsibility requirements for their handling. Only then can
the problem be reduced to plans, programs and implementation. Reports to the New York State Planning
Committee on Mental Health by the Task Force on Addictions have provided data and recommendations that
apparently have not yet been fully utilized. In
particular, planning of the comprehensive units of
health services should include specific provision for
control and treatment of what is now generally recognized as "one of the largest and most troublesome
social and health problems of our times."

Ambulatory Care

Between 1950 and the present, the number of visits
to hospital out-patient clinics and emergency departments has increased from 6.6 million to over 8 million.
Although this increase has been due primarily to a
sharp rise in emergency department visits, the implications for ambulatory services as a whole cannot be
ignored. The nature of the outpatient functions of
hospitals is changing.

Numerous reasons have been noted for this revolutionary expansion of ambulatory services. In one of
the many special studies focusing on the subject,
E. R. Weinerman speaks of the effects of "changing
social environment and advancing frontiers of science"
on both the form and content of medical care, and in
particular on the ambulatory services of general hospitals which include medical training programs. Among
the most influential social changes, he lists the
growing importance of long-term health maintenance
services for chronic illnesses, the need for coordination of patient care in a setting of intense medical
specialization, the emergence of the general hospital
as the community health center, and the trend toward
more prepayment and tax support of medical care
services.

In their report on "Organized Ambulatory Medical
Care Services" (November 1965), the Health and Hospital

Planning Council discusses the pressures for augment-
ing ambulatory services that have been created by such
demographic changes as increasing numbers of the very
young and the very old in the total population. During
the decade preceding 1964, the population of New York
City increased at the rate of about 20,000 persons per
year in both the under-15 and the 65-and-over age
groups. This has led to an increased utilization of
pediatric out-patient care and of organized ambulatory
services for chronic and functional diseases of the
aged, utilization trends expected to continue for at
least several more decades.

Most studies attribute the shift of traffic from
in-patient to out-patient departments to the rising
costs of in-hospital care and to a lack of physician
services in depressed communities. Rising costs was
given major emphasis in a conference sponsored by
The New York Academy of Medicine to consider the problem. Executive Secretary Becker termed the expanding
role of ambulatory services in hospitals and health
departments as "the most important change in the organization of health care that has occurred since the
widespread adoption of the voluntary prepayment mechanism for financing acute hospital care."

Growing evidence that a significant proportion of
emergency department visits are non-urgent (an average
of 70% has been estimated), helps explain the dramatic
increase in the emergency room census (e.g., there were
about two-and-one-half times the number of emergency
department visits in 1964 as in 1950) as compared to
a relatively small increase for out-patient clinics
during the same period. Why are patients selecting
the emergency room over the OPD? Though no empirical
proof has been tabulated, it is believed that this is
occurring because of the chaotic confusion and long
waiting lines, unsatisfactory medical service, inconvenient operating hours of the clinics, and lack of
physician services in the communities.

These overt problems of the OPD are, in fact,
symptoms of fundamental problems underlying clinic
organization and practices. Overcrowding of facilities
increasing specialization in medicine, shortage of
manpower, obsolescence of facilities, and lack of
planned community relationships, have caused a gradual
development of fragmentation and lack of coordination
in the delivery of medical care.

It has been recognized that correction of these
central problems will require a major reorganization
of the traditional health delivery system. The fundamental need for comprehensive, continuous health care
for the whole family would have to be met out in the
community. Therefore, arms of the hospital that would
reach out to the people would be a far more effective
approach to the problem than merely extending the
hospital services within their present geographical
limits.

Initial planning has developed a general framework for such a neighborhood health complex. This is
shown schematically in Figure 5.

A detailed proposal for implementation of this
plan is being prepared by Mary McLaughlin, M. D.,
("Public Health and Medical Aspects of Neighborhood
Ambulatory Health Services." April 24, 1967). Although
this proposal is still in a formative stage, with numerous problems in the actual specifications remaining
to be worked out, provision has been made in the 1967-
1968 budget to continue with initial planning and
development. Basic requirements, components, and standards of medical care to be considered in the planning,
as envisioned by Dr. McLaughlin, will be summarized
briefly here.

The first requirement is defined as a redistricting of the city. Then, successively or simultaneously,
three stages are described as fundamental to effective
implementation: the integration of preventive and
treatment facilities in Health Department facilities,
the institution of family-centered general clinics in
local hospitals in those cases where the hospitals are
not near a health center ambulatory care unit, and the
establishment of satellite neighborhood health clinics
in those areas of need where there is no hospital or
health center available.

Redistricting of the city automatically calls for
certain precautions. It is pointed out that making
coterminus all health, hospital, and mental health
districts (and, ideally, welfare districts also) is
essential for the efficient coordination of health
services in the city, but one major problem, at least,
is immediately clear: Care will have to be taken to
retain the integrity of the statistical analyses and
valuable health indices that have been prepared through
the years by the separate departments with respect to

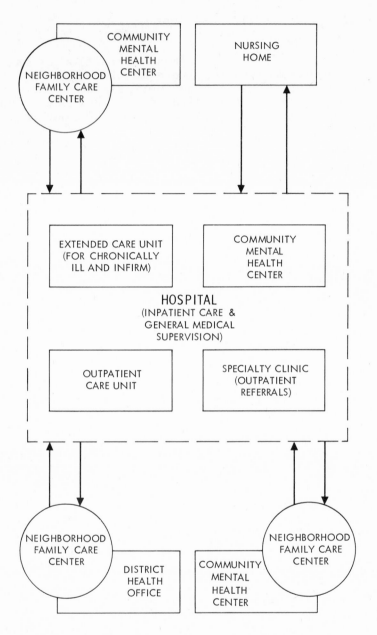

Figure 5.   The Neighborhood Health Complex

(Each service area will include a varying number of
related public and private health facilities depending on population, density, degree of medical indigency, etc.)

their particular districting systems. Master planning
for the community mental health centers has met this
problem by designing catchment areas to coincide with
sets of health areas (not districts).

Regarding hospital districting in this comprehensive plan, Dr. McLaughlin points out the necessity of
assuring "equality of opportunity of the municipal and
voluntary hospital to care for the indigent and medically indigent according to their ability to provide
a service meeting prescribed standards." She reports
that a planning grant has been obtained from the U.S.
Office of Economic Opportunity for developing an
approach to this particular problem.

The program would be coordinated on a district
basis, with clinics operating under the medical supervision of a "back-up" hospital depending upon the
number of doctors and the measure of need evaluated
for that district. Although the clinics would be
offering a "local doctor's office" for the medically
indigent, patients would have the option of visiting
a local private physician. Utilizing the group practice system, the clinic staff would take care of over
80% of the health problems of the family. More extensive diagnostic or therapeutic service would be
handled by the hospital.

Dr. McLaughlin has suggested eight basic components of service for the neighborhood ambulatory care
units: medical care for (1) children, (2) adults, and
(3) pregnant women; (4) a small mental health unit;
(5) dental service; (6) capacity for routine laboratory testing; (7) capacity for routine chest and long-
bone x-ray; and (8) a pharmacy.

Five basic standards of medical care have been set
for the new ambulatory care units. It is specified
that there would be a full-time medical director for
each unit. Secondly, this director would have a staff
of full-time or half-time personnel including general
practitioners under the direct supervision of, and in
consultation with, board-qualified or eligible internists and pediatricians; board-qualified or eligible
obstetricians; board-qualified or eligible psychiatrists; licensed general dentists with referral to
specialists on need; a public health nurse available
for consultation to staff and patients and to coordinate the service with the field activities of public
health nurses; a full-time case worker, social service
aide, or social worker; and necessary supporting staff

including "out-reach" personnel. Underlying the
entire staffing philosophy would be the goal to offer
medical care on a "family physician" basis.

A third basic standard specified for the neighborhood ambulatory care units regards the keeping of
records. In proposing that the unit record system
for each satellite be coordinated with the back-up
hospital's system, the additional suggestions are
made that a listing of all members of the family with
their unit numbers would be on the face sheet of each
record, and that basic information on each record conform to the standards as described by the Health Depart
ment Office of Program Planning. Critical problems
have been observed in the unit record system of the
municipal hospitals (reported on in some detail elsewhere in Parts Two and Three). These problems would be
multiplied with the addition of satellite clinics to
the system, particularly in trying to establish a
data processing system for record-keeping.

A six-day-week schedule, including evening hours
and 24-hour emergency service, has been proposed as
a standard for these clinics. The emergency coverage
could be handled either through a phone call to a
physician of the unit or to a physician on the local
hospital staff. Basic plans also call for an appointment system that is flexible enough to allow for
emergency or unplanned visits to the clinic. Appointments would be worked around 30-minute first visits
and 15-minute return visits. Obstetrical and gyne-
cological visits would be scheduled at 20-minute
intervals. Clinic schedules would also be such that
adults and children could be seen on the same visit.

Special procedures for physical examinations
constitute the fifth and final basic standard recommended for the ambulatory units. A routine medical
auditing service by the Department of Health would
enforce the specified standards, and reporting mechanisms would be set up at the clinics to advise the
Health Department regularly of the status of the
ambulatory care service.

So far as administration of the ambulatory units
is concerned, the plan proposes that a specific set
of responsibilities be decentralized to the health
officers in the districts. This would be a new role
for the district health officer and it has been suggested that he should receive an appointment as

assistant administrator of the back-up hospital.
Assisting him would be a hospital-appointed director
of ambulatory care who would be the medical supervisor
of all clinics in the health center. The director
would report to and assist the health officer in the
integration of the therapeutic and diagnostic services
of the district. It is believed that this team approach would enable the epidemiology, case-finding,
sanitary health programs, etc., of the Health Department to become an integral part of all the components
of the comprehensive medical care in and out of the
hospital. (An alternative administrative structure
will be proposed in Part Three.)

     In addition to his new duties, the health officer
would continue to report to the Associate Deputy
Commissioner through the Assistant Commissioner for
Community Health Services for the total health program of the area.

     The back-up hospital is seen by Dr. McLaughlin
as the provider of staff and medical supervision for
the program, as well as a needed consultation service
in specialties--at the hospital or by appointment
at the ambulatory care unit. It would also be expected
that referrals from satellite clinics and requests for
hospitalization would be honored almost immediately;
that referrals from the ambulatory care unit for out-
patient or in-patient service would be accepted "with
ease and priority"; where possible, continuous care
by the clinic doctor would be continued in the hospital (with the specialists taking only temporary control of the case for the necessary period); and that
the hospital would operate a family ambulatory care
unit for residents of the immediate vicinity of the
hospital.

     The original planning also emphasizes integration
of public health and ambulatory care. Absence of such
integration, it is stressed, would "perpetuate and
exaggerate the present situation of fragmentation of
medical care." Also emphasized is that, "basic to the
entire philosophy, is the necessity for a comprehensive
neighborhood program for the area administratively
under one person. It is mandatory that such a person
incorporate into the district program all the programs
relating to health whether they be related to preventive medicine or the diagnosis and treatment of illness. Medical care can no longer be a separate entity
from public health."

Those preventive medicine components which are seen as essential integral parts of ambulatory medical care are (1) early case-finding; (2) public health nursing; (3) health education and nutrition; (4) epidemiologic study and control of infectious and chronic disease; (5) the use of sanitary health services; and (6) the use of records and reporting systems.

The initial plan for the neighborhood ambulatory units calls for 30 centers in the city, each to serve a district of between 10,000 to 30,000 persons. Not all of these would be freestanding units. As discussed above, some hospitals would still provide an ambulatory unit. This would be the case when the satellite clinics are at too great a distance from the hospital to serve the basic objectives of the plan.

Provision in the current city budget has considered both the renovation of some of the hospitals that will have an ambulatory unit within the central building, and the initial planning of approximately half of the freestanding units. Based on the rule of thumb of one square foot per patient, the freestanding units are planned to be approximately 30,000 square feet. An estimated annual census for each unit is 150,000 visits.

PROGRAMMATIC CONCEPTS FOR THE DELIVERY OF HEALTH SERVICES

Four major health problems have been emphasized as involving most of the communities of all boroughs:

- Care of the aged

- Mental health

- Addiction

- Ambulatory care.

Given these four areas of effort as the foci for strategic planning, suitable tactical plans--sets of programs--may be prepared for carrying out strategies. At the operating level, programs for the next decade are likely to be shaped significantly by four forces:

- The need to facilitate and control shifts in medical responsibility between and among the private and the public sectors.

- The need to increase community involvement in health programs. "Involvement" relates to both the support and the use of health services.

- The need to provide continuing, in-service education for medical and para-medical personnel.

- The need to better the cost/effectiveness ratio for the delivery of health services.

Controlling Shifts in Medical Responsibility

The historical role of local government in health services has been to improve the environment, to offer preventive services, and to care for the health needs of the poor. Historically, government directed its services to those needs not met by the private sector. With increasing amounts of state and federal money available for the relief of the medically indigent, the two domains, public and private, have begun to merge. The indigent patient may now seek his physician where he wishes.

Local government rightly is undertaking to enlarge its concern from the delivery of health services in city facilities to the planning and con-ceptualizing and coordination of such services through-out the community. This larger concern will be manifested, in part, by a greater (but enlightened) reliance upon the private sector (as a "partner") for the operational delivery of health services. Private institutions already provide at least part of the professional staffs in most city hospitals. Similar affiliations can be expected to produce staff for the array of satellite facilities to be planned and built. It is likely that the private sector will undertake to build certain of these satellite facilities. Further, it is appropriate that city hospitals in the not-too-distant future become community hospitals with their doors open to private patients.

It is likely that the city's brick-and-mortar role in health services will retain its traditional

aspects--to build facilities where private agencies
do not find it feasible to do so--adding community-
wide construction planning to its concerns. But
unlike the past, the services offered in these
facilities will be increasingly like the services
offered in the private sector--and often managed by
the private sector. The gain in human dignity is
not the least of the virtues that will attend a
properly managed shift in the character of public
health delivery.

Increasing Community Involvement

A great potential for fiscal economy and for a
"profit" in lives saved exists in preventive medicine
and in home-care programs for persons who do not
truly require a hospital bed. To fulfill this potential, the health services system must manifest itself
deeply in the community. It must make itself available. It must become identified with the local community. It must "explain itself" through information
programs that improve community understanding of
available services and possibilities for self-help.
The interface between the community and its health
services must be made as uncomplicated, inviting and
efficient as possible.

It is widely held that these aims can best be
served by placing multi-service centers in the community. Health offices would be only one component
of such a center. For the decade of the '70's and
beyond, this concept anticipates that persons who
turn to such a center for help would find what they
need without excessive waiting and without further
travel. They would not find themselves being shuffled
at their own expense from one part of the city to
another.

Such centers are complicated to plan and difficult to place geographically. They must be relatively
large but functionally flexible. Each in its planning
will call for an extensive interplay of persons,
offices, agencies, and other interests.

An alternative scheme foresees smaller, specialized facilities located where need for given services
appears to be greatest. Their planning would seem to
be less complicated. There would be more of them;

each would serve a smaller community and, potentially
at least, would enjoy a closer involvement in community life. It appears, too, that a configuration of
smaller parts can more economically be adjusted to
changing community needs (and to advances in medical
practice) than an arrangement of larger components.
However, this arrangement would be limited in requiring an effective information program to insure that
each person in the community knew which center to
visit for a given service. It would also require
that trained, informed, and courteous persons be at
the door of each facility to direct people in a responsible and helpful way. (Too often, the present
health services system has a reputation in the community for indifference and rudeness. This must be
overcome, whatever the cost, if out-reach into the
community is to be improved.)

The private physician is an important potential
tie to the community. Ways must be found to bring
him into an active role in the larger system. Converting city hospitals to community hospitals will
assist in this, assuming a sound program of physician-
hospital affiliation. (In this regard, specific
recommendations are offered later in this report.)
Satellite facilities may also be adapted to selected
roles in support of private practice.

Ways must also be sought to bring the medical
schools, "the centers of excellence," into active
and first-hand contact with the problem-community.
Medical schools and teaching hospitals rightly speak
of their need to stand apart from the routines of
medical practice in order to work for betterment. On
the other hand, as the standard bearers of the profession, they must be enabled (are perhaps obliged)
to extend their supportive and guiding influence into
the farthest reaches of the community either with or
through these new endeavors.

The health facility as an economic resource in
the community must not be overlooked. It is a source
of jobs and potentially a training ground for clerical
and para-medical personnel. It would be desirable
for health facilities in deprived communities to be
largely staffed by persons living in the neighborhood,
with many having learned their work within the very
walls. As one physician said, "You are not likely to
go to the Bronx to hire a typist for Harlem Hospital."

Providing In-Service Education

In terms of physicians, this is a problem of two parts. The first is the simple need to keep the physician abreast of his art. The accelerating inventiveness of this era makes this difficult enough. The matter is worsened with increasing value placed on continuing care and family-based care. In these connections, there is envisioned the patient and his family in a prolonged relationship with either a medical team or a general practice physician. In either case, a broad base of information about a range of specialties must be developed within one person, if only for purposes of sound diagnosis and correct referral. A well-designed, continuing educational program can help physicians meet this need.

The second part of the physician/education problem lies in the fact that several thousand physicians in New York City do not enjoy staff privileges in a hospital. The worst among them can be viewed as poorly trained men and women whose work must be upgraded to protect the community that they serve. The best among them (and there are many) must be viewed as a partially wasted resource. If they are excluded from hospitals for professional reasons that can be resolved with additional training, then such training should be afforded and made attractive as a mutual benefit to physicians and their communities.

In both its aspects, this problem of continuing education requires that the physician stand in a professional relationship with a medical school or teaching hospital (whether directly or at one or several levels removed in relation to satellites, etc.). His work should come under the scrutiny of other physicians; he would in turn be obliged to observe and discuss their work. This suggests that a tie to a medical school (perhaps through an intervening institution) must be established for each medical facility in the system.

Para-medical personnel are in short supply across the nation. Health facilities can well be the focus for training programs to help provide such people. (Specific recommendations appear in a later chapter.) Such training programs require that buildings afford more space than is needed for purely medical purposes. They must provide working room for students and teachers. Teaching programs must be evaluative as

well, and must help to provide a clearer understanding
than we now possess of job content and requisite skills
in the para-medical realms.

Improving Cost/Effectiveness Ratios

Effectiveness in the delivery of health services,
not cost, is the primary issue. On the other hand,
an enormous capital construction program must be
carried out in the years ahead to renovate and re-
construct the city's out-dated hospitals and medical
facilities-- municipal, voluntary, and private. Ways
must be found to contend with rising personnel costs
and the cost of new diagnostic and therapeutic equipment. Even with the influx of state and federal funds,
one can spend without end for health services. On the
other hand, given a surfeit of money, one can arrive
at that point where an additional dollar spent for
medical service buys only a penny's worth of improvement. The city is at neither extreme. With the
implementation of sound programs, the city would be
in a position to buy much improved medical service
for the dollars that it spends.

Already mentioned are some concepts leading to
this end. Increasing emphasis on preventive medicine
(requiring close community involvement) is a case in
point. Generally speaking, prevention costs less
than cure--at least up to a point as yet unreached
by urban medical delivery systems. Home-care programs
will speed the patient's departure from the acute care
or extended care bed that he now occupies past the
time of real need--to the exclusion of someone else.

By building separate facilities for separate
purposes (keeping extended care units separately
identified from acute care, for example) the most
economical construction techniques and floor plans
commensurate with a given use can be employed. Multi-
purpose facilities, on the other hand, tend to be
constructed to suit the most demanding of their several
uses. A maximally flexible physical plant (built of
relatively small modules) promises savings when plant
changes are called for by changes in community needs
and medical practices. The positive contribution of
flexible plant to the long-term cost/effectiveness
ratio for health services cannot be overemphasized.

Acute general hospitals appear to be most economical if they are in the range of 350 to 700 beds. Fewer beds cannot support modern surgical suites, intensive care units, laboratories, and radiology departments. Larger hospitals become difficult to serve and manage. The years ahead will likely bring about the merger of many smaller hospitals to produce relatively fewer institutions of optimum size. This will additionally reduce the duplication of expensive units devoted to surgery, radiology, and intensive care.

The operating schema that appears most effectively to serve the set of needs just described consists of five subsystems, one for each borough, that take the form represented in Figure 6. In the model, medical school and teaching hospital lie at the center of each subsystem, as do certain centralized services; these are tied to acute general or teaching hospitals farther out (the general model does not distinguish between municipal, voluntary, and proprietary hospitals); and around the general hospitals are a variety of strategic satellite facilities in the neighborhoods of the city.

We can expect that the geographic bounds for such a subsystem must accommodate many significant factors among which are travel time between components and to river barriers within the city, place of existing facilities, and need patterns. A natural gross compromise is to equate a "subsystem" with the existing borough structure; it should not attempt to reach across county lines except temporarily; it may embrace less than a county.

Queens and Richmond lack medical schools. Planning for a school for Queens should be completed as soon as possible. It may prove feasible to serve Richmond for, say, five years from Brooklyn and Manhattan. Eventually Richmond, too, must possess a medical school; planning for it should begin now.

The responsiveness of this system model to the system needs described above lies in five characteristics of the model:

- The array of satellites

- Specialization of facilities

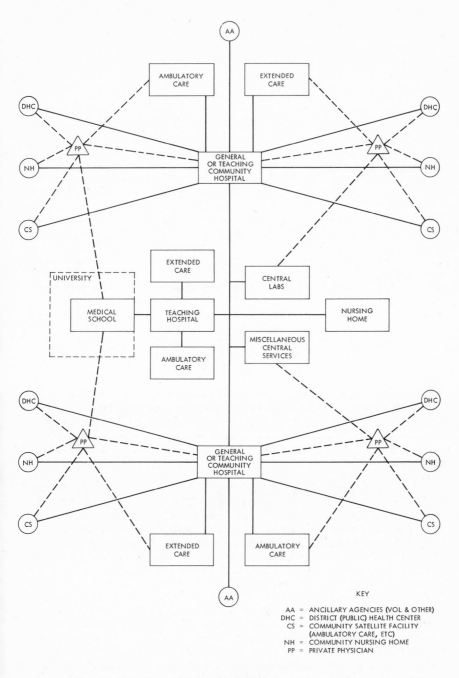

Figure 6. Simplified Schematic System Model
(One, Two, or Three per Borough)

KEY

AA = ANCILLARY AGENCIES (VOL & OTHER)
DHC = DISTRICT (PUBLIC) HEALTH CENTER
CS = COMMUNITY SATELLITE FACILITY
(AMBULATORY CARE, ETC)
NH = COMMUNITY NURSING HOME
PP = PRIVATE PHYSICIAN

203

- The tie to a medical school

- Other affiliations (and the closer integration
  of public and private effort)

- Localized, integrated administration.

The concept of an array of satellites is perhaps the most significant element of the operating
system of the next decade for the delivery of health
services. This concept bears on all the needs discussed earlier: the shift in private/public roles,
community involvement, bettering the cost/effectiveness
ratio, and continuing education.

City planning currently is addressed to two long-
term programs for developing satellite facilities.
One program will eventually provide 30 family-care
centers (ambulatory care with some number of "overnight" acute beds) placed in neighborhoods of greatest
need. Eight new centers appear in the current capital
budget as do funds for renovating eight similar facilities in existing health district offices. Some standardization of design is desirable and appears likely;
at present two basic designs are under consideration,
one based on the HIP infirmary at Montefiore Hospital,
the other based on ambulatory care facilities of the
California Kaiser/Permanente health plan. The cost
estimate for both designs is the same, two million
dollars for buildings and equipment apart from land.
Each facility is designed to serve 30,000 people.

Extensive planning under way for Community Mental
Health Centers has been cited. The "catchment areas"
for these centers are not necessarily coterminus with
the ideal service areas for the ambulatory care centers
described above. As noted, the city has long been
troubled by the lack of congruence among out-patient
districts, ambulance districts, health districts, and
welfare districts. Federal funds may bring with them
their own requirement for districting, as in the case
of mental health catchment areas. Perhaps there is
good in this. Where a common districting scheme for
all services might have appeared desirable, it would
very likely have called for disadvantageous compromises along many boundaries. Greater usefulness would
appear to lie in establishing decision rules for ignoring district boundaries in accomplishing the job
to be done.

If trouble caused by a badly placed boundary can be overcome by adjusting procedures, one need not enter the negotiations necessary to adjust a vested but meaningless historic boundary.

Twenty-seven community mental health centers are in the planning, at least to the extent of tentatively establishing hospital affiliations for staffing and in-patient back-up. Twelve centers are listed in the current capital budget, seven of them for planning funds only. The estimated costs included in the budget for individual facilities range from a little over $5 million to $17.3 million.

Apart from coordinated city-wide plans such as these, individual hospitals are extending their reach into the community via satellites. Lincoln Hospital is operating a small out-patient service at St. Francis Hospital, a few blocks away. Lincoln also has an O.E.O. grant of $578,500 to operate a neighborhood service center, as well as a Children's Bureau grant, exceeding $1.2 million for 1966-67, to develop maternity centers. Roosevelt Hospital operates two storefront clinics in the neighborhood and also conducts a single-room occupancy program in psychiatric care for the inhabitants (70% of whom are on welfare) in an impoverished residential hotel. Grant-seeking for satellite programs is active at Brooklyn Hospital. Montefiore operates the HIP infirmary on its grounds. These activities, though not part of a coordinated plan, are under the purview of both the Health Services Administration and the Health and Hospital Planning Council. We can expect, in years to come, that a more unified, city-wide direction will be applied to this expanding program.

The concept of specialization of facilities is implicit in the array of satellites. It can be expected to manifest itself in other ways as well in the programs of the next decade, and is of special significance in matters of cost/effectiveness.

Already suggested is that the buildings of a given facility be specialized to some advantage. Thus the concept of a "tower of acute beds" is under study in connection with renovation and rebuilding plans for existing city hospitals. Under this concept, construction of a new building alongside an existing hospital is favored, housing acute beds, operating rooms, and intensive care units, the old building then undergoing renovation to accommodate offices, laboratories,

teaching areas, research facilities, and quarters
for house staff. (Advocates of this plan point out
that research grants provide money for remodeling
existing facilities, as necessary; rarely do they
provide for building new facilities.)

This two-part arrangement differs from the more
common view of the hospital as a "single box" to be
renovated or re-built as a whole. The box concept
has produced cost estimates for rebuilding Kings
County Hospital in the range of $70 to $93 million.
The tower of acute beds, plus renovation of existing
plant, yields a first rough estimate materially less.
Prudence imposes the assumption that additional planning will force any figure upward. It appears,
nevertheless, that it would remain well below the "box"
estimate for Kings County Hospital.

It may be expected that certain laboratory
services will be centralized in the health services
system of the future, whether in city facilities or on
contract to private companies. Laundry services are
already centralized for many city hospitals. Opportunities to centralize other services should be inves-
tigated. Present laundry services are far from
satisfactory. This is attributable to reasons familiar
in the city: The operators are neither responsible to
those whom they serve, nor are they in positions of any
real authority over their operations.

In the city hospitals today, there is found a
struggle for balance between patient care, teaching,
and research (to be discussed in subsequent chapters).
In the system of the future, most physicians and para-
medical workers will find themselves in programs of
medical education as teachers or students, or (more
likely) both. Research programs, too, many of them
funded by grants, will and should be carried on at any
number of facilities. Patient care, in these circumstances, can easily become a forlorn endeavor. It
should not be assumed, as some would have it, that
good patient care is a sure result of teaching and
research. The role, or roles, of any given facility
at any given time must be carefully spelled out to
avoid worsening the present state of cross-purposes.
While good definitions can change as need or opportunity arises, clarity of purpose for each person,
each service, and each facility must be established.
Certain institutions, for instance, should clearly
be designated as centers of medical education. The

city appears to enjoy that state now; but in fact,
in the present program of affiliations, physicians
who are skilled and valuable as teachers find their
time and their energies drained away in a flood of
activities at the level of signing requisitions for
paper clips. Some clearer definitions are in order.

In earlier passages on the subject of medical
and para-medical education lie at least some of the
reasons why a tie to a medical school is a centrally
important element of the health system of the future.
Through that tie the excellence of the medical schools
can spread more widely through the system resulting
in an improvement of the skills of the physician in
the system. Communication between the schools and the
problem community would expand.

None of this will be easy. On the subject of
in-service training for physicians, one encounters
a range of viewpoints that can briefly be paraphrased:

Private physician: "You can't talk about medical
    practice without talking about medical edu-
    cation. Practicing physicians don't want
    conferences and seminars. They want long-term
    educational programs leading to clear pro-
    fessional betterment. They will welcome this."

Private physician: "I can't keep up with the
    literature. Impossible. I need concentrated
    courses and seminars."

Medical school professor: "In-service training
    is a problem that we must attack. A very
    difficult problem."

Medical school dean: "The in-service programs
    that we've tried are greeted with enthusiasm,
    then attendance falls off, and after a while,
    no one shows up."

Medical school professor: "Many of the physicians
    we're talking about are foreign-trained doc-
    tors, so poorly prepared that they couldn't
    possibly benefit from study at advanced levels."

(These are expressions of opinion noted in interviews.)

At St. Luke's hospital, in-service training programs are being emphasized, with reports of success. The problem must be studied and successful experience utilized.

City-operated "health-careers institutes" appear to be a sound idea for the future. These institutes would devote themselves to formulating system-wide programs in medical education, to developing new teaching techniques and materials, and to providing needed courses not available elsewhere. They could provide special instructional needs at all levels of the health careers hierarchy.

The system model implies not only internal ties to medical schools but any number of other ties or affiliations between facilities. These are essential to making it a system. No facility in the model functions alone. Satellites are backed by acute care hospitals. Municipal and private institutions intermix. The patient who must move from one facility to another for care does not find that he drops from one physician's responsibility and enters another's. By and large, he enjoys continuity of care. Implicit in this and not evident in the model shown in Figure 6 must be improved management information and transportation programs to tie the parts together.

CHAPTER **4** SURVEY OF
THE MUNICIPAL
HOSPITAL SYSTEM

INTRODUCTION

Periodically, intense controversy has centered
on the management and operation of the city's municipal hospitals. A recent and protracted recurrence
of this controversy led the Commission staff to undertake an investigation of the status, role, character,
and operation of each such institution. The survey
was structured with two conditions in mind: (1) to
contribute to the inquiry of this Commission; and
(2) to avoid overlapping studies underway by other
Commissions or agencies (generally having to do with
fiscal practice and aspects of resource utilization).

At all of the 21 municipal hospitals, intérviews
were conducted with a number of administrative and
staff personnel, beginning usually with the administrator of the hospital. In each instance the plant,
the general personnel picture, and the management
problems of the hospital were probed; determination
was made of the hospital's major programs (if any),
its major problems, and its evolutionary role as an
institution. To the staff's knowledge this is the
first instance of an investigation of these matters
that included on-site visits to all of the municipal
hospitals within the same study. Particular attention
was directed to out-patient and emergency room services,
since these functions represent the prime hospital interface with community health needs--indeed, they often function as the "community physician."

A specific, basic purpose of the hospital survey was to determine a probable "best evolution"
for each institution. This pattern of evolution or
disposition as ultimately determined would, if
carried out, make possible relinquishment by the city
of a number of its hospitals, retention of others

209

under a new form of control, and the maintenance of
direct but altered administration for the remainder.
Ultimately, this pattern would call for some change
in geographical location of several of the hospitals,
for programs of rebuilding and renovation, and for
extension into the community of ambulatory care and
other satellite facilities. Details of this suggested evolution are specified in Part Three within the
framework of the present volume, some general conclusions from the survey of the municipal hospitals
can be stated:

1. There is a most serious and debilitating
   waste of available resources.

2. There are serious inadequacies in the
   delivery of medical care to patients.

3. In the long run, neither of these conditions needs to be tolerated if appropriate
   remedial actions are taken in a timely
   manner.

The material in Chapters 4 and 5 is closely in-
terconnected: Chapter 4 presents selected observations made and commentary recorded during visits to
the municipal hospitals. (Hospitals are discussed in
alphabetic order.) Full transcripts of visit notes
would be impractical to include here and would be so
redundant (with respect to problems cited) as to mask
items of individual significance in the case of each
institution. Notes presented will accomplish the
latter and will highlight basic system-wide problems.

Interpretive caution is recommended. While
editing has removed nearly all personal references
and the controversial opinions of those interviewed,
readers are cautioned to avoid the acceptance of implied criticism of persons or agencies. In later
discussion, basic causes of difficulty and disaffec-
tion will be examined.

The topic of affiliation contracts is treated
briefly and anecdotally in each of the following sub-
sections on individual hospitals, but comprehensive
discussions of contracting in general is to be found
in Chapter 5.

Matters pertaining to medical records functions
and to program planning for the separate boroughs

were sufficiently complex and compelling to warrant independent treatment. Discussion of these topics will also be found in Chapter 5 .

Following the complete survey of the municipal hospitals, and in keeping with the mayor's charge to the Commission, a similar but limited survey was undertaken of major university hospitals, major voluntaries, medium- and small-sized voluntaries, proprietary hospitals, state and federal hospitals in the city, and voluntary and proprietary nursing homes. Visits to these institutions are treated in summary as a last section in Chapter 5. Again, major findings and recommendations are held for Part Three.

BELLEVUE HOSPITAL CENTER

Plant and Services

Bellevue Hospital Center has a capacity of 1,617 and a complement of 1,520. It functions at an average of 68% of complement with an average daily census of 1,052. Psychiatry, with a complement/capacity of 582, functions at over 100% (recently at 107.8), having an average daily census of 628. Chest, with a 310-bed complement, has an average occupancy rate of 79%.

Bellevue is old, dirty, and a management nightmare. It has been described as a "standing ruin." Logistic and systems circumstances are diametrically opposed to efficient management or good provision of services to patients. The morale of much of the staff is low; they feel "always criticized, never helped."

Physicians

Historically, Bellevue has provided excellent medical care. There is deep pride in its role in American medicine. Since the hospital became affiliated, care has been provided on a more regular basis, perhaps more frequently, and with more equipment than in periods prior to affiliation. Research has experienced an increase, and some of the services have been enabled to stabilize their respective activities. There does not seem to be any major problem in recruiting physicians. The major problems are in getting the physician to the patient.

Other Professional Services

Budget inflexibility and lack of funds combine to produce a shortage of R.N.'s providing bedside care.

A staff member describes a case in point: "There is no provision for hiring (therefore it is not legally possible to hire) a part-time nurse. Desperation for a head of nursing led to innovation. A part-time nurse was hired by paying her on a full-time basis, but skipping every other pay check. This nurse is absolutely essential to good patient care, but must be deviously hired to meet the urgent need."

By "isolating" themselves (and by paying supplements to the R.N.'s), the voluntary hospital affiliates have been able to staff their own services in Bellevue. But there is still an over-all shortage. Clearly, this pattern of accommodation thrust upon the voluntary affiliates, the municipal administrators, and the employees is detrimental to patient care.

Support Activities

There is never enough equipment to clean the hospital thoroughly. Though enough is ordered, deliveries are "cut back." There is only one supervisor to every 40 housekeeping employees and these are not trained supervisors. This is not adequate for good supervision. To maintain any semblance of cleanliness the housekeeping personnel must function as "handy men" even though there are rules against their going beyond the scope of their stated responsibilities. Hiring practices for these support positions are self-defeating: a high school diploma is required; when hired, the employee must wait six to eight weeks for his first paycheck. Other constraints apply in the dietary function that prevent employees from doing their jobs well; for example, they often cannot get hot food to patients because of the labyrinth of halls, buildings, and elevators that must be traversed.

Affiliation

Bellevue has been affiliated with three different institutions, New York University, Columbia, and
Cornell.

Some negative aspects of affiliation are present;
for example, there are laboratories that are locked
at night and to which the Bellevue administrators
have no keys. Wards operated by the affiliation
staff reflect selective admission practices.

In fortunate contrast, the affiliates have
brought great staff strength to Bellevue and have
greatly increased the quality of medical service
available.

Bellevue is in a state of transition. Two
affiliations phasing out are the Columbia and
Cornell general surgical divisions (discontinued on
July 1, 1967), and the Columbia and Cornell general
medical divisions (July 1, 1968). With the latter
termination, the sole affiliation will be with New
York University, which has carried the major load
for both in-patient and out-patient services. With
the withdrawal of Columbia and Cornell, more physical
space will be available; this may help in relieving
the now over-crowded clinics. (The anticipated
change provides some rationale for rejecting requests for more space and/or physical changes within
the present quarters.) A second major change in the
offing is the "new Bellevue." It was commented that
the new hospital will have a smaller bed capacity
and will provide new quarters for the out-patient
and emergency services. Building activity often is
taken as a reason for minimum renovation of present
facilities.

Administration

From the administrator's point of view, the
management and coordination of Bellevue is a difficult and frustrating responsibility. "Business must
be done by personal contact" and this is not to the
advantage of the patient. Administrative criticisms
have been chronic for many years. "They say we don't
make decisions and we're low caliber, but they won't
even let us buy pencils." The hospital system is
"comprehensively inefficient." "Plans for the new

hospital were <u>done</u> in 1956-1957, and now--10 years
later--steel <u>is up</u> for the first six floors." It
was observed that "the city is operating in a depression orientation." Most of the civil service
staff (who live to work) are ready to retire; the
younger generation refuse the evident conditions.

There is little or no feedback from the central
office (Department of Hospitals). "Sometimes we don't
get answers to letters for--literally--years. In
addition, there is a lack of clarification, backing
and guidelines."

Morale is chronically low. It is said that this
is due first to constant criticism, second to poor
working conditions, and third to a system that is so
thoroughly bureaucratic that one "can hardly ever do
anything about anything." For example: if an employee is two or more hours late he can be docked
for a half day. "If he is late by one hour and 59
minutes, you can't do anything to him." The administrative system is such a labyrinth that the following is common: the supervisor keeps a record of an
employee's lateness and reports it to payroll monthly
(it takes from four to six months to "make a case");
then there is intercession for the employee, the
argument being that (a) an employee should not be
punished twice (if you've docked him at all) and
(b) lateness has been allowed for four to six months,
therefore he cannot be fired now. Employees know
this procedure and too often take advantage of it.

The personnel department handles 6100 employees
and the following functions: (a) budget, (b) vacancy
control, (c) 20-year service pins, (d) retirement,
(e) pension, (f) bonds, (g) counseling, (h) health
programs, (i) social security, and (j) records. This
office does not have an adding machine; there is no
private place to conduct hiring interviews.

Physical Deficiencies

- A change-over from DC electrical current to
  AC electrical current has been needed for
  many years.

- Ice-makers are needed on the wards; the
  present brine system is obsolete.

- For privacy on the wards, cubicles and screens are needed.

- Screens are needed on the windows.

- An efficient security system is needed, with clock rounds for watchmen.

- Many areas of the hospital are in need of painting.

- A better extermination and pest control program is necessary.

- Sinks should be installed on the wards and toilet facilities improved (portable toilets might be considered).

- Elevators throughout the institution are in need of constant repair; some are in need of synchronization.

- The roofs of the institution are in need of repair and preventive maintenance.

- The air-conditioner in the operating room breaks down intermittently from causes beyond the scope of the hospital to control.

- Air-conditioners are needed in all intensive care units and on the disturbed wards of the psychiatric building.

- Redesign of some nursing areas on the wards is needed.

- Redesign of the central supply department is needed, taking advantage of industrial engineering techniques.

- Reconditioning of the laundry area and laundry equipment is needed.

Some not atypical equipment-procurement cases illuminate the problem of physical deficiencies:

- A striker frame, ordered on an "emergency" basis, took fourteen months to obtain.

- The hospital ordered an incubator, requesting that it be delivered inside and that it be CO_2 adaptable. One-and-a-half years after bids were let (with the two requests above-mentioned denied to save money), the equipment arrived. City officials who examined the device on the loading dock believed that it wasn't the standard small equipment; they then had to contract separately for inside delivery. This required a crane to lift the equipment, and the removal of a section of wall and a window. When inside and uncrated, it was discovered that the incubator was not CO_2 adaptable. In all, three-and-a-half years were consumed. Today, the equipment sits useless in the hospital.

Outpatient and Emergency Room Services

Administration of these services is fragmented, which causes some intrasystem communication problems. One administrator directs OPD and home care; another is assigned to emergency/admitting, dietary, prisons, general surgery, surgical specialties, disaster squad, ambulance service, transportation, and garage.

The major problems reported were insufficiency of space and of clerical personnel. Apparently there are adequate staffs of physicians and nurses, but the latter are "bogged down with clerical details."

One way to cope with the space problem is to stagger the schedule of clinic hours for better utilization of available room. The schedule for Bellevue's clinics exemplifies the problem and is typical of all municipal OPD's visited. Its complexity, however, leads to complaints that doctors give patients misinformation about clinic dates and times.

Leniency in admission policy was said to be a problem. It was estimated that approximately 30% of the patients come from out of the district, most of these being admitted either for special teaching purposes or for nonmedical reasons; it was implied that the staff could better deal with large patient loads if the clientele were limited to those who should be admitted.

The Bellevue plant contributes special problems for OPD. Originally a two-and-a-half floor dormitory, it was renovated to eight floors that were "never set up for a clinic." The organization is confusing, and a particularly sore issue is that only two of the four "antiquated" elevators go to the eighth floor. The other two are part of the old building, going only to the third floor, yet "the major traffic load is beyond the third floor."

It was also pointed out that those coming in the emergency walk-in entrance (which, in fact, is next to the ambulance entrance) must pass through the chaos and confusion of stretcher beds, patients waiting in wheelchairs, etc. Further, those being treated are in full view of the waiting patients. A little more room, it was suggested, would help alleviate this situation. Space provision should be made not only for a well-organized clinic, but for the morale of the staff. There is no place for the staff to relax; even toilet facilities are inadequate.

The OPD staff would favor a community health service, provided through small centers in outlying areas, for the purpose of "taking the hospital to the patient." It was said that "Bellevue doesn't know the community and its problems"; there is too little active participation by the hospital staff in community activities, nor is sufficient effort made to hire community people. It was pointed out that there are only about 259 home-care patients, all of whom were referred by the doctor upon dismissal from the ward. Considering that an average of 250 patients are discharged from the ward daily, the question was raised whether the hospital really knows where these people go and what their needs are. Without home care, how are the remainder of the discharged patients carrying themselves through the usual post-hospitalization convalescent period?

The community was described as "in transition." Although still primarily low-income, new housing projects are apparently bringing in some middle-class residents. It was explained that many of the low-income people are older, and many are living in ghettos, including Italians, Germans, and some Jews. Puerto Ricans in the community were reported to use the ER more than the clinics and higher income persons to use the hospital only for emergencies (otherwise going to voluntaries or private hospitals).

Greenwich Village is in this district, as is the
Bowery--of whose destitute alcoholics the ER is
"reluctant to take care." The balance of the community is made up of those who work in offices and industry but live in other districts. For the most
part, Bellevue's district is an area "north of
Houston Street, south of 42nd Street, and from river
to river."

BRONX MUNICIPAL HOSPITAL CENTER

Plant and Services

Officials describe this plant as "a campus
setting." There are three main buildings (Abraham
Jacobi Hospital, a general hospital with 816 beds;
a nurses' residence and school; Nathan B. Van Etten
Hospital, with 417 beds, for T.B. and thoracic surgery) and several smaller buildings--all in an open
park. A 1964 map shows eight buildings. Jacobi was
completed in 1954, Van Etten in 1955. The Jacobi
emergency room was renovated last year. Much of the
plant was recently repainted. To the eye, the plant
is clean, modern, and hospital-like; nevertheless,
a lack of space is evident everywhere, and other
problems typical of the municipal hospital are evident. The radiology department has equipment that is
outdated, inadequate, and in bad repair. Not long
ago, a piece of X-ray equipment fell, hitting a
patient.

Distances between buildings create special problems. Transit is always difficult for elderly or infirm persons. Supplies and laundry must be tran-
shipped from outbuildings. Bad weather compounds
these difficulties. Snow removal equipment is not
easily available. Ambulances can leave the grounds
only via a narrow, one-way access road that may be
wholly blocked by other departing vehicles. Requests have been made for a different ambulance road
to be cut directly into an adjoining street, but
without success. The "campus" needs trucks and
shuttle vehicles.

This is a general hospital center engaged in
patient care, research, teaching, and community education. Over 100 out-patient clinics are available

in Jacobi and Van Etten. Patient load increased
from 1960 through 1965 (see table following), but
seemed to level in 1966.

	1960	1965		1966
Admissions	14,248	21,653	(+52%)	21,490
Births	1,738	2,665	(+53%)	2,621
Out-patient	237,956	292,090	(+23%)	282,010
Emergency	93,290	133,147	(+43%)	135,575

The community is not a slum. Much of it is middle income--a mixture of native whites and Puerto
Ricans. There are many elderly people. The hospital
sees relatively few OB cases, it was said, for these
patients tend to prefer other care under medical insurance. (On the other hand, statistics cited earlier show births increasing at the same rate as other
services.) The hospital receives some patient overflow from Lincoln Hospital. Much of the load is active trauma comprising emergency cases from a large
area including many miles of highways and beaches.
Nighttime clinics are needed.

Physicians

The administrator's 1966 report said that she
had "been able to maintain a full complement of interns and residents on all major and most specialty
services." In 1964 there was a house staff of 385,
consisting of interns and assistant residents. The
1966 report noted a request for additional house
staff lines because teaching programs were expanding
under the guidance and direction of Albert Einstein
College of Medicine.

Other Professional Services

The 1966 report speaks of the "best nurse staffing picture in the municipal system." The report
also speaks of a threatened nurses strike (rather,
a mass resignation) that was abated by a salary adjustment constituting a "satisfactory settlement."
Nevertheless, there is a nurse shortage. Nurses'
aides do dietary aide work. To compensate for the
system constraints, some nurses work double shifts
and work on their days off. Additionally, nurses
are faced with a number of serious problems: the
laundry is closed on holidays and weekends and there

is always a critical shortage of linen supplies;
there is not adequate space for storage, so nurses
must continually call on central supply for materials
that ought to be at hand. (Forty percent of the head
nurse's time is spent in "search and find" activities.) Perhaps the nurses' dilemma is best pointed
up by the statement that nursing is a twenty-four-
hour operation and support services operate on an
eight-hour basis. "It is not possible to catch up."

The recommendations here are for: (1) expansion
of support services (pharmacy, dietary, clothing,
laundry, etc.); (2) provision of clerical assistance;
(3) creation of ward-manager positions; (4) subsi-
dizing of housing; (5) provision of transportation
(especially for the night shift).

The record room is not functioning properly because it lacks adequate space and personnel.

The social service department is excellent owing to a supplement that raises salaries to competitive levels.

Budget for supplies is inadequate (X-ray supplies being a case in point).

Support Activities

Preventive maintenance is not possible. The
maintenance staff numbers approximately 25. The administrator estimates that 60 to 90 would be needed
to carry out a proper job of preventive maintenance.
A consequence of this shortage is that an earlier,
excessively expensive degradation of plant will occur
with respect to normal expectancy.

The city has not met the hospital's needs in
maintenance, housekeeping supplies and personnel.
For example: examination of a ward linen closet at
noon revealed no linen there. The linen delivery
from the laundry was not scheduled until after 3:00
p.m. For a period of several hours, a disordered
bed in that ward could not have been changed without
a time-consuming search through other wards for linen.

Affiliation

Laboratory services are provided under the affiliation contract. Home-care services were in negotiation for fiscal 1967-1968. Staff services are provided by physicians from Yeshiva University (Einstein Medical College). The proposed contract for laboratory services is $2 million (as in 1967); for home care, $537,500.

The relationship between this hospital center and Einstein is one of the best in the city. Initiative and open-mindedness on both sides suggest that the new affiliation contracts can achieve milestones by including program definitions, goals, provisions for community extension, and desirable constraints.

Administration

Some staff members chose to comment on the hospital commissioner's roles with respect to hospital administration. "What could they accomplish in their length of time in office? They were in office just long enough to learn, then they were gone." It was felt that some commissioners had viewed the job as a stepping stone. "They were not one of us. They seemed to look down on persons in civil service. Every commissioner has asked what the troubles are. Some did not stay long enough to hear the answer." (Generally speaking, this study has found that commissioners are not at fault, though often targeted for blame. Local attitudes of hospital staffs are honestly expressed, but are really indicative of much deeper problems, which will be discussed in Volume II.)

"Perhaps civil service has outlived its usefulness," says one senior staff member. "It used to protect against undesirable employees and political maneuvering. Now the reverse is true." On the other hand, some real dedication is evident: nurses in their 60's, with swollen ankles, were observed carrying major work loads.

The procedure for administrative action is said to involve these steps:

- Request

- Follow-up calls and memos

- A detailed report of impending crisis

- A call to the assistant hospital commissioner

- A second detailed report of specifications to
  the assistant commissioner.

It was said that "to improve the city hospitals,
either city organization must change or the hospitals
must be removed from city administration." (This attitude was often expressed by interviewees throughout
the hospital system.)

Budget inflexibility is a problem. Overages
are inevitable and call for added work in preparing
memos of justification. "You don't look good if you
overspend." Here (as elsewhere in the hospitals surveyed), salary supplements seem justified. In the
course of a recent denial of this administrator's
supplement, she "was made to feel like a thief"
(again, a common finding).

Disposition of cases back to the community is a
major problem. Grant money is a help in some ways,
notably in supporting a program for comprehensive
community pediatric care. To speed the discharge of
patients from Van Etten, the administrator wishes to
establish a Welfare Department satellite office on
the grounds. This office would see to clothing and
housing for the patients. (Welfare has declined in
view of its policy against field offices.)

Under the provisions of Medicare legislation,
this hospital has an automation utilization review
committee. The administrator proposed that the hospital join in a nationwide program for computer analysis of discharge statistics being developed under
the auspices of PAS (Professional Activity Study);
the hospital has acted accordingly.

Outpatient and Emergency Room Services

OPD 1966 Census, 248, 840
ER 1966 Census, 135,575
Home Care 1966 Census, 85
OPD Hours/Days, A.M. and P.M., Mon. through Fri.

The chief administrator of the OPD and ER at
Bronx Municipal feels that, "at one time we had a

model OPD. Then the hospital demand grew past the
point of good handling." This "point of no return,"
as he termed it, was reached about 1961, approximately six years after the hospital was built. For one
thing, he points out, "when all the physicians were
volunteers, they were more motivated." Now, of the
staff of 600 (varying from full-time to part-time),
only two-thirds can be paid under the budget allocations. The remaining 200 volunteer doctors rebel
against working for nothing, yet continue under the
arrangement for the status of association with Albert
Einstein Medical College.

The major problem, it was reported, is that the
city has not increased the budget in proportion to
rising needs, which accelerated when the district was
enlarged. This extension of district boundaries occurred because the hospital has been running a low
occupancy rate, so the ambulance (not OPD) district
was widened. However, since ER cases are generally
referred to the clinic for follow-through, the new
limits ultimately affected the OPD also. This problem was countered with a strict policy of treating
only district residents. Other patients who come in
may be given one treatment if it is deemed necessary.
This tightening up apparently helped balance the
great rise experienced over the preceding years.
"If we opened our doors," said the director, "we'd
have many more Bronx patients because of our excellent service." (Similar comments were made in most
of the OPD's visited in this study.) Reportedly, 20
to 30 patients per day come from outside the district
asking for admittance because they "don't wish to go
to 'X' Hospital for various reasons."

The situation of the volunteer vs. paid physician poses several problems. First, which 400 of the
600 doctors should be paid? Second, there is so much
work that those who are paid for two hours on any
given day may actually average three hours of service.
As a consequence, it was reported, doctor morale is
sometimes low and patient care sometimes suffers.
Apparently, also, the hospital's particular affiliation arrangement causes some annoyance to the staff.
Bronx Municipal and Einstein have always been affiliated, but the affiliation has not always involved
money. In exchange for the use of the facilities,
the medical school has provided some staffing. The
expense of this arrangement can no longer be carried.
The upcoming contract may alleviate this worsening
condition of dual standards.

To handle its rising load of patients more efficiently, Bronx OPD limits the doctor-patient ratio to six per doctor per hour. Those who cannot be taken care of on a given day are asked to return the next day, or in cases of emergency are referred to the ER. Hence, the administrator said, they "cope with overload with, possibly, less than a complete job."

This administrator feels that Bronx OPD has reached the limit of its facilities. He said that if they could "afford" to stay open evenings and weekends they would serve more people. However, in addition to the financial problem of extending hours, it apparently is just as difficult to get personnel to work here at night as in other OPD's in the city.

The basic problem, according to this administrator, is the unrealistic budget. It is said to require at least $20 million to run the hospital, but they are allotted $16 to $18 million. Many absolute musts have to be achieved on emergency requests. This, then, leaves nothing for growth, innovation, research, etc. The feeling was expressed that money should be available to them to use with "experience justification."

As an example of their difficulties in meeting critical needs, an instance of low oxygen supply was described. The regular distributor could not fill their order, so they requested authority to purchase a supply from another dealer. The red tape that followed took so much time that they had to resort to small containers on hand (for example, from the ambulances). When they called "downtown" once more to report the urgency, a clerk (their contact in purchasing) asked, "Why do you need oxygen?"

Speaking to the complaint that the central office "is unaware of real problems and needs" in the individual hospitals, a spokesman proposed that although some areas--for instance, automation--should be handled centrally, operational decision-making in general should be decentralized with provision for accountability. Citing another example of wasteful central purchasing, he spoke of the penicillin that was purchased from Italy "at a great saving." Unfortunately, its form required a larger needle than is stocked in the American hospital. Patients were

caused unnecessary pain and, in many cases, the doctors "wouldn't even use the stuff," making it a
"total waste."

One further key problem was reported: the geographic positioning of the OPD and ER at this hospital. The two services are at opposite sides of the
building, yet must work together. Sometimes emergency cases must be rushed across the main lobby
(perhaps in a critical state) in a wheelchair to the
ER. The ER here meets the same weekend problem as
do most of the hospitals--that of the nonemergent
cases who "won't wait" until Monday for attention.
(The wait for attention was in the order of four to
six hours in the ER until a special attending physician was assigned to take care of nonemergent cases
on weekends.)

The need for machine processing was pointed out.
"People can't handle all this information!" They do
not have an addressograph machine (the city will not
provide this until affiliation is completed). They
are so far behind, it was reported, that necessary
statistics for 1966 are still not available. Further, in January 1966 additional file space was requested.   Sixteen months later, records are still
being stored in boxes in the halls. In this matter,
the staff is falling further behind every day.

The community served by Bronx Municipal is primarily residential. Often, people own their own
homes. However, clientele is between 80 and 90 percent indigent by Medicaid standards. It was the
opinion of the OPD/ER home care director that they
are meeting the medical needs of the community, except for preventive medicine. This, he said, is what
the Department of Health is set up for; to put it all
under the responsibility of the Department of Hospitals
"would be very expensive." This administrator feels
that Bronx Municipal is well established in the community and that it is "one of the best hospitals in
the world." However, he adds, the hospital facility,
in terms of its physical capability to contain and
support more units, more beds, more nurses, etc.,
reached the saturation point about 1961--and still
the patient load increases. Under these conditions,
every new patient is simply a new increment of in-
escapable overload. Therefore, "compared to what we
used to be able to do, we're failing." This kind of
awareness and concern deserves an effective response.

BIRD S. COLER HOSPITAL

Plant and Services

Coler is a chronic-care hospital, built in 1952. It contains 919 long-term care beds (89% occupied) and 749 infirmary beds (93% occupied). The hospital is located at the north end of Welfare Island, isolated from the city, without public transportation. As hospital personnel emphasized, it is often "viewed as a prison." Its location shows little wisdom or planning. "This is the place where the community files away its problems." The plant is clean, its walls are tiled. It looks like a hospital.

Two factors shape the clinical services at Coler. First is the emphasis on the patient, not merely disease as such. However, while the medical college is departmentalized, the hospital services accordingly organized, ailments of the elderly are not easily "departmentalized." Each patient must be treated as a person. To meet this fact, a significant team innovation has been employed. The chief component in the Coler structure is the "professional practice unit," consisting of an internist, a psychiatrist, a social worker, and a nurse. They work in concert in dealing with the patient.

A second factor shaping the clinical services at Coler (or beginning to) is the belief that if one is to treat patients instead of diseases, he must become part of the community and must understand the way the community organizes itself for the treatment of disease. He must reach the patient before the latter arrives at Coler. This raises a set of problems treated below under "Administration."

It should be noted that Coler, unlike hospitals such as Harlem or Bellevue, does not relate to a given community or region within the city. This cheats it of volunteer services from the community and compounds the problems of the Coler physician who wishes to influence the community's handling of health and disease.

Physicians

The affiliation contract with New York Medical College provides for complete services by physicians

for operating the hospital, except for interns and
residents who are to be paid by the city. The contract also provides for "the clinical staff and special faculty to provide undergraduate, graduate, and
postgraduate training to members of the health professions...." The physicians who work at Coler, including residents and interns, also rotate through
Metropolitan Hospital and Flower Fifth Avenue
Hospitals.

Other Services

There is a nurse shortage here, as at other city
hospitals, worsened by the hospital's isolation and
the attendant transportation problems. Housekeeping
and maintenance personnel are in short supply. Laboratory services are covered by the affiliation
contract.

Affiliation

As noted above, the affiliation with New York
Medical College provides physicians, except for interns and residents, and laboratory services. The
affiliation also provides technical and ancillary
personnel in physical therapy, occupational therapy,
sociology, speech, and rehabilitation services. The
1966-1967 contract cost $2,236,000. The same amount
is planned for 1967-1968.

The belief was encountered at Coler that an
equivalent level of service could be maintained were
the contract money made available directly to the
hospital administrator, without passing through an
affiliate.

Administration

The crisis in the city hospitals, in the view
of the staff at Coler, is not in money but rather
in the inability to move--to innovate. They are persuaded that their hospital is viewed throughout the
city as the end of a process; patients who arrive
here have "gone through the works." They are here
to be out of sight. Thus, the city finds it hard
to relate to a struggling program in community

medicine. Staff members say, "we've created problems
in attempting to improve."

One senior medical staff member commented on requirements to enable the city structure to react to
pressure for change. In his view, the city departments are not geared to do adequate planning. Only
a few people carry the real work. Moreover, there
is no continuity at the commissioner level. The individual commissioner has not been able easily to relate to planning or to the long view. Continuity--
the long view--can be found in universities. On the
other hand, universities cannot undertake service
commitments. The medical schools are evolving toward pure science. The answer has to lie in some
sort of partnership between the political structure
(the city), the university, and the community.

Another problem is lack of communication among
the city hospitals. Are conferences a partial answer?
An ongoing study group on chronic diseases is needed.
Coler is presently working with Harlem, Metropolitan,
and Lincoln Hospitals in an effort to "get into the
process of acute care earlier."

An experimental program now in the design phase
at New York Medical College was discussed. This program is built on the assumption that the doctor's
education must start in the community with a concern
for health as well as disease. Neighborhood health
centers are to be the focus. The experimental design
calls for three centers serving 50,000 people. Groups
of students will follow given families, as need arises,
through diagnostic centers, to community hospitals, to
university hospitals.

Staff members speculated about this kind of
plan: Metropolitan Hospital might become a university hospital and drop from 1000 beds to perhaps 400.
Smaller 100- to 200-bed units could "surround" the
hospital. At the family/system interface, the
internist-pediatrician would function; at the next
level, the specialist in the diagnostic center. In
such an arrangement, Coler would become an experimental center for chronic disease. Comment was made
also on the widespread belief that chronic disease
beds should be available in general hospitals: namely, that this would perpetuate the tendency of medical staff (except in isolated cases) to look at
chronic ailments strictly in a disease sense.

While none of this says a great deal about the mechanics of administration of Coler Hospital today, it does cast a provocative light on the broader questions of hospital administration at the planning level. More particularly, it reflects keen insight and concern regarding community medicine and chronic disease on the part of the Coler staff.

CONEY ISLAND HOSPITAL

Plant and Services

Coney Island is a relatively new hospital with a bed capacity of 567. Its complement is 467 with 77% average occupancy rate. The average daily census is 364 and, in 1966, 8,774 patients were admitted (1,157 D.O.A.). It is only moderately active in OPD visits (125,709). The old Coney Island is now used as an infirmary (among other uses); it has a capacity of 283, a complement of 101, and is 90% occupied.

Coney Island is not located in a markedly im-poverished community per se, as are most other city hospitals. A good number of the residents in the community are retired or, at least, older people. Consequently, there is a large number of what are referred to as "disposition" cases at the hospital. The building itself is attractive, and there are not the numerous problems of structure that plague many other municipal hospitals. The full range of ser-vices of a general hospital is offered. An enlarged psychiatric service is in the planning stage, as is a new building.

Physicians

Physician services, in general, have been vastly improved. Evidences of "payroll padding" have been alleged (Procaccino, Thayler reports were cited), which are purported to have had a demoralizing effect on hospital personnel. Community programs have been instituted in which all M.D.'s in the area have been invited to participate.

Other Services

Nursing continues to be a critical problem for the hospital. Numerous efforts have been made to

correct this situation, all of which have failed.
Only three nurses tend patients on the night shift,
and the affiliate institution has recently withdrawn
supplement pay support to the nurses' aides who had
filled in.

Pharmacy has also experienced severe personnel
shortages, and the affiliate in this instance provided additional people.

The same personnel situation obtains in dietary
and housekeeping functions: namely, shortages.

Affiliation and Administration

There is a sense of "distance" between the two
administrations of the affiliated hospitals, Maimonides
and Coney Island. The city administrator states that
he had inadequate cooperation and information concerning the operations of the hospital. He is "not included or consulted, but simply informed--sometimes--
of the decisions regarding Coney Island." He has
been a highly vocal critic of affiliation contracting
in general, and Maimonides in particular. His feelings about cooperativeness are, in general, said to
be shared by other staff members. The administrator
feels that the city should recognize differences
among affiliate hospitals (their philosophies and
capabilities) and should organize more effective relationships between them and city hospitals.

CUMBERLAND HOSPITAL

Plant and Services

Cumberland is pleasantly located (by comparison
to many others). It is well-kept and clean. It was
constructed in 1922 and renovated nine years ago.
The hospital has a bed capacity of 451, but staff
shortages have caused the bed count to be reduced to
401. The average rate of occupancy in 1965 was 90%,
and it is running at approximately 85% during the
early months of 1967. Cumberland experiences many
of the same problems as do the other municipal hospitals, but not to the same extent. It offers the
full range of services of an acute general hospital

and has the additional great advantage of having its
affiliate hospital about one block away. Low-income
housing developments surround the hospital; ghettos
lie beyond. The community is predominantly Negro and
Puerto Rican. Cumberland has taken steps to increase
community support for the hospital. The area is "in
transition" and the lay board is still mostly of non-
community representation. The hospital sponsors various functions to which community members are invited.
It sends out releases and brochures describing the
institution.

Physicians

Medical staff is provided by the affiliation
with Brooklyn Hospital and includes the benefits of
faculty appointment. There is also access to the
facilities and equipment of Brooklyn Hospital. Some
of the chiefs of service are concerned with lack of
equipment, delays in personnel acquisition, and the
fact that the "city has not kept its part of the bargain" in terms of research opportunity. At least one
chief indicated he might seek another position.

Other Services

The finding and hiring of nursing personnel is
a considerable problem, although proximity to Brooklyn
Hospital has been of some help in this matter.

Again, the familiar personnel problems pertain
to ancillary personnel: their availability, and the
hospital's freedom to hire and/or replace.

Affiliation

The affiliation with Brooklyn Hospital appears to
be in good order. There was no observable indication
of discord. The contract includes medical records,
physicians for all clinical activities, laboratories,
diagnostic radiology, home care, and psychiatry. The
executive vice-president of Brooklyn Hospital feels
that the contract has been "mutually beneficial."
One of the interesting statistics cited was the decrease in the mortality rate at Cumberland: pre-
affiliation, 10%; post-affiliation, 3.5%. The value
of the contract is $4.5 million.

Administration

One strongly voiced complaint was that there were "twenty or more different agencies that have veto power" over local administration without any accountability relationship with the hospital. Also, administrators and service chiefs pointed to the severely limiting disparity in salary levels for the same job in different institutions; the example was given of the physical therapist: city salary, $6,100; voluntary, $7,000; proprietary, $9,000.

Outpatient and Emergency Room Services

OPD 1966 Census, 194,875
ER 1966 Census, 101,586
Home Care 1966 Census, 129
OPD Hours/Days, 8:30-5:00, Mon. through Fri.

Although the OPD and ER are separated physically and administratively at Cumberland, functionally they overlap at the admitting desk. Oddly enough, the ER appears to be without any serious problems, whereas the OPD seems to have more than its share. The OPD director said, "What we're up against is having too big a load for the size of the institution." There is a tremendous and observable space problem. Reportedly, the staff is qualitatively adequate, but quantitatively insufficient for the needs of the OPD.

On the other hand, the ER has very new and very modern facilities and the director considers his staff quite adequate both quantitatively and qualitatively. During the hours of observation in this survey, it was clear that this ER does have a very smooth operation. It was reported that since the construction of the new quarters, the ER census has steadily increased. For example, in 1963 the visit number was approximately 77,000; in 1964, approximately 86,000; in 1965, approximately 100,000.

One of the real problems in the Cumberland OPD is the fact that the hospital is not yet totally converted to the unit record system (and this is the root of other problems). There is inadequate clerical staff in the records department. Therefore, rather than progressing, administrative support is getting so far behind in setting up its records and correspondence handling that the present staff may never get the task done. It was reported that the staff comes in weekends to try to catch up, but to comply with the city's overtime compensation policy, they must take several days off later to compensate for the weekend work. The work falls behind again on those days. Initiative has tended to be self-defeating. This clerical shortage is characteristic of all the clinics in the OPD. Nurses are doing clerical work and are unhappy about it.

To counter the space and volume problems, a proposal has been made that the clinics stay open evenings. It was said, however, that the staff works on session hours and "simply will not make themselves available." It is hoped that ultimately the originally planned three additional floors for the building will be raised, thus alleviating the space problem. Even so, insufficiency of personnel will remain a severe problem.

Equipment procurement, too, has apparently caused problems in the OPD. Staff members report waiting over a year for certain new, vital equipment that, ordered as an "emergency," was to have been supplied "immediately."

These shortages seem not to disturb the ER. There is a problem of inadequacy of ancillary staff; the RN shortage has affected the ER only slightly, but a fairly serious shortage of practical nurses and nursing aides is reported.

Good facilities and staff attract patients from other districts who, in selecting the Cumberland ER, add to its patient burden. These patients are treated once, then their records are stamped "Out-of-District," and they are referred back to the clinics in their districts.

An excellent relationship appears to exist between the OPD and ER. Nonemergent cases that come to the ER are examined, then given appointments with the screening clinic in the OPD. This is accomplished in the admitting room, which is the common "walk-in" entrance for both the OPD and the ER, and the provision is made for this service around the clock. The OPD has a mental hygiene clinic, a cancer detection clinic, and a fairly active teaching program (e.g., diabetes, prenatal, nutrition, etc.).

A unique arrangement was reported for transferring patients from Cumberland. A patient has to
be diagnosed as transportable if he is to be transferred. If it is inadvisable to move him, he is put
in the holding ward or in the regular wards (or held
even if he has to be put in a corridor).

However, if he is movable and there is no room
for him at Cumberland, arrangements are then made by
telephone to move the patient to one of five hospitals with which they have this arrangement. A physician accompanies the patient to the other hospital,
taking with him all necessary papers and copies of
any applicable X-rays.

With respect to the community, OPD and ER personnel feel they have a "rapport" with the people they
serve, claiming that many who went to other hospitals
want to "come back to Cumberland." Possibly, they
suggest, this is because the teaching group takes
more interest in the individual case. The population is predominantly Negro and Puerto Rican and the
patients "receive the service well."

FRANCIS DELAFIELD HOSPITAL

Plant and Services

This is a 295-bed cancer hospital. The administrator describes its purposes as patient care, training, and research in that order. The hospital was
built in 1955. A new laboratory and X-ray area have
just been added, funded in part by a federal grant
obtained by Presbyterian, and in part by the city.

It was stated that the hospital does not get
enough patients. Its occupancy rate in 1966 was
60.8%. The hospital works closely with Harlem and
Presbyterian in obtaining patients. Patients transferred from other hospitals "are generally past
hope." Some patients are self-referred, others come
from neighborhood doctors, some from the Garment
Workers' Union Clinic.

A senior medical staff member asks whether the
city should be in the business of running a cancer

hospital. Once, as he put it, only the city hospitals (with city funds supporting them) could offer radiological facilities at the leading edge of the art. Today, a number of hospitals match and often exceed city facilities. Patients, he stated, do not like cancer hospitals. They find them depressing and morbid.

Another kind of difficulty was alluded to in an instance where a medical staff member brought a private patient in for radiotherapy, before comparable facilities were available elsewhere. Although the patient was prepared to write a check to the hospital on the spot, the "welfare people put him through a three-hour interrogation."

Physicians

Doctors under the city affiliation contract must be distinguished from doctors who work at Delafield under the long-standing teaching affiliation with Presbyterian. Certain key staff members are on city pay: the director of radiology, the director of OPD and medicine (who receives his OPD pay from the city), the dentist, and the director of the blood bank (who receives a resident's salary). All other doctors and X-ray technicians, it was said, "are under the affiliation."

Department staffs in surgery, medicine, and gynecology are not supported by contract. Physicians here are paid by Presbyterian and spend part of their time at Delafield in fulfillment of the teaching affiliation. Eighteen attending surgeons, for instance, are provided by Columbia under this arrangement.

The published summary of affiliation contracts shows three for Delafield/Columbia: one for anaesthesiology ($105,397), one for diagnostic radiology ($329,214), and one for radiation therapy ($251,284).

Physicians not covered by the affiliation contract sometimes bill patients under Medicare, providing the services are clearly personal and identifiable. The money goes into a fund at Columbia, pending a clearer definition of the legality of the process. Presumably, funds will someday be apportioned.

Other Professional Services

Nurse lines at Delafield are reasonably well filled with the major exception of staff nurses, as the following table shows.

	Lines	Filled	
Supervising nurses	13	12	
Head nurses	20	18	
Staff nurses	118	9	(+ 2 part-time)
P.N.'s	65	59	
Aides	47	135	
	263	233	

The assistant director of Nursing services spoke of a good orientation program at Delafield for P.N.'s and aides, but pointed out that nurse recruits are sometimes lost because of the four-week wait for a first pay check.

Nursing, according to all persons interviewed, is a basic problem at Delafield. There, nurses must work with inadequate staffs and supporting services. An added difficulty is that night X-ray and laboratory services are inadequate.

The ancillary facilities are inadequate. The physical plant does not allow for adequate research facilities.

Affiliation

Columbia and the city are moving to consolidate the many fractionated affiliation contracts. However, there seems little hope of basic improvements in their provisioning. In the case of Delafield, it is thought that Columbia will seek coverage for medical services.

Administration

Delafield's administrator is innovative. When city channels could not produce an audio paging system, the administrator convinced the medical board to fund necessary parts, then hospital electricians were used to install the system. This is a clean hospital with an undersized houskeeping staff.

"I tell the staff, if they don't help keep the place clean, they're the ones who have to walk around in the dirt."

Difficulties were pointed to that arise because administrators do not participate in drawing contracts. For instance, X-ray service went to contract with no provision for ancillary personnel. Pathology is responsible for autopsy, but not the morgue. Ordinarily, the pathology department runs the morgue. All contract accounting is worked out directly by the commissioner's office.

Out-Patient and Emergency Room Services

OPD 1966 Census, 28,257
OPD Hours/Days, 9:00-5:00, Mon. through Fri.

Because of the special function of Delafield, the in-patient, out-patient, and emergency services do not have the same operational distinctions as at other hospitals. One staff covers all of the services, out-patient and in-patient, and as one nurse said, "the OPD is the emergency room."

Although lack of space was mentioned as a concern, the primary problem was reception-room space; clinic patients have to wait in the corridors. Need was also observed for private areas for examining and treating the patients. However, the shortage of nurses noted above is a greater problem than are the crowded corridors. Nurses now must run back and forth between the wards and the clinics to serve the doctors in each and perform other nursing tasks in both areas. It was pointed out that not only are there not enough nurses, but those whom they do have are not given enough "status," i.e., there is no lounge or conference room provided as for other professionals. "Fortunately our nurses have been around here a long time and are all dedicated," commented the hospital administrator.

An interview with the nurse in charge of the OPD revealed another side to this problem. Nurses do feel abused with overwork and low status, but a major complaint is weekend duty tours. Apparently the clinic has to be staffed on weekends to take care of the emergency cases, but the nurses tend to believe that most of these cases are not emergent and that patients are taking advantage of the system. Further, nurses who work on weekends must take days off during the week, so the already short staff is even more handicapped on such days.

The community served by Delafield is not limited to a district. All cancer patients in the five borough are treated at Delafield if necessary and desired. Although the neighborhood has been labeled "crime-ridden," the hospital administrator stated it is well policed, and they have few problems in this regard.

CITY HOSPITAL CENTER AT ELMHURST

Plant and Services

This hospital opened in March 1957. It is a 941-bed hospital; in 1966 its occupancy rate was 89%. Home care patients numbered 240 at the time of this survey; the year's average was 264 (said to be second only to Bellevue). Although the hospital has not been painted in ten years, it still appears well-kept.

X-ray and laboratory areas are "grossly under-planned." A feasibility study by Skidmore, Merrill, and Owings is underway to see to expanding the radiology area, along with the emergency service and the OPD. Money is budgeted for an expansion of 200,000 sq. ft.; at this point in the study, the architects advise that 394,700 sq. ft. will be needed. Another generalized space problem lies in the fact that no expansion of areas ancillary to the affiliated areas has been possible.

Although the hospital is just ten years old, it has become a "community landmark." It has an active ladies' auxiliary. There is a close relationship with the Health Department, and with the Queensbridge Project. The project area is four miles from the hospital, with poor transportation between. Today, doctors from the hospital visit the project; when necessary, patients are admitted from there without difficulty or interrogation.

In enumerating the services of this hospital, the administrator spoke especially of large psychiatry and rehabilitation units, a premature-infant center, a male T.B. service, extended care service, a

coronary care unit (three beds), a speech and hearing
unit, and a mental retardation unit. He hopes to
extend the social services.

The hospital serves a community of 800,000 people of mixed origins and ages. The obstetrical overflow from Greenpoint comes to Elmhurst.

Physicians

Physicians of all clinical services, including
interns and residents, are provided under the affiliation contract with Mt. Sinai. There are 16 full-
time chiefs of service. Before affilation, the
physicians were voluntary or on sessions.

Other Professional Services

The administrator believes that Elmhurst comes
the closest of any city hospital to filling its nurse
complement. Of 400 budgeted R.N. lines, 230 are
filled by registered nurses. Thirty of these are
full-time equivalents on per diem. The hospital has
worked to achieve its nursing staff. Success is attributed to good recruiting, to relieving nurses of
non-nursing duties and to refresher courses that attract inactive nurses. Twenty joined the first refresher course, twenty finished, and "seven or eight"
accepted work as per-diem nurses. The chiefs of medicine and pediatrics have started evening symposia
for nurses.

Support Activities

Already noted are difficulties in laboratory
areas and in radiology. In addition, it was said that
requests for equipment and reconstruction take two
years to process. Mt. Sinai has speeded this in some
cases by hiring architectural services to prepare
plans to accompany requests, thus cutting the processing time. Some $50,000 of Mt. Sinai money has been
spent for this purpose this year, according to the
administrator.

Affiliation

Two contracts are proposed for 1967-1968: medical
services for $9,990,000 and psychiatric services for

$1,130,996--total: $11,120,996. This would repeat
prior arrangements for 1966-1967. The contracts
cover physicians for all clinical services, complete
laboratory services, social services, radiology, home
care, and medical records.

Administration

This administrator believes that ways should be
sought to place fiscal responsibility in the hospital,
with controls, and with adequate staff to meet local
responsibility. He believes in "system engineering"
as a road to solving many hospital problems. He spoke
of some success with work simplification techniques
and of having, in effect, gained people by simplifying and combining jobs. With respect to personnel
matters performed by nurses, this work was shifted to
the personnel division thus "gaining a nurse" for the
patient floors.

He believes that the administration of the city
hospitals has been strengthened in recent years by obtaining trained administrators. He believes that
Dr. Trussell's program of sending several administrators and assistants for training at Columbia was an
important step in the right direction. Middle management (the division heads) needs strengthening in the
city hospitals. (Several other administrators voiced
this opinion.)

Administrative personnel are interested in programs for improving hospital utilization. Where surgery is indicated for an out-patient, administrators
want a complete work-up in OPD and careful scheduling
of surgery so that the patient is admitted the day
before his operation, and not a week before.

The hospital is planning to participate in the national Professional Activities Study (PAS) to gain better statistical information about hospital activities.

An unusual "problem" reported was that there are
certain facilities exclusive to Elmhurst and therefore
unavailable to any but the indigent. For example, the
speech and hearing clinic has equipment that is unavailable elsewhere in the city. The administration
finally succeeded in widening limits of accessibility
outside the Elmhurst district, making eligible the indigent of the five boroughs. Nonindigent city citizens cannot have the advantage of this equipment;

there is nothing equivalent elsewhere. Apparently a
similar situation exists in their physical medicine
department. It is claimed that more and better facilities exist there than in any of the other hospitals,
city or private, yet the service is restricted to the
Elmhurst district.

Out-Patient and Emergency Room Services

OPD 1966 Census, 194,831
ER 1966 Census, 89,980
Home Care 1966 Census, 270
OPD Hours/Days, 8:30-4:00, Mon. through Fri.

It was reported that this OPD has been undergoing a steady increase in load of about 8% a year,
yet--as is common elsewhere in the municipal hospital OPD's--facilities are not growing with the census. To meet this problem of space, there is hope
of staffing evening clinics to take some of the load
from daytime sessions. Also, it has been found that
afternoon clinics were empty of patients before the
closing hour; therefore, the schedule will be reorganized so that two sessions can be run during the
afternoons.

As to staff, the common difficulties were discussed. There is a shortage of ancillary personnel,
but not of physicians. Most of the doctors are post-
affiliation. At the time of the affiliation contract,
those doctors who were eligible were moved on to the
Mt. Sinai staff. The rest, it was commented, "have
faded away." It is a concern of the administrators
that nurses cannot also be moved to Mt. Sinai lines,
as the administrators feel more could be done for the
nurses in this way.

Elmhurst is particularly active in community
affairs. It was reported that this community represents a higher socio-economic group than character-
izes most of the city hospitals--more "affluent,"
as it was expressed--though within the range of eligibility. Examples described of the community activities of this hospital were:

- Queensbridge Health Maintenance Service for
  the Elderly (noted earlier). An extension of
  the Elmhurst Clinic within a housing project,
  this project began with a grant and developed

into an active and successful demonstration.
It is staffed and controlled by the Elmhurst
Clinic in cooperation with the Department of
Health.

- Community Rehabilitation Service. This activity provides concentrated rehabilitation
  services to the community: vocational, therapeutic, and psychiatric. Both services and
  facilities are offered by the hospital to
  patients through the orders of ward doctors,
  private physicians, etc.

- A Lay Advisory Board. This board interprets
  the hospital's role to the community and provides a means for the community to define its
  needs to the hospital.

- Day Camp Program for Geriatric Patients.
  This plan makes it possible to take these
  patients to the Golden Age activities and
  facilities in the city.

- Active Recreation Therapy Department. This
  provides a program to help elderly, indigent
  patients "back into the business of living
  again," rather than just "living out their
  lives in the hospital," and crowding the
  wards. Guided by the general belief that
  patients can be energized and returned to
  the community, the program has special activities both outside the hospital and participation in activities within the hospital.

JAMES EWING HOSPITAL

Plant and Services

Ewing is one of the city's two cancer hospitals.
It is relatively new (1950). It is well equipped,
and its condition is good. It has a bed complement
of 240 and has experienced a slow but steady decline
in both admissions and patients treated. In 1965,
the occupancy rate was 73%; in 1966, 70%. On the day
of this survey, occupancy was about 60%.

It is a 17-story structure, compactly built with
connecting corridors to Memorial Cancer Hospital

(a 273-bed voluntary), which owns the ground on which
Ewing is built. Ewing was to be one of two cancer
research and care centers for New York City. This
objective never fully eventuated, as almost all hospitals have their own cancer care and research centers. Memorial was principally interested because
its opportunities for research were limited in a
field requiring much research. Indigents value the
hospital and cooperate accordingly. Memorial uses
a carefully specified consent form. Twenty-five per
cent of the beds at Ewing are "for study purposes,"
and are maintained mostly by grants. The present
commissioner has stated that Ewing will be "given,
sold or leased" to Memorial Hospital.

Physicians

The services of physicians are provided by
Memorial under affiliation contract; there are no
city medical staff members. Pediatric patients are
cared for in the pediatric ward at Memorial Hospital.

Other Professional Services

There seem not to be any significant laboratory-
related problems, with the exception of equipment.
Nursing, on the other hand, is a major problem. In
the administrator's opinion, this is the only really
significant problem. Ewing is presently at about 50%
staffing of its 150 R.N. lines, if one counts nurse
interns (these interns are foreign-trained R.N.'s).
Presently on the staff are 64 American-trained R.N.'s.
Sloan House and Memorial have helped in providing
money for supplements.

Support Activities

There was no indication of excessive personnel
shortage problems. In one instance--a need in the
telephone and information service--a position was
borrowed from nursing.

There are no evident problems with maintenance
or short supplies (reflecting new plant and lowered
usage). Ewing benefited from good planning and budgeting from the beginning. Other hospitals have not

been able to increase their personnel budgets to
meet changed and enlarged needs.

Affiliation

The city entered into a contract with Memorial
which, in turn, has affiliations with Cornell Medical
College and New York Hospital. The amount of the city
contract in 1966-1967 was $3,225,000; proposedfor
1967-1968 is $3,465,000.

Administration

The largest and most difficult problem that the
administration has had to deal with is disquiet among
city employees upon learning of the possible transfer
of Ewing to Memorial. The administration has attempted to assure them that they will be given preferential
consideration if the transfer occurs (i.e., the city
will help find them new jobs).

Perhaps the most troublesome problem observed
was that Ewing operates on a selective admission
basis as if it were a voluntary hospital. It does
not accept patients who might "come in off the
streets"; all of its patients come via an elaborate
pre-admission procedure. Very few come from other
hospitals. A question was raised as to whether other
hospitals offered the same care to the cancer patient
as does Ewing. The answer: "yes, today." Some
years ago this was not true. The two city cancer
hospitals were ahead of the general hospitals in
their techniques of surgery and radiology. Other
hospitals have now caught up.

Ewing is remarkably well cared for and has enjoyed unusual success in obtaining most of its needs.

FORDHAM HOSPITAL

Plant and Services

Fordham is a free-standing, 450-bed hospital, not
adjacent to a medical school or a voluntary hospital.
Photographs were shown, dating from the early 1920's,
when this was the "famous city hospital." Today the

building is worn-out, dingy, crowded, dark, and
unfriendly. The interior walls are old paint
and plaster, hard to keep in repair. The hospital
fronts on a park, in a depressed neighborhood of
apartments, tenements, and stores. Bus transportation appears good, at least in daytime. The plant
includes four auxiliary buildings. Plant deficiencies stand second to the nurse shortage on the administrator's list of major problems.

This is an acute general hospital. It operates
45 clinics. The following figures, extracted from
the hospital's published statistics, 1962 through
1966, show constancy in some areas, great change in
others:

	1962	1966
Total admissions	11,652.0	12,502.0
Newborn admissions	1,714.0	2,156.0
Average daily census	369.4	349.0
Home care daily census	136.4	125.2
Operative procedures	1,791.0	2,682.0
Laboratory procedures	185,432.0	800,545.0
Death rate	8.9%	5.7%
Clinic visits	89,450.0	113,784.0
Emergency visits	51,698.0	89,404.0

Physicians

Physicians of all clinical activities, including
in-patient, out-patient, and emergency services, are
provided by the affiliation contract with Misericordia
Hospital. Diagnostic radiology is similarly covered.
The contract provides for home care of not more than
200 patients at any one time, "except as otherwise
provided." Psychiatry is excluded, except for in-
patient psychiatric consultations.

Other Services

The administrator names the shortage of registered professional nurses and of licensed practical
nurses as the hospital's major unresolved problem.
The hospital is authorized to employ 199 nurses; 83
are currently in service.

Fordham participates in a student nursing program with the Misericordia Hospital School of Nursing and with Bronx Community College. In the past year, 40 student nurses from Bronx and 36 from Misericordia participated in this clinical affiliation. Ten newly recruited nurses from Misericordia were slated to start work at Fordham in July 1967.

There are personnel shortages in the housekeeping, security, stores, maintenance, dietary, and pharmacy staffs.

Affiliation

The administrator believes that Fordham could not function as it does without its contractual affiliation. He believes that the two managements function as an effective team. Nursing stations have been provided by Misericordia from its own funds, an example of benefits accruing to the city from the affiliation. The amount of the contract for fiscal 1967 is $3.5 million. The same amount is projected for fiscal 1968. Laboratories, blood bank, and medical records are covered by the affiliation contract.

Administration

Argument was made for increased autonomy for the hospital. It was pointed out that the administrator has no real standard by which to measure performance. The administrator does not, for instance, know his "income," but the Welfare Department does. With the advent of Medicare-Medicaid, and the increased income for service that these programs offer, information about their funding should become an important management tool.

Local administration does not regard its budget as a firm ceiling. Given a crisis, there is overspending as necessary. (Contrast this attitude with that of the administrator who says, "You look bad if you overspend.")

Out-Patient and Emergency Room Services

OPD 1966 Census, 112,839
ER 1966 Census, 89,404

Home Care 1966 Census, 139
OPD Hours/Days, 9:30-3:00, Mon. through Fri.

This hospital has two long-range goals for its
ambulatory care activity: (1) to be able to assign
each patient to a particular physician; and (2) to
provide a group system of physicians for continuous
and comprehensive care of patients. In reaching for
these goals, it is realized that the staff will have
to go through a long "phase of disappointments";
patients must learn to adapt to the system.

The general feeling of those interviewed was
that "a great job has been done at Fordham with very,
very limited facilities and space." Believing that
it is "self-defeating to simply cope with atrocities
by taking emergency measures," they have preferred to
"make a big noise" and try to handle resources as
efficiently as possible.

There was evidence that much is being accomplished in spite of difficulties, but the difficulties were also quite apparent. Their buildings are
old and facilities outdated. Clinics are crowded,
and it was clear that they are operating with minimum
staff. The supervising nurses of the OPD and ER, both
obviously proud of their work, are competent and dedicated professionals who appear to be capable of
achieving high-quality work with minimum tools and
assistance.

In the ER it was reported that only 35% of the
emergency visits turn out to be nonemergent. This
is in marked contrast to the New York State average
of 70%. Staff members could not explain this difference (which they claim is true of weekends as well).

Most of the OPD clinics are scheduled for morning
sessions during the week, and the big rush is between
8:00 and 9:00 a.m. Clinic personnel have found it
extremely difficult to shift patients' habits to attending afternoon clinics and believe it would be
even more futile to try to train them to accept evening or weekend clinic hours. This, they said, means
breaking down a system that has been in existence a
long time. However, because the ER is overcrowded
on the weekends, they would like to relieve that traffic of at least the 35% nonemergent cases--but this
solution leads to a staffing problem.

Although Fordham is on the unit record system, a deviation exists in procedure. Different unit numbers are given in the ER from those used in the OPD and the wards. Only when a patient goes from the ER to the OPD or to the wards is he assigned a number in the central system.

A long-range plan discussed with the OPD/ER director was the establishment of planning groups for both patients and hospital personnel. Specifically, he wants to provide a "dynamic environment" in which "both kinds of participants" might move from the normal routine of task-orientation to one that is growth-oriented. This is seen as a way of "getting out of the rut" as well as of presenting a fuller set of possibilities (in terms of kinds of service) to the patient for exploration and discussion. The central hospital staff supports this approach for OPD, and application has been made for a grant from the Office of Economic Opportunity. Also, it is anticipated that this may stimulate the establishment of health centers in the community, which will serve as satellite clinics for both preventive and curative medicine.

With respect to the community, staff members claim that they take many patients "who would not be welcome anywhere else," and they feel that in this respect they are serving at least one vital need. They characterize the community as "unusually urban" and vitally interested in the hospital. To the community, Fordham Hospital is "as traditional as the local church or school." As proof of this strong attachment, the community has continually opposed closing down the hospital even though the building was already old and obsolete in the 1950's. At times, authorities have wanted to close it.

It is curious that the "community" does not surround the hospital, but rather, is south and east of it. The population is predominantly Puerto Rican and lower-middle-class Caucasian. An indigenous Italian enclave lives in a ghetto that has seen little change in 50 years. Staff members estimated a constant distribution of children, middle-aged, and elderly patients using ambulatory services, but commented that they seldom see working-age young males or teenagers.

With respect to participation of the hospital staff in community activities, one organization in particular was discussed--the East Tremont Neighborhood

Association. In the future, it was stated, the staff hopes to reach out even more into the community than they have been able to do in the past.

GOLDWATER MEMORIAL HOSPITAL

Plant and Services

The Goldwater long-term-care unit, located on Welfare Island, has a capacity of 802 and a complement of 762 beds which are currently occupied at a rate of 75%. The average daily census is 675, and 1966 brought 812 admissions. The separate infirmary, with a capacity of 448 and a complement of 438, was occupied at an average rate of 96%, having an average daily census of 345, and having 258 admissions for the year. The Goldwater plant is in moderately good condition. Access to it is limited to one vehicle approach from Queens.

Physicians

The fact that the AMA will not approve a separate residency program in chronic disease makes adequate availability of physicians difficult. Most hospitals are now building, or planning to add, their own rehabilitation facilities, thus further complicating professional personnel problems for Goldwater.

Other Professional Services

Nursing is a critical problem at Goldwater. Sometimes there is one staff nurse for the entire hospital at night, one or none in the afternoon. The director of nursing feels that this is truly a crisis, and that patient care suffers dangerously with this shortage.

Support Activities

Once again the common finding: "The city does not keep its bargain." Supplies and personnel in housekeeping, clerical, records, and dietary are chronically short.

Affiliation and Administration

The administrator applauds what the affiliation with New York University has brought: some prestige and money (in the forms of equipment and medical services). However, it has also brought duplication of effort in such areas as purchasing, bookkeeping, records, and personnel, and has fractionated the authority of the city administrator. There is the feeling that New York University has been "around so long that it has grown conservative in its efforts and has begun to accept the 'substandard' conditions as standard." (This was a common complaint in the survey regarding affiliate hospitals. More interesting is the fact that this common complaint is expressed by both city and affiliate staff members. Affiliate administrators often evidence a growing lack of hope for the city's reform as a contractual partner.)

GOUVERNEUR AMBULATORY CARE CENTER

Plant and Services

Today Gouverneur is a district ambulatory care unit operating as an extension of its affiliate hospital, Beth Israel. The new Gouverneur Hospital, near the present ambulatory care facilities, is nearly ready to go into service. It is not presently planned as a full-service general hospital.

The plant is old. Up to 1959 it operated as an acute general hospital. The commissioner of hospitals at that time called it the worst hospital in the city, not only for its plant, but also for the level of medical services offered. One of its two main units was later reopened by the state as a treatment center for mentally retarded children.

The community fought the closing; the reopening of Gouverneur in 1961 as an OPD center was the city's compromise. Community pressure has forced a redesign of the "new Gouverneur" Hospital now under construction four blocks from the present site. The new building was originally planned as a 200-bed chronic care hospital. It is now designed with the first six floors for ambulatory care, but the use of floors seven to twelve remains in debate; they appear to be shaped for 124 acute-general beds and 87 extended-care

beds. Beth Israel will serve as back-up to this facility, but will provide obstetrical and surgical
services at its own site.

The Gouverneur neighborhood is the traditional
landing-place in America of foreign-born persons.
Some 30,000 low-income housing units are in the area.
Union-sponsored housing also exists. In the words
of the Gouverneur administrator, "these developments
have tended to drive out the middle class and have
institutionalized the slums."

Ten to fifteen years ago, an influx of Negroes
and Puerto Ricans began. Street gangs brought special
problems which impelled the creation of neighborhood
associations and the appearance of professional social organizations. These groups are sources of the
community pressures so evident in Gouverneur's history.

Affiliation

All personnel at Gouverneur are provided under
the affiliation contract with Beth Israel. The
amount of the contract is $1,683,046. It was the
first, and remains the only, comprehensive affiliation contract in the city. It is probably to be regarded as the most workable, and probably the most
successful, of all affiliation contracts.

Administration

Gouverneur is unique in its reputation as a
place where the Departments of Health, Mental Health,
and Hospitals have learned to work together at the
community level. Strong attempts have been made to
bring the Department of Welfare into this family of
cooperation. However, such items as orthopedic shoes,
artificial limbs, and support stockings are often
provided by Beth Israel (at no cost to the city) because the city appears unable to respond to requests
for such items in a timely way.

Out-Patient Services

OPD 1966 Census, 255,000
Home Care 1966 Census, 49
OPD Hours/Days, 9:00-9:00, Mon. through Thurs.,
            9:00-5:00, Fri.

OPD activity is, in fact, an extension of the
Beth Israel Medical Center into this community, hence
this affiliation is something more than is implied by
the usual contract. It is an actual off-shoot of the
hospital, established in response to a particular community need. As an ambulatory care unit, with comprehensive affiliation, it started in 1961 "with a
clean slate." No traditions, personnel, or policies
were inherited. Consequently, innovation was possible
and good working relationships were established among
the institutions involved.

The facility staff reports that they have local
control of their budget, and therefore more freedom
to achieve efficiencies than do the municipal hospital OPD's. Further, they believe the morale of their
personnel is exceptionally high. This is reflected
in attitudes toward, and interest in, their work.

Another unique feature is that Gouverneur has
hired most of its clerical staff and aides from the
community itself. They have been trained in the OPD.

Three features reported indicate the kind of progress that has been possible at Gouverneur, as far as
general procedure is concerned. Without traditions
to break before new systems could be implemented, this
OPD has been able to build a staff of full-time doctors, achieve a successful "real" appointment system,
and eliminate "sub-sub-specialty" clinics that generally develop within a teaching situation. A guiding
philosophy has been that Gouverneur doctors are to be
"internists first, consultants to their peers second."
Further, the OPD has opened medical and pediatric
clinics four evenings a week, with no great difficulty
in procuring staff. OPD personnel reported that if
and when funds are available they will open the basic
clinics on the weekends also and ultimately around the
clock through the full week.

The staff at Gouverneur is actively involved in
community affairs, and the community has been involved
in health services. One matter given more attention
here than in other OPD districts is that of dissemination of information in the community regarding health
services available to citizens. Even though hard-sell
advertising is professionally unacceptable, there is
the attitude that "the word has got to get around,"
and the staff is willing to go to "many lengths" to
accomplish this. A satellite program has already begun.

No other OPD visited has such extensive information
on where its patients live, and who receives its
health services. The hospital determined both the
areas it does serve and those it does not, and has
developed a sound basis for locating satellite clinics.
An OEO grant has been applied for to develop these
clinics.

Signs in the regular clinics reflect a multi-
lingual neighborhood. They are printed not only in
English and Spanish (common among OPD's), but in
Chinese and Yiddish. (Ten percent of the population
resides in Chinatown.) It was pointed out that Puerto
Rican patients are more highly represented in the
clinic population than in the community population.
Apparently this is because the Puerto Rican population
comprises many young families who seek a great deal
of medical and dental care.

There is a high level of narcotic addiction in
the community served by Gouverneur. Special care is
provided for this problem, both in the OPD and in
community agencies. The narcotics center has both
helped and (inadvertently) worsened the problem.
Complication has been caused by certain requirements:
the minimum age, 21, is a legal necessity; and the
maximum age, 50, has been set because of the effects
of methodone on the body. Treatment will be given·
only to those who have been addicted for four or more
years and who have experienced repeated failure at
other attempts to "kick it." It was pointed out that
these requirements, while necessary, eliminate care
for many who need help.

Intimate involvement in "research" was also reported as characteristic of the community. Presumably
the community engages in constant self-perusal and, in
some respects, is unusually willing to try new ideas.

GREENPOINT HOSPITAL

Plant and Services

Greenpoint is a "free-standing" series of eight
buildings which are in poor condition (one is condemned)
and poorly located with respect to the population
served. The hospital was built in 1914, and for approximately 20 years was a good teaching hospital.

Deterioration began in full after World War II. Five
years ago staffing fell to one full-time physician and
a few part-time professionals; the hospital exhibited
a nearly complete disintegration of services. In 1959
the hospital was closed, with only out-patient services remaining. In 1961 (July) Mt. Sinai undertook an
affiliation agreement for Greenpoint, and, in July
1962, Brooklyn Jewish became the affiliate; it remains
so today, providing a full range of medical service.
Greenpoint is very difficult to manage and maintain
due to its separate facilities. Survey observations
underscore the seriousness of the physical condition
at Greenpoint, a hospital heated by hand-stoked coal.

Physicians

Prior to the original Mt. Sinai affiliation, most
of the residency programs had lost their approval and
services were curtailed. Physicians' services were
limited because Greenpoint could not attract new,
young, qualified physicians. Since the affiliation,
the number of active attendings rose from 82 to 202
over a four-year period; the percentage of board-
qualified physicians rose from 50% to 84%, and board-
certified from 17% to 54%. Full-time physicians increased from 1 to 39; the average age is now 43. There
are now 34 residents and interns compared to the
earlier 19. Yet serious problems confront the hospital in terms of professional accountability--actual
physician time on the premises.

Other Services

Nursing continues as a serious problem. Location
and noncompetitive salary scale are cited as major
factors.

Support services pose equally serious problems.
Again, noncompetitive salaries and rigid over-
centralization were cited as major causes. (The
head of housekeeping earns $90.00 per week and has
responsibility for eight buildings.) Equipment and
supplies also constitute a severe problem.

Affiliation and Administration

As indicated earlier, the affiliation has
brought much to Greenpoint and, as such, has been
invaluable.

However, the laxity in the contract structure and the
unrealistic quality of many of its provisions are said
to constitute major problems. There is built-in
noncooperation, nonaccountability, and duplication.
There are no guidelines, and the city administrator
cannot perform administrative functions responsibly
but is rather a "baby sitter" to the institution.
There needs to be a tighter control of the affiliation,
and the authority of real management is needed within
the hospital.

Outpatient and Emergency Room Services

OPD 1966 Census, 184,213
ER 1966 Census, 66,401
Home Care 1966 Census, 102
OPD Hours/Days, 8:30-9:00, Mon. through Fri.

Not only are the OPD and ER physically separated
at Greenpoint, but the OPD itself is housed in several
scattered locations. Patients must sometimes be transported from the ER to the clinics, from clinic to clinic, or from a clinic or the ER to the wards, and this
invariably means going outdoors. Considering New York
weather variations, these trips cause considerable
difficulty. Staff members observe, "This hospital was
not built for sick people." Not only are there separate buildings for different functions, but there are
no ramps for wheelchairs.

Problems of record keeping in a multiple-building
situation were reported. To make the unit system work,
duplicate sets of cards are necessary, but the OPD
has neither the clerks nor the equipment to make this
possible.

The common problem of space shortages has prohibited teaching. To perform the necessary teaching in
the obstetrics clinic, it was reported, the nurse must
go from room to room. None of these problems is being
dealt with currently, it was explained, "because a new
building is anticipated in the near future."

In both the OPD and ER, physician staff was
reported to be adequate in quantity and quality, but
"desperate" shortages exist in nursing and ancillary
personnel. With respect to staff needs (as well as
equipment), the comment was, "It's very difficult to
get anything through city channels."

It was observed that the OPD and ER were oper-
ationally--as well as physically--separated at Greenpoint. Each unit reported contact with the other to
be limited to "referrals only." The ER director feels
that his operation is, traditionally, the stepchild of
the hospital. "Greenpoint is still an in-patient institution, with appended OPD and ER." Yet, in terms of
census statistics, the reverse relationship would be
expected. The ER is under the direction of the department of surgery, a matter of administrative difficulty.
ER staff would prefer departmental autonomy because--
more and more--to the patient, "the ER is the hospital."

With respect to the problem of space, it was
pointed out that seven acute emergencies at a given
time is the maximum that can be handled, but this figure is commonly exceeded on weekends.

Although it was reported by OPD staff that a
major despair is the space limitation for community
teaching (which they believe to be an important
function), one special need has been met with respect
to community need. The community is predominantly
Puerto Rican, characteristically of low income, and
heavily burdened with emotional problems. Greenpoint
has added social service people to its staff for the
specific purpose of screening for psychological problems. Patients are then referred to staff psychiatrists. This has proved to be so popular an offering
at the OPD that there is a waiting list for months
ahead. This development has not defeated the program's
objectives, however; the psychiatrists' schedules are
cushioned to make immediate attention available to
those who must receive it.

The OPD staff at Greenpoint feels that one of
its greatest services to the community is its evening
clinic session. It seems ironic, however, that the
people do not take full advantage of the opportunity.
Evening hours are from 5:00 to 9:00 p.m., but the rush
does not start until 7:00 p.m. because of the conflict
with the supper hour. To date, appointment-setting
has not solved this problem, but efforts continue because a major objective is to achieve (ultimately) a
one-to-one relationship between the patient and a
doctor of his choice.

The problem of "phoney" addresses was discussed
as common. Wrong identification is given deliberately, it was reported, particularly in cases of positive serology and positive chest problems. Apparently

patients know when they have these diseases and want
to avoid recall to the OPD for treatment. There is
no way of tracing these cases, though a strong effort
is made.

HARLEM HOSPITAL CENTER

Plant and Services

Harlem is a general care hospital having 777 beds
and an average occupancy rate of 85% in 1966. There
were 17,264 admissions and over 250,000 clinic visits
in 1966. The psychiatric service (142-bed complement)
functioned at an average occupancy rate of 96%, T.B.
(20-bed complement) at 92%, and the infirmary (120 beds)
at 95%. Harlem is a sprawling collection of buildings
with "about one hundred routes to the outside." The
earliest structure was built in 1906; the most recent
was occupied in 1956. A "new Harlem" is presently
under construction with completion estimated by 1970.
(Accustomed to delays in city construction, the hospital staff tends to doubt this estimate.) Some of the
old plant will still be useful, other parts should be
demolished. In some areas lighting is poor and walls
and floors are in need of repair. There are severe
space shortages in medical wards and for social service functions.

Physicians

Doctors are not in shortage at Harlem, but there
are complaints about the lack of "reciprocity" in
training with respect to rotation of staffs.

In many services there have been exceptional recent improvements in medical staffing. This year, for
the first time, Harlem got 16 out of 21 requests in
the intern matching program. Money and equipment,
along with the prestige of the Columbia affiliation,
have made this possible.

Other Professional Services

There is, as in all other city hospitals, a shortage of nurses. Also, there is shortage of laboratory

space and related professional services. Here, the
city has not been able to evidence ability to provide
the needed personnel.

Support Activities

The same circumstances obtain for ancillary personnel: inadequate protection in the form of security
guards, and inadequate help in the form of dietary and
housekeeping personnel.

Affiliation and Administration

Medical staff and other personnel brought in with
the affiliation with Columbia University (or because
of it) would "leave if the arrangement were discontinued." Others, who would see more "responsible" roles
and "two-way" rotations, are bitter. The latter complain that Columbia practices discrimination against
them. Some stated that even when they have board and
state certification, they are not allowed to do patient
care at Columbia.

Once again, the basic contract fractionation produces discord and difficulty in management, and inadequate controls.

One staff physician stated that, before the affiliation, in one service there were only three physicians
on duty and a patient had to wait up to five hours for
emergency service; now there are five times as many
physicians, and patients have to wait only three hours!
Clearly, whatever the true case, there is a need for
more efficient management in the delivery of health
care. (Again, caution is suggested in the matter of
attributing cause and blame. Observations of the kind
cited are indicative of system-wide problems only
incidentally related to the Columbia-Harlem affiliation

Out–Patient and Emergency Room Services

OPD 1966 Census, 251,135
ER 1966 Census, 124,885
Home Care 1966 Census, 213
OPD Hours/Days, 8:00-4:00, Mon. through Fri.

When Dr. Jacob Horowitz (formerly assistant commissioner of hospitals) went to Harlem in September 1966, his mission was "to see what he could do about the problems at Harlem." Consolidated under his direction were the ambulatory services of the OPD, ER, home care, medical records, pharmacy, and employees' health service, and he was assigned the additional task of coordinating with several community organizations. His job, then, as he said, was "to integrate services within the hospital and within the community." He reported that the Harlem OPD and ER serve a community of some 400,000 people, as well as maintain a mental health clinic, several health centers, and well-baby clinics (operated by the Health Department). An objective accompanying the integrating of services has been that of bringing together preventive and curative aspects of medical care and also to "bring medical services to people in the community--to set up satellite units."

In subsequent interviews with the heads of divisions, a number of problems were discussed. A major concern for all was the inadequacy of space. Another difficulty expressed was that of the relationship with the Welfare Department. It was reported that there is no direct contact with the Welfare Department, yet "a majority of our patients are welfare recipients."

Apparently the Welfare Department refuses to consider physical coordination unless it can be housed directly in the hospital, and this, it was explained, is physically impossible. The Harlem OPD is short of social workers. A large proportion of this hospital's patients live in boarding rooms and, when hospitalized even briefly, they lose their rooms. Hence, upon discharge, these patients are not only alone, but have no place to live. The staff believes problems of this nature should be the concern of the Welfare Department.

Also, in the records department, where correspondence is handled, they feel they are doing another of the Welfare Department's jobs: answering the never-ending stream of letters requiring verification for insurance, etc. A third source of similar burden was observed in almost all OPD's: the processing and collection of Medicaid and Medicare forms must be shared by OPD clerks. Representatives of the Welfare Department were observed to be registering applicants, but this appeared to be the extent of their responsibilities.

Procurement of supplies was discussed with each person interviewed because each was disturbed by the problem. Apparently it takes approximately six months to receive supplies of common drugs. An anecdote will suffice to indicate the kinds of difficulties encountered. When the OPD ran out of sterile gauze pads and could not get any more for some time, aides packaged unsterile gauze into squares and took them to another department, where the autoclave is kept, for sterilization. Because these aides should have been carrying out other tasks, it was suggested that the waste in man/hours cost more than any saving on these disposable supplies. (It was further pointed out that shortage of disposable supplies is not uncommon; they often run out of such items as syringes.)

In another instance, aides were assigned to clerk jobs dues to a need for "hands"; there were resultant difficulties with the union. As soon as it was possible to supply the OPD with the additional clerks needed, the affiliate did so, and the aides were returned to their regularly assigned jobs. Because of this, it was reported, the union was concerned that "they were taking the aides' jobs away."

The Harlem community is at least 95% Negro (possibly higher), though the hospital is "beginning to see more white patients lately," mostly Puerto Rican. The staff is candid in stating that they really don't know the community well, nor do they feel the community knows about the services offered at the hospital. The comment was made that if the people were educated as to what their needs really are, they would "push" to get these services and the hospital would rise to meet the needs. So far as types of cases are concerned, typical at Harlem are gunshot and knife wounds, drug addition (high in mothers and babies), alcoholism, and respiratory diseases related to smog and smoke.

In its annual report, Harlem discusses a number of community activities in which the hospital participates. Given greatest attention are the Peoples' Civic and Welfare Association, the Lay Advisory Board, a Health Career Project for young people, and training in fire prevention and disaster control.

KINGS COUNTY HOSPITAL CENTER

Plant and Services

This is a 2,709-bed hospital, the largest in the city system. A plot plan shows thirty-six buildings. The larger among them are the hospital itself (built in 1932), the institute of pathology, the T.B. and cardiovascular surgery building, the psychiatric building (1942), the outpatient building (1942), and the two nurses' residences (one built in 1942 and the other not dated on the plot plan). Downstate Medical Center and University Teaching Hospital face Kings County across Clarkson Avenue. A nursing school adjoins Kings County on the same grounds.

One of the smaller buildings is a cancer hospital. Another is the neurology and neurosurgical building. A third is devoted to psychiatric research.

Portions of the main building have been renovated. A walk around the grounds reveals broken windows, an occasional window askew in its casement, and missing screens. Now obsolete is the existing feasibility study for reconstruction and modernization of the hospital. The estimated cost: $92,860,000--$20 million over the approved budget. Much more may be needed. A new feasibility study is called for.

Here are some basic statistics from 1966:

Average daily census, hospital	2,169
Average daily census, home care	248
Average patient stay, hospital	14.0 days
Average patient stay, home care	10.4 days

Ambulance calls in 1966 exceeded 50,000, said to be the largest number in the city; and pediatric emergency runs at 170,000 visits a year. The staff assumes that a large part of this represents overflow from other hospitals in the area.

Physicians

The city pays 350 residents and interns at Kings County. The affiliate, Downstate Medical Center, adds

88 positions to this number. Both groups rotate
through Kings County and University Teaching Hospital.
The affiliation contract presently covers only pediatrics and clinical psychiatry.

Other Professional Services

About 50% of the nurse positions are filled with
R.N.'s. Night coverage is difficult. Perhaps 500
student nurses are enrolled in the nursing school;
they are able to help in emergencies.

Support Services

The budget for surgical equipment is $100,000;
need is closer to $250,000, not counting major instal-
lations, cobalt units, construction, and so forth.
Much equipment throughout the hospital is provided
by Downstate, some of it via grant funds and foundation
money. Downstate has "issued an ultimatum" that equipment, space, and support services in pediatrics--an
area now covered by affiliation contract--must be made
adequate, or the college will be forced to withdraw
its medical services.

A pneumatic tube system is needed in the hospital
for medical records. The system would link the central
record room, emergency, pediatric emergency, and the
OPD record room. A secretary should be provided for
each chief of service.

Affiliation

While the present contract with Downstate covers
only clinical psychiatry and pediatrics, there is
expectation that new contracts will cover other medical
services.

Other than pediatrics, additional needed services
have often been provided by Downstate, especially in
pathology.

Like a number of other city hospital administrators, the Kings County administrator believes that he
could, given the necessary authority, have put the

contract funds to comparable use directly without
dependence upon an affiliate. (The present study
throws grave doubt on the probability of obtaining
"the necessary authority.")

Administration

The administrator reports that he has long forgotten many of his requests for equipment, personnel,
and construction. He keeps no logs. Perhaps this is
a measure of futility. He is not alone among the
city administrators in these matters.

Out—Patient and Emergency Room Services

OPD 1966 Census, 525,942
ER 1966 Census, 150,000
Home Care 1966 Census, 248
OPD Hours/Days, 8:00-4:00, Mon. through Fri.,
   with 24-hour screening in pediatrics.

This OPD is one of the most active in New York
City.

Professional staff considers it ironic that this
is the only OPD without clinical clerks. Only two
clerks are available, one for registration and one for
making appointments and taking care of traffic in the
diagnostic clinic. In attempting to counter this
problem, seven people were "borrowed" to serve as
clerks while "awaiting an allocation of additional
personnel." These borrowed clerks consisted of two
OPD aides, two persons from housekeeping, and three
aides transferred from other services. This move was
absolutely essential when Medicaid and Medicare came
in with W-300 forms to add to the over-burdened nurses'
chores. A staff member stated, "Four million dollars
per year is at stake in patient benefits. There are
over 500,000 visits per year for which the city is
supposed to be reimbursed $8.23 per person per visit."
Without personnel to handle the billing, it was asserted, "the city will miss out."

It was reported that someone from central offices
came out to Kings and agreed to provide them with part-
time personnel on an hourly basis as a temporary measure, but nothing has developed from this offer. They
say they have constantly asked for lines in their

budget (originally 10 were requested, but with Medicaid and Medicare, 20 are now necessary), but no response has been made to these requests.

Operations in this OPD/ER differed from others in the city in several ways. For one thing, they have not yet converted to the unit record system. Separate numbers are issued in the in-patient department and in ER and OPD. Currently they are moving their records from closed files to open shelves, and plans are underway for coordinating the various filing systems.

Another unusual feature observed, in relation to other OPD's in the city, was that there apparently is a scarcity of clinic doctors. "Session doctors are hard to find," explained the director. He said he has no direct responsibility for procuring them. They are appointed through the medical board. His busiest clinic, the medical, suffers the most from this "sad lack of professional staff." There are five physicians in this clinic to see 100 patients in two hours, or a ratio of 1:10 per hour. In contrast, the ER reportedly has a "good" staff of physicians.

As in all the OPD's and ER's, space is a dominant problem. Both functions have grown in the past six to eight years at a rate close to 15% annually. This rapid growth caused an urgent situation in the pediatrics OPD. Apparently patients had to wait six to eight hours, during which time some children became dehydrated and other serious consequences developed. A separate structure, designed to handle a volume of 125,000 patient visits, was then planned for the Kings County pediatrics clinic. This new area was occupied in February 1966, but one year later the census had increased to 170,000. The director stated there is "absolutely no room for expansion."

Along with their problems of space and number of doctors, the OPD reported that, because of their being affiliated with a state hospital, they do not get the extra support they would like in obtaining supplies that are difficult to order through city channels. There is always a delay, they said; in fact, items are "sometimes obsolete by the time they are received." Curiously, the ER reported that it has no problem in procuring supplies. It even gets them a month in advance of need.

Regarding the affiliation with the Downstate
Medical Center, another problem was discussed. Patients who are sent to the Downstate Clinic from
Kings County (because they are "interesting" medical
cases) are returned to Kings County for all medical
care other than specialized treatment. The problem,
it was said, is that no record of what was or was not
done is sent with the patient. Apparently such information can be obtained only on request, and then it
comes weeks too late to be useful. It was suggested
that this communication problem might be solved with
an interchangeable record system.

A visit to the pediatrics OPD uncovered another
critical problem. It was reported there that some time
ago a contract was approved by the Board of Estimate
to hire 35 physicians who are desperately needed in
the pediatric clinics. However, the director stated,
the city controller would neither sign this contract
nor communicate with them about it.

Specifically, this was a $1.5 million contract
different from existing hospital affiliation arrangements. It was a separate agreement made in response
to an emergency need. It was said that Commissioner
Terenzio, in fact, had been so sure of its validity,
and of approval for this emergency need, that he
advised Dr. Achs, the director of this pediatrics OPD,
to proceed with hiring. However, she elected to
wait until final official approval, which, she reported,
had not yet been received.

A comparison should be made between the enormous
Kings County ER operation and others surveyed. The
Kings County ER plant is in the worst condition of
all ER's observed in this survey. The director says
he has been submitting renovation plans for 14 years,
and there has been no action. He stated that two years
ago some plans were made for a total rebuilding of the
area, but this activity never got beyond the planning
stage. Dr. Brown visited as HSA administrator; after
seeing the facilities, he demanded immediate changes.
Nothing has happened.

Briefly, the emergency room is very crowded. No
privacy is allowed the patients. Apparently there is
not sufficient police coverage or hospital security,
and thievery is common. The staff is obviously too
small and the space problem is undeniable. In the
corridor at the time of the interviews were sick people,

a man on a stretcher (an "overdose" case), friends
and relatives looking lost and desperate, and general
chaos and confusion. There was even a prisoner in
the holding ward with a guard (when acutely ill,
prisoners cannot go to the regular prison ward but
must stay in the ER under guard). To quote one of
the staff, "This really is where the buck stops."

All that was reported on the community is that it
is made up of approximately 58% Negro, 40% Puerto
Rican, and 2% "white" (representing many nationalities).
Clearly, the staff is much too busy with the demands
of treatment to develop broader concerns about the
community.

LINCOLN HOSPITAL

Plant and Services

Lincoln Hospital consists of two large red-brick
buildings plus some smaller structures. It is an old
plant of 345 beds. One of the main buildings is the
hospital proper; the other, until the early 1960's,
was the Lincoln Hospital School of Nursing. Now it
accommodates the psychiatric service, provides office
space, and houses residents and interns. Interior
walls at Lincoln are painted, except for certain tiled
areas such as the surgical suite, and so are subject
to peeling, fading, and chipping. Of four elevators
in the plant, two are running. Generators installed
in 1927 cannot handle the electrical loads. Furnaces
are coal-fired. Air conditioners in the surgical re-
covery room do not work. A request for window screens
for certain of the wards has been in process "downtown"
for over two years. The lights above the pediatric
examining tables were bought several years ago by
Dr. Einhorn (today, chief of pediatrics) out of his
own pocket. Otherwise, only the ceiling lights in
the room would have been available for examinations.
In his resident days at Lincoln, Dr. Einhorn also
won a crash repainting of the pediatric service, after
fruitless requests and follow-ups, by producing a
chemical analysis showing the existing paint to be
28% lead.

A new Lincoln Hospital is in planning, to be
located about four miles away, nearer the center of

the out-patient area. It is tentatively scheduled for completion in five years at a cost of $66 million.

Lincoln is an acute general hospital. The administrator speaks of patient care and teaching as the hospital's central concerns. Yet community service is patently vigorous at Lincoln; it includes the running of the neighborhood maternity centers, a high-school program for pregnancy force-outs from the schools, a health-career training program, a program for training obstetrical technicians, and a program under which Lincoln trains people to run the community services. Most of these programs are financed by federal agencies or foundations. Certain of them are aimed at obtaining skilled help for the hospital within the community it serves.

This entire survey noted no higher level of initiative for community extension than that found at Lincoln. (For the most part, these programs are not funded by the city, a matter to be discussed.)

Physicians

The bulk of the medical staff at Lincoln is provided under the affiliation contract with Einstein Medical College. The affiliation has accounted for significant (in some instances, outstanding) improvements in medical staff.

Other Professional Services

Of the 176 professional nurse lines on the table of organization for Lincoln Hospital, 36-$\frac{1}{2}$ are filled. Nine beds in the intensive care unit require two and one-half nurses. Per-diem nurses are brought in, when possible. They must wait three weeks for their first pay. Thirty student nurses from Bronx Community College are receiving clinical instruction at Lincoln. The night service is very hard to staff. The subway is two blocks distant and the neighborhood threatening. The neighborhood is second only in its crime rate to the Bedford-Stuyvesant area. Purse-snatchers have been known to work in daylight on the Lincoln doorstep.

A unit-manager program is underway at Lincoln to relieve the professional nurse of "the management activities associated with the ward environment, equipment, and supplies." The object: to give the nurse

more time for patient care. (A problem here: Many
nurses find it difficult to delegate tasks to the
unit manager.)

Support Activities

The hospital loses clerks of long experience
because they pass examinations that qualify them for
higher positions. Openings cannot be provided at
Lincoln, and so these experienced personnel go elsewhere. Eight months ago the hospital asked for lines
for three bacteriologists in order to hold three
qualified people who had learned their work at
Lincoln. Telephone calls and follow-up memoranda
have so far produced no result. The hospital is
using contract money to hold these people.

Linens are in short supply. Laundry service
(Welfare Island) takes inordinately long.

Affiliation

The Lincoln affiliation is with Einstein Medical
College (Yeshiva University). The contract amount in
1966-1967 was $3,465,740. It covered anaesthesia, ob-
stetrics/gynecology, pediatrics, psychiatry, surgery,
and a survey of the medical service. For 1967-1968, an
over-all contract is proposed for $6,672,330.

The administrator points to changes resulting
from affiliation: in 1965, 42 persons worked in the
hospital's laboratories, with inadequate supervision.
In 1967, the number is 89, including an effective
proportion of supervisors. The history of the blood
bank shows, first, a nurses' aide in charge, then a
technician in charge, now a physician in charge. At
one time, anaesthesia was the province of two part-
time anaesthesiologists, with help from resident surgeons who had undergone a 15-lecture training course.
Now, six full-time anaesthesiologists are on the
staff. In 1963, two foreign-trained, unlicensed
physicians constituted the emergency staff. The emergency room gave the hospital the reputation in the
community of a "butcher house." Today, the emergency
room is properly staffed, full-time, in all sections.

The administrator feels comfortable with the
management arrangements for this contract. The

affiliation staff report to him; he reports to the director of the medical school in matters of professional service. He is not bypassed in his own hospital (an unusual, almost unique, experience among city hospital administrators).

The affiliate is providing certain persons not covered under the affiliation contract. These include the ward managers (unit managers, as described above) and administrative assistants to nurses on certain services.

Administration

The administrator commented at length (as did all hospital administrators) on the inflexibility of his budgets and his inability to move funds from one budget category to another in order to meet needs.

His staff budget is the same as it was three years ago except for the addition of certain lines meant to offset the increased service expected to result from the closing of St. Francis Hospital in the Lincoln outpatient district. Each year the administrator submits budgets to meet his needs but the budget is set elsewhere. He "feels free" to exceed his budget for "life and death" items. Last year these exceeded budget by $2 million.

The hospital's extensive community service programs are financed largely by money from sources other than the city. Funds have come from the mental hygiene board of the National Institute of Mental Health, from the Office of Economic Opportunity, from the Federal Child Service Bureau, from the Commonwealth Foundation, and from the Council on Health Education for Living.

A hospital steering committee has been established for the various community training programs.

Outpatient and Emergency Room Services

OPD 1966 Census, 195,893
ER 1966 Census, 182,094
Home Care 1966 Census, 157
OPD Hours/Days, 8:00-3:30, Mon. through Fri.

A procedural problem related to record-keeping was described by Lincoln personnel as second only to the space problem in urgency. Lincoln has not yet converted to the unit record system because it is "too expensive to convert and no particular advantage is seen." The existing numbering system causes many problems. The patient gets a temporary number in the screening process in order to identify his X-ray and lab tests; he gets another number in X-ray, which is a permanent number in this department; if he is assigned to a clinic, he is given a "clinic number," which is good for one visit only. Each patient is filed by name, date, and day on every visit he makes to the OPD.

Inadequacy of space is a major problem in this OPD. Originally there were to be four floors for the clinics, but only two were built. (Even the elevator indicates four floors.) The basement of this building, which might be used to relieve crowding somewhat, has been taken over for another hospital function. A further source of discontent is that the building was supposedly designed for air-conditioning, but "it was never installed"; thus, there is inadequate insulation against heat. Summer conditions were reported as "the worst they could possibly have."

The space problem is worsened by an admissions problem. Policy is to accept every patient even if it means squeezing another bed in the corridors. However, Lincoln has an arrangement with Bronx Municipal to cover instances in which there is simply no more room and the patient is transportable. Plans for the patient's transfer are made on the telephone and a physician accompanies him in the ambulance.

The third problem of deepest concern at Lincoln is staffing. Though Lincoln's ER staff is reported to be adequate, the OPD situation was reported as "bad." This, it was explained, is because the OPD is still in the very early part of the affiliation program and the community session basis is relied upon primarily. They have, then, good physicians as well as many who are not board-certified or board-eligible. Prior to the affiliation, it was commented, "turn of the century" medical care was practiced. Two factors, however, make it difficult to change the situation as rapidly as they would like. First, because of the ever-increasing volume of patients, quality control of physicians is hard to maintain. Second, Lincoln

prefers not to dismiss these less-than-qualified
physicians when there is opportunity to help up-grade
them. To this end, the affiliation staff has initiated
a continuing education training program for all doctors. With private funds, they have enlarged the complement of full-time physicians, trained them, and
paid them while attending the training function. Their
hope is to put residents in each of the medical clinics and in each of the subspecialty clinics after
1 July 1967.

In further assistance to the medical staff,
private funds have been used to build and staff a
laboratory for the ER. Also, a large number of clerks
have been placed on "college lines," not only because
of the unavailability of city lines, but because
Lincoln would prefer to have them on college lines.
("You have no idea what it takes to fire someone on
the city payroll.")

Exemplifying the many improvements the affiliation
is trying to achieve at Lincoln is the improvement in
ambulatory service over the past several years. It
was stated that, "The revolution in the quality of
medical care is beyond anything that the public could
imagine. It's an overnight revolution--expensive, but
necessary--wrought not only to change incompetency to
acceptability, but far more. Medical care is better
at Lincoln than at many proprietary hospitals. World-
famous consultants are available here, something which
is rare in private hospitals."

There is a shortage of nurses at Lincoln, as at
all the hospitals. To compensate for this lack and to
relieve the present staff, Lincoln has supplemented
the R.N.'s in the OPD and ER with practical nurses,
nurses' aides, and specially trained bilingual aides.
"Some of the best nurses at Lincoln are in the emergency room," it was reported. Some OPD personnel feel
that not as many nurses are needed as is commonly
believed. Physicians in the clinics can use aides or
a secretary for some of their needs, it was commented.

Some of the "city" staff were interviewed separately and another set of problems was revealed. In
particular, discriminatory practices were reported:
city staff are paid less than the affiliate doctors;
the latter have air-conditioning in their offices,
and there is parking space provided for affiliate
residents but not for the city staff (primarily

attending physicians). As a consequence, doctors are
frequently forced to double-park. Apparently the
salary situation was approached once by proposing
supplementation for some of the city salaries, but,
reportedly, "Procaccino took all this away" (except
for the nurses). "The mayor should do something
about this salary problem," they said.

The community served by Lincoln was characterized
as "youthful." Its population is, historically, migratory. The Irish and Jews were there first, then
Negroes became dominant, and the Puerto Ricans followed.
Although most of the Irish and Jews have been pushed
out, a few are left. The new groups, being migratory,
leave "before they become old," hence the community
is unique by being an "acute medical population."
The proportion of young to old is different from other
general city hospitals. The largest clinic loads are
in gynecology and pediatrics. Lincoln does not en-
counter many strokes or coronaries. "People are
dreadfully ill or injured when they go to Lincoln,"
it was pointed out. Statistics show a small percentage
of elective admissions (which indicate the chronically
ill).

The distribution of population was reported as
approximately 60% Puerto Rican, 30% Negro, and 10%
Irish and Jewish. One physician said that a "really
basic problem" is New York City's attempt to assimilate
600,000 Puerto Ricans. "The minute they arrive at the
airport," he claimed, "they're told about Lincoln."
Lincoln, then, becomes a social problem center for them
and the hospital's task becomes more than narrowly
medical. "We should be teaching them, too," was the
common feeling expressed. Apparently the Health Department began a teaching program, but ran out of supporting funds.

To accommodate the Spanish-speaking community,
the affiliate hired a bilingual physician to screen
patients immediately upon their entrance in the ER
(i.e., directly after registration). This service is
offered 24 hours a day. As noted earlier, affiliation
money has also been used to train indigenous people
in clerical and aide work to supplement the work of
the bilingual physicians and assist as interpreters
to other doctors.

When opinions were asked about solutions to the
many problems of the city hospitals, the answer was,

"The city has turned its back on the hospitals. If
the colleges don't help now, there is no answer. The
city should turn their hospitals over to privately run
institutions. What they need is a 'hiring agency.'
There's so much red tape that you never get anything."

METROPOLITAN HOSPITAL

Plant and Services

Metropolitan has a bed complement of 1000 and the
average rate of occupancy has been approximately 86%.
The hospital opened in 1955, having been built from
plans drawn in 1940. A new psychiatric wing is under
construction.

The walls are tiled, the lobby is open and attractive, but the hospital is overcrowded and its 1940
design is not functional in terms of medicine in the
1960's. Parking is a problem. Grassed areas exist
on the grounds, but cannot be converted to parking
"for esthetic reasons."

Physicians

The New York Medical College provides a large part
of the medical staff and major difficulties result from
the complex administrative organization. Doctors are
responsible to the affiliate and not to the city hospital administrator. This produces confusion and
duplication for all concerned. The result is often
double equipment orders, the neglect of priorities,
and confusion. Other doctors are on sessions or are
on the city payroll. Session doctors "arrive late and
leave early," in the words of one chief of service.

Other Professional Services

Administrative personnel submit the following
problems in the area of nursing:

- Shortage of registered professional nurses on
  all wards.

- When a position becomes vacant, the hospital is
  not permitted to appoint anyone to the position
  for 30 days. This is very frustrating.

- The hospital has been requested to move
  practical nurses and nurses' aides out of
  registered-nurse line positions. Because
  of this, two jobs may be tied up for four to
  six weeks.

- New employees have to wait four weeks for
  their first paycheck. Registered nurses--
  with years of experience--are paid at the
  minimum rate and have to wait an undefined
  length of time for the monies allotted for
  steps I, II, and III (years-of-experience
  salary increments).

- There is no subsidized housing at Metropolitan
  Hospital, a large factor in hiring difficulties.

- At the present time, nursing personnel are
  performing housekeeping functions, dietary
  functions, clerical functions, and messenger
  functions--all of which interfere with the
  accomplishment of nursing activities.

- Shortages of linen supplies, such as work
  clothes, bath towels, pajamas, etc., make it
  extremely difficult for nursing personnel to
  meet patients' needs. This, in turn, creates
  "low morale" as employees face this constant
  problem on a daily basis (the problem inten-
  sifies on weekends, as there is no delivery
  of linen on Sunday). Since the majority of
  patients are medically indigent, they do not
  have the means to provide for their own
  toothbrushes, combs, and soap on admission.
  A very minimal supply is distributed to each
  ward.

- Shortages of stationery items hamper both
  clerical and medical functions--there are too
  few pencils, sharpeners, yellow pads, X-ray
  request cards, blood-test forms, etc.

Support Activities

Metropolitan Hospital has only one paid supervisor
for its 37 employees in the maintenance department.
Twenty-five of these people are semiskilled and work
under four skilled mechanics. If a skilled man is out,
that shop is not able to function (because of rules

that necessitate supervision). In addition, the skilled man cannot do his own work for all the supervising that he must do.

The need for flexibility is strongly expressed-- for example, the authority to call in local people for various small jobs. (Replacing part of a lighting fixture, it was claimed, costs $6.00 when done locally and $27.00 when done through the "normal city channels.") An example of excessive time and dollar waste was cited: A three-month contract was let to a number of contractors (in the usual manner) to install an air-conditioning system in a nursery. Twelve months have passed and the job is not yet completed. This reason was offered: There are no penalty clauses and the contractors do not feel any obligation to perform, or to conform to the agreements. They are said to use city contracts as "fill-in" work. "The minimal clauses that are in the contracts are not enforced. Since there is no prime contractor, there is no one responsible for the entire job. When it comes to the mess that accompanies such a job (i.e., plumbing, electrical, etc.), everyone blames someone else--no one will clean up." In this case (as in others), a separate, "extra" contract was let for the cleaning.

Affiliation

There are mixed feelings concerning the affiliation. Equipment is poorly utilized; the affiliate was said to have little knowledge or interest in the real needs of the hospital; too often it has its own interests in what is attempted. The present contract covers medical records, pathology, anaesthesiology and radiology. A large contract is pending.

Administration

Regarding administration, these attitudes were expressed:

- Control of hospital administration should rest with the municipal administrator.

- The administrator should be able to select qualified personnel to assist him.

- All plans for modification of services should be the result of conferences between the affiliate and the administrator.

- All monetary expenditures affecting the hospital within the budget allotment should be controlled by the administrator, with the proper advisement of the financial office. There should be local flexibility in disbursement.

- The affiliate should submit its reports to the municipal hospital administrator.

- The services of an architect are needed to plan with the hospital administrator for the best possible expansion of X-ray, laboratory, and medical record areas. Under the present circumstances, such plans would be drawn by the architect and, when completed and ready for implementation, would be shown to the administrator who would have no opportunity to change them.

Out-Patient and Emergency Room Services

OPD 1966 Census, 434,599
ER 1966 Census, 127,262
Home Care 1966 Census, 190
OPD Hours/Days, morning and afternoon,
                Mon. through Fri.

Metropolitan's OPD and ER are housed in relatively new buildings. However, closer inspection reveals that most of the other hospitals' problems are shared. The building was in the process of construction from 1940 through 1955 and was outdated by the time it was completed. It was designed for 200,000 patient visits per year, and there are now more than 500,000. In terms of the rule of thumb of one square foot per patient served, the 30,000 square feet of this OPD facility are markedly insufficient.

Reportedly, the OPD staff is not large enough to meet patient needs. However, the director pointed out, within the present space allocated they cannot handle any more personnel.

Uncoordinated planning between central and local staffs was observed to add to the fragmentation of services in this OPD. In the pediatric clinic, for example, it was reported that one day "a wall was put up" in the center of the clinic with no reason given. Personnel are now carrying on their work on both sides of the wall with considerable communication difficulty. The administrator in charge of this clinic predicted that ultimately the area on one side of the wall will be taken from her, and she does not know how she will continue to cope.

Crowding in the ER has added to its problems. For example, the three-sided examining rooms provide little enough privacy for patients, but the situation is made worse when waiting patients must sit in an area where they have a full view of patient examinations. Unless curtains are carefully drawn, patients being treated are not hidden from this "audience." (It was observed that lighting is better if the curtains are not pulled.)

Problems of the ambulance system were discussed with an administrator in the ER. There is a critical need, he reported, for more direct communication between the people who need and call the ambulance and the hospital to which they will be transported. The present system requires a call to the police, who determine the district in which the emergency problem exists and from which hospital an ambulance should be sent. The call is relayed to that hospital and, presumably, the ambulance (with a driver and attendant) is dispatched immediately. Examination of statistics reveals a number of "unanswered calls." Individual hospitals are held at fault for these "errors," but many, if not all, "unanswered" calls were never relayed to them. As "proof," Metropolitan keeps a log of all calls and can show that they were never directed to the "unanswered" cases.

A final problem reported at Metropolitan is similar to one found at Harlem. The correspondence division of the medical records department is not adequately staffed; correspondence is slipping further behind each day. The staff feels that they will never catch up. Equally disturbing to them is the condition of their typewriters. Because all their correspondence is directed to the public, they feel the letters should be neat. However, this is unachievable on the typewriters presently assigned them. Resolution of these problems requires at least two more typists, two more clerks, and new typewriters.

MORRISANIA HOSPITAL

Plant and Services

Morrisania is a 415-bed general hospital. With its ancillary buildings, including a former nurses' residence now adapted to other uses, it occupies a city block in the Bronx. Apartments and small businesses surround the hospital. A mixed population, largely Negro and Puerto Rican with some white, constitutes the community.

Physicians

All physicians at this hospital are provided by the affiliation contract with Montefiore Hospital.

Other Professional Services

Certain affiliation funds are allocated to recruit nurses, assist in their housing, and pay their salaries (the only instance in the city of nurses provided under affiliation funds--a very promising innovation). Of the 103 staff nurses presently at the hospital, 54 are on the affiliation payroll, 49 on civil service. The hospital needs 147 staff nurses, and has asked for 54 added lines in a new category to be called "assistant head nurse." Also needed are 46 head nurses. These numbers do not include supervisors.

Affiliation funds have been used to underwrite nurses' apartments near the George Washington bridge, seven minutes by bus from the hospital. When these apartments are rented, their cost to the city is $12 to $15 per nurse per month.

A recruiting brochure has been prepared by an organization of recruitment professionals. One full-time recruiter has been working for the affiliation. This excellent program has added nurses to the staff.

Pre-affiliation, there was only one night nurse-supervisor for the entire hospital. Now there are three (four, counting one per-diem nurse).

Support Activities

The hospital administrator states that supply problems are no longer chronic, but episodic. Nurses, on the other hand, complain chiefly about supply problems. They learn to live with peeling paint, according to the superintendent of nurses, but they are troubled by short supplies. There is too little linen. Deliveries from the laundry on Welfare Island arrive late in the day and may not return enough linen for one day's care. The nurses improvise by using spreads for sheets and by using incontinence pads with no bottom sheet. Storage space is inadequate. The superintendent of nurses believes that unused porches might be covered and used for storage.

Nurses make many trips to the pharmacy because space is inadequate for floor stocks. The hospital administrator has planning underway for the floor delivery of drugs on an automated order system.

Affiliation

Morrisania has two affiliation contracts. A contract with Montefiore Hospital covers physicians for all clinical activities, social services, laboratories, diagnostic and therapeutic radiology, a mental hygiene clinic and psychiatric consultation for in-patients, certain nursing services and the medical records. This contract cost $5,879,710 in 1966-1967. The amount proposed for 1967-1968 is $6,925,385. It was stated that Montefiore spent $28,000 of its own money to open a pediatric out-patient department.

A second contract with Bronx-Lebanon Hospital covers ambulatory care, including physicians, nurses, technicians, laboratory assistants, and other professional and administrative staff as necessary. This contract cost $363,000 in 1966-1967; $438,000 is proposed for 1967-1968.

What is left for the administrator to run, in his own words, is "the hotel."

Morrisania exhibits one of the closest interplays between hospital administrator and affiliation coordinator encountered in the survey. Their plans are laid in close cooperation; in the absence of one, the other assumes his tasks and responsibilities.

Administration

Three elements of the management processes within this hospital were noteworthy. First was the interplay of administrator and affiliation coordinator mentioned above. Second was the penchant for stretching rules in the interest of direct and reasonable action. Third was the effort, still in its early stages, to assemble meaningful cost and statistical data covering the hospital's operations; Morrisania offered the best cost documentation encountered in the course of the survey.

Out-Patient and Emergency Room Services

OPD 1966 Census, 162,857
ER 1966 Census, 123,359
Home Care 1966 Census, 136
OPD Hours/Days, 8:00-4:00, Mon. through Fri.
        Evening hours, Mon., Wed., Thurs.

The most salient problem observed here was that of inadequate space. In both the OPD and the ER, conditions were chaotic because of concentrated activity within small areas. Recently, the hospital tried to alleviate this problem by separating the pediatric OPD and ER from the adult facilities, whereupon, the pediatric OPD daily census leapt from 250 to 350 in five days (overcrowding the new quarters), and adult clinics continued to expand and overflow the space alloted to them. Maintenance is obviously difficult under such conditions, and the need for renovation was dramatic at this hospital.

The need for longer clinic hours is recognized, but a common problem was reported as inhibiting this solution: adequate staff cannot be induced to work in the evening hours. It was reported that this hospital has always had an excellent attending and teaching staff since its beginning in 1929. Interns have been attracted to Morrisania from all over the country. During World War II, however, there was a great shortage of doctors, and interns who were available chose to go to the university hospitals. Therefore, as have all the city hospitals since the war, Morrisania suffered from "chronic under-financing and under-staffing." There has been no alternative to hiring foreign-trained physicians, many of whom have been less than qualified.

The feeling at Morrisania is that the affiliation contracts offer the best solution to these problems. The hospital feels particularly fortunate that its contract with Montefiore covers nursing staff as well as physicians. This has made possible its well-known advertising campaign for nurses and other attractions for employment such as apartments at $65.00 a month. These tactics have proven successful, and the nursing problem at Morrisania is met more adequately than it is at any other city general hospital.

This, however, applies to the total hospital. Within the OPD and ER facilities, shortages exist primarily because space limitations do not permit a larger staff. In particular, the clerical shortage imposes serious burdens. In 1960, two clerks were assigned to handle a certain load of correspondence in the OPD administration. Seven years later these same two ladies are still trying to handle the greatly increased job.

The introduction of Medicare and Medicaid added to clerical loads. During a survey interview, the difficulties of filling out Medicare forms were demonstrated in actual practice; it was clear that the present clerical staff cannot perform the task without more help. The OPD director mentioned that there had been a slight drop in the OPD census, a phenomenon that he does not attribute to a decrease in actual patient visits, but to the "slipping through" of many patients without registration. The clerk's work load has become physically impossible to sustain, and the only expedient solution may be to send patients through the system without the specified forms (thus denying reimbursement to the city).

Interviews with the clinic and ER staffs revealed problems in requisitioning of vital supplies. For example, a linen shortage was reported that is forcing them to use paper sheeting on the examining tables.

The primary reason for these shortages, the administrator explained, is an unrealistic budget. Projected costs are based on expenditures of a year or two ago--the most recent figures available at the time the budget was compiled. Given the tremendous growth in patient visits during these same few years, the budget allocation is totally inadequate. As an example, the administrator pointed out that they had budgeted $320,000 for pharmacy in 1966-1967, but they spent $450,000. Citing this as a prime example of problems caused by centralized decision making, he said the big danger is "over-simplification. We know what we need, but the system continually negates it."

QUEENS HOSPITAL CENTER

Plant and Services

Queens Hospital Center has a total bed complement of 1,761 and has been averaging approximately 80% in occupancy rate. Admissions were slightly down from 1965, as was the average daily census. Ambulatory visits were up from 1965, as were almost all laboratory activities.

Physicians

The medical service is organized into two divisions, with two-thirds of the patients on the Long Island Jewish Division and the other third on the Mary Immaculate Division. There continues to be some voluntary staffing beyond affiliation levels, though the affiliation contracts are supposed to provide these services. Several satellite clinics have been organized, mostly at the initiation of the affiliate.

Other Professional Services

Only 184 of 487 nursing positions are filled by R.N.'s. Though in dire need of nurses, Queens counts itself fortunate in having the nursing school students available. This also allows them a first opportunity to recruit new nurses from the graduating classes.

A major problem here is that Queens must offer some
incentive for nurses to work in a hospital far from
their homes.

Laboratories present an equally serious problem.
They are critically short of space and equipment.

Support Activities

Currently, the most vexing problem that confronts
Queens Hospital Center, according to the administrator,
is the retention and recruitment of housekeeping
personnel. Noncompetitive salaries seem to be the
major difficulty, magnified by a tightening market in
this field. The supply of linen is not sufficient
for patient needs, especially on weekends.

Affiliation

Under the affiliation program, medical care responsibility was developed for city cases in two nursing
homes totaling 400 beds. Several satellite clinics
have been organized. Basically, the affiliation has
brought a stabilized staffing program to Queens. The
affiliation programs are these:

Long Island Jewish Hospital:	Laboratories, home care, medical records, all clinical services except psychiatry, two nursing units in medicine, and certain medical clinics in the OPD.	$9,120,000
Mary Immaculate:	Clinical services for two nursing units in medicine and certain medical clinics in the OPD.	732,400
Hillside:	Physicians for psychiatric services.	830,000

Administration

The administrator feels that he could have done
as well in meeting the problems of the hospital if
he had been directly given the money with which to

work and the freedom to spend it. He expresses a
sincere dedication to the municipal system, as well
as deep frustration and unhappiness that the situation
has deteriorated as it has.

Out-Patient and Emergency Room Services

OPD 1966 Census, 173,897
ER 1966 Census, 84,503
Home Care 1966 Census, 204
OPD Hours/Days, 8:00-4:00, Mon. through Fri.

In OPD and ER the usual problems were observed:
crowded corridors full of waiting patients and rushing
staff; reports of inadequate personnel, space, and
equipment; problems with maintenance; and complex,
ill-conceived arrangements (such as an archaic telephone system in the registration area).

The director is disturbed about the "stockyard
operation" of the OPD, difficulty in destroying the
image of the unlamented "charity" hospital, and the
rising problems of fragmented service. To counter
these trends, he has worked out a system for comprehensive care on a continuing basis. In essence, his
plan for "core" medical and surgical clinics represents
an effort to relate physical design to organization and
function. He pointed out that the core of the hospital
is medicine, yet the medical section has no permanent
location at Queens. Although he has proposed very
simple and inexpensive changes, he stated that he has
encountered "enormous difficulties--almost unbelievable"
in the implementation of these plans. "To put it
through the city," he said, "is almost an insurmountable problem. It would take two-and-a-half years on
a crash program." Unhampered by red tape, he maintained, a few people could go into the building and
take care of changes "overnight." He was told when
he assumed his job that he could make any changes he
wished, and that he would have the money to make them.
Now, he reports, he cannot make even "utterly essential
changes."

In addition to the thwarting of reorganization
plans for the Queens clinic, three other kinds of
problems were noted:

1) The clinic will soon be the recipient of a
federal grant for a fully qualified gynecologist to

perform pelvic examinations--a necessary service
for preventive medicine. It has been estimated that
6000 to 8000 patients will be examined in the first
year alone. Yet no money or plan is forthcoming to
provide space or essential facilities for this activity. Within the present physical setup, there is no
room for it.

2) The rehabilitation building has no ramp, but
a large number of the patients are severely disabled
children. It is necessary, then, to carry these patients up the staircase. Since there are no porters,
the task remains for the over-worked nurses and doctors. A memorandum describing the situation is two
years old, the problem itself has been urgent much
longer than that, but the necessary ramp has been
denied because (it is said) the building is obsolete
and does not warrant renovation.

3) It was reported that the obstetrics department has a medical consultation one day a week during
which X-rays are examined. For years they have been
requesting a viewing box; at present examinations have
had to be made by holding the films up to the light.
Their request has never been responded to. (One of
the doctors, however, managed to "borrow" a portable
viewing box.)

When asked to suggest changes that might improve
the delivery of personal health services in the city
hospitals, one director said, "I'd get the city out
of the hospital business. In some way they ought to
be able to unload this thing." He doesn't think the
voluntary hospitals want to own city hospitals, however. "The best solution is a quasi-official organization like the New York Port Authority. That is,
something that is of but not in the city--with a
centralized board of trustees and perhaps also centralized advisory groups of technical specialists with no
authority. Then decentralize.

"Set up a voluntary board of trustees for each
hospital and let them operate. They would have to be
fiscally accountable to the state and to the people,"
he added, "but they would operate with state and
federal allocations on decentralized budgets.

"There should be a regional planning division in
which we would all be participants. I hope we won't
be too frustrated in another year or two, and want to

throw in the sponge. Twenty years ago city hospitals
were much better, though they were never any great
shakes. Then came along research, and clinical
teaching went to pot."

The community contains a heterogeneous population,
and is not situated in the middle of slums. There are
many economic levels, including wealthy and poor
Negroes and wealthy and poor whites.

SEA VIEW HOSPITAL AND HOME

Plant and Services

Sea View Hospital and Home consists of 92 buildings scattered over 300 acres near the center of
Staten Island. The hospital opened in 1912 for T.B.
care, its nucleus eight 4-story pavilions, its total
capacity over 2000 patients, Eight miles of concrete
road (much of it in bad repair) connect the buildings.
Only a dozen or so buildings are still in active use.
The beds number over a thousand:

Hospital

Two (of eight) pavilions and a geriatrics building (1935)	244
Isolation building, serving all Staten Island for T.B. and communicable diseases	34
Total	278

Home

Six nursing home buildings	558
Custodial section for home-less aged	228
Total	1,064

The "home" section opened in 1908 as "Farm Colony."
In July 1961, the hospital (no longer devoted to T.B.)
and the home were combined under one administration.

While plans are 80% complete for a new extended care building, it is believed that construction will not take place.

There is a geriatric facility. Its occupancy rate in 1966 was 85.2%. Patients come here only when their relatives cannot handle them. Twelve patients were admitted the day prior to this survey visit; none could care for himself. The patients here are senile, incontinent, incapacitated. Only about 5% of the patients are ever discharged. There is no out-patient or home care. The hospital does offer a full range of in-patient clinics.

The condition of the physical plant--the scarcity of elevators, the distances between buildings--are major handicaps in delivering good patient care. But the patients, according to the administrator, love Sea View, atop its wooded hill.

Physicians

There is no affiliation contract here. Two pathologists and two radiologists are on city pay. Some 20 other services are manned by 150 to 160 physicians on session pay. Each physician serves one day in seven, visiting the hospital that day and serving on call for 24 hours. He has a "ward of basic responsibility," where he sees to record-updating, annual examinations, and intensive care of a limited number of patients. Under this arrangement, continuity of care comes hard. No night physician is on the grounds.

The administrator cited three factors basic to holding this staff: enthusiasm and dreams of a better place; the fact that this is a selected and well-motivated staff; and the belief that care of the aged is a coming endeavor. He would like to combine some resident job lines, now unfilled, to provide salary for some night physicians.

Other Professional Services

Many of the "T.B. nurses" are still here. Of 200 nurse lines, 90 are filled. The physical therapy department is training its own aides. Salaries appear to be the main problem in recruiting nurses, technicians, speech therapists, and social workers.

Support Services

Laboratories and radiology are in buildings separate from patients. An X-ray examination may require the services of eight people at various places to move one infirm patient from bed to car to laboratory to car and back to bed.

Equipment comes slowly. Four hundred hi-lo beds were requested "years ago." Eighty have arrived via the annual budgets. Word that 45 more were in transit came in June 1967.

Affiliation

As noted, there is no affiliation here. St. Vincent's Hospital (Staten Island) accepted a $35,000 study contract to examine Sea View in terms of possible affiliation. The staff at Sea View are somewhat resistant to this possibility.

Administration

Everything here is patchwork. Great effort is required just to slow the pace at which one loses ground. The decaying plant, the distances, the many empty buildings--one can almost forget that there are patients here. Potentially, however, the Sea View site is one of the most valuable and useful to the future health system of the city.

SYDENHAM HOSPITAL

Plant and Services

Sydenham is a small 218-bed hospital located only a mile and a half from Harlem Hospital. The average daily census in 1966 was 149, with an average of 17 admissions per day. Per cent of occupancy was 67% for the year. The building is in need of maintenance, and there are persistent, serious problems with broken water mains. Like Sea View, it has no contractual affiliation.

Sydenham was acquired by the city in 1949, when the former voluntary found that it could not sustain

itself. In an attempt to protect the practice of the
community physician, the city agreed to maintain a
private facility on the premises. Thus Sydenham has
two distinctions: 1) its proximity to another and
larger municipal hospital; and 2) its unique character
as the only municipal hospital with private and semi-
private facilities.

The latter circumstance requires some explanation:
Physicians with private practice can admit their
patients to the hospital and provide for their care,
the patient making his own arrangement for payment
with the doctor. The hospital charges the patient
for his stay, and the revenue from this enterprise
amounts to approximately $400,000 per year. This
money is surrendered to the general fund of the city
from which no return to the hospital is made.

Space is a major problem here; there is virtually
no room for expansion in the present site. Alternating
current source is inadequate and there is no emergency
generator. The Joint Commission on Hospital Accreditation granted Sydenham conditional accreditation,
outlining the following conditions for full
accreditation.

Alter and renovate:	Laboratory area
	Kitchen and dietary area
	Maternity suite
	Medical records department
	Operating suite
In addition, provide:	New X-ray equipment
	Emergency generator
	Adequate AC

Physicians

Since Sydenham is not affiliated, the medical
staff is on city payroll. There are also physicians
on session pay. The chiefs of service complain of
inadequate numbers of doctors; this, in turn, is
related to its accreditation problems. Patients are
sent to Harlem Hospital when that is deemed advisable.
Sydenham relies on other hospitals for ambulance
service, having none of its own.

Other Professional Services

There is a severe nursing shortage at Sydenham, particularly on the night shifts. The neighborhood does not lend itself to safe travel and, with other fringe benefits absent, this hospital has a great problem in attracting nursing personnel. As mentioned, laboratory and equipment shortages are extensive.

Affiliation

Although there is no centractually funded affiliation, Sydenham has made arrangements with other institutions for help. Sometimes they borrow equipment; in some cases they have initiated agreements to send patients (to Harlem) and receive patients (from Towers, Mayflower, and College View Nursing Homes).

Administration

Sydenham has been neglected for a number of years and, in some important ways, continues to be neglected. Renovation costs have been estimated at over $3 million. Sydenham's administration evidences most of the basic problems noted in other city hospitals.

CHAPTER **5** SPECIAL TOPICS: THE
MUNICIPAL AND OTHER
HEALTH CARE AND HOSPITAL
SYSTEMS

STATUS OF MEDICAL RECORD FUNCTIONS: MUNICIPAL HOSPITALS

Investigation was made of the medical records departments of five municipal hospitals (Bellevue, Elmhurst General, Harlem, Queens General, and Metropolitan), and at Downstate Medical Center. Interviews were held with the records librarians, and a facilities inspection was conducted at each institution.

1) Functions of the Medical Records Area as a System. The medical records functions at municipal hospitals include: (a) checking, assignment, and dissemination of patient identification numbers for use in controlling patient care throughout the hospital; (b) collecting individual forms and reports, filing on a unit record basis and returning the unit record; (c) statistical summaries of hospital, patient, and health care events and activities; (d) statistical analyses and data collection in support of various medical research projects; (e) information and fact retrieval in support of medical billing and insurance functions; (f) information and records retrieval for various investigatory, legal, and administrative personnel; (g) correspondence such as employment, health, and hospital release certifications; and (h) typing, transcription, and distribution of narrative medical summaries of patient diagnosis and treatment.

2) Characteristics of the Processes Performed. The processes performed to meet the characteristics of the functions cited above, it was found, can be presented in terms of the type of activity, the skill level involved, the time to perform the process, the cyclic nature of the process, the deterministic or nondeterministic sequence of events, the number of

people involved, the inputs to the process, the outputs from the process, the ability to change the process, etc.

3) Characteristics of the Information Transfer and Communication Links. Here, the parameters involved were found to be related to the media used to transfer information--such as the unit record, a phone call, a letter, or a transcription tape. In each case, the duration, distance, volume, source, and destination become meaningful characteristics.

4) Characteristics of the Information Storage and Filing Media. The parameters involved herein were found to emphasize space, type of storage, accessibility of files, volume, etc.

In each of these areas, an attempt was also made to visualize the impact of automated data processing equipment upon the specific problem areas cited in the interviews. However, as will be shown by later examples, it soon became apparent that examination from the viewpoint of a systematic approach to data collection highlighted the lack of an underlying system concept for planning, monitoring, and controlling the evolution and change of the medical records tasks. Furthermore, it became increasingly apparent that system development of the medical records departments could not be accomplished as a narrow, independent program. To accomplish this, it would be necessary to integrate the vital information flow, information storage, retrieval, presentation and information processing tasks of these departments in relationship (1) to the rest of the administrative and medical areas within the hospitals, (2) to the centralized budgetary, fiscal, procurement, data, and logistics management processes, and (3) to the community.

Individual Institutions

A brief summary follows of the implications of this investigation for each institution surveyed.

Bellevue offers a typical example of a records room with massive and voluminous files that reach from floor to ceiling in row after row. Space is a major problem. Furthermore, as in most of the municipal hospitals, accessibility to the files is extremely awkward, as a person must alternately stoop

and stretch from floor level to 10-foot ceiling level
to retrieve files.

Information concerning hospital statistics at
Bellevue was extremely limited, and in some instances
nonexistent. Similarly, performance information concerning the records room was not available. For example, no information was available on the average
time to access a file, or the average number of times
a file is accessed in a year, or on the volume of
information in a record.

Generally, it was felt that because of the every-
day volume of tasks, a personnel problem has developed.
Aides were doing clerical jobs.

Bellevue is in a unique state, of the hospitals
visited, in that a five-year project is underway with
adequate resources to investigate ways and means of
applying automatic data processing (ADP) capabilities
to the medical records functions. ADP equipment is
being installed on an exploratory basis. Programs are
planned to:

1. Perform scheduling and control functions
associated with the appointment system;

2. Retrieve and check patient identification
numbers;

3. Perform the medical narrative analysis on a
key word basis;

4. Summarize such diagnosis and patient population data as age, sex, etc.

Bellevue is in a state of transition in the medical
records area. The development of ADP potentials has,
to some degree, forced the medical records functions
to be first organized, then systematized. The initial
system logic, in a manual mode, is being worked on at
this time. Effort is being expended in forms control,
transmissions, communication links, error detection,
and conversion of medical summaries from voice to
typewriter using MTS typewriter and typing pool. A
remote tie-in between Metropolitan, Cumberland, and
Bellevue hospitals is under discussion.

Organizational, personnel, and equipment problems
were cited in discussions at Elmhurst General.

The need for a centralized records system standardized for all municipal hospitals was mentioned. It would be one way for the records librarian staff to "fight back against the medical staff's demands for information." These requests may be inconsistent, redundant, or seem to be meaningless and yet, regardless of effort required, must be complied with immediately. "A medical prima donna feeling doesn't help achieve the personal motivation factor inherent in high performance output," according to an interviewee. Intra-hospital organization lines of authority do not allow for effective personnel relationships on a team basis. This lack of teamwork was said to be characteristic of the city-wide system. In the entire tenure of one records employee at Elmhurst, no member of the city administration had visited or been in direct contact with the staff.

Morale is extremely low and said to be aggravated by the difference between city and other benefits for personnel doing the same job. Personnel resentments between the groups was regarded as a major problem.

Equipment problems were generally associated with delays in obtaining anything from a Xerox machine to paper clips. Space problems could be resolved to some extent by the use of ADP equipment. However, it was felt that only 25 per cent of the 60-person staff would be useful or retrainable for an ADP (or advanced) system.

These additional recommendations or comments were offered:

1. Microfilming should be done after three years.

2. Billing should be integrated into the records function, as pulling of the files is not always adequate. (Some records involving lab tests require six weeks to be completed.)

3. Records must be returned or "stolen back" each night.

4. Approximately 1,200 records are retrieved each day.

5. A three-shift operation is used--the second shift for filing and the third shift for retrieving the scheduled records for the next day.

6.   Phone links are better than in most municipal hospitals but a 30-foot walk from the files to
the phone is still required.

At Harlem Hospital, medical librarians are being
used to expedite the acquisition of desks, lights,
fans, space, coolers, etc. to prevent dirt and construction debris from falling into records and to
protect the records from being lost, torn, or otherwise mishandled. The jack-of-all-trades nature of
the job, is evident as the basic factor in the work
of this department. "Make do with supplies and people" was said to be the order of the day for a medical librarian directing an information center in a
municipal hospital.

Personnel problems were cited. Generally, it
was felt that the better medical records librarians
were receiving their training at the municipal hospitals and then leaving for better jobs. No incentive
was available to keep trained personnel. Concurrently,
the affiliation contract has resulted in an expansion
of the size of the staff from 23 to 60 people. The
result has been a staff characterized by inexperience,
capable but not necessarily efficient, and suffering
from poor working circumstances.

Some areas for improvement were suggested by
those interviewed:

1.   Develop in-service training programs and
maintain incentives.

2.   Standardize forms and prohibit various departments from using their own versions.

3.   Microfilm records as early as possible.

4.   Provide central storage for older records
and improve control and retrieval capability.

At Metropolitan Hospital, the major problem cited
was space. (Active records number 400,000, with 1,500
to 2,000 records being retrieved daily.) Access is so
limited that any accident, such as collapse of a file
cabinet or a small fire, would endanger personnel.
Access to most file corridors is possible at one end
only and they are extremely narrow. Files are kept
on windows and on desks, as there just isn't any
other available space. Personnel available through

affiliation cannot be effectively used because of lack of space for their physical movement, for desks, typewriters, and tables. Examples of equipment problems are:

1. Microfilm equipment is urgently required but even if it were made available, there would not be sufficient space for it. (A centralized city service in this area would be very helpful.)

2. Covers for folders were of such poor quality that frequent mending was required.

3. No water coolers were available for the staff working in the records room. Jars with ice were kept in the windows, competing with files for space.

4. A replacement fan for a minimum circulation of air was not forthcoming after considerable delay.

Personnel problems are also very important:

1. Medical records librarians are scarce; registered personnel are almost impossible to obtain. The starting salary of $4,750 is considered to be one of the lowest for any professional category.

2. Morale would be enhanced if the function were given some glamour such as calling it "information center" instead of "records room." (This department should not be a basement activity.)

Performance problems are these:

1. Four messengers are required to carry records for OPD to the record room, a distance of approximately one-half mile.

2. A basic patient identification problem exists, namely, "How do you differentiate the medical records of 1000 'Jose Rodriguezes' who can be expected to move frequently within the same region?"

3. A five-year backlog of indexing exists.

4. Reproduction requires a folder separation. Staples must be pulled. Errors, lost records, and pilfering are encouraged by this procedure.

Some improvements are taking place although major efforts are required. A dictating system was under

installation so that all narrative information may
be dictated and typed. The resident physician will
provide a checking function and then sign each insert
to the record.

At Queens General, a major reorganization is
required in order to improve the functioning of the
medical records department, according to persons
interviewed. The records staff is not able to plan
effectively, it is not able to be responsive, and
its performance is worsening. Some specific examples
are these:

1. The entire unit record concept for maintaining patient data is confused. It is a "unit" in name
only, as it cannot keep up with multiple inputs and
multiple outputs of information. The system must
accommodate itself by such strange means as having
a patient make separate visits to two clinics because
the records cannot be transferred from one to another
within the same day. Furthermore, as satellite
centers are developed, it will be impossible to copy
the unit record and maintain it at both locations.

2. The phone lines between the department and
the rest of the hospital are limited to two extensions. Considering the role of information in every
department, it is no wonder that serious delays occur.
As delays become excessive, various actions are taken
without necessary records information, producing
errors and more delay. For example, patients may be
assigned new identification numbers because a phone
line is busy.

3. The distance from the records room personnel
to the files in the basement is 100 yards and one
floor level. No intercom exists.

4. The files were moved to the basement on a
crash basis as workmen started to build a wall divid-
ing the room. No advance notice existed for the move.
The relocation was to a basement area with no lights,
ventilation, windows, or adequate shelving. At the
time of this survey, a bare minimum level of lighting
existed and most records were on shelves. It was
said that candles were used to retrieve files during
the interim. The stench anticipated during the summer
from sewer drain was already producing concern.
Debris and miscellaneous material awaited removal.

5. One of the main functions of the records librarian was to act as a construction engineer.

No guidelines for over-all improvement or direction were apparent. Questions as to the role of microfilm, ADP, etc., did not seem to have any clear answers. Planning seemed nonexistent.

Downstate Medical Center was visited because of its progressive approach to computer-based innovation.

Extensive ADP support is used at this state hospital to perform many of the laborious checking functions associated with medical records. Computer capabilities exist to (1) check patient identification numbers from the admissions areas, (2) update medical data from charts in the ward, (3) schedule appointments, (4) store patient data, (5) schedule and check prescriptions, and (6) perform research functions.

A foundation of information, based on a system concept of a central computer record with auxiliary processing, is being developed. Problems--such as difficulty in using the social security number as the controlling identifier for the patient--are being worked out. Attempts are being made to achieve a faster response time for new social security numbers between the medical center and the Social Security Administration. Matters of children's control numbers, errors, and lost numbers are all being systematically worked on.

It should be noted that the administrative needs, and the use of ADP support, observed at Downstate are not necessarily comparable with those of the city hospitals, nor is it implied that their ADP approach constitutes the best system or one that would necessarily work in a municipal hospital. The respective functions, objectives, and health care environments vary. Nonetheless, the ADP system underway at Downstate provides an important local example of what can be done for medical records administrations with computer-based innovation.

Findings and Recommendations

At present, medical records information flow in the municipal hospital is laborious, time-consuming, repetitive, fraught with potential for errors,

restrictive in growth, and expensive--for the medical
records staff, the medical staff, the hospital, and
the patient. Efficient health care delivery in many
ways depends upon accurate information that is easily
collectable and accessible, responsive in time, selective in content for various users, cost/effective, and
controllable in the light of changing medical and
hospital needs. These objectives cannot be met by
adding more personnel, space, etc., if applied merely
to an extension of present-day practices. These practices are inherently inefficient.

Today, vastly improved capabilities are a practical, obtainable reality at the present time for
ADP-supported information handling. However, both
information control and data management must be integrated into a city-wide system to attain the benefits
of:

- relieving the workload and paperwork burden
  on the medical, hospital, and records staffs;

- improving the information availability, accuracy and usefulness of each of the various
  levels of use;

- decreasing the patient time at, and number of
  visits to, municipal hospitals through information control;

- increasing the timeliness of information;

- providing information capabilities to planned
  satellite and community health centers;

- supporting information needs of research and
  public accountability functions.

Certain key problems leap to the eye as appropriate choices for a first application of the power
of automated information handling. Three such probable first-choices are noteworthy.

It is recommended that plans be developed for a
city-wide medical information system as part of an
over-all integrated reorganization of health care
delivery. Called for would be continuity of information system characteristics city-wide. (The larger
system proposal is presented in conceptual form in Part
Three.) Decentralized control of daily operations

would be provided in one mode of operation and yet
regional and city information needs would be available in another mode based upon preplanning, scheduling, and concurrence. This design would require
and assure standardization of reports, formats, file
structure, programs, and equipment across the participating institutions.

Determination would need to be made of the best
basis of a city-wide patient identification system.
Several approaches are conceivable, but the most
likely is the use of the Social Security number as
the patient identification number. However, several
actions would need to be taken prior to the establishment of this approach:

- Agreements with the Social Security Administration to furnish ID numbers on a real-time
  basis for persons not having them (approximately one minute).

- Agreements with the Social Security Administration to furnish ID numbers on a real-time
  basis for children at birth.

- Agreements with the Social Security Administration on performing checks on a real-time
  basis for persons forgetting or losing their
  Social Security numbers.

An ADP-supported system implies that the master
record would be in the computer. All inputs would be
directly inserted via remote stations. Legally, the
physician's signature is required on various medical
documents to certify actions taken and to afford validation checks. Frequently, the law is influenced by
what is practical and expedient. For example, a signature is sometimes accepted under the law in the
forms of stamping, printing, or typewriting, in recognition of the business practice of "signing" letters
and other instruments by mechanical means. Provisions
should be made to ascertain what and how signature
requirements can be met for this application of a
digital information system. Security provisions can
be achieved for inputs to medical records by individual code number or ID card for each valid user of the
system.

The larger significance of medical records processing specifically--and medical management information flow generally--will be brought into more meaningful context in Part Three.

AFFILIATION CONTRACTING

During the course of the Commission's inquiry,
a special subcommittee of the Medical Advisory Group
was requested to provide a position paper regarding
affiliation contracting. The subcommittee members
were George Baehr, M.D., Henry L. Barnett, M.D., and
E. Hugh Luckey, M.D. The following introduction to
the topic of affiliation contracting is taken from
that excellent paper.

The city's affiliation contracts with voluntary
teaching hospitals for the professional staffing of
municipal hospitals were recommended five years ago
by a study commission appointed by Mayor Wagner, and
the recommendation was subsequently carried out by
Commissioner Ray Trussell during that administration.
In almost all instances, the affiliations have been
successful in raising the professional standards of
the city's hospitals through the employment of competent full-time and part-time professional personnel
operating under the supervision of chairmen of the
various clinical and laboratory divisions of teaching
hospitals. Those municipal hospitals which were
affiliated with strong voluntary institutions have
become teaching hospitals and, as a result, have been
able to recruit increasing numbers of interns by the
intern-matching plan and have significantly increased
the number and quality of residents in residencies
approved by the American Medical Association.

Although firm criteria are lacking for assessing
improvement in the effectiveness of health care as a
result of the affiliations, it is appreciated that a
modest increase in the size or improvement in the
professional training of the hospital staff does not
in itself insure improved services. However, as
happened at Lincoln Hospital between 1958 and 1967,
when the staffing of a pediatric service containing
80 in-patient beds and a very large ambulatory service
was increased from a house staff of 2 foreign-trained
interns and 3 part-time attendings to a house staff
of 25 interns and residents including 10 university
faculty members and an additional staff of 25 attending and consultant pediatricians, there can be little
question concerning the improvement in medical care.
Striking improvement in staffing at all professional
levels also followed the affiliation of Morrisania
Hospital in 1962, Greenpoint Hospital in 1962, City
Hospital at Elmhurst in 1964, and Harlem Hospital.

Although the quality of in-hospital patient care depends largely upon the quality and adequacy of the house staff and the time devoted to their supervisory duties by a well-qualified attending staff, it also depends upon the availability of up-to-date clinical, laboratory, and X-ray equipment and upon an adequate staff of nurses and ancillary personnel. In many of the city hospitals replacement of obsolete equipment has been long delayed by red tape and, when equipment has been acquired, delays in installation have been frustrating. Nurses are still in gravely short supply. As a result, the full benefits of the affiliations have not as yet been achieved.

In a few instances, affiliation contracts were made with relatively weaker voluntary hospitals because the number of strong voluntary hospitals with superior standards and full-time professional leadership had been exhausted. In such instances, the benefits of affiliation have been less than satisfactory. These should be critically reexamined.

The funds available under the contracts may have materially benefited the small voluntary hospitals professionally, and this has tended to improve the care of city-pay patients hospitalized in the parent institution, although this was not the primary purpose of the affiliation. The strong voluntary hospitals have benefited less in this way, although the affiliations have provided them with additional opportunities for good clinical teaching of medical students, residents, attending staff, and neighborhood physicians, as well as additional full-time clinical and laboratory professionals required for this purpose.

Scope of Affiliation Contracting

The annual contractual value of affiliation services has grown explosively since the early period, from 1958 to 1961 (see Tables 5 and 6). Hospital Department records show these gross annual budgets:

FY 1961/62	$ 2,530,580
FY 1962/63	11,024,516
FY 1963/64	16,403,371
FY 1964/65	37,662,688
FY 1965/66	57,731,355
FY 1966/67	76,230,788
FY 1967/68 (est.)	96,890,290

Table 5. Contracts Anticipated by Dept. of Hospitals
at Close of FY 66/67

Hospital	Affiliate	Service	Effective Date	Expiration Date
Bellevue	Columbia University	Chest & Medicine	7/1/67	6/30/68
Bellevue	New York University	Medical Records	4/1/65	6/30/68
Bellevue	New York University	Pathology	7/1/67	6/30/70
Bellevue	New York University	Radiology	7/1/66	6/30/69
Bellevue	New York University	Psychiatry	10/1/66	6/30/69
Bronx Municipal	Yeshiva University	Anaesthesiology, Laboratories, Radiology	7/1/64	6/30/74
Bronx Municipal	Yeshiva University	Home Care	10/1/66	6/30/74
Bird S. Coler	New York Med. Coll.	Professional	7/1/67	6/30/70
Coney Island	Maimonides Hospital	Professional	7/1/67	6/30/70
Coney Island	Maimonides Hospital	Psychiatric	7/1/67	6/30/70
Cumberland	Brooklyn Hospital	Professional	7/1/66	6/30/69
Francis Delafield	Columbia University	Anaesthesiology	7/1/65	6/30/68
Francis Delafield	Columbia University	Laboratories	7/1/66	6/30/69
Francis Delafield	Columbia University	Diagnostic Radiology	7/1/65	6/30/68
Francis Delafield	Columbia University	Radiation Therapy	7/1/65	6/30/68
Elmhurst	Mt. Sinai Hospital	Professional	7/1/67	6/30/70
Elmhurst	Mt. Sinai Hospital	Psychiatry	7/1/67	6/30/70
James Ewing	Memorial Hospital	Professional	7/1/65	6/30/68

(Continued)

Table 5 (Continued)

Hospital	Affiliate	Service	Effective Date	Expiration Date
Fordham	Misericordia Hosp.	Professional	7/1/67	6/30/70
Goldwater	New York University	Professional	6/29/65	6/30/68
Gouverneur	Beth-Israel Hosp.	Ambulatory Unit	12/1/64	11/30/67
Greenpoint	Brooklyn Jewish	Professional	7/1/67	6/30/70
Harlem	Columbia University	Professional	7/1/67	6/30/70
Harlem	Columbia University	Psychiatry	7/1/65	6/30/68
Kings County	Downstate Med. Center	Pediatrics	2/1/67	6/30/68
Kings County	Downstate Med. Center	Child Psychiatry	1/1/66	6/30/68
Lincoln	Yeshiva University	Professional	7/1/66	6/30/69
Lincoln	Yeshiva University	Psychiatry	7/1/66	6/30/69
Metropolitan	New York Med. Coll.	Professional	7/1/66	6/30/69
Morrisania	Bronx-Lebanon Hosp.	Ambulatory Unit	7/1/66	6/30/69
Morrisania	Montefiore Hospital	Professionals & Nurses	7/1/65	6/30/68
Queens	Hillside Hospital	Psychiatry	7/1/67	6/30/70
Queens	Long Island Jewish	Professional	7/1/67	6/30/68
Queens	Mary Immaculate	Medical	7/1/67	6/30/68

304

Table 6. History of Annual Expenditure,
Dept. of Hospitals, Contractual Services

Code	Title	1966-67 Budget as Modified	1967-68 Budget Request	Increase or *Decrease
68-477	Special Clinical Services	$76,230,788.00	$96,890,290.00	$20,659,502.00

To provide funds for the following contracts:

Institution	Affiliation	Service	Contract Amount 1967-68
*Association for Homemaker Service, Inc.			
Bellevue	N.Y.U.	Medical Records	$ 60,000.00
Bellevue	N.Y.U.	Psychiatric	393,546.00
Bellevue	N.Y.U.	Radiology	4,160,006.00
Beth Israel - Man. General		Narcotics	1,665,000.00
Bronx Municipal	Yeshiva	Home Care	1,000,000.00
Bronx Municipal	Yeshiva	Laboratories	537,500.00
*City	Mt. Sinai	Medical	2,000,000.00
*City	Mt. Sinai	Psychiatric	9,990,000.00
*Coler	N.Y. Med. College	Professional	1,130,996.00
*Community Blood Council			2,236,000.00
*Coney Island	Maimonides	Medical	62,500.00
*Coney Island	Maimonides	Psychiatric	5,016,000.00
Cumberland	Brooklyn	Professional	800,000.00
Delafield	Columbia	Anaesthesiology	4,569,000.00
Delafield	Columbia	Diagnostic & Radiology	105,397.00
Delafield	Columbia	Radiation Therapy	329,214.00
Ewing	Memorial	Professional	251,284.00
			3,465,000.00

(Continued)

305

Table 6 (Continued)

Institution	Affiliation	Service	Contract Amount 1967-68
*Fordham	Misericordia	Medical	$ 3,500,000.00
Goldwater	N.Y.U.	Professional	4,640,000.00
*Gouverneur	Beth Israel	Amb. Care	1,683,046.00
*Greenpoint	Brooklyn-Jewish	Professional	3,200,000.00
Harlem	Columbia	Anaesthesiology	781,200.00
Harlem	Columbia	Medicine	3,145,000.00
Harlem	Columbia	Obs. - Gyn.	973,482.00
*Harlem	Columbia	Pathology	660,000.00
Harlem	Columbia	Pediatrics	782,000.00
Harlem	Columbia	Psychiatry	783,100.00
*Harlem	Columbia	Diagnostic Radiology	600,000.00
*Harlem	Columbia	Surgery	2,117,500.00
Kings County	Downstate Medical	Child Psychiatry	1,387,716.00
Lincoln	Yeshiva	Medical	5,691,750.00
Lincoln	Yeshiva	Psychiatric	980,580.00
*Metropolitan	N.Y. Med. College	Professional	1,500,000.00
Morrisania	Bronx-Lebanon	Amb. Care	438,000.00
Morrisania	Montefiore	Medical & Soc. Serv.	6,925,385.00
*Queens General	Hillside	Psychiatry	830,000.00
*Queens General	Long Island Jewish	Medical Services	9,120,000.00
*Queens General	Mary Immaculate	Medical Services	732,400.00
*Increase - Estimated Renewals			8,647,688.00
			$96,890,290.00

Code	Title	1965-66 Budget as Modified	1966-67 Budget Request	Increase or *Decrease
68-477	Special Clinical Services	$57,731,355.00	$74,296,129.00	$16,564,774.00

To provide funds for the following contracts:

Institution	Affiliation	Service	Contract Amount 1966-67
*Association for Homemaker Services Inc.,	N.Y.U.		$ 50,000.00
Bellevue		Medical Records	366,102.00
Beth Israel		Narcotics	1,000,000.00
Bronx Municipal	Yeshiva	Laboratories	2,000,000.00
City	Mt. Sinai	Medical	9,990,000.00
City	Mt. Sinai	Psychiatric	1,130,996.00
Coler	N.Y. Medical	Professional	2,236,000.00
Community Blood Council			62,500.00
Coney Island	Maimonides	Medical	5,016,000.00
Coney Island	Maimonides	Psychiatric	800,000.00
*Cumberland	Brooklyn	Professional	3,569,500.00
Delafield	Columbia	Anaesthesiology	102,320.00
Delafield	Columbia	Diagnostic Radiology	317,697.00
Delafield	Columbia	Radiation Therapy	240,105.00
Ewing	Memorial	Professional	3,225,000.00
Fordham	Misericordia	Medical	3,500,000.00
Goldwater	N.Y.U.	Professional	3,650,000.00
Greenpoint	Brooklyn-Jewish	Professional	3,200,000.00

(Continued)

Table 6 (Continued)

Institution	Affiliation	Service	Contract Amount 1966-67
Gouverneur	Beth Israel	Amb. Care	$ 1,683,046.00
Harlem	Columbia	Anaesthesiology	726,700.00
Harlem	Columbia	Diagnostic Radiology	600,000.00
Harlem	Columbia	Medicine	2,330,000.00
Harlem	Columbia	Obs. - Gyn.	823,482.00
Harlem	Columbia	Pathology	660,000.00
*Harlem	Columbia	Pediatrics	525,000.00
Harlem	Columbia	Psychiatry	769,306.00
Harlem	Columbia	Surgery	2,117,500.00
*Lincoln	Yeshiva	Anaesthesiology	522,000.00
*Lincoln	Yeshiva	Medicine	250,000.00
*Lincoln	Yeshiva	Obs. - Gyn.	748,000.00
*Lincoln	Yeshiva	Pediatrics	640,000.00
*Lincoln	Yeshiva	Psychiatry	470,740.00
*Lincoln	Yeshiva	Surgery	835,000.00
*Morrisania	Bronx Lebanon	Amb. Care	363,000.00
Morrisania	Montefiore	Medical	5,879,710.00
Queens General	Hillside	Psychiatry	830,000.00
Queens General	Long Island Jewish	Medical Services	9,120,000.00
Queens General	Mary Immaculate	Medical Services	732,400.00
*Increase - Estimated Renewals			3,214,025.00
			$74,296,129.00

308

Code	Title	1964-65 Budget as Modified	1965-66 Budget Request	Increase or *Decrease
68-477	Special Clinical Services	$37,662,688.00	$53,709,371.00	$16,046,683.00

To provide funds for the following contracts:

Institution	Affiliation	Service	Contract Amount 1965-66
Bronx Mun. Center	Yeshiva	Laboratories	$ 1,500,000.00
City Hospital	Mount Sinai	Medical Services	9,300,000.00
City Hospital	Mount Sinai	Psychiatry	1,034,474.00
Coler Hospital	NY Medical	Medical Services	1,760,000.00
Coney Isl. Hosp.	Maimonides	Medical Services	4,560,000.00
Coney Isl. Hosp.	Maimonides	Psychiatry	600,000.00
Cumberland Hosp.	Bklyn. Hosp.	Medical Services	3,569,000.00
**Delafield Hosp.	Columbia	Radiation Therapy	144,500.00
**Delafield Hosp.	Columbia	Anaesthesiology	66,440.00
**Delafield Hosp.	Columbia	Diagnostic Radiology	148,000.00
Ewing Hospital	Memorial	Laboratories	1,800,000.00
Fordham Hospital	Misericordia	Medical Services	3,000,000.00
Greenpoint Hosp.	Bklyn. Jewish	Medical Services	2,700,000.00
**Gouverneur Hosp.	Beth Israel	Out-Patient	1,330,834.00
**Harlem Hospital	Columbia	Anaesthesiology	196,900.00
**Harlem Hospital	Columbia	Obstetric & Gyn.	523,482.00
Harlem Hospital	Columbia	Pediatrics	525,000.00

(Continued)

309

Table 6 (Continued)

Institution	Affiliation	Service	Contract Amount 1965-66
Harlem Hospital	Columbia	Psychiatry	$ 481,500.00
Harlem Hospital	Columbia	Pathology	600,000.00
Harlem Hospital	Columbia	Surgery	1,925,000.00
Harlem Hospital	Columbia	Radiology	550,000.00
Harlem Hospital	Columbia	Medicine	850,000.00
**Lincoln Hospital	Yeshiva	Obstetric & Gyn.	550,000.00
**Lincoln Hospital	Yeshiva	Anaesthesiology	213,000.00
**Lincoln Hospital	Yeshiva	Pediatrics	536,000.00
Lincoln Hospital	Yeshiva	Surgery	835,000.00
Lincoln Hospital	Yeshiva	Psychiatry	470,740.00
**Morrisania Hosp.	Montefiore	Medical Services	3,215,501.00
Morrisania Hosp.	Bronx Lebanon	Amb. Care Unit	363,000.00
Queens Gen. Hosp.	Mary Immaculate	Medical Services	665,800.00
Queens Gen. Hosp.	Long Island Jewish	Medical Services	8,065,000.00
Queens Gen. Hosp.	Hillside	Psychiatry	583,000.00
Increase - Estimated Renewals (**)			795,000.00
Undistributed			202,200.00
Home Care			50,000.00
			$53,709,371.00

310

Code	Title	1963-64 Budget as Modified	1964-65 Budget Request	Increase or *Decrease
68-413	Rental of Office Equipment	$ 51,696.00	$ 52,696.00	$ 1,000.00
	To provide funds for rental of IBM Machines, Postage Meters and Xerox Lithomaster Processor.			
68-415	Rental of Other Equipment	16,500.00	16,500.00	-
	To provide funds for rental of Motion Pictures, Radium and other medical equipment.			
68-421	Cleaning Services	101,000.00	101,000.00	-
	To provide funds for cleaning services--curtains, uniforms and rugs. Also to clean hospital windows at least twice a year. A minimum of $60,000.00 is required for exterminating services.			
68-442	Transportation of Patients	3,000.00	3,000.00	-
	To provide funds for transportation of patients to State Tubercular and Mental Institutions.			

(Continued)

Table 6 (Continued)

Code	Title	1963-64 Budget as Modified	1964-65 Budget Request	Increase or *Decrease
68-451	Ambulance Service	$ 1,077,000.00	$ 1,077,000.00	$ —
		To provide funds for contracts with voluntary hospitals for ambulance service.		
68-475	Research Services	365,000.00	365,000.00	—
		To provide funds for contract between Francis Delafield Hospital and Columbia University for Laboratories Services.		
68-477	Special Clinical Services	16,403,371.00	18,260,022.00	1,856,651.00
		To provide funds for the following contracts:		

Bronx Municipal Center - Yeshiva - Laboratory   1,500,000.00
Cumberland - Brooklyn Hospital - Medical Services   3,245,000.00
Delafield - Columbia - Radiation Therapy   144,500.00
Delafield - Columbia - Anaesthesiology   66,440.00
Delafield - Columbia - Diagnostic Radiology   148,000.00
Ewing - Memorial - Laboratory   1,800,000.00
Gouverneur - Beth Israel - Out-Patient   1,330,834.00

312

Greenpoint - Mount Sinai - Medical Services	$ 2,911,125.00
Harlem - Columbia - Anaesthesiology	196,900.00
Harlem - Columbia - Obstetric & Gynecologic	336,482.00
Harlem - Columbia - Pediatrics	475,000.00
Harlem - Columbia - Psychiatrists	412,500.00
Lincoln - Yeshiva - Obstetric & Gynecologic	550,000.00
Lincoln - Yeshiva - Anaesthesiology	213,000.00
Lincoln - Yeshiva - Pediatrics	536,000.00
Lincoln - Yeshiva - Surgery	795,000.00
Lincoln - Yeshiva - Psychiatric	383,740.00
Morrisania - Montefiore - Medical Services	3,215,501.00
	$18,260,022.00

(Continued)

313

Table 6 (Continued)

Code	Title	1962-63 Budget as Modified	1963-64 Budget Request	Increase or *Decrease
68-413	Rental of Office Equipment	$ 45,000.00	$ 47,062.00	$ 2,062.00
	To provide funds for rental of IBM Machines, Postage Meters and Xerox Lithomaster Processor and Camera			
68-415	Rental of Other Equipment	16,500.00	16,500.00	-
	To provide funds for rental of Motion Pictures, Radium and other medical equipment.			
68-421	Cleaning Services	100,000.00	100,000.00	-
	To provide funds for cleaning services - curtains, uniforms and rugs. Also to clean hospital windows at least twice a year. A minimum of $60,000.00 is required for exterminating services.			
68-442	Transportation of Prisoners & Inmates	3,000.00	3,000.00	-
	To provide funds for transportation of patients to State Tubercular and Mental Institutions.			

314

Code	Title	1962-63 Budget as Modified	1963-64 Budget Request	Increase or *Decrease
68-451	Ambulance Service	$ 1,143,000.00	$ 1,143,000.00	$ —

To provide funds for contracts with voluntary hospitals for ambulance service.

68-475	Research Services	365,000.00	365,000.00	—

To provide funds for contract between Francis Delafield Hospital and Columbia University for Laboratories Services.

68-477	Special Clinical Services	11,024,516.00	11,986,103.00	961,587.00

To provide funds for the following contracts:

James Ewing & Memorial Hospitals - Laboratory	1,800,000.00
Bronx Mun. Cen. & Yeshiva - Laboratory	1,500,000.00
Delafield & Columbia - Radiation Therapy	100,000.00
Delafield & Columbia - Anaesthesiology	66,440.00
Delafield & Columbia - Diagnostic Radiation	148,000.00
Lincoln & Yeshiva - Pediatrics	360,000.00

(Continued)

Table 6 (Continued)

Gouverneur & Beth Israel - Out Patient	$ 1,061,666.00
Greenpoint & Mount Sinai - Medical Care	2,555,932.00
Harlem & Columbia - Obstetric & Gyn.	336,482.00
Harlem & Columbia - Psychiatry	412,500.00
Lincoln & Yeshiva - Obstetric & Gyn.	525,000.00
Morrisania & Montefiore - Medical Care	2,923,183.00
Harlem & Columbia - Anaesthesiology	196,900.00
	$11,986,103.00

68-482 Visiting Nurse Service	$320,000.00	$320,000.00 -

To provide funds for Visiting Nurses for Home Care Program.

316

When contractual negotiations for FY 1967/68 are completed, the necessary budget (subject to accrual
adjustments) will probably have increased.

It is clear that the contractual delivery of
personal health services has become very big business.
This practice has now reached a volume and established
a tradition sufficient to make evident (agreeable or
not) the fact that public hospital administration and
function in this city is undergoing fundamental, inevitable change.

In recent months the practice of affiliation
contracting has been the subject of great controversy--
so much so, that additional exposure of its inevitable
faults of growth need not be detailed here.

This study has been concerned with the fact of
its continuing utilization, with the potential for
improving the provisions of these contractual agreements, and with the potentials of affiliation contracting for an improved system of personal health
delivery.

Some Broad Conclusions

The present study affords certain convictions:

- Recent fault-finding in affiliation practices
  ultimately will result in more progress than
  harm; much of the recent controversy rests
  upon real problems; however, the era of fault-
  finding per se has served its purpose and
  should now be closed.

- For the foreseeable future, affiliation contracting is here to stay.

- Affiliation contracts can and should embrace
  far more precedent-setting provisions dealing
  with programs, goals, roles and desired at-
  tainments than have been given serious attention by contractual principals to the present
  time.

- The city has failed as a partner to the contracts, far more seriously and consequentially
  than have voluntary agencies; means must be
  found for relieving the city of its role of
  "supply and support partner."

- Given the presence of an effective means
  for so altering the city's role, affiliation
  contracts are more likely to move toward
  comprehensiveness (Gouverneur-Beth Israel;
  Morrisania-Montefiore) than toward fractionated services.

Analysis of Contract Provisions

Because affiliation contracting is the current,
yet faltering, vehicle for a major part of the delivery of health services by the city, two aspects of
these contracts should be clarified: (1) their present, generally common characteristics, and (2) how
those characteristics could be strengthened.

- Responsibilities are presently divided between
  the voluntary hospital and the city. The city
  is no more able to meet its responsibilities
  now than in the past, i.e., no real progress
  seems possible in the present arrangement.

- Contracts call for the provisions of services
  but do not specify what is to be accomplished
  by the provision of service; there are no objectives or goals specified.

- There is no provision for accountability other
  than a post-audit of the voluntary hospital's
  books.

- Procurement of equipment, supplies, and services authorized by the contract and to be
  provided by the city are subject to the same
  maze of governmental controls as when the city
  ran the entire system, and with the same unin-
  tended yet paralyzing effects.

- The contracts are still oriented toward the
  solution of the original staffing crises;
  i.e., they have not been broadened to deal
  with additional problems.

- Their frequent specificity of orientation
  toward clinical delivery (good in itself) has
  been permitted to preempt their potential for
  community orientation.

- In a very real sense, they have tended to perpetuate and amplify fractionation. (Whereas

the city fractionates administrative matters, the voluntaries have often fractionated medical delivery services.)

The Commission staff's analysis has derived a number of means by which these affiliation contracts might be strengthened:

- Include specific program goals in positive and quantifiable terms such as, "The goal of the program is to reduce infant mortality in the South Bronx by __% in the next five years."

- Specify accountability procedures in terms such as, "All expenditures in behalf of this program shall be certified by the head of the medical service directing the program as necessary, in his professional opinion, to the successful pursuit of the program goals as specified herein."

- Extend coverage of contract to ensure that all equipment alterations, services, and personnel necessary to the operation of the contracted program are the responsibility of the contractor.

- In the process of contract negotiation, include the signing of a performance certification typical of that appearing in contracts between the Community Mental Health Board and community voluntary agencies who may carry out activities for CMHB.

Following are illustrative excerpts from one affiliation contract--that between the city and Columbia University to provide surgical services at Harlem Hospital. Subsequently, examples are cited of the kinds of provisions that would greatly strengthen such a contract.

1) ". . . the University will have the exclusive responsibility of nominating the members of the clinical and other professional staff required for the said surgical services . . ."

2) ". . . the City retains the University to provide the professional surgical staff (excluding residents and interns who shall be employed by the City) and ancillary personnel to furnish all surgery services

required in the operation of the in-patient, out-
patient, emergency and admitting services and for
consultative needs of patients having surgical conditions at said hospital."

3) ". . . the University agrees to render all
services for which it is responsible in a competent
manner and to the best of its ability . . . "

4) ". . . the City shall operate the surgery
services in the hospital . . . in a manner which will
maintain accreditation by . . ."

5) ". . . the University shall keep separate
accounts . . . and such accounts shall be open to inspection by the Commissioner of Hospitals . . . at
any mutually convenient time or times."

6) ". . . within one hundred eighty (180) days
after the close of each contract year, the University
shall furnish a certified statement of income and
expenditures under this agreement . . . such audit
shall be certified by independent Certified Public
Accountants . . ."

7) The Harlem/Columbia contract also contains an
18-page list of items (surgical instruments and equipment) to be purchased by the city. Each item is listed
by catalog number, name of article, unit need, unit
price, and total price. It is understood that city
purchasing procedures insist on no deviations from the
listings except in case of emergency.

As can be seen, these passages are simultaneously
vague and restrictive. The contract could be materially improved by wording replacement passages in ways
calculated to enhance the following objectives:

1) Clear statements of positive goals, such as,
"The University shall fill the following positions
with men of the following specifications within the
next 18 months . . . "

2) Clear statements regarding review of progress,
such as, "The University and the City shall review
progress toward these goals in the form of Quarterly
Technical Program Review Conferences, which will consider (a) status and progress of operational activity,
(b) fiscal matters, (c) problems or obstacles in
either area, (d) need for program modification."

3) <u>Clear statements as to how goals shall be accomplished,</u> such as, "Whereas the University has submitted a step-by-step plan for accomplishment of these goals, as specified in Attachment I . . ."

4) <u>Clear statements of program accountability,</u> such as, "The University hereby undertakes to accomplish the goals according to the plan submitted and will deviate from the plan and time schedule only after written agreement from the City that the deviation is deemed necessary and in the best interests of the public . . .," and, "Expenditures of funds not anticipated in the plan but judged as necessary or advantageous to the accomplishment of the goals as planned or amended shall be accounted for in the following manner: (a) the head of service shall prepare a document stating that in his opinion expenditures of the specified class are in the best interest of, and consistent with the goals of, the program, (b) a copy of the document shall be promptly forwarded to the City, and (c) all accounts kept by the University of such expenditures shall reference the document as authority for such disbursements."

5) <u>An effort to provide an incentive to superior performance,</u> such as, "The University and the City agree that the attached plan, time schedule, and budgeted costs constitute reasonable expectations as to the University's performance during the contract period. Should the University, however, exceed expectations by achieving the goals of this contract at a cost less than budgeted, the University shall have been deemed in this regard to have performed in a superior manner. (Determination of such savings shall be made annually, but reviewed and projected quarterly during such annual period.)   When substantial savings are apparent an optional application of such saved funds may (for example) take the form of funding special innovative programs of great interest to the University and the public--as negotiated and agreed upon between the City and the University." (Other examples may include the addition of special personnel or equipment. Many options are possible.)

Additional Findings and Suggestions

The hospital survey exposed a good deal of facilities discrimination in the sense that the affiliate medical staff, when in the municipal hospital, enjoys

better physical circumstances (by a wide margin in
some cases) than do the staff members of municipal
hospitals not on the affiliate payroll. Would it be
possible to develop a nondiscrimination statement
with respect to these physical circumstances? If it
is possible for an affiliate staff member to work
under air-conditioned circumstances, the same circumstances should be accorded to a comparable member of
the municipal medical staff. Overt variances in
working conditions are a cause for lowered morale and
some bitterness.

Some laboratories or other specialized facilities
are available only to affiliate physicians and in no
way help the municipal medical staff member. Such
areas frequently are closed off at night and locked.
Can joint programs be encouraged that will allow
municipal staff members to benefit from such specialized facilities?

Would it be possible to develop a "best efforts"
clause that would stimulate the affiliate, over time,
to develop community-related group practice in relation to the municipal facility? In this same regard,
would it not be possible to stimulate the affiliate
to develop specialized programs relating the hospital
to the private physician in the community (who may
not now have hospital privileges)? This has been
initiated by at least one affiliate.

Would it not be desirable to develop a "community
programs clause" that would encourage the affiliate to
develop such programs under the general approval of
the commissioner of hospitals? In this regard it
would not be at all out of order to insist that in
due time there be appointed a "Chief of Community
Health Education and Services." This person and his
staff would be concerned with the problem of developing sound community relationships and developing
attitudes within the community that would foster the
use of local health facilities.

In addition, it would be appropriate to stimulate
the affiliate to shape the OPD and Emergency Room
capabilities of the municipal hospital to the end of
developing a community medical service center facility.

Along this same line the affiliate could be
encouraged to develop and specify at an early date a
fully defined extended-care program within the municipal hospital, indicating the number of beds and wards

so assigned, the types of cases that would be handled, and the circumstances under which these cases would be selected and cared for. In this same sense a carefully defined home care program with rotation of staff would be of great benefit. Finally, in this same vein, some encouragement to the affiliate within the contract for involvement in a chronic care facility planning program in the community, in working relationship with the municipal hospital, would be very desirable.

Some motivation should be written into the contract to cause the affiliate to scrutinize questionable cases of patient transfer and questionable practices of patient selection.

In a number of instances, heads of service in the affiliate hospital are giving lip service to their presumed role in the municipal service (by telephone and a few annual "inspection visits"). The contract can be written so as to stop this kind of performance.

In other instances, interns and residents of the affiliate hospital are not rotated regularly through medical assignments in the municipal hospital and, on the other hand, medical staff members on the municipal payroll are sometimes not allowed certain desirable interactions in the affiliate's facility. Both of these matters should be attended to, so that rotations are evident and regular, and so that municipal staff training and updating in the voluntary hospital are encouraged. (A good example is the practice of exchanges between Montefiore and Morrisania.) Rotations should involve non-physician staff and para-medical personnel.

Within the next three years--that is, the term of duration of most of these contracts--there will in all probability be developed a city-wide medical information system. The contract should require the cooperation of affiliates and municipals in the development of common criteria for this system and for cooperation in its early stages of development.

Finally, and in connection with the community development incentives, the affiliate should be required to "survey" and to report upon the probable cognizant community surrounding the hospital, as well as that of the affiliated municipal, to determine

what medical facilities of other kinds are present,
how many physicians are practicing there, how many
physicians have hospital privileges, how many do not,
and--generally--to develop community-oriented incentives for the cooperation of these facilities so that
a more coherent delivery system at a local level can
be achieved.

MUNICIPAL HOSPITALS: SUMMARY IMPRESSIONS

Patients' View

The patient in the municipal hospital system
experiences difficulties from the time he attempts
to enter a hospital for treatment up to and including the time he leaves the hospital.

The investigating staff has found evidence,
heard testimony, and examined documents which indicate clearly that at least some of the city hospitals
are subject to the practice of selective admission.
Once admitted to the hospital (or in the emergency
room) a patient can wait many hours for service.
Needed service can be as relatively minor as an X-ray
or as major as the treatment of an open wound.
Patients are concerned and have expressed fear at the
possibility of being "experimented" upon. During a
patient's stay, it would not be too uncommon for him
to share one toilet facility (which may be in poor
repair) with an entire ward of other patients. He
might not get clean sheets as often as he should,
and he may have to sleep in the hallway. His bedside
care will often be minimal or, under some circumstances, unavailable.

Professionals' View

The professional staff of the public hospitals
are agreed that there is inadequate support for their
needs--in the form of nurses, nurses' aides, technicians, messengers, supplies, and equipment. They
feel that they are often overloaded with patient bed
care and other responsibilities. Doctors were observed being used as messengers to deliver needed supplies or reports. Adequate laboratory facilities are
sorely lacking because of space, money, or organiza-
tionally related shortages. There are no clear guidelines governing patient care, teaching, and research

responsibilities, and the desirable balance among
these.

Often, doctors become over-involved in one or
another of these activities, but aren't certain they
are really "doing their job." Finally, they express
confusion and concern over the split nature of the
management of their institution. With two separate
administrators, the efficient handling of and vital
coordination of their needs are left to chance. Affiliations have helped a great deal, but still leave
much to be desired.

Administrators' View

The municipal hospital administrators have serious and too often justifiable grievances. They are
truly "damned if they do and damned if they don't."
The administrator receives an unrealistic and inadequate budget, and later finds that his budget is
monitored and delayed, and his needs denied. Finally,
he finds that his budget is administered elsewhere.

In many hospitals, there has been no change in
level of operating dollars for a number of years--no
matter how service needs may have changed. (Of course,
there have been salary increment adjustments over the
years to accommodate raises, etc.) This is also true,
often, with regard to personnel and equipment; in
both areas many of the hospitals have been functioning
years behind the times. What money the administrator
does have, he cannot put to current best use.

If he determines a critical need for a nurse, and
he has "unused" clerk lines, he cannot take appropriate advantage of them. He is bound hand and foot to
inflexible procedures and regulations and remote
decision-making that operate to the detriment of the
hospital and ultimately the patient. Usually, he is
without authority as regards medical services; in
most hospitals he can neither coordinate them nor is
he sufficiently a part of their planning. Excess or
deficiency in patient care, teaching, or research is
not an issue he is authorized to deal with--even when
he is persuaded that a particular voluntary hospital
cares more about "teaching" value than the patient
value in a given case. The dual administrative arrangement all too often creates management confusion
and seriously affects patient care.

Out-Patient Departments and Emergency Rooms

This survey has gathered data for three areas of interest:

- System or procedure followed in the OPD and in the ER.

- Major problems encountered (distinct from expected problems in these operations) and ways in which these difficulties have been dealt with.

- Characterization of the community served and evaluation of whether the hospital is meeting the needs; if not, plans and/or hopes for the future.

Variations were found in OPD procedure but each of the 15 departments surveyed falls within the framework described in Figure 7. (Brief examination of the flow pattern illustrated will be instructive with respect to system problems in OPD functions.) In most cases, admission to the hospital is through the emergency area. There is no separate admissions desk as in a voluntary or private hospital. More and more, to the patient who walks in or is brought in by ambulance--whether he is actually an emergency case or not--the emergency room is the hospital. An estimate was quoted for the State of New York that 70% of the walk-ins to emergency rooms are nonemergent. This phenomenon occurs, reportedly, for a number of reasons. Possibly the clinics are closed at the most convenient hour for the patient to attend them. Sometimes the patient cannot distinguish between real urgency and a problem that can wait. Further, many patients elect to go to the emergency room because they know they cannot be turned away (the city hospital ER must treat anyone who presents himself for medical care, no matter his economic or residential elegibility; patients know they will get much faster help than in most of the crowded clinics). In some rare cases, it was observed that the ER has more staff and better facilities than the OPD, and patients had made this discovery.

It can also be generalized that the OPD and the ER, the two major elements of ambulatory service in the city hospital, are separate activities, both physically and functionally. But, whether under the

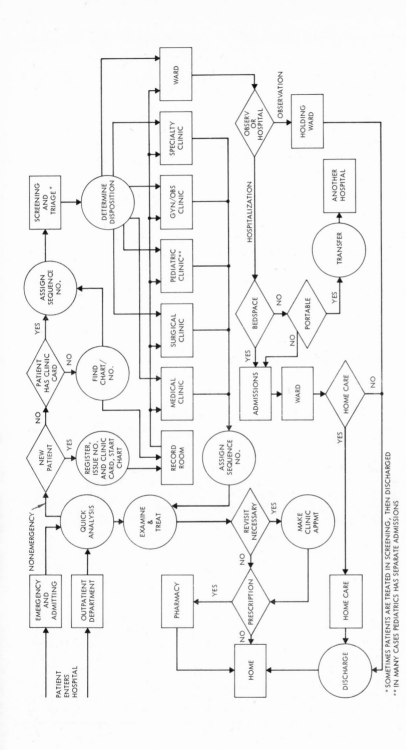

Figure 7. Generalized Flow Diagram of Typical Out-Patient and Emergency Room Functions

* SOMETIMES PATIENTS ARE TREATED IN SCREENING, THEN DISCHARGED
** IN MANY CASES PEDIATRICS HAS SEPARATE ADMISSIONS

327

direction of a single administrator or separated administratively, the departments are closely related in operation.   In fact, in those cases where they were located in separate buildings, this was reported as an inconvenience and the cause of many problems. (Although detailed descriptions of the procedures followed by each of the institutions that were studied were obtained, they will not be presented in this report.)

A difference was found in the meaning of "Ambulatory Services."   Essentially, the term refers to medical attention for ambulant patients, i.e., non-bed patients.   This attention is slowly being extended from treating the sick to administering preventive medicine as well, and the set of services is widening to include home care, extended care, rehabilitation service, etc.

Not only are hospital administrators becoming aware that the ER/OPD operation is the hospital in terms of community perception, but, possibly more important with respect to medical care, it is becoming increasingly clear that the ER/OPD is the family physician for the indigent population.   Through education and the experiencing of improved and widening medical services, the public utilizing OPD and ER services is slowly beginning to expect comprehensive care on a continuing basis: cancer detection clinics; chest X-ray facilities; teaching in nutrition, family planning, the care of diabetics, etc.; along with the concept of the physical examination before treatment in the clinics.   These expectations are encouraging the idea that the hospital is for both well and sick people.   It is a "health" institution, and the term "health" is changing in meaning for the population at large.

Major Problems

Problems that were reported fall into the ten general categories of: inadequate space, facilities, and personnel; resistance to change from within the system; difficulties of procuring supplies and effecting renovations because of external resistance and red tape; physical separation of interdependent functions; unrealistic budgets; burdens of constraints placed on the system by central policies, union policies, etc.; increasing number and complexity of forms; general

negation of progress by the larger system of which
the hospitals are a part; and the continuing degradation of morale--hence performance--of personnel as a
result of frustration and discouragement. In some
cases, it would appear that difficulties encountered
are draining even the most dedicated staff members of
the desire to function effectively.

It was found, however, that attempts to change
things in the interest of progress are thwarted with
almost equally frustrating intensity from within as
from without the system represented by each individual
institution. For example, old dispensary habits, and
the "newly outlawed" distinction between private and
public medical care in the city hospitals, are examples
which persist and resist reform movements. Further,
present personnel policy set years ago, along with some
union regulations, often aid and abet conditions which
inhibit efforts to improve services.

The common goal to offer a family-physician type
of service in the OPD/ER was reported to have been
achieved by only one of the facilities observed. This
was at Gouverneur where apparently a "real" appointment system is being made to work. In all other municipal hospital OPD's observed, discouragement was
reported in this area. It seems to be generally recognized that a long and tedious appointment stage must
be experienced before patients will be educated to
assume their responsibilities in establishing a one-
to-one relationship between doctor and patient. Currently there is approximately a 50% "no-show" for
appointments, and these are generally block appointments. Only in rare cases, as in specialized clinics,
have personal appointments been made and kept with any
record of success. The effort, of course, is being
made not only to shorten the wait for patients and to
offer them personalized service, but also to relieve
the congestion in the clinics.

A contributing force to this problem is a social
factor. It was reported that the OPD is like a club
for the indigent. Many patients arrive at 8:00 A.M.
(opening hour) or before, no matter the hour of their
appointment at the clinic they are visiting. It was
conjectured this is either because they enjoy coming
and sitting and visiting--or they want to be sure to
get in line early.

Regarding efforts to make appointment systems
work and to try to achieve a continuing relationship

for a patient with a given doctor, typical comments
were: "We're prepared for a long, hard battle to
make this work"; "We'd like to be the family physician for our people and are trying, but it's very,
very difficult"; "Once we did have that relationship,
but since our census took the big leap it did several
years ago and we reached the point of no return, we
have had to give up trying to achieve a one-to-one
relationship." It was observed that administrators
are more hopeful of success in meeting this problem
than are the medical personnel--probably because the
latter are closer to the reality of the situation.
"Impractical," they say, but they keep trying new
ideas.

Physicians themselves are the target of criticism in the hospital system. For example, session
doctors not familiar with the hospital drug list may
prescribe out-of-stock drugs, thereby causing confusion and long waits; ward doctors apparently sometimes
"forget" to advise the clinics of follow-through cases,
frequently find referral to home care "too much
trouble," or often direct ward patients upon discharge
to a clinic--but give the wrong day--thereby causing
confusion for both the patient and the clinics. The
criticism was also voiced that some physicians specify
a quantity for a prescription that exceeds the amount
needed before the requested return visit. Invariably,
it appears, the patient will then wait until he has
finished his prescription before returning--ignoring
his appointment and expecting attention when he does
arrive.

Other internal problems observed included: the
reluctance to extend clinic hours into the evening
and over the weekend (this apparently causes bad feelings in the ER, and among administrators with community
service consciences who want to change the hours but
cannot procure needed staff); "oldtimers" who continue
long-time routines in spite of changes--and, it was
reported over and over, it is "impossible to fire anyone"; and the usual variety of administrative conflicts, caused primarily by personalities, that work
to the detriment of every system.

It is redundant to relate the personnel problems
imposed by "time-off" policies and union regulations,
but these stories were heard everywhere and the effects
on the efficiency of the OPD and ER were reported as
great.

Variations in the kind of contract signed at the time affiliations were effected have worked to both the advantage and disadvantage of the hospital system. For example, Morrisania Hospital has been able to deal adequately with the nursing problem because of the specificity of their contract with Montefiore. This is the only contract covering nursing provision. Some affiliates have been particularly generous in extending their support to the purchase of supplies or equipment too difficult to obtain through regular channels; but apparently not all affiliates have, and the hospital staffs resent the differentiation. Another problem reported was that a discrepancy exists between advantages given "city-paid" physicians and affiliate-supplied medical staff. The former are on a lower salary in many cases and inequities exist in such areas as parking facilities and the provision of air conditioning.

A problem common to most of the hospitals that were observed is the nature of relationships with Welfare Department personnel and services. This is closely related to the increasing number and complexity of forms to be processed in the clinics--with inadequate clerical staff to perform the task. Representatives from the Welfare Department were in most of the OPD's. Sometimes a group of them concentrated in one area; other times individuals dispersed among the crowds of waiting patients. OPD staffs reported that these people function only in the capacity of accepting applications and determining eligibility. The processing of the forms and the collection procedures, then, are the responsibility of the OPD's.

But an additional Welfare Department conflict was reported in some of the institutions. Apparently, correspondence relating to insurance claims, verification of hospitalization, etc., are handled by OPD staff and this seems to be a task assigned to records departments. It was observed that in each of these cases the work load was piling up faster than the available clerical staff could possibly progress with the job. In one hospital they are now a year behind and slipping further back every day. The director of ambulatory services in that institution complained that this is a responsibility of the Welfare Department and therefore an unjustified burden on the hospital personnel.

The Community

The community of the city hospital OPD and ER
can be generally defined as low-income, low-education,
predominantly Negro and Puerto Rican, at least 80%
indigent, and generally depressed and distressed.
Medical problems run the full continuum. Of high
incidence are TB, VD, addiction (drug and alcohol),
and geriatric problems.

However, there are unique features of each of
the communities served by individual hospitals.
Not as much was learned about the health care needs
of these communities as hoped for from hospital
staffs because they do not have good knowledge of,
or on-going study of, these needs. In some cases
they referred to studies that had been done, but they
did not seem to be familiar with their contents. In
other infrequent cases, however, it was learned that
some hospital staff members participate actively in
community affairs, assist and encourage community
leadership, and are personally concerned with community
problems. (Three special instances of this occured
at Lincoln, Gouverneur and Elmhurst.) Unfortunately,
it would appear that most of the hospital administrators are so enmeshed in the trials of survival of
their institution that they are unaware of the increasing and probably undefined needs around them.

The greatest need that was pointed out is that
of extended care. Much has been written about this;
it will not be elaborated here. "We need a place,"
said more than one physician, "that we can call and
say, 'I have a terminal cancer patient (or any number
of other hopeless problems) and am sending him over
now.'" It is commonly known that many social problems
(mostly old people without homes, family or health),
drunks, and numerous other "unwanteds" are passed from
one emergency room to another. They get "dumped" into
a holding ward until a social worker can find a solution or until they are in good enough state to wander
back into the community.

Satellite Clinics

It would appear that, concurrently, plans are
being made for family health centers that, if implemented, will relieve the responsibility of the hospital units considerably, but there is little or no
communication of these ideas among those who will be

affected directly. To the extent that this observation is correct, it must be commented objectively that two things are happening that are not in the best interest of the future of the delivery of ambulatory health services in the City of New York: (1) Central planners have not yet found means for taking advantage of the experience and capability of the men and women in the OPD/ER facilities who can help them most; and (2) wasted effort and anxieties are being poured into duplicative planning.

Conclusions and Recommendations: OPD/ER

In the crowded corridors and dreary examining rooms of the out-patient departments and emergency rooms of the municipal hospitals medical care is evolving through historic developments. Traditional charity clinics are being transformed--agonizingly slowly--into an organized system of ambulatory service for the total population; turn-of-the century medical practice is being gradually replaced with quality "that even money can't buy"; and the conflicting forces of major trends in medical care are being exposed. But the evolution will require decades for fulfillment. It is curious that the very system in which this drama is unfolding should repress its progress with incredible unawareness of its basic needs and apparent reluctance to respond to its clearly evident requirements and to local initiative.

The problems that these developing ambulatory units are encountering are many and, it would seem, vastly more than there should be. Clinics and emergency rooms of the city hospital are the laboratories of the medical schools, the family physician for thousands of families, and probably the most dynamic, exciting aspect of the hospital's operation today. Yet it would appear that those who have been assigned the responsibility for the very survival of the institutions have to face insurmountable difficulties in performing even the fundamental daily tasks. Within the old buildings, many of which are poorly equipped and most far too small for the ever-rising needs, research is yielding important gains in medical care while more and more of the medically indigent flock to the doors because they are learning that it is there where they will find a doctor when they are sick, and they are learning that he is a good doctor and one who cares. More recently, they have been learning that the clinic is a place to go in order to stay well, too. But limitations of physical space constrain the expansion of these developments. Indeed, it was estimated by many directors that there is not room for the thousands they now serve--for even curative medicine, let alone space to expand to fulfill the teaching and preventive work they feel they should be doing.

The clinics are also the meeting ground of at least two powerful and competing forces in medical care. Specialization, the trend that has hastened progress toward the obliteration of much disease, has also produced fragmented service, a problem which is brought into full focus in the hospital out-patient department. Scheduling of some 50 to 70 clinics within a 10-session week is a complex task in itself-- without the added burden of matching the puzzle with session doctors' schedules. Although screening may save the patient the frustration of finding the right doctor for his problem, fragmentation makes it ever more difficult to achieve the consistent patient-doctor relationship for which all the out-patient departments are striving. This, then, is the opposing force to specialization: the balancing trend toward treating the whole patient, manifested through efforts at group practice and finding a really rich seed bed in the hospital clinics. There, somehow, group practice must succeed, so it is there--in the clinics--that systems are being tested by trial and error.

Other interesting changes are occurring in the ambulatory care units of the city hospitals. Once, and apparently not too long ago, these were rather static operations. Physicians reported that when the affiliations were effected, "turn-of-the-century" medicine was being practiced in the clinics of some of the hospitals. Thanks to the affiliation contracts, many changes have been wrought in a relatively short time. These improvements and innovations stand out against the inert backgrounds of aging buildings and ideas.

At the Lincoln Hospital, yellow and red lines are painted on the Out-Patient Department and Emergency Room floors to lead the patients to particular areas. At Gouverneur, the walls outside the clinic doors are painted different colors, thereby simplifying directions to specific doctors for the patients, many of whom have difficulty reading English. Communication is facilitated, too, with bilingual screening physicians and specially trained bilingual clerks in some

OPD's and ER's. The pregnant woman, for example, is
given priority in most OPD's, with such innovations
as separate registration areas, immediate reception
by the conference nurse, a direct line to the doctor
where she is examined as quickly as possible, and
special classes held for her throughout her pregnancy.
The number of women reporting to the hospital in their
second trimester is increasing because of the education
that has been possible. At Harlem, there is a special
pharmacy window just for pediatrics--for the purpose
of helping mothers and small children to avoid long
lines. And in many of the OPD's, space is being
cleared for a room for waiting children. In another
OPD it was observed that cribs were placed throughout
the many clinics for restless infants.

Creative thinking--by the clerks, by the professionals, by the administrators--was evident in many
areas. Particularly impressive were the shortcuts and
many efficiencies that have been instituted from sheer
necessity. How to handle the herding masses that grow
larger every day? Innovations in grouping and in appointment systems were observed. How to make the
pharmacy line shorter? A third or fourth window had
been added by cutting a hole in a door and locking
the door shut; a numbering system was devised; new
prescription forms were designed. To practice good
medicine, the physician needs good tools and good
aides. It was clear in this survey that much is happening in terms of upgrading and organizing--even
though the task is made unrelentingly difficult by
the constraints of the system within which the clinic
must operate. Two general observations are basic:

1) Working against the many efforts of competent
and dedicated people to adapt to a rapidly changing
medical world are such basic system problems as unrealistic budgets, centralized purchasing, inhibiting
personnel policies, lack of coordinated planning, and
responsibility without authority at the local level.
This report has cited many instances of attempts to
meet the inevitable problems of inadequate space and
clerical help, as well as efforts to make economical
renovations of present inadequate facilities, all of
which are thwarted by system constraints. Local
autonomy must be achieved.

2) It was observed that 14 municipal hospitals
are all struggling with precisely the same problems
and working toward precisely the same goal. Yet it

was noted that they constitute a set of competitive
sub-systems, not a cooperative situation whereby problems might be solved more quickly through coordinated
planning and work.   Other than arrangements between
emergency rooms to transfer patients, no evidence was
observed of inter-municipal-hospital operation.   Undoubtedly this would be difficult within the present
system, so the problem goes back to point 1, above.
Further, with respect to the satellite clinic concept,
it bears repeating here that no coordination was observed between the central planners and the directors
of present hospital ambulatory services who are closest to the problems and who have had opportunity to
gain much helpful insight.   When achieved, local
autonomy must operate within the framework of over-
all system specification and planning.

Recommendations

It follows from these conclusions that at least
two kinds of planning would be advisable immediately:
long-range and interim.   It is presumptuous to be too
specific regarding long-range planning.   Clearly,
there are fundamental system problems that can be
dealt with only through a complete reorganization
(developed in Part Three). And until long-range changes
are possible, the basic problems reported here have no
chance of real solution.

Suggestions, however, for interim revitalizing
of the separate hospital system can be made.   First,
a communication system should be initiated among
those people who are involved in and concerned with
the present and future of ambulatory care in New York
City.   This group should include at least all key
administrators and medical staff of the OPD's and ER's
in the municipal hospitals--and possibly in the volun-
taries--along with those engaged in central planning.
The separate planning of each should be made available
to all to avoid duplication of work and frustration of
effort.   It would be hoped that the dissemination of
information among these persons would stimulate group
action and eventually the activation of smaller coordinating councils (with authority).

Second, these same channels (or a separate one)
should be used to articulate the most pressing needs
of each of the operations.   Representative of the
needs would be instances such as the correspondence
division of the record departments where work, already

a year in arrears, continues to slip back daily because there are not personnel to handle it; the need
of a ramp on a rehabilitation center building where
cripples must somehow ascend a great number of stairs;
or linen supply in emergency examining rooms where
either paper sheets have been resorted to or linens
must be used for several persons before changing.
Ultimately, these kinds of problems could be met
through decentralization of the budget or at least
realistic allocation of funds. They will continue
for some time, however, unless they are channeled to
a central authority capable of real action.

Summing Up: The Crisis

The crisis in health services has a two-fold
expression. The first is in what is provided by the
system; the second is in what is not provided because
needs are unmet and unrecognized.

The medical care provided to the city's indigent
generally is miserable. And this is demonstrated by
any objective measure of the well-being of the people
whose health care is a city responsibility. What the
city is providing in most of its own facilities is
shameful in medical and personal terms. It is demeaning to everyone involved--the patients, the doctors,
the hospital employees, and the hospital administrators; and it is a disgrace to the city. What the city
purchases in care for indigent patients in the voluntary hospitals is a markedly superior treatment of
disease, once the patient is in the hospital, but an
archaic and expensive pattern of medical relief in
the hospital or clinic.

The dual system and the segregation of hospital
resources results in uneconomical multiplication and inflexible use of facilities and personnel. This means
a fragmentation of patient care which is incompatible
with effective continuity and economy of medical care.
A city hospital serving only the medically indigent
is not providing the quality, scope, flexibility and
economy of services that should be provided.

The locus of the medical treatment provided to
the city's poor is an institution not a doctor; the
OPD, the emergency room or the hospital bed, are the
primary sources of what may more accurately be called
medical relief. What are the faults?

- It is episodic acute treatment, depersonalized and dehumanized, without consistency of relationship between doctor and patient.

- Sick poor often are receiving dispensary-level care from transient medical staffs. Some institutions undertake no responsibility for providing continuing or comprehensive care oriented toward the prevention of disease, the minimizing of disability, or the restoration and maintenance of health. Patients must go to different clinics or subclinics for each ailment. Diseases are treated, not people.

- Often, responsibilities stop at the hospital door.

- Every canon of good medical care may be violated by some of the arrangements.

- Inadequate staff, especially on the nursing and para-medical levels, prevails.

- Inadequate equipment and supplies, and badly operated run-down facilities, are the rule.

- Medical records are in shocking disarray in many instances.

- General amenities are largely or completely absent. The city's hospitals are usually depressing, often in bad repair, and personal treatment can be disgraceful.

These matters have been in evidence--to the eye, in documents, in statistics, and in testimony--throughout this survey, in most hospitals in the municipal system. They are sufficiently pervasive to be regarded as the real symptoms of the basic illnesses of the institutional system as a whole. Part Three of this report will deal with their causes and treatment. Before such considerations can be meaningful, however, additional areas of concern must be appraised in chapters to follow.

Reports of hospital visits have been presented, preceded by analyses of the health needs of the communities borough by borough. Now in order is a summary of recommendations for comprehensive program needs in each of the five boroughs.

PROGRAM PLANNING NEEDS: THE FIVE BOROUGHS

Manhattan: Health Services Programs

Important in shaping health programs for comprehensive planning are these characteristics of the
borough:

- The need for medical centers along Manhattan's
  West Side to serve as hubs for better-organized
  patterns of health services.

- The need for certain smaller hospitals to
  undergo merger among themselves or with hospital centers.

- The presence of Harlem--America's archetypal
  ghetto.

- The overload on Metropolitan Hospital's OPD.

- The low utilization of Sydenham, Ewing, and
  Delafield Hospitals.

- The isolation of Bird S. Coler and Goldwater
  Memorial Hospitals.

- Inadequate hospital coverage in the Lower West
  Side and upper Harlem.

- Poverty pockets in affluent areas.

- Care of the aged.

- Addiction.

- Mental health.

- Ambulatory care.

- The need for coordinated planning and delivery
  of medical services.

These needs and problems are addressed in various
ways in the programs discussed below.

Bellevue

If the OPD in the new Bellevue is taken as the primary ambulatory care facility for the neighborhood, it will be inadequate. A new OPD wing will be called for when the present construction is finished. On the other hand, the family care center being planned through renovation of the Lower East Side District Health Center will affect the patterns of ambulatory care in the area. (The center is across the street from the hospital.) The relationship of the two facilities must be carefully coordinated. The capital budget for 1967-68 (CB '68) records an estimate of $1.4 million for facilities at Bellevue for the treatment of burn victims. A $4.5 million "crash" program is in process (under the Bureau of Maintenance, Department of Hospitals) to renovate two pavilions and to build a new emergency unit. Bellevue is next door to New York University Medical Center. A comprehensive affiliation with NYU should be sought to place the two medical establishments under a single administration. The city in such an arrangement would relinquish operating management of Bellevue, but retain program control and policy direction.

Bird S. Coler Hospital

The location of this hospital on Welfare Island emphasizes the tragic isolation from society of its elderly and chronically ill patients. Access to the island is difficult. The transportation problems of the staff and of visitors are the problems of a very small minority in the city and are in very small prospect of improvement. Any change in Coler's role and circumstances depends upon the development of adequate extended-care facilities elsewhere in the city. If this can be accomplished, Coler should be remodeled to function as headquarters for the city's health agencies (access from Manhattan required). A very rough estimate of this cost is $2 million.

Francis Delafield Hospital

In the years 1964-66, the occupancy rates for Delafield were 54.8%, 57.7%, and 60.8%. It is not in the public interest for the city to continue operating a specialty hospital at a conspicuously low occupancy. The cancer services of Delafield are no longer without peer in the city. Other uses should be sought for this

facility. Ambulatory care is one possibility, but
an unlikely one because of (1) the new private-
practice clinic building under construction a block
away at Presbyterian, and (2) the proposed renovation
of the district health center immediately north of
Presbyterian. A more feasible prospect for Delafield
is conversion to an acute general hospital for the
area, so that Presbyterian might pursue the selective-
admissions policy indicated by its role as a teaching
institution. A rough estimate for converting Delafield to either use is $4 million. There is likeli-
hood that the community can support Delafield as a
voluntary institution. Ways should be sought for a
mutually satisfactory transfer of this property to
Presbyterian Hospital. Failing this, a comprehensive
affiliation should be established to place the two
hospitals, in their proximity, under a single administration. As with Bellevue, the city in this arrangement would retain program control in the public
interest. CB '68 records a single project for Dela-
field--an estimate of $52,700 to create an experimen-
tal pathology laboratory under the auspices of the
Health Research Council.

Goldwater Memorial Hospital

This institution shares with Coler the disadvan-
tages of Welfare Island. Given needed development of
adequate community and extended care facilities elsewhere in the city, Goldwater should be remodeled to
serve as a health-careers institute (as specified in
Part Three). Design and renovation costs for this project, including equipment, may be estimated at $4
million. CB '68 lists three programs for Goldwater
that total an estimated $5.54 million. One program
($2,800,000) provides a new addition for auditorium,
chapels, canteen, and related facilities. A second
($2,255,000) is for general alterations and renova-
tions. A third ($486,600) provides for renovating
the cardio-respiratory laboratory under the auspices
of the Health Research Council.

Gouverneur Ambulatory Care Center

Construction of the new Gouverneur is underway.
Original plans called for a 204-bed general care
hospital. New plans call for 124 acute general beds

and 87 extended care beds. This has required redesign
of floors 7 through 13. The Lower East Side Health
Center and a Community Mental Health Center are part
of the Gouverneur project. The new building offers
no obstetrical facilities, no surgical suite. Beth
Israel Hospital is to provide these services. The
medical programs for the new facility and the detailed
working arrangements with Beth Israel are by no means
final. In all probability there will be need (1) to
make Gouverneur Hospital full-service, and (2) to develop satellite community clinics.

Harlem Hospital

Work is in process on a new 800-bed hospital.
CB '68 provides $8 million this year to complete the
funding of this $45 million project. A crash program
has been inaugurated to provide needed painting, electrical work, refrigeration work, and other renovations
in the existing facilities. CB '68 lists an estimated
cost of $13.6 million to construct a Community Mental
Health Center at Harlem Hospital. This hospital should
be developed as a major, independent community medical
center.

James Ewing Hospital

Like Delafield, Ewing's occupancy rate is chronically low (73.8%, 72.5%, and 70.2% in the years 1964-
66). Ewing stands adjacent to Memorial Hospital.
Connecting corridors link them. Efforts are underway
to work out mutually satisfactory arrangements for
transferring ownership of Ewing to Memorial Hospital.
At its low occupancy rate, this hospital does not
justify retention in the public sector.

Metropolitan Hospital

If Coler continues in its present function, Metropolitan and Coler could constitute a medical center in
affiliation with Flower and Fifth Avenue Hospitals and
the New York Medical College. A comprehensive affiliation should be established to enable these institutions
to function under a single administration, with the
city retaining program control with respect to Metropolitan's responsibilities. A new psychiatric wing
is under construction at Metropolitan and is to include
a psychiatric laboratory and community mental health

facilities. The estimated cost of this project
shown in CB '68 is $16 million. CB '68 also shows an
estimated cost of $26 million for a new building,
including site, to expand services at Metropolitan.
A better solution would involve: closing Coler,
moving New York Medical College to Queens, affiliating
Metropolitan with Mt. Sinai.

Sydenham

        Certain facts about Sydenham should be noted.
First, the occupancy rate for the years 1964-66 was
low: 70.6%, 67%, and 60.4%. Second, the physical
plant is cramped and out of date. There is no room
within the building for effective remodeling nor is
land available for expansion. Third, the hospital is
too small (218 beds) to justify operation by the city
as a general hospital. Sydenham maintains 59 beds
for the private patients of Negro physicians in the
area. This is a carry-over from Sydenham's original
role (pre-1949) as a voluntary institution. Occupancy
in these beds runs 90-95%. Given a general program
to introduce private beds into city hospitals, this
unique service of Sydenham will no longer be a factor
in charting its future. Two courses suggest themselves. One is conversion of Sydenham to an ambulatory care facility, satellite to Harlem Hospital.
The other is merger with Knickerbocker Hospital (221
beds, one-half mile north of Sydenham) and possibly
with the Hospital for Joint Diseases (330 beds, three-
quarters of a mile east) to form a large, general
hospital serving the West Side between St. Luke's at
113th Street and Presbyterian at 168th Street. Pending definitive plans, modernization and reconstruction
of the present plant is necessary, with special reference to the electrical system. CB '68 records a total
estimated cost of approximately $1.1 million for
renovation.

Satellites

        In the preceding sections plans were touched on
for developing ambulatory care centers--"Neighborhood
Family Care Centers"--through construction and renovation programs at Gouverneur and at the Lower East
Side District Health Center. Both projects are listed
in CB '68. CB '68 also provides for renovation programs ($600,00 each) to develop family care centers at

East Harlem and Central Harlem District Health Centers, and provides an estimate of $1,184,340 for a "comprehensive health center" at Washington Heights.

In addition, two new free-standing family care centers are in the current planning for Manhattan, listed in CB '68 at an estimated cost of $2 million each. A status report dated July 13, 1967, comments on these projects:

> Riverside - Site Acquisition Board has been requested to locate space in the vicinity of 82nd Street to cover health areas 34 and 35.
>
> Central Harlem - Site Acquisition Board has been asked to acquire space in the Milbank-Frawley Urban Renewal Area. A possibility exists that New York City Housing Authority will provide space in Foster Houses.

Already mentioned is the incorporation of community mental health centers in the building plans for Harlem Hospital, Gouverneur, and Metropolitan Hospital. The plans for Bellevue also provide for such a center. Table 7 lists community mental health centers (including the four just named) proposed for Manhattan over a 20-year development program. The list also shows hospitals in the catchment area for each center and gives the catchment population.

Independent satellite programs, many of them funded by federal grants, are increasingly being undertaken by hospitals in New York City. These programs promise to play a growing role in the delivery of health services in Manhattan. Some examples: Harlem Hospital, in company with the board of education, has made use of a neighborhood community center to provide a school program for unwed pregnant girls, who by law cannot continue in a public school. Roosevelt Hospital operates two store-front clinics in its neighborhood and conducts a single-room occupancy program in psychiatric care in a former residential hotel. New York Medical College is searching for ways to extend certain of its maternity and child-care programs into the community.

Table 7. Community Mental Health
Centers Proposed for
Manhattan

Key: * - Proposed affiliate for staffing and
          back-up.
      f - Certain funds provided in the Capital
          Budget for 1967-68.
      b - Project carries a budget code but is not
          yet funded.

Community Mental Health Center	General Hospital In or Near Catchment Area	Population of Catchment Area
f Bellevue East------	*Bellevue---------- University	127,409
Bellevue West------	*Bellevue---------- French New York Polyclinic St. Clare's	120,890
f Central Park No.---	Flower-Fifth------ *Mt. Sinai	105,935
East Side----------	Lenox Hill-------- New York	70,797
Greenwich Village--	Beekman----------- *St. Vincent's	124,017
f Harlem-------------	Harlem------------	184,488
Inwood-------------	Jewish Memorial--- St. Elizabeth's	114,897
f Lower Manhattan---- (Gouverneur)	Beth Israel------- Columbus *Proposed Gouverneur New York Infirmary	172,891
f Metropolitan-------	Doctor's---------- *Metropolitan Trafalgar	173,985
Morningside--------	*St. Luke's-------- Sydenham	162,827
b Washington Hgts./ West Harlem------	*Columbia Presby- terian---------- Knickerbocker	166,433
f West Side----------	Roosevelt--------	173,712
	Total:	1,698,281

345

It is absolutely imperative that all independent activity in support of ambulatory care facility development be welded into one borough-wide plan.

The Private Sector

Relationships with the private sector have been noted above for city hospitals in Manhattan. For Bellevue and Metropolitan: comprehensive affiliations that remove the city from operating management of these hospitals. For Ewing: transfer to Memorial. For Delafield: transfer to, or comprehensive affiliation with, Presbyterian. For Sydenham: the possibility of merger with Knickerbocker and the Hospital for Joint Diseases, or satellite to Harlem Hospital.

Earlier mentioned was the need to develop certain voluntary institutions as medical centers along the West Side. St. Luke's, Roosevelt, and St. Vincent's Hospitals appear suited to this purpose. City and other support should evolve for the development of satellites to these hospitals. Community mental health centers are already proposed for each. The Riverside and Lower West Side District Health Centers are in the communities served by St. Luke's and St. Vincent's Hospitals. The free-standing family health center proposed for the vicinity of 82nd Street is a possible affiliate for Roosevelt.

Bronx: Health Services Programs

Certain problems and circumstances appear to lead the forces that shape program-planning for the delivery of health services in the Bronx:

- The thin spread of hospitals in the Bronx, calling for coordinated planning of all hospitals in a cooperative pattern.

- The lack of hospital facilities in the southeast Bronx.

- Mott Haven--among the three most depressed areas in the city.

- City commitments from previous administrations to build at Montefiore and St. Francis.

- Care of the elderly in the Bronx.

- The obsolete and run-down city hospitals in the west Bronx--Fordham, Lincoln, and Morrisania.

- Aggressive medical leadership at Montefiore and at Einstein College of Medicine.

- Poor transportation in the Bronx.

The programs that follow respond in various ways to these needs and circumstances. One general observation must be made: In the Bronx there is displayed an exciting vigor in planning and action for improved health delivery, unduplicated for an entire borough elsewhere in the city. Leadership is being expressed in most of the major agencies of the borough.

Bronx Hospital Center

The capital budget for 1967-1968 establishes funding for an $855,000 project to expand and reconstruct the laundry facilities at the Bronx Hospital. Budget codes have been issued for two other projects that do not appear in CB '68. One is a 400-bed public home infirmary care building, tentatively budgeted at $18,240,000 for 455,000 sq. ft., but estimated in an architect's study to require $21,784,000 for 751,000 sq. ft. Further work here is held up pending development of a total Bronx plan. The second unfunded project is a public home infirmary ambulatory care building to cost $10 million. This project is also affected by the total plan.

The Department of Public Works is preparing a program to expand the Bronx Hospital emergency room and radiology facility, and to establish a 200-bed mental health unit. Over time, one may expect the Bronx Hospital, in its affiliation with Einstein College of Medicine, to become the hub of an array of satellite facilities. A tower of acute beds is a feasible concept for Bronx Hospital, in company with a renovation program for the existing structure to provide teaching, office, and research space. While the present plant is relatively new, it is functionally out of date.

Fordham Hospital

CB '68 establishes initial funding for a $19.8 million project to relocate Fordham Hospital to the

grounds of its affiliate, Misericordia, in the north
Bronx. The Health and Hospital Planning Council has
recommended that Fordham be moved southwest instead,
to 180th Street and 3rd Avenue. Current opinions in
the city indicate a location another half-mile southwest, closer to the Grand Concourse at Tremont or
Burnside Avenue. There is some possibility that construction of a family care center can begin now on
land next to the present Fordham. (In any event, such
a center should be established when Fordham moves.)
CB '68 initiates funding on a $4 million crash program
to provide needed alterations in surgery, radiology,
the food services, laboratories, and the ambulatory
care services. Rebuilding of Fordham at Misericordia
would appear to be a poor plan.

Lincoln Hospital

Initial architectural planning is underway for
a new Lincoln, located northwest of the present site.
CB '68 provides starting funds for this project,
estimated at a total cost of $66.7 million, including
a community mental health facility. Actual bed complement is not firm. If Fordham moves to the southwest, 750 beds will serve at Lincoln. However, commitments exist to provide 500 general-care beds and
200 psychiatric beds for the community. How many
long-term beds should be provided? Either new under-
standings of bed use must be reached, or the bed-
count raised above 750.

Morrisania

Commitments exist from previous city administrations to construct a new Morrisania Hospital on the
grounds at Montefiore Hospital, the Morrisania affiliate. Current city planning is to meet this commitment with a wing on Montefiore, possibly in the
form of a tower of acute beds. A new program must
be devised for the present Morrisania. Extended
care needs are great in the community, as is the
need for a family care center. Lincoln is to move
toward Morrisania, Fordham is likely to do so, and
such shifts will ease the demand on Morrisania for
acute general services. However, the present Morrisania should be rebuilt or renovated, at least to provide ambulatory care.

St. Francis Hospital

The city faces a commitment to buy St. Francis;
CB '68 provides $3 million for this purpose. Ambu-
latory care seems the most feasible use for this
property.

The Bronx Plan

The Bronx is thinly covered by hospitals. To
move one is to affect the others. The potential
effect of satellites, especially of comprehensive
family care centers, must also be weighed. Figure 8
pictures a feasible arrangement of city hospitals
and family care centers. District health centers
have also been sketched in.

Satellites

CB '68 provides initial funding for renovations
to establish family care centers at the Tremont and
Mott Haven District Health Centers. An HSA status
report dated July 13, 1967, notes that Tremont "may
have to withdraw because of inadequate space." Also
provided in CB '68 are initial funds for two free-
standing family care centers, their total costs estimated at $2 million each. The July 13th status
report comments on these projects:

> Morrisania--Three possible loca-
> tions have been suggested by the
> Borough Director: (1) Vicinity of
> West Farms Road (11,000 square
> feedt); (2) Star Theatre--163rd St.
> and Southern Boulevard (presently
> occupied by the Bronx Community
> Progress Center); and (3) A YMCA
> which was renovated four years ago
> and is presently for sale.

> Mott Haven--Site Acquisition
> Board has been requested to ac-
> quire the St. Francis Hospital
> parking lot. The District Health
> Officer has suggested that the
> community would prefer a site at
> 153rd Street and Union Avenue,
> which is city-owned and in the
> Hunts Point Multi-Service Area.

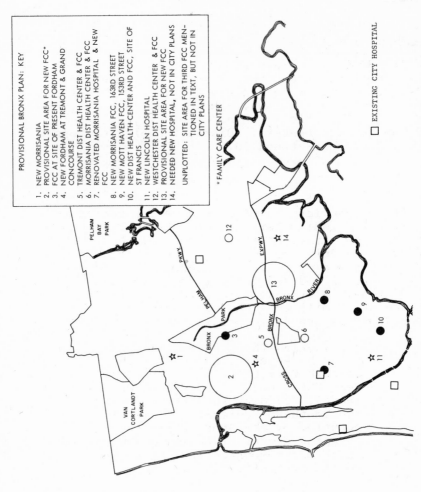

PROVISIONAL BRONX PLAN: KEY

1. NEW MORRISANIA
2. PROVISIONAL SITE AREA FOR NEW FCC*
3. FCC AT SITE OF PRESENT FORDHAM
4. NEW FORDHAM AT TREMONT & GRAND CONCOURSE
5. TREMONT DIST HEALTH CENTER & FCC
6. MORRISANIA DIST HEALTH CENTER & FCC
7. RENOVATED MORRISANIA HOSPITAL & NEW FCC
8. NEW MORRISANIA FCC, 163RD STREET
9. NEW MOTT HAVEN FCC, 153RD STREET
10. NEW DIST HEALTH CENTER AND FCC, SITE OF ST FRANCIS
11. NEW LINCOLN HOSPITAL
12. WESTCHESTER DIST HEALTH CENTER & FCC
13. PROVISIONAL SITE AREA FOR NEW FCC
14. NEEDED NEW HOSPITAL, NOT IN CITY PLANS

UNPLOTTED: SITE AREA FOR THIRD FCC MEN-
TIONED IN TEXT, BUT NOT IN
CITY PLANS

* FAMILY CARE CENTER

□ EXISTING CITY HOSPITAL

Figure 8. Proposed Medical Facility Locations: The Bronx

CB '68 provides $3 million for the "acquisition and conversion" of St. Francis Hospital into a family care center, satellite to Lincoln Hospital. While three million dollars is the current asking price for this property, conversion to ambulatory care will require additional funding. It would be reasonable, in long-range terms, to plan eventually to move the district health center to the St. Francis site, even though renovations to the center are called for now to provide needed family care.

The feasibility of constructing family care centers on the sites of Fordham and Morrisania are under study, in anticipation of possible relocation of the present hospitals. Within the next five years, planning is in order for at least three additional free-standing family care centers.

Community mental health centers, three in number, are afforded initial funding in CB '68. Two of these, however, at Lincoln and Morrisania, are to be incorporated into the new hospitals bearing those names. ("Morrisania" thus refers to the new structure planned at Montefiore.) Action on these centers must await hospital plans. The free-standing Crotona Park Community Mental Health Center, its estimated cost $17.4 million, also receives initial funding in CB '68. The possibility exists that this center will be merged with the planning for the new Fordham Hospital.

Table 8 lists community mental health centers proposed for the Bronx over a 20-year development period. Also shown are hospitals in the catchment area for each center and the catchment population.

Hospitals in the Bronx, in the fashion of the era, are launching independent satellites--independent, at least, in the sense that they are not part of a long-term, city-wide or borough-wide program. They frequently share the resources of other institutions. Montefiore, for instance, with funds from the Office of Economic Opportunity and in cooperation with the Department of Health, has established a demonstration program involving family medical care, training for health workers, a planned effort in community involvement, and a plan for project evaluation. The base is the Morrisania District Health Office; smaller satellites extend from there. Lincoln Hospital, among its community-oriented projects, has an O.E.O. grant of $578,500 for neighborhood service centers and a

Table 8. Community Mental Health
Centers Proposed for the
Bronx

Community Mental Health Center	General Hospital In or Near Catchment Area	Population of Catchment Area
Bronx Municipal-----	Bronx Municipal------	133,452
Crotona Park--------	Bronx-Lebanon-------- (Concourse and Fulton Divisions)	170,823
Fordham-------------	Fordham-------------	158,458
High Bridge---------	Bronx-Lebanon-------- (Concourse Div.)*	147,256
Hunts Point---------	Proposed Lincoln*----	149,014
Lincoln-------------	Proposed Lincoln----- St. Francis	195,164
Morrisania----------	Montefiore----------- Proposed Morrisania Union	160,650
Soundview/ Throgs-Neck-------	Bronx Municipal*-----	178,602
Williamsbridge------	Misericordia---------	131,396
	Total:	1,424,815

---

* In periphery of catchment area.

352

Children's Bureau (HEW) grant of $1.2 million to
develop maternity centers. These programs are in
affiliation with Einstein Medical College. Effective
city-wide planning for health services must eventually
encompass such programs.

The Private Sector

Albert Einstein Medical College adjoins Bronx
Hospital Center; Montefiore property is the proposed
setting for the new Morrisania. In the interest of
unified, simplified, and more effective management,
the two voluntaries should undertake the administration of their related city hospitals under comprehensive affiliations. This is for the purposes of operating management; program control over the hospitals
should remain in city hands.

The voluntary sector should be probed for interest and resources, in cooperation with the city, to
construct a general hospital in the southeast Bronx
to serve the Soundview--Throgs-Neck area. Active
planning on such a hospital is needed now.

Queens: Health Services Programs

The borough characteristics that appear of special weight in shaping future programs are these:

- The relatively large proportion of proprietary
  hospitals and private physicians.

- The general lack of strong affiliations between
  municipal and voluntary institutions within the
  borough.

- The lack of a central, major community hospital. (Long Island Jewish Hospital fits the
  definition for quality, programs, and leadership, but is at the far edge of the borough.
  Thus additional community hospital orientation
  is needed elsewhere in the borough.)

- The relative lack of health facilities in
  Jamaica, where a major poverty pocket has
  developed.

- The appearance of isolated poverty pockets in relatively well-off communities.

- The lack of a medical school.

In various ways, these needs and circumstances are addressed in the programs that follow.

Queens Hospital Center

Plans are emerging to strengthen and enlarge Queens as a community hospital. The capital budget for 1967-68 (CB '68), as an information item, listed plans for a chronic care building to cost $26.1 million. A community mental health center is in the planning. The concept of a tower of acute beds, plus renovation of the existing plant, is feasible for consideration at Queens Hospital because of the available land. Renovation for expanded ambulatory care will be important in conversion to a community hospital.

Elmhurst Medical Center

Here, as at Queens, plans are emerging for development as a community hospital. As an information item in CB '68, the costs of renovation and new construction, including site, are estimated at $13.5 million. Here is another place where it is feasible to think of building a tower of acute beds and renovating the existing plant for ambulatory care, offices, laboratories and teaching. Elmhurst was built in 1955. It is nonetheless an outdated hospital.

Riker's Island

The adult sentence unit on Riker's Island contains a 200-bed infirmary; an examining area and 80-bed security ward are housed in the reception unit. These two units are in separate buildings and under different wardens. Surgery and acute care are provided in prison wards at Bellevue. Transfer of a prisoner between these facilities calls for two guards, handcuffs, a vehicle and driver, and the exercise of an impressive array of security procedures. A 500-bed security hospital would produce long-term personnel savings. This goal can be realized by adding a

250-bed unit to the infirmary at Riker's Island, but
staffing would be a major problem. Strong affiliation
with Bellevue-NYU would be necessary. (The infirmary
was once an active teaching hospital. Isolation and
the many gate checks necessary to enter or exit eventually cost the hospital the majority of its professional staff.) A somewhat less attractive alternative is to build a security hospital at Elmhurst, the
municipal hospital nearest Riker's Island. A new
wing on the Island infirmary would cost approximately
$25 million; a new building at Elmhurst, approximately
$50 million.

A Medical School for Queens

The need is clear. The cost to the city would
depend upon the availability of federal or state funds
and upon the possibilities for cooperation with an
established university and medical school. The city
cost may range from $30 to $50 million, in terms of
very rough estimates for moving an existing school.
The location could be either Queens or Elmhurst (with
the edge to Elmhurst if a prison hospital were to be
built there with its potential as a teaching hospital).
An attractive and promising additional alternative is
association with Long Island Jewish Hospital. The
city should explore funding arrangements for a medical
school and possible affiliations, with a view to early
action.

Satellite Facilities

CB '68 provides for renovating the Jamaica District Health Center to provide neighborhood family
care services. Affiliation planning is underway for
this facility with Mary Immaculate Hospital.

Also planned for renovation as family care centers (though not in the current budget) are the
Astoria-Maspeth and Corona-Flushing District Health
Centers. Planning is underway to add these centers
to Elmhurst's program.

A community mental health center (new building)
is listed as an information item in CB '68. It is
contemplated to add this facility to the affiliation
program at St. John's Hospital (Queens). Table 9 lists
community mental health centers proposed for Queens
over a 20-year development program.

Table 9.   Community Mental Health
            Centers Proposed for
            Queens

Community Mental Health Center	General Hospital In or Near Catchment Area	Population of Catchment Area
Elmhurst-----------	Elmhurst-----------	198,356
Kissena Park-------	Booth Memorial-----	85,238
Little Neck--------	Hillside**--------- Long Island Jewish	195,935
North Shore--------	Flushing-----------	127,627
Queens Hospital----	Interfaith--------- Mary Immaculate Queens	195,790
Queens Village-----	Hillside*---------- Queens*	172,185
Rego Park----------	St. John's--------- Wyckoff Heights	193,844
Richmond Hill------	Jamaica------------	168,659
South Shore/ Rockaway---------	Peninsula---------- St. Joseph's	109,173
Steinway-----------	Elmhurst*----------	192,185
Woodhaven----------	Elmhurst*---------- St. John's* Wyckoff Heights*	170,586
	Total:	1,809,578

---

 * In periphery of catchment area.
** Psychiatric hospital affiliated with Long
   Island Jewish Hospital.

The Private Sector

In addition to the satellite affiliations with
St. John's and Mary Immaculate, the city is exploring
the purchase of an existing 200-bed general hospital
to convert to ambulatory care under an affiliation
with Jamaica Hospital. Whatever the outcome of this
question, Jamaica Hospital, because of its location,
appears a likely candidate for city support in the
development of satellites in Jamaica.

Brooklyn: Health Services Programs

Among the factors that dictate health services
program needs for Brooklyn are these:

- Obsolescence: Sixteen of 41 Brooklyn hospitals studied by the Health and Hospital Planning Council in 1966 were judged obsolete.
This is nearly 40 per cent.

- Maldistribution of health services: The
southeastern area has over 35% of the population and only 9% of the hospital beds.

- The out-patient overload on Kings County
Hospital.

- A multiplicity of services and variations in
the quality of care.

- The lack of borough-wide organization for the
delivery of health services.

- Inadequate programs for the mentally ill, the
aged, and the addicted.

These needs and circumstances are reflected in
various ways in the following programs.

Cumberland Hospital

Cumberland Hospital is affiliated with Brooklyn
Hospital, four blocks away. The two function well as
a single center. An $8 million renovation program
for Cumberland is shown in CB '68. A budget code
(without funding, as yet) has been established to provide an estimated $11.2 million for building an extended
care unit and a community mental health center on

city-owned land adjacent to Brooklyn Hospital. Studies are underway of the feasibility of reversing this
plan, so to speak, by converting Cumberland to extended
care, ambulatory care, and mental health, and constructing a new acute-care facility next to Brooklyn
Hospital.

Coney Island Hospital

CB '68 shows a $2.3 million program for hospital
renovation and alteration. CB '68 also lists a community health center and research facility for Coney
Island Hospital, the cost being $10.3 million. The
community around Coney Island Hospital is very largely
middle-class, and appears capable of supporting a
voluntary hospital. In progress are studies of possible ways that the hospital might be transferred
from public to voluntary auspices to the satisfaction
of both parties. Whatever the outcome, Coney Island
should undergo additional renovation to adapt it to
private patients so that it can serve as a community
hospital.

Greenpoint Hospital

CB '68 provides for an expenditure of $53 million
to construct a new general hospital at Flushing and
Sumner Avenues. This cost covers both the site and
the addition of a community mental health center. The
disposition of the present facility is an open question. Tentative planning calls for converting part
of the facility to ambulatory care. But the location,
relatively isolated and in an area that is largely
industrial, does not speak wholeheartedly for even
this reduced use. This hospital should be rebuilt
and developed as a major, independent community medical center.

Kings County Hospital

CB '68 lists (for information only) a sum of $93
million for replacements, reconstruction, and modernization of Kings County Hospital. Action on this
program has been postponed for the drawing up of a
clearer statement of role for Kings County. With
University Hospital, Kings County should serve as

the medical hub of Brooklyn, with other hospitals
functioning in relationship. The bed count should
be reduced. Ambulatory care facilities in other
locations should be developed to ease the pressure
on the ambulatory services of Kings County. The
concept of a tower of acute beds seems a feasible
application here, at a great saving in cost. Pending the over-all development, a crash program is in
order to improve conditions in the emergency room,
surgery, OPD, and radiology laboratory.

In addition to the above, CB '68 provides
$85,300 for renovating the TB research laboratories
at Kings County, under the auspices of the Health
Research Council. CB '68 lists (for information)
$788,000 for laboratories for the Health Research
Council "in certain existing buildings" at Kings
County.

Satellites

CB '68 estimates a total cost of $600,000 each
for renovating the following District Health Centers
to provide neighborhood family care services: Brownsville, Fort Greene, and Sunset Park. Amounts in the
neighborhood of $2.2 million each are estimated in
CB '68 for building additions to established family
care centers at Brownsville and Bedford District
Health Centers. The same budget estimates $2 million
each for three free-standing family care centers in
Brooklyn. (The following comments on these three
programs have been provided by an HSA status report
dated July 13, 1967:)

> Bedford -- St. Mary's Hospital has
> offered land on the grounds of the
> hospital itself and this is immedi-
> ately available.

> Brownsville -- Free community parti-
> cipation in selecting a site at
> Pennsylvania and Pitkin Avenues.
> Site Selection Board requested to
> acquire this site.

> Bushwick -- New York City Housing
> Authority may be able to provide
> site on Housing Authority proper-
> ty. This program is hampered by
> the fact that no commitment has

been received for back-up services, and hospitals in the
area are limited.

Already mentioned are community mental health
centers as part of the building plans for Coney Island,
Cumberland, and Greenpoint Hospitals. In addition,
CB '68 estimates $17.4 million for a Bedford-Stuyvesant
Community Mental Health Center.

The sum of $9.5 million is projected in CB '68 to
construct a new home and hospital for the aged at Manhattan Beach, Brooklyn.

Table 10 shows the full array of community mental
health centers currently proposed for a 20-year development plan. General hospitals in or near the catchment area for each center are shown, as is the current
population of the catchment area.

The Private Sector

To facilitate the operation of Brooklyn and Cumberland Hospitals as a single center, Cumberland
should be placed under a comprehensive affiliation
with Brooklyn. The city in this arrangement would
retain program control over the combined operation;
operating management would be in the hands of Brooklyn
Hospital. In addition, an affiliation with Brooklyn
should be established to provide staffing for the
family care center being planned at the Fort Greene
District Health Center. The two institutions, hospital and health center, are two blocks apart.

Similarly, a comprehensive affiliation should be
arranged between Kings County Hospital and the Downstate Medical School. Already mentioned is that the
private sector should be explored for arrangements to
operate Coney Island as a voluntary hospital. If
these plans can be fulfilled, the city will be left
with full administrative responsibility for one hospital in Brooklyn: Greenpoint.

Planning is underway, as stated above, to place
the new Bedford Family Care Center on the grounds of
St. Mary's Hospital. A mental health center is also
planned for St. Mary's.

St. John's Hospital, in the present planning,
will affiliate with the family care center to be

Table 10. Community Mental Health
           Centers Proposed for
           Brooklyn

Community Mental Health Center	General Hospital In or Near Catchment Area	Population of Catchment Area
Bedford Stuyvesant-	St. Mary's*-------- St. John's Episcopal	189,502
Bensonhurst--------	Coney Island*------	184,887
Brookdale----------	Brookdale---------- Lutheran Hospital of Brooklyn	123,073
Canarsie/ East New York----	Brookdale*--------- Lutheran Hospital of Brooklyn*	175,400
Coney Island-------	Coney Island-------	188,895
Cumberland--------	Brooklyn---------- Proposed Cumberland	135,971
Dyker Beach--------	Victory Memorial---	95,000
East Flatbush------	Kings County*------	189,582
Greenpoint---------	Proposed Greenpoint	116,818
Kings County-------	Kings County------- St. Mary's Unity	174,960
Maimonides---------	Lutheran Medical--- Center Maimonides	103,922
Midwood/ Flatlands--------	Community Hospital- of Brooklyn Proposed Providence	192,930
North Brooklyn-----	Proposed Cumberland* Proposed Greenpoint*	143,799
Park Slope---------	Caledonian--------- Methodist	126,150
Red Hook/Prospect--	Adelphi------------ Jewish Hospital of Brooklyn Long Island College (Main and Prospect Heights Division)	174,520
Ridgewood----------	Bethany Deaconess-- Evangelical Deaconess Proposed Greenpoint* Wyckoff Heights	186,454
Sunset Park--------	Maimonides*--------	125,456
	Total:	2,627,319

* In periphery of catchment area.

361

developed at the Bedford District Health Center. A
community mental health center is also planned for
St. John's.

Other hospitals that appear suitable for joint
effort with the city are these:

> Brookdale -- A community mental
> health center (funded under
> Brookdale's own auspices) and
> the family care center at the
> Brownsville District Health
> Center (budgeted in CB '68).
>
> Long Island College Hospital --
> A family care center for Red
> Hook, not yet budgeted.
>
> Lutheran Medical Center -- The
> family care center at the Sun-
> set Park District Health Center
> funded under the hospital's own
> auspices.

Planning is currently underway among the Catholic
institutions of Brooklyn for mergers of smaller institutions with a view to building a major general hospital, probably (in the current planning) in Canarsie.
(The Catholic hospital and health service planning
program is excellent.)

The Health and Hospital Planning Council has
recommended that many of the smaller voluntary and
proprietary hospitals be merged and mostly rebuilt.
It is very likely that this will have to be accomplished with the assistance of public funds. HSA
staff have emphasized that "much of the final plans
for Brooklyn cannot be laid until the availability of
public capital becomes clear."

Staten Island: Health Services Programs

These problems and characteristics of the borough shape its health program needs:

- A lack of low-cost nursing homes.

- No psychiatric beds.

- Poor transportation.

- A single, 160-bed general hospital in South Richmond.

- Air and water pollution.

- An in-patient overload on the borough's four general hospitals. (An estimated 75-100 medical/surgical beds are needed now; 100 or more by 1970.)

- No room for expansion at Staten Island Hospital (274 beds).

- Limited voluntaries.

- Sea View: An obsolete and deteriorated plant--possibly the worst in the city--but situated on an excellent site.

- Future need for a medical school.

- A mobile low-income population; no clear poverty pockets.

These matters are reflected in the programs that follow:

Sea View Hospital and Home

Key findings here are obsolescence and deterioration--old people and old buildings grown hopeless together. Sea View consists of five basic components:

- Two ward pavilions containing 244 hospital beds.

- The geriatrics building for treating chronically ill, aged men and women.

- The isolation building (Richmond Boro Hospital) of 34 beds for tuberculosis and communicable diseases.

- The Home section: 558 nursing-home beds in six buildings.

- A custodial section of 228 beds for homeless old men and women.

Offices and service facilities are scattered among the more usable of the 92 separate buildings on the Sea View grounds.

The Sea View program can be tied to the larger needs for medical services on Staten Island. The city, in partnership with Staten Island Hospital, should construct on the Sea View grounds:

1) A 500-bed acute general hospital, designed with teaching in mind.

2) An attached (and expandable) building for administration, physicians' offices, ambulatory care, and hospital services.

3) A 400-bed nursing home; and nursing/para-medical training center.

4) And, ultimately, a medical school.

Renovation of the custodial care units on the Sea View grounds is also in order.

At St. Vincent's Hospital, at the north end of Staten Island, a second 400-bed nursing home should be built, with city participation if necessary.

CB '68 provides initial funding of an estimated $2.7 million for alteration and renovation of the geriatrics building at Sea View. Architects' plans for a new extended care facility at Sea View (esti-mated cost approximately $6.8 million) are over 80% complete, but work has stopped pending definitive programs for Staten Island as a whole.

The Private Sector

The city should have limited (if any) direct engagement in the operation of health services on Staten Island; it should devote its resources (for such time as necessary) to assisting in the build-up of voluntary strength to satisfactory levels. The medical program at Sea View is sound--given the gray and crumbling plant and the shortages characteristic of the city system--but this is a monument to individ-uals, to the medical director in particular; there is no promise whatever of long-term continuity.

With the consent of the city, St. Vincent's Hospital is seeking state funds to acquire Sea View, but this hospital has land for expansion at its present site. A nursing home and extended care facility should be built here to give St. Vincent's a share of the health services responsibility now borne by Sea View. St. Vincent's should additionally be looked to for the operation of satellite programs in its community.

If Staten Island Hospital is to grow, it must move. This hospital, as reported elsewhere herein, is developing a long-range plan for improvement and expansion. Initial-phase cost is estimated at $9 million, for which federal funds will be sought. These circumstances encourage explorations into the possibility of a joint undertaking with the city at Sea View.

The city should begin inquiries into the private sector to initiate planning for a medical college on the Sea View grounds. This is a long-term project, with the start of definitive planning a year or two away.

While we can expect family care centers--ambulatory care centers--to be built on Staten Island, no specific plans have been formulated. Two community mental health centers are in planning. One of them, North Richmond CMHC, is afforded initial funding in CB '68. The total estimated cost: $5,057,000. St. Vincent's will staff and operate this center. There is some possibility that St. Vincent's will undertake its construction as well.

SURVEYS OF NONMUNICIPAL HOSPITAL AND NURSING HOME SYSTEMS

Having focused primary attention upon the municipal hospitals in comprehensive investigation, Commission perspective required a sampling survey of all other classes of hospitals. Comparable staff visits were made to selected:

- University teaching hospitals.

- "Medium-size" voluntaries.

- "Small-size" voluntaries.

- Proprietaries (including an osteopathic hospital).

- State mental institutions in New York City.

- Federal institutions in New York City.

The staff wishes to highlight certain observations regarding each. (Extensive visit reports for each institution surveyed in the various classes have been omitted, with reluctance, for reasons of space in this report.)

Teaching Hospitals

The medical schools and teaching hospitals view themselves as "centers of excellence." They believe that they in fact function in this role, except when their efforts are diluted by activities not related to teaching or research. Affiliation programs, for instance, are sometimes seen as forcing their staffs into trivial administrative concerns that are wasteful of their professional talents.

The schools point out that each physician's work in teaching hospitals is constantly under the scrutiny of students and other physicians. They believe (and the survey staff is persuaded) that this is the ultimate guarantor of good patient care. For this among other reasons, the teaching function should be extended into the farthest reaches of the health system, very likely on a regional (borough) basis, with a given medical school at the hub.

The faculties insist that selective admissions are essential to the basic roles of the teaching institution. They are worried about the effect of Medicare on the available stock of teaching material. One professor pointed out that Medicare has only highlighted what has always been a gnawing ethical question: "On whom should the medical student perform his first appendectomy?" It may well be that, in times to come, the patient who seeks the excellent medical services of the teaching hospitals must do so with the understanding that he will be used as teaching material.

In this tour of municipal, voluntary, and proprietary hospitals, more than once the opinion was encountered that one cannot talk about the delivery

of health services without talking about medical education. Are not the departmentalized structures of
the schools, which are carried on into practice, destructive of patient-oriented medicine? And what
about continuing education to keep the practicing
physician abreast of his art and to upgrade the poorly trained (usually foreign-trained) practitioner?
These questions cannot be addressed without working
changes in the medical schools. The forces of tradition have so far held the upper hand. Programs
must be worked out actively to measure the stated
problems and test feasible solutions. This is possible, and the affiliation contract may be a framework in which first, perhaps tentative, directions
may be set.

        In summary, it seems evident that a university
teaching hospital should be actively engaged as the
medical leadership apex of every broad system of
institutional health delivery for a borough or a major part of a borough (vide Figure 6). In other words,
a model should be formed, and patterns set so that
the University Hospital can provide its most beneficial effects upon associated voluntary and municipal
institutions. This principle should hold even in
cases where a borough does not now enjoy the presence
of such an institution.

        In this latter regard, the staff has foreseen
an early need for a medical school in Queens and,
within the next five to ten years, on Staten Island
at the Sea View site. Continued clustering of medical schools in Manhattan has led to system imbalances
for the city as a whole. Ultimately, schools in
Queens and Staten Island would probably come about
through principal joint sponsorship by CUNY, the city,
and voluntary institutions.

Voluntary Hospitals

        Growth and expansion is the pattern for the larger
voluntaries visited and for certain of the smaller.
Often, construction is underway or plans are on the
drawing boards. Satellite programs are contemplated.
The voluntaries are alert to sources of federal and
state money. They are concerned with fitting themselves into the developing schema for a health services
system, coordinated city-wide.

Voluntary hospitals visited were:

Bronx Eye and Ear Infirmary	Bronx	58 beds
Brooklyn Hospital	Brooklyn	373 beds
House of St. Giles the Cripple	Brooklyn	44 beds
Interfaith	Queens	90 beds
Jamaica Hospital	Queens	295 beds
Maimonides Hospital	Brooklyn	565 beds
Midtown Hospital	Manhattan	59 beds
Misericordia Hospital	Bronx	332 beds
Roosevelt Hospital	Manhattan	514 beds

A concern for improved management practices is evident among the larger voluntaries. (Administrators at smaller voluntaries manage in terms of first-hand information: "I know how that department's doing, because I'm there every day.") At two hospitals in particular, questions brought forth a wealth of operating information from documents readily at hand. One administrator, for instance, explained his building programs in terms of service statistics that were plotted historically and projected into the future. At the same institution, the controller was developing automated accounting procedures and taking pains to teach the department heads how to interpret and use the operating reports. One hospital was endeavoring to develop program budgeting techniques, but with indifferent success, in spite of hard work and sizable assistance from outside consultants. (There is a lesson here: for hospitals, the phrase "program planning and budgeting" is easy to voice, hard to implement. Its application city-wide will call for education, effort, and time.)

Not infrequently it was found that the administrator could not produce historical analyses of his hospital's operations, well documented plans, or current measures of actual expenditures against budgets. No inference is made here about the quality of management and certainly not about the level of patient care in these hospitals. But changes must come about in reporting techniques and management style if institutions such as these are to participate effectively with one another and with the city in a coordinated health services program.

At another hospital, the adminstrator had developed a seminar program to help the members of his board of trustees to carry out their responsibilities.

His goal: "To teach them what questions to ask."
His was largely a new board, replacing one with a
long history of indifference, that had in his judge-
ment let the institution slide into the hands of its
physicians, to the detriment of its physical plant,
its planning program, and its potential role in the
community.

In two of the larger voluntaries, ward patients
were found (the medically indigent patients) in quarters not different from the more deteriorated wards
at Bellevue, Greenpoint, or Fordham. In the smaller
institutions, where the "wards" were six to eight
beds, there was no discernible difference in terms
of paint and plaster from the private-patient areas.
Some of the larger voluntaries, too, had their ward
patients attractively housed.

The administrators of the smaller voluntaries
find themselves searching for plans. They cannot
offer the equipment and services of the larger hospitals. They feel that this, in some cases at least,
represents disservice or active risk to the patient.
On the other hand, they pride themselves on the personal quality of the care they deliver. They may
have a proud tradition of service. One of them would
like to transfer its name and its specialty services
to the grounds of a large voluntary. Another is buy-
ing land in its vicinity in hopes that it can expand
to a size approved by the Health and Hospital Planning Council. But the available land may not be such
that it can do this.

Long-range comprehensive health facility planning
for the metropolitan area should anticipate a gradual
evolutionary change in the status and role of voluntary hospitals. In general, these changes should be
aimed so that any given hospital ultimately fulfills
one of these roles:

- Expansion to a 300- to 400-bed general
  hospital;

- By conversion, a major community-oriented
  ambulatory care center, satellite to a general hospital;

- Relocated to be physically adjacent to a
  large general hospital, with functions aligned
  appropriately;

- Conversion to an appropriate form of long-term nursing home and rehabilitation center.

In any event, all medium- and small-size voluntaries should be in active affiliation with large general hospitals, should serve as a point of working relationship with community physicians, and should evolve according to comprehensive city planning which they have had a part in bringing about.

Proprietary Hospitals

The staff visited these proprietary hospitals:

Interboro	172 beds	Brooklyn
Lefferts General	160 beds	Brooklyn
Parkway	220 beds	Queens
Westchester Square	224 beds	Bronx

The newest of these hospitals is clean, open, efficiently arranged, attractive to the eye. The oldest is clean and well-kept. In no particular of architecture or housekeeping are they inferior to well-run voluntaries of comparable age.

The negative incentives are clear: one administrator spoke of inspections every 70 days by one city agency or another, plus inspections by state agencies. The hospitals tell of deficiency reports having been written for a cigarette butt on a stockroom floor, for dirt on a refrigerator fan that the inspector uncovered by unscrewing the refrigerator's backplate, and for water splashed on the floor beside a dishwashing sink. To a follow-up letter from the city asking what had been done to remedy the latter condition, the hospital replied, "We mopped it up."

The Fire Department noted deficiencies in one hospital (according to the hospital staff), but advised that corrections be postponed because new codes were in preparation. The Department of Hospitals then responded to the uncorrected deficiencies by revoking the institution's one-year license and issuing a punitive 90-day license in its place.

This survey cannot offer first-hand observational experience with respect to the quality of medical care in these hospitals. These are common charges levied by critics of the proprietary system:

They do not buy adequate equipment. Asked
one voluntary administrator: "Would they
spend $8,000 for a magnet to remove metal
splinters--an instrument that they would
use twice a year?"

They hospitalize people unnecessarily and
perform unnecessary operations and laboratory tests, all to boost income.

The quality of patient care is not under
the kind of scrutiny that you find in
teaching hospitals--with students and
other physicians looking in on each case.

They admit unqualified physicians to their
staffs, as long as the man provides patients to fill empty beds.

To rephrase for emphasis: This survey cannot
comment on the validity of such charges. It seems
evident that certain of them would disappear if the
proprietaries could be incorporated into an integrated
system with the voluntaries and the municipal hospitals (probably without substantial change in their
operations!).

One of the hospitals is studying the advisability
of seeking voluntary status. The administrator named
his reasons:

Proprietaries are out of the mainstream of
medical care. They can't hire interns,
can't teach. Laws are restrictive. (The
proprietary system depends for its staffing upon the independent-practice physi-
cians--a resource and relationship to be
rediscovered and newly redeveloped by the
other classes of hospitals.)

Harassment. An inspection every 70 days.
"Deficiencies and violations, real or
alleged, reported at the drop of a hat."

The Blue Cross formula favors voluntary
and teaching hospitals by allowing more
expense items.

Low morale: proprietaries are looked down
upon by persons in other institutions.

In summary, present findings afford these observations:

- As a class, these institutions have been subjected to what they believe to be harassment at the hands of those who prefer that there be no "private" hospitals, i.e., no "profit" in medicine. (This concept is found to be a source of much confusion; it needs investigation, clarification, and resolution.) In this regard, the staff investigators believe that independent objective study should be made by competent <u>disinterested</u> parties; in all probability, outcomes would include recommendations for legislative, regulatory, and functional changes.

- A means of affiliating proprietaries with large hospital centers should be evolved.

- Those who hold controlling interest in each proprietary should undertake self-examination to determine (1) the desirability of changing to voluntary charter, (2) to evolve toward one of the end-forms suggested above for medium and small-size voluntaries, and (3) in any event, to establish effective means of participating in total community health planning.

- The entire medical establishment should encourage open-minded, objective concern for the problems of this class of hospital. It comprises a significant health system resource in New York City.

Other Government Hospitals

The staff visited these hospitals in the state and federal systems:

Manhattan State Hospital	3300 beds
Manhattan Veterans Admistration Hospital	1218 beds
Bronx Veterans Administration Hospital	1220 beds

In 1946, the V.A. hospital system became the largest in the world, with 165 hospital and 95 clinics. (For central organization, see Figure 9.) Wherever possible, their hospitals affiliate with other local

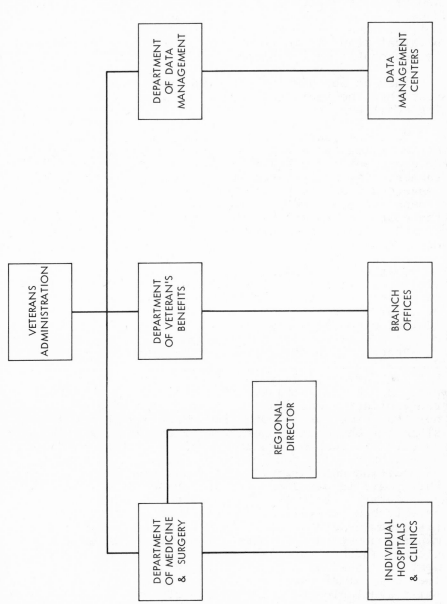

Figure 9. VA Hospital System: Central Organization

373

hospitals--Manhattan V.A. is affiliated with six.
Nonaffiliate visiting physicians are brought in as
consultants, as necessary. This hospital adjoins
Bellevue and New York University Hospitals. The
physical plant is in good to excellent condition and
is reasonably well equipped.

They do not have the nursing problem to the extent that the municipals do--140 filled of 175 nursing positions.

Veterans (particularly those with service connected ailments) are given preference in admission.
No questions are asked regarding ability to pay;
rather, they are treated free of charge. Nonservice-
connected disability veterans are asked to list their
assets and state whether they can pay any or all of
the costs. They are taken at their word (an "affidavit" system desperately needed in the local urban
hospitals).

Charge schedules are determined by a survey of
five local (nonfederal) hospitals in the area. Average costs are determined for a variety of medical
procedures and are communicated to patients in an
admission counseling session.

Decentralized operating control exists in the
V.A. hospitals. In 1953, a reorganization of the
V.A. was affected as a result of a two-year study
performed by consultants. The basic feature of the
reorganization was a decentralization to the local
hospital director of authority which made him responsible for the entire operation of the hospital. He,
in turn, is responsible to a regional director who
acts as a coordinator for the chief of the Division
of Medicine and Surgery. The annual budget (starting
this year) is based on patient turnover (as in a
proprietary hospital). Once the total amount is
established, the director can allocate his money as
his judgment dictates. He can authorize $20,000
minor-improvement projects out of his budgeted funds
with no further approval. Equipment, new or replacement, and new construction, are funded separately.
The hospital director can do his own contracting,
shift available money and personnel, and can reorganize within departments. He is the only person at the
hospital with authority to communicate to Washington.

The Bronx V.A. is not as new as is the Manhattan
V.A. The newest building there is 27 years old and
the oldest 65 years. But the administrative structure
is identical with Manhattan's. Both administrators
agree that the budget has become even more restricted
in recent years, with more money being specifically
allocated, but the essential ingredient, they feel,
is the fact that they can function as administrators
and they do "run the hospital."

Manhattan State Hospital, on Ward's Island, is a
unit of the State Department of Mental Hygiene. Yet
it must be considered an integral part of the city
system for treating mental illness. Its patients
come from the city. The city institutions function
as receiving and screening hospitals. City treatment,
according to the state administrator, does not exceed
30 days, except by consent of the patient and for
teaching purposes. Admissions to the state hospital
are for 60 days or less, but this can be extended.
The hospital admits 2,300 patients yearly. An out-
patient service operates, but only for former in-
patients.

Who pays for patient services? A sliding scale
is employed to enable the patient to pay what he can.
no investigation is made of the patient's resources.
A simple affidavit serves the purpose.

The hospital works closely with city agencies.
It is participating in the development of a federal
community mental health program that places participating hospitals in three administrative groups:

Metropolitan	Presbyterian	Bellevue
Harlem	St. Luke's	NYU Hospital
	Roosevelt	Beth Israel
		St. Vincent's

The administrator enjoys operating latitude within his budget. The budget contains only _fifteen_
lines. The categories are necessarily broad, and
afford freedom of movement to meet local needs.

Staff visits to state and federal hospitals in
the city have served to point up these findings:

● It is possible for public institutions to improve upon the medical support staffing characteristic of city hospitals in the neighborhoods in which they exist.

- It is possible to administer a local public institution within the contained management of that institution.

- The basic characteristics of the V.A. hospital system in particular contain lessons for the public hospital system of New York City.

Nursing-Home Facilities

The staff visited these institutions:

Aron Manor	Proprietary	Midtown Manhattan
Beth Abraham	Voluntary	Central Bronx
Eastchester	Proprietary	Northeast Bronx
Fairview	Proprietary	Forest Hills
Surfside	Proprietary	Far Rockaway

The Health and Hospital Planning Council reported in 1966 that 150 nursing-home facilities exist in New York City. Eighty-seven were proprietary (58%). Newer nursing homes built by law to the "Trussell Code" are markedly different from the older homes, many of which are located in converted homes and apartments. Apparently, older homes cannot by law be renovated or expanded.

A visit was made to one in this class. It was characterized by drabness, narrow halls, some patient rooms that must function as hallways, a minimum of natural light, and countless compromises needed to adapt the building to its present use. Rehabilitation facilities were at a minimum. Nevertheless, cleanliness was satisfactory, and this home was no worse than others in terms of the characteristic nursing-home odor.

Newer homes are open, light, and often colorfully decorated. Space and equipment are devoted to rehabilitation programs. In one home, there was no odor whatever. The administrator attributed this to prompt changes of linen and plenty of fresh air.

It is said that perhaps ten proprietary nursing homes in the city do not accept welfare/Medicaid patients. In others, the mix of private and public patients varies. The newest and most attractive of the homes visited reserves 30% of its beds for welfare patients "as a public service," even though some financial loss is alleged.

These are some comparative weekly rates:

Home	Private Patient	Welfare/ Medicaid	Medicare
A*	$100 minimum	$ 91.62	Unreported
B	$120 - $160	Unreported	$107.88
C	$125 - $170	$122.54	Unreported
D	$150 - $175	$122.54	Unreported
E**	$164 - $238	$150.22	$148.63

Medicare is bringing many convalescent patients into nursing homes, where once the primary service was custodial. Some number of homes may be expected to shift into this area of business. Chronic-care patients may find real difficulty in getting into homes that are near hospitals.

Effective functioning of nursing-home staffs at the orderly and aide level is essential to proper care of the aged. One administrator spoke of indifference and occasional cruelty toward patients on the part of his lower-level personnel. Even trainee help would be of assistance in these areas. This need should be addressed through certain of the paramedical training programs in planning throughout the city (and as later recommended in this report).

Findings may be summarized as follows:

● There are two groups of nursing homes from the viewpoint of physical acceptability: the new ones and the old ones.

  - Old homes are constrained from improvement by many internal and external forces. This debilitating, intentional "deadlock" on improvement must be broken equitably.

  - In their range of fair to excellent, the new homes demonstrate a highly promising potential for this class of health institution.

● There is a fundamental problem of definition of services for "nursing homes." Some virtually

---

*The oldest home in the group.
**Could be (and has been) classed as a chronic-care hospital; offers many medical and rehabilitative services.

are limited hospitals; others are chronic-
care homes; others are detached extended
care facilities.

- There are inadequate long-term and custodial
  care beds in the city.

- The location of some beds means removal of
  the patient from the community.

- There is lack of responsible planning for
  this entire area of vital care on the part of
  the city and other agencies.

- New federal and state funding sources will
  force changes in patterns of care. These
  changes should be directed in the public
  interest.

Due note should be taken of the need for the
city to either initiate or motivate others to initiate a comprehensive, planned program for nursing-
home facilities. In the process, the entire system
of regulation, inspection, and licensing should be
examined objectively and revised where needed. Deficient nursing homes of the older sort should not
be allowed to drag on as they are. Either effective
renovation programs should be permitted (this need
not mean expansion in bed count) or they should be
equitably phased out in a planned program.

All long-term care beds should be located either
adjacent to general care hospitals or have the in-
house advantage of some medical staff specializing
in geriatrics. All nursing homes should be affiliated with strong general hospitals; all should have
strong rehabilitation services.

These aims can be met only with legislative
changes, comprehensive planning, and vigorous public
leadership. All recommended provisions should apply
to every nursing home--whether private, voluntary, or
public (as in the case of those which could replace
the need for Coler and Goldwater Hospitals).

CHAPTER 6 MEDICAL MANPOWER: PRINCIPAL ISSUES

Throughout the preceding chapters there have been numerous references to the shortage of professional staff nurses. This chapter is devoted principally to a survey of that and similar problems, and of the factors contributing to them. It reports on some special considerations pertaining to para-medical personnel who also deliver bedside care, and considers briefly some of the factors relating to physicians in private practice who often do not enjoy the benefits of staff privileges in hospitals.

The first part of this chapter is a largely noninterpretive reporting of interviews with a number of persons who are knowledgeable in the problems of in-patient nursing. Numerous reports, articles, and statistics were also obtained and considered. The second part is a selective, interpretive report leading to recommendations regarding treatment of the basic problems in the area of medical manpower as observed.

THE INVESTIGATION

Interviews with Directors of Nursing

At Bellevue Hospital, the director of nursing described some of the factors that contribute to the shortage of nurses there and the actions underway to alleviate the shortage.

In examination of both the unrenovated and renovated sections of the plant, a range from "the incredible to the livable" is apparent. There has been a marked lift in nursing staff morale as a result of the beginning of renovations. Inappropriate clerical assignments for nurses have sometimes been reduced. For example, an addressograph machine has been installed to prepare the many labels needed for each patient's records.

The table of organization for nurses in Bellevue calls for 667 R.N.'s, a number estimated as being about 75% of optimal staffing, while the number of positions filled, 169, represents about 25% of the allotted number in the table of organization.

Administrative steps have been taken that are apparently effective in holding some staff nurses; other steps are planned. Two-and-a-half years ago, a "clinical nurse" program was instituted. R.N.'s in this program were relieved of any duties but that of bedside care. They did not supervise nurses' aides or practical nurses (P.N.'s) but, should one of the latter wish to learn, the R.N. was free to teach her. This program was started within one medical service; other services are beginning to ask for similar programs. Nurses in the program could not be "borrowed" by another service short of help. Turnover was reported as practically nonexistent and absenteeism among associated nurses' aides and P.N.'s has dropped spectacularly. There are plans to so improve each service one at a time as numbers of personnel permit.

Many nonworking nurses live in an apartment development within walking distance of Bellevue. In an effort to attract some of these nurses back to work, a committee was formed and charged with establishing a nursery school at the hospital. There are some administrative problems to be met in this matter. More security guards are needed for the safety of nurses.

The director of the Bellevue Hospital School of Nursing reported that the school, which offers a two-and-one-half year diploma curriculum, is being phased over to a four-year program at Hunter College.

At Harlem Hospital, the director of the school of nursing reported that their training program will be taken over by Manhattan College. It was her view that unless the hospital is affiliated with a training institution, recruiting and accreditation will become increasingly difficult.

She reported that the greatest shortage of nurses at Harlem Hospital is in OPD, medicine, and surgery services that are always overcrowded--thus causing nurses to experience heavy overloads.

At Harlem there is lack of security guards, shortages of supplies, shortages of messengers and escorts and clerks, thus forcing staff nurses to do support tasks. From a nursing point of view, affiliation contracting has led to many improvements in equipment and supplies.

The nursing director has instituted a ward manager program, which is said to be beneficial. There is notable need for a nursery school program for nurses who have children, and a need for parking space for nurses' automobiles.

Public Health Nursing and Visiting Nurse Service

It was reported that there are now available only about half as many public health nurses as were available before World War II. One nursing official stated, "I would hate to see an epidemic here." She obviously felt the matter to be critical.

Some of the factors contributing to the shortage of P.H.N.'s are other shortages in clerical personnel, which throw extra loads on the nurses. Also, there are more attractive openings for nurses in the voluntary and industrial sectors, with better pay scales. Also significant are shortages of social workers, lack of means for nurses to interchange with hospital staffs (for upgrading), and a lack of programs for training in nursing schools. An official observed, "Some nurses are not getting good training. These nurses are scared to deal with patients."

One lamentable "benefit" was reported as a product of the shortage of P.H.N.'s--a reduction in the instances of "case finding."

In 1948, a public health aide program was begun. The P.H.A.'s are given a short period of general training, including orientation to department goals, personnel policies, and job responsibilities, after which they are trained on the job. About 50% of these aides are men. Women selected are of "the motherly

type"; they often have had door-to-door selling experience. It was stated that the city could use 100
more.

It was observed that nursing as a profession is
nearing the stage where it must be managed as a scarce
resource. Unfortunately, nurses are being drawn into
such jobs as school nursing and other nonhospital
pursuits "to deal with the healthiest part of the
population"; this, of course, draws them away from sickness and bedside care.

The Department of Health contracted with the
Visiting Nurse Service to provide some 41,000 visits
at a cost of something over $300,000 in 1966. Of these
visits, 78% were made for morbidity, 17% for well
patients, 5% for office or nonhome visits. Of the
total, 54% of the cases required care while the remaining 46% were for infant and child care consultations.

Less than 20% of approximately 200 new P.H.N.
recruits each year are from outside the greater metropolitan area. Most P.H.N. employees are drawn from
the city's suburbs and work on a per-session pay basis
(a session is four hours).

The Visiting Nurse Service was organized in 1893.
Currently it employs 189 field personnel: 80 fully
qualified P.H.N.'s, 34 licensed practical nurses,
46 R.N.'s and 74 home health aides (all women). Eight
employees are part-time. Turnover is high.

The V.N.S. is a nonprofit corporation geared to
provide "instant response" to nursing needs. The service has contracts with the Department of Health and the
Department of Welfare in terms of a letter of agreement. It bills on the basis of the number of visits.
Services include home visits to crippled children, TB
patients needing home care, maternal/child health
matters, etc. The V.N.S. accepts referrals from OPD's
and hospitals.

It was reported that there are now some 5,000
fewer visits per year being made by nurses in training. It was said that nurses in training today are
being overly protected and that nursing curricula
should be adjusted to give more practice with patients.
Two-year programs were said to produce nurses who were
"not qualified to function well but were trainable."

From four-year graduates, leadership is expected. It was emphasized that there is clear need for a legal re-evaluation of the "giving of medication" by aides.

Staff Nurses' Views

Voluntary hospitals offer more than the city in salary and benefits. Additionally, working conditions (sanitation, supplies, etc.) are better in the voluntaries and, if they don't provide apartments, they offer a subsidy. There is more "floating" in the municipal system (nurses taking jobs until a good spot opens up). There are too-frequent changes in shifts in the city hospitals, too much pressure, and the "psychological load of a job half done."

One R.N. reported on her experience in applying for a part-time job at Bellevue. The physical examination, which should have taken about half an hour, in fact took over three hours because each part of the physical was given in a different location in the hospital. She was infuriated by the attitudes of the clerks she encountered. As she saw it, the clerks felt that a nurse should be "eternally grateful" for an opportunity to work at Bellevue.

One view, expressed in various ways, was that R.N.'s do not wish to escape from caring for city patients but they feel driven away by poor neighborhoods and poor working conditions at city hospitals.

Nursing As a Profession

Nursing is often viewed by its organized leadership as a profession that is finally "standing on its own feet" and demanding economic recognition. Some feel it has waited too long: 50% of all nurses are not in practice. Where there has been noticeable improvement in pay, large numbers are returning to employment. (San Francisco, for example, is reported to be over-staffed at the present time.) In contrast, in New York, pay raises granted on May 18, 1966, had not yet found their way into the paychecks of municipal nurses at the time of this inquiry.

For many nurses, two major barriers to returning to practice are the nondeductible costs of child care and the tax-bite when their income is added to that of their spouses. To return to work is to work for very little.

The need for nursing services calls for unusual hours--6:00 a.m. to midnight, with 3:00 p.m. to 7:00 p.m. being "disaster time."

In 1965, new standards for the organization of nursing services were issued. It is felt that some impact is now evident. Nursing is beginning to take a stand on what is and what is not nursing. There are those who are not certain whether the situation today is a matter of shortage of nurses or a shortage of nursing. Nurses have traditionally done many things that are now being defined as non-nursing duties. Many nurses are reported as uncertain about what they would do if non-nursing duties were taken away.

Before World War II, 6.5% of the young women graduating from high school entered nursing training. At present, only 4% enter training. One official holds that all R.N.'s should have four years of training. Another states that there are two levels of nursing needed: professional and vocational. Still another states that R.N.'s can be prepared in two- or three- or four-year programs. All agree that there is a lack of trained teaching personnel, and some report that many curricula "grew like Topsy" and need revision. Widely deplored is the tendency to train nurses narrowly and mechanically rather than to train for thinking and for a broad orientation. Master's degree programs, from which instructional personnel often are drawn, graduated 100 fewer nurses in 1966 than in 1965. There has been no increase in the bachelor-level graduates--probably a decrease. The two-year programs are said to be booming, but one official feels these programs will not have real impact for several years.

A trend that appears to be emerging is the provision of nursing services on a contractual or fee-for-service basis.

Nurses' Aides and Practical Nurses

There were widespread complaints about nurses' aides and practical nurses, and some praise. Most of the criticism focused on what was said to be protection given incompetent workers by the union. (Other testimon

indicates that unions are taking strong, laudable
measures toward the up-grading of members through
training.) On the other hand, the N.A.'s and P.N.'s
were praised for their reliability. It was pointed
out that most of them live in the local neighborhood.
Few have the funds to go on for any advanced education
and are fixed at their present levels. Many are older
women with years of experience. It is not infrequent
that they treat new R.N.'s with disdain, indicating
that there is little justice in having to teach an R.N.
her job when the R.N. is receiving more pay. They
also resent the fact that during night hours they have
to take on the responsibilities of a staff nurse but
without additional compensation or recognition. (They
are amused about their "variable" competence--what can
be expected of them suddenly grows as the sun disappears, and as suddenly disappears as the sun rises.)

By and large the satisfaction with N.A.'s and
P.N.'s is greater where good supervisory practices
exist.

Staff members at the City University of New York
are studying the possibility of a new career-ladder
training program for these categories of personnel.

Private Physicians

Attitudes regarding private practitioners who do
not maintain hospital affiliation cover a wide spectrum, from great regard to great reservation. Some
feel that a disturbing percentage of these physicians
are not well qualified and should not be allowed to
practice in city or voluntary hospitals. Still others
feel that if the city is to improve over-all health
delivery, served by limited physicians, then it must
find some way to up-grade them to mutual advantage.
Efforts to offer training over TV have had, at best,
limited effect. There appears to be increasing
acceptance of the private practitioner as a "time-to
time" member of the hospital staff, with the same
restrictions and responsibilities as other nonresident
professionals such as attending teaching rounds, accepting supervision of the chief of service, pooling
in-patient care fee collections, and being paid a
commensurate salary in return.

One authority believes that when the Medicaid
funds assure the physician his fees, and when he is

given hospital staff status, much will have been done
to stop or even reverse the flow of physicians from
poverty areas.

A preliminary report entitled, "Physicians in
New York City," prepared by the Urban Medical Economics
Research Project, indicates that in 1966 there were
22,241 active physicians, 59% (13,122) of whom are
principally in private practice. The data, however,
contained no information on the numbers of physicians
without hospital affiliation; thus it is not possible
to assess accurately the size of the manpower pool
that unaffiliated physicians constitute.

At this point only gross guesswork can be brought
to bear on the numbers involved. (One often hears the
estimate that "some 5000 to 7000 private-practice
physicians in New York City do not have hospital staff
privileges.") Table 11 contains figures taken from the
above-cited report regarding the numbers of physicians
by specialty in private practice in the city. One
could assume that most of the specialties are either
hospital based (and the physicians are already affiliated) or that the specialty does not need hospital
facilities. The four major specialties in which
physicians might bring their patients to a municipal
hospital (if this were possible), or to other hospitals
are general practice, internal medicine, psychiatry and
pediatrics. Assuming that as many as 50% (and this
seems high) of the physicians in these specialty areas
were not affiliated with a hospital, this calculation
would result in an estimate of about 4000 unafilli-
ated physicians. While this is a sizable number, it
is clearly below traditional estimates. On the other
hand, a lower actual population of unaffiliated physicians does not reduce the need for and desirability of
affiliation improvement.

The opening of municipal hospitals to private
patients (discussed as appropriate elsewhere in this
report) would present a great opportunity for a new
program of physicians' affiliation. Requirements for
such affiliation have been considered by a subcommittee
of the Medical Advisory Group in support of the present
Commission. These considerations are reproduced as
follows (The investigating staff has no basis on which
to evaluate these particular provisions).

All licensed physicians who do not hold appointments in voluntary hospitals should be invited to

Table 11. Physicians in Private Practice by Type of Practice in New York City, 1966

Primary Specialty	No.	Primary Specialty	No.
Unspecified	0	Otolaryngology	301
Administration	0	Pathology	67
Allergy	80	Pediatrics	639*
Anaesthesiology	313	Pediatric Allergy	5
Aviation Medicine	1	Pediatric Cardiology	3
Cardiovascular	130	Physical Medicine & Rehabilitation	52
Child Psychiatry	38	Plastic Surgery	90
Diagnostic Roentgenology	3	General Preventive Medicine	0
Dermatology	269		
Forensic Pathology	0		
Gastroenterology	85	Colon & Rectal Surgery	59
General Practice	3,819*	Psychiatry	1,477*
General Surgery	1,104	Public Health	0
Internal Medicine	2,110*	Pulmonary Disease	53
Neurological Surgery	64	Radiology	242
Neurology	91	Therapeutic Radiology	1
Obstetrics-Gyn.	880	Thoracic Surgery	54
Occupational Medicine	33	Urology	229
Ophthalmology	437	Other	84
Orthopedic Surgery	275		
		Total:	13,088

* Likely principal sources of non-hospital-affiliated physicians.

become staff members of an affiliated municipal
hospital in their borough, provided they agree to the
following requirements:

   1) Restrict their practice within the limitation
of their training and experience as recorded in the
directory of the State Medical Society and according
to the regulations of the Departments of Health and
Hospitals.

   2) Abide by the regulations of the hospital's
medical board and accept supervision of their professional conduct and in-hospital practice by the chairmen
of their respective clinical departments or those
persons' designated representatives.

   3) Attend a substantial percent of the teaching
rounds, the clinical pathological conferences, and
other educational exercises of their department.

   4) In recognition of the fact that in-hospital
practice differs from solo practice in that it involves
the collaboration of many other staff physicians and
hospital services, pool all in-patient income from
private patients with all other professional income
of the medical staff of their respective departments
(except official salaries) and accept in return an
adequate monthly payment from their department based
on rank, hours of attendance, and other regulations of
the medical board.

THE INTERPRETATION

Basic Findings

   The delivery of personal health services is a
rapidly expanding field. As it grows in scope and
complexity it demands more specialty training. By
reason of the fact that city positions are civil service and are thereby tied to a personnel system that
must keep salaries in the health field "equitable"
with salaries in other governmental agencies (which
are not undergoing comparable expansions in the
quality and quantity of services they render), the
city simply cannot compete with the much larger system
of nongovernmental health institutions and agencies.
A way must be found to permit the health care system
to be competitive in its search for personnel.

Further, the staff finds that the shortage of
personnel engaged in bedside care is critical, sometimes bordering on the scandalous, and growing worse.
In addition to salary matters, this continuing deterioration is contributed to by several factors. Physical
working conditions are often quite undesirable, as are
living conditions. Para-medical support to professional medical personnel is inadequate. Hours and utilization policies are variable to poor.

Most important, however, the staff finds two sins
of omission which, if corrected, would eventually end
the shortage of (nonphysician) health services personnel. The first of these omissions is the absence of
meaningful career ladders for nurses' aides and practical nurses to advance professionally. The second is
the absence of a meaningful career ladder that would
attract males into the health field in large numbers
in positions other than that of physician.

The Nursing Shortage

In 1940 there were 216 R.N.'s for every 100,000
people. By 1950 this had increased to 249 R.N.'s per
100,000 people. By 1958 the number had increased to
268. By 1964 the number had reached 306, and by 1966,
the number had reached 319. Today there are approximately 50% more nurses per 100,000 people than there
were 25 years ago.

During the Great Depression there was no nursing
shortage.

It seems clear that the "need" for nursing is in
part a function of economics. In a depressed society
where the individual cannot afford medical care, there
is relatively little demand for nursing services. In
an affluent society the demand is great and the supply
is small.

The Surgeon General's Consultant Group on Nursing
states that the need for nurses in 1970 will be 850,000
yet only 680,000 are expected to be obtainable. The
basis for determining whether there is or is not a
shortage would seem to be a judgment closely allied to
the values held by a society at a given moment in time,
although not completely separable from the fact that
nursing care can and does save lives. There seems to

be no clear "base line" for what constitutes a nursing
shortage except demand.

It is an increasing shortage of nurses--in this
"demand" sense--that constitutes the problem today,
especially the shortage of professional nurses giving
bedside care, for it is at this point that the shoe
pinches. Professional nurses are finding their way
into useful nursing employment, but not nearly so often
at the bedside. Clearly they are seeking jobs that
bring them into contact with more healthy people
(school nursing) and regular hours (industrial settings
or private practitioners, for example.)

Why are nurses increasingly drawn away from bedside care?

During the depression of the 1930's there was no
shortage. When there is no shortage, standards rise.
As standards rise, academic performance becomes emphasized. As academic performance is emphasized...the
sequence of events is painfully clear.

Nursing leaders today specify that "this ideal of
going to college is on every girl's mind! We must make
our training collegiate!"

Nursing, as a profession, is changing--at least
in its image. There are nurses' aides, practical
nurses, professional nurses and non-nursing personnel
such as ward managers. The nursing profession is a
"house divided against itself." As one examines the
diversity of training programs being offered in
New York State alone (Table 12), it becomes clear
that the profession projects no clear image as to just
what constitutes "nursing."

It seems clear that nursing as a profession is
moving away from (1) its traditional source of recruitment, namely girls in the upper levels of the lower
class, and (2) its "psychological" source of recruitment, namely girls who want to "be of help."

Just as doctors have increasingly specialized, so
have professional nurses--as propelled by higher academic training. Accompanying the shortage of the
"general practitioner," is an equivalent shortage of
the "general nurse."

Table 12. Types of Nursing Programs
Offered in New York State

1. Eighteen-month school for graduate practical nurses.

2. Two academic years, Associate in Arts and Sciences degree, community college.

3. Twenty-two-month diploma program.

4. Twenty-four-month diploma program.

5. Twenty-seven-month diploma program.

6. Thirty-month diploma program.

7. Thirty-three-month diploma program.

8. Thirty-six-month diploma program.

9. Four academic years, Bachelor of Science degree.

10. Four academic years, plus one, two, or three summers, B.S. degree.

11. Five academic years, B.S. degree.

12. Two academic years, plus three calendar years, B.S. degree.

13. Two academic years, plus 22 months, B.S. degree.

14. Two academic years, plus B.S., equals Master of Science degree.

It is estimated that only 62% of all trained nurses are employed. As of 1966, it is estimated that 379,000 nurses are at home caring for children. It is conceivable that if suitable child-care facilities were furnished by hospitals, many nurses might be brought back into employment.

One thing is clear: given today's standards for nursing care, there is, and will continue to be, a national shortage of nurses that will be felt most strongly in terms of hospital bedside care.

Implications for New York City

As one would expect, there is little shortage in New York hospitals willing to pay and located in good neighborhoods. One voluntary hospital is operating with 92% of nursing positions filled and with low turnover.

The situation in the municipal hospitals is markedly different. At the best, one hospital has only 45% of its staff's nursing positions filled. At the worst, one hospital has but 1% of its staff's nursing positions filled as of February 1967 (Table 13.)

Additionally, throughout the hospital system, the turnover rate is about one-third per year. Note, however, that the hospitals, for the most part, are manning supervisory positions rather well.

Of 5,721 positions authorized in 1966 for professional nurses (to serve as staff nurses), only 1,363 are filled by R.N.'s, while 3,696 are filled by P.N.'s, nurses' aides, and other personnel. When trends are analyzed (Figure 10), it is clear that bedside care is increasingly being delivered by other than registered nurses.

The city has reached a point where determination must be made as to whether bedside care is to be furnished by professional nurses or whether the care furnished by subprofessionals is adequate. And the nursing profession should determine whether or not its emphasis on collegiate training may not be leading to the abandonment of an important arena that is, traditionally, in the nursing domain.

Table 13. Professional Nurses Employed in City Hospitals
as of February 28, 1967*

	Admin. & Superv.			Staff Nurses		
	Auth.	Emplyd.	%Filled	Auth.	Emplyd.	%Filled
Elmhurst	132	123	93	273	121	45
Bronx Municipal	169	137	80	438	183	42
Morrisania Only	72	42	60	140	28	20
(incl. Montefiore)			(92)			(42)
Seaview	54	51	94	138	51	37
Coney Island	80	65	80	177	65	37
Queens	168	140	89	487	140	29
Ewing	34	30	89	130	30	23
Greenpoint	45	44	97	93	27	22
Cumberland	57	44	79	93	44	21
Bellevue	363	286	80	963	190	20
Kings	371	337	91	1070	203	19
Lincoln	70	64	90	176	34	19
Metropolitan	156	132	85	277	53	19
Sydenham	39	37	95	86	16	19
Harlem	153	137	90	389	67	17
Fordham	66	63	95	134	19	14
Delafield	38	32	84	118	11	10
Goldwater	107	70	65	341	10	3
Bird S. Coler	101	67	67	200	2	1

* Source: New York City Department of Hospitals Report.

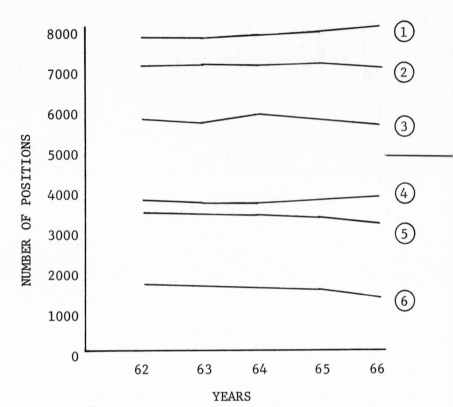

NUMBER OF POSITIONS

YEARS

① Total R.N.'s Authorized

② Total Jobs Filled

③ Total Staff Nursing Positions
Authorized

④ Staff Nursing Positions Filled by
P.N.'s, N.A.'s, and Others

⑤ Total Nursing Positions Filled by R.N.'s

⑥ Staff Nursing Positions Filled by R.N.'s

Figure 10.   Staffing of Nursing Positions
in City Hospitals

Source: Nursing Education and Nursing Service
N.Y.C. Department of Hospitals, 1967.

394

As recently as May 4, 1967, Commissioner Terenzio stated that "weakness in security protection and miserable hospital sanitation have done more to discourage nursing morale than any other single factor I know." Incredible as the working conditions are in many municipal hospitals--conditions that force staff nurses to points of complete frustration--a truly significant fact seems to have been entirely overlooked. Most of the nurses interviewed in this study expressed in one way or another that they received a high degree of satisfaction from serving the poor ("They are so grateful for any little thing you do for them"), and little satisfaction from serving the rich ("They treat you like a maid; 'Get me this,' 'Get me that,' 'Fluff my pillow,' and so on"). If the city can overcome poor working conditions, it will probably overcome the worst obstacle to adequate nursing in the municipal system.

Further alleviation of the shortage can be accomplished by these provisions:

- Increasing pay and differentials to compete

- Increasing fringe benefits

- Providing housing or subsidy

- Undertaking long-overdue renovations

- Providing equipment and supplies

- Improving sanitation

- Providing nursery schools for working mothers

- Improving standards of maintenance

- Providing adequate security

- Stepping up recruitment programs

- Providing more in-service training

- Instituting training in how to supervise P.N.'s, aides, etc.

- Providing good refresher/orientation programs for returnees

- Training administrators in manpower management

- Eliminating assignment from pools

- Better use of part-time nurses

- Relieving nurses of non-nursing duties

- Instituting ward-manager programs

- Assignment to beds in terms of nursing care needs.

The improvement of working conditions for R.N.'s will, however, do only part of the job of meeting the total shortage of support manpower in the delivery of personal health services.

What seems equally promising is to create a new career position--the nurse clinician. (This title is in use--and in controversy--for a related application; nonetheless, it is appropriate here.) This position would provide career specialists in bedside care, and could permit advancement to R.N. and other capacities, with further education and training (Figure 11).

The name for this career line was deliberately chosen in order to emphasize the notion that training would be focused on bedside care. The training envisioned would cover a 30-month tuition-and-expense-paid period, including a year of rotational clinical training, and an intensive six months of selected specialty training on the job. Recruits to this position might be drawn from high-school graduates and personable, bright drop-outs in poverty areas. Graduates would be certified and registered.

It is probable, however, that all of the above provisions will fail to meet medical support manpower needs in this era of accelerated medical-social legislation. An additional major innovation could close the gap.

Males constitute a personnel pool largely overlooked in nursing today. A new career line, masculine in image, might complete the range of solutions to the personnel shortage (nationally, as well as in New York City). Nursing as a profession is clearly feminine in its image and attracts few males. Concepts such as "corpsman" and "physician assistant" are clearly masculine and desperately needed.

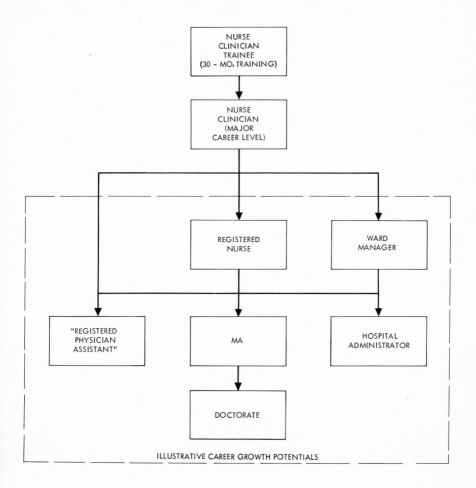

Figure 11. Suggested Ladder for the "Nurse Clinician"--
A Special Nursing Role

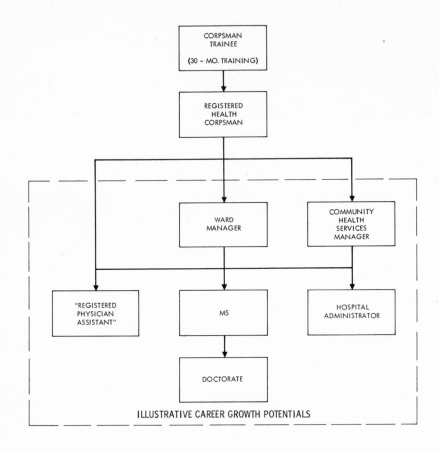

Figure 12. Suggested Ladder for the "Corpsman"--
A Masculine-Image Nursing Role

It is recommended that a "health careers institute" under HSA establish positions and training programs for the male career line depicted in Figure 12.
The idea of such a career line has already been given
initial trial elsewhere, and shows great potential.
Again, entry level would draw heavily upon the
high-school graduate and personable, bright drop-outs
in poverty areas. A 30-month tuition-and-expense-paid
training period would consist of a mixture of academic
and apprenticeship training with emphasis not on nursing skills, but on skills that would directly assist
physicians in diagnosis and treatment of patients,
on skills suited to emergency room service, and on
skills to support administrators and others in hospital
functions. Too, such trainees would be available to
community health functions, mental health facilities,
ambulatory care centers, the private physician, long-
term care programs, and specialty programs such as
narcotics rehabilitation.

It is recognized that professional groups in
medicine might at first be wary of such a career line
but experience and need strongly suggest that acceptance would follow in due course.

It is estimated that the full array of medical
services and agencies of New York City could today
readily absorb approximately 5,000 of the two new kinds
of trainees recommended.

Finally, a health careers institute should pioneer
in the development of completely new health career
training programs for para-medical skill clusters requiring three to twelve months of training; laboratory
aides, ward manager aides, medical records aides, medical welfare community workers, and so forth.

CHAPTER **7** FLOW AND
IMPACT OF
PUBLIC FUNDS

THE NEW LEGISLATION

In 1965, Congress ended a bitter debate that had lasted 20 years. At issue: Is medical care a right or a privilege? In response to public demand and political pressure, Congress enacted "Social Security Amendments of 1965," Public Law 89-97, effective July 1, 1966.

Part A of Title XVIII, "Medicare," provides for hospital and medical services for all persons over 65 years of age, regardless of economic status.

Under Medicare, 19 million men and women over 65 years of age are now assured of medical treatment determined by their needs for care and not by their pocketbooks.

Despite warnings that American medicine would collapse immediately under the weight of millions of the aged demanding health handouts, the first six months of Medicare's use were remarkably orderly. The increase in hospitalization amounted to approximately five per cent. Except for problems in a few hospitals, the transition has been smoother than expected, though costs have skyrocketed--see Table 14. (All statistics, quoted rates, applicable operational procedures and other findings in this staff study were obtained or examined in the period May-June 1967.)

Medicare provides hospital care for a period of 90 days after payment of a deductible of $40.00, and coinsurance (20%) after 60 days; care for 100 days in an approved extended care facility, with payment by the patient of $5.00 per day after the first 20 days; extensive out-patient diagnostic service after a

Table 14. Gross Expenditures for Medical Care,
Reflecting Increases Related to
Titles XVIII and XIX, PL 89-97

(thousands of dollars)

	May 1965 - Feb. 1966	% of Total	May 1966 - Feb. 1967	% of Total	% Change From Prior Period
N.Y. City - Total	$125,234	100.0	$184,815	100.0	47.6
Hospital	76,160	60.8	134,902	73.0	77.1
Nursing Home	27,777	22.2	26,947	14.6	- 3.0
P.H.I.	11,217	9.0	11,773	6.3	5.0
Physician's Serv.	1,336	1.1	1,431	0.8	7.1
Dental Care**	995	0.8	287	0.2	- 71.2
Drugs	1,349	1.1	1,780	1.0	31.9
All Other*	6,401	5.1	7,695	4.2	20.2
Upstate - Total	79,983	100.0	106,839	100.0	33.6
Hospital	32,133	40.2	38,844	36.4	20.9
Nursing Home	13,348	16.7	17,913	16.8	34.2
P.H.I.	19,037	23.8	22,211	20.8	16.7
Physician's Serv.	4,487	5.6	9,364	8.7	108.7
Dental Care	1,960	2.5	5,971	5.6	204.7
Drugs	4,750	5.9	7,650	7.2	61.1
All Other*	4,257	5.3	4,886	4.6	14.8

(Continued)

Table 14 (Continued)

	May 1965 - Feb. 1966	% of Total	May 1966 - Feb. 1967	% of Total	% Change From Prior Period
N.Y. State - Total	$205,221	100.0	$291,653***	100.0	42.1
Hospital	108,301	52.8	173,747****	59.6	60.4
Nursing Home	41,127	20.0	44,860	15.4	9.1
P.H.I.	30,256	14.7	33,984	11.7	12.3
Physician's Serv.	5,823	2.8	10,794	3.7	85.4
Dental Care	2,956	1.4	6,257	2.1	111.7
Drugs	6,100	3.0	9,432	3.2	54.6
All Other*	10,658	5.2	12,579	4.3	18.0

Note: Detail may not add to total due to rounding.

* Includes such items as: clinic, physical therapy, prosthetic devices, visiting nurse, etc.

** These were salaried dentists in N.Y.C., so the figure does not reflect current trend properly.

*** There is an additional $74,599,109 for care of aged in mental hospitals that is not included in the table.

$20.00 deductible and (20%) coinsurance; and home
health follow-up for 100 days. Each patient may
choose his or her own physician or hospital "if such
institution, agency or person undertakes to provide
him such services" and is entitled to semiprivate accommodations during each "spell of illness."

Reimbursement to the hospital and extended care
facility, and for costs of the diagnostic services,
is made on a "reasonable cost" basis from the Federal
Hospital Insurance Trust Fund, which is made up from
the increased Social Security taxes--and from general
tax revenues ($600 million the first year) since the
former source alone is not adequate to meet the obligations of the trust fund. Physicians' fees will not
be paid from the fund, but from Part B.

Part B of Title XVIII, "Supplementary Medical
Insurance Benefits for the Aged," provides for the
payment of physicians' fees for patients over 65 years
of age in the hospital, office, extended care facility, or home at the "usual" or "going" rate of compensation after the deductible of $50.00 and a 20%
coinsurance feature. These payments to the doctor
may be made by one of several methods: through a
designated "intermediary financial agency," or by
direct billing to the patient under the rules for
payment mentioned above. Physicians are not paid
directly by the government. Special problems arise
in the instances of salaried staffs or physicians on
other plans of compensation. The payments are made
from a Federal Supplementary Medical Insurance Trust
Fund derived from voluntary contributions ($3.00 per
month from individuals over 65 years of age, matched
by the government) plus appropriations from general
tax revenues since the fund is not self-supporting
($900 million was appropriated for the first year).

The second section of "Social Security Amendments
of 1965," is Title XIX, "Grants to States for Medical
Assistance," which under certain conditions pays for
medical and other health services for anyone of any
age.

Title XIX received little attention at the time
of its passage. It may, nevertheless, become the
most significant piece of social legislation enacted
since the Social Security Act of 32 years ago.

The goal of Title XIX, called Medicaid in New
York, is to abolish charity medicine. Under it,
those with insufficient income to pay medical bills
are to be treated by the same private physicians, in
the same hospitals, and at the same rates as others
in the community. Bills for these services will be
paid by the state, with the federal government assuming 50 to 83 per cent of the cost. Each state must
pass enabling legislation to participate. States
that have not joined by 1970 will no longer receive
federal funds for their various aid-to-the-indigent
programs; more than 30 states now participate.

Title XIX consolidates and expands five other
Social Security Amendments, including the Kerr-Mills
Act, maternal and child health legislation, and
school and preschool child health services, as examples. It has a potential coverage of 36 million
people under 65 years of age and persons over 65
years of age after their benefits under Title XVIII
have been exhausted. It pays for all medical expenses
of individuals "whose income and resources are insufficient to meet all of the costs" of their medical
needs. Eligibility is determined usually by state
welfare departments and varies with each state. In
New York, "medical assistance provides unlimited
medical benefits for persons, regardless of age, who
cannot pay for such services, as determined by a
means test."

The "means test" is the net annual income, allowing for the number of children, savings, life insurance, other assets, and the amount of the medical
expenses, possibly including unpaid deductibles or
coinsurance charges under Titles XVIII and XIX and
instances of catastrophic costs of a given illness.

The state decides how much money a family may
earn and still be eligible. The scale ranges from
a high of $6,000 net income a year in New York, for a
family of four, to a low of $2,448 in Oklahoma.
New York's law states that the $6,000-a-year family
must pay 1% or $60 toward its medical bills; $4,500
is the ceiling for fully free care.

Under "Medical Assistance," physicians will be
paid at the going rate of charges that are regarded
as reasonable. Payments will be routed either
through an approved "provider of services" such as
the United Medical Service or a commercial insurance

carrier. Physicians in the future will be entitled
to collect fees for services rendered in the past on
a voluntary basis. The new laws will be a major
source of new money for practitioners, hospitals, and
clinics. Many details of administration, including
utilization review procedures for example, have yet
to be worked out.

The total costs of the several programs to the
federal government will be huge--much greater than
predicted. They will increase in the future, especially if amendments to Public Law 89-97 are approved later to extend benefits and lower or remove
contributions by users. Generally, tax costs to
state and local governments are likely to increase
substantially under the formulas. New York City is
an exception since this city has for decades been
carrying a very heavy burden of public financing for
medical indigency.

How the Program Is Administered

Each state operates its own program under welfare administration policies administered by the
Bureau of Family Services. From the outset, states
were required to include all recipients of public as-
sistance--the aged, blind, disabled, and families
with dependent children. States can extend coverage
to comparable groups of medically needy people--those
who have enough for daily living but not for medical
expenses--and also to all children under 21. But by
1975, state medical assistance programs must cover
all who cannot afford the care they need. (Under the
reimbursement formula provisions, a state medical
assistance program will be funded in most instances
by tax monies from federal, state, and local sources.
There has been much confusion regarding this matter.)

Eligibility standards and services for the
various age and disability groups are to be equal in
scope, duration, and amount. After July 1, 1967,
each state program must include at least five basic
services: in-patient and out-patient hospital care,
physicians' services, skilled nursing home care (for
adults), and laboratory and X-ray services. States
should show steady progress toward the 1975 goal of
a comprehensive range of high-quality services, including dental care, prescribed drugs, home health
care, prosthetic devices and eyeglasses, and necessary transportation.

Eligibility

To qualify for federal funds, state programs must be operated on a state-wide basis, allow all needy persons to apply, and have fair hearings for dissatisfied applicants. States must set up medical care units staffed by medical and social work personnel and assisted by advisory committees representing both providers and users of service. Applicants may not be required to have residence in the state for any period of time. Relatives' responsibility must be limited to "spouse for spouse," and parents for children under 21 or children of any age if blind or permanently and totally disabled. If states do not set up medical assistance programs by January 1, 1970, they will lose federal financial aid for medical care of public assistance recipients.

PARTICIPATION AND EARLY PROBLEMS

It was necessary for each state wishing to participate in the medical assistance program to provide a plan from its state department of social welfare to the federal Department of Health, Education and Welfare for approval before grants could be made.

New York was the ninth state to qualify for medical assistance. Notice was given of willingness to participate on May 1, 1966. Previously, on January 1, 1966, seven other states committed themselves to proceed; California began its program in March of that year. The program in New York City did not begin until October 1966, although an earlier preliminary grant was made.

The delay was costly, as can be seen in the figures comparing the states of California and New York in Table 15. Although California was late in signing up for medical assistance, it applied the sum of $159.8 million for the four months of fiscal 1966. Of that amount, $79.9 million was reimbursed by the federal government. In the two months that New York State's program operated, its total expenditure by comparison was $38.9 million, of which $18.1 million was reimbursed by the federal government.

New York's state law was passed on May 1, 1966. It is not clear why New York City did not get its program working until five months later. However,

Table 15. Comparative Medical Payments:
New York vs. California

(thousands of dollars)

Type of Service	New York	California
In-Patient Hospital Care	$ 14,913	$ 34,441
Nursing Home Care	17,820	54,913
Physicians' Services	1,562	24,689
Other Practitioners' Services	35	2,682
Dental Care	627	9,835
Prescribed Drugs	1,798	18,095
Other	2,168	15,144
Total	$ 38,922	$159,799

(Continued)

407

Table 15 (Continued)

Source	New York Per Cent	New York Amount	California Per Cent	California Amount
Federal Funds	46.6	$18,129	50.0	$ 79,899
State Funds	26.7	10,398	22.2	35,528
Local Funds	26.7	10,395	27.8	44,371
Total:	100.0	$38,922	100.0	$159,799

Total Payments Including Federal, State and Local, for:

	Total Vendor Payments	Aid to the Blind	Aid to Families with Dependent Children	Aid to the Permntly. & Totally Disabled	Medical Assistance	Medical Assist. for the Aged
California	$294,974	$1,672	$12,000	$11,265	$159,799	$ 82,824
New York	233,620	1,164	32,260	23,429	38,922	121,371

it can be estimated that the gross loss was in the order of $60 million. This is not untypical of the laxity in a number of related programs in which the city is involved.

The tardiness may be partly explained by delays in the organization of the federal program. The federal policy did not get to the states until June 1966. Nevertheless, some states (seven in all) made short forms applying to the law and were ready to receive funds by April of 1966.

The state and the city can take pride in the commitment of public assistance with respect to the other states participating in the program. For a family of four, the income fixed in most states cannot exceed $3,000 to $3,200 per year. The income allowable in New York is $6,000 per year for a family of four. The standard of the state exceeds federal requirements, and in some cases benefits are extended to persons whom the federal ruling would not classify as indigent. For this reason, as noted in Table 15, the percentage of federal aid given New York is less than that given California.

Federal requirements have been sufficiently lenient to permit city and state estimates to stand in lieu of the otherwise necessary claims for grants. In some cases the federal government has allowed some retropayment of monies, based on predicted expenditures for specified periods in the absence of complete justification. However, this period of tolerance has ended. The Chief of State Grants Branch, U.S. Department of Health, Education and Welfare, states that federal quality control will be implemented stringently after July 1, 1967. Thereafter, it will be necessary for all cities and states to meet the approved plan for authorizing recipients and receiving reimbursement. In neither respect are the city's practices yet adequate. The Department of Welfare's sampling technique, basic to reimbursement estimation, does not accord with state and federal requirements.

There are several means of auditing the recipients of medical assistance. One is the audit agency of HEW. Another is the General Accounting Office, the arm of Congress that monitors all government expenditures. A third is the New York State Audit Agency, whose methods are known to New York City.

In the course of the present study, it became abundantly clear that audit vulnerability is likely for
all social assistance programs examined, and that
local traditional practices should be aired, revised,
and tightened.

Establishing Eligibility for Medicaid

Figure 13 (four parts) reproduces Form MA-11, the
application questionnaire that each seeker of Medicaid
assistance must fill out. Suppose, for the moment,
that you are the mother of a very sick child, whom
you have brought into an emergency room for treatment.
You are Puerto Rican, and speak only a few words of
English. You find, before your child can be helped,
that you must provide information on your wages for
the past eight weeks, on your insurance benefits, on
your real property, and (God save the mark!) on your
stock portfolio. It is obvious that this form, in
itself, constitutes a major bottleneck to successful
operation of the Medicaid program. The City of New
York, in an attempt to simplify matters for its medically indigent population, produced a revised version
of Form MA-11; the "simplified" version is _four_ pages
long rather than two.

Supporters of the Medicaid questionnaire offer
justifications for each blank on the form. In general,
the justifications state that many items of information may be of later help in determining the possibility of other sources of entitlement. It is argued
that these possibilities could total quite a significant sum for the city, which it is not now receiving.
This may be so, but surely some assessment is needed
of the amount of effort expended in obtaining this
information, compared to the amount of money that
could be saved if the questionnaire were truly simplified, or if it were replaced by an affidavit of
eligibility.

It is estimated that more than 60% of the children in New York City belong to families qualified
for public assistance or medical assistance under the
$6,000-or-less per year, "family-of-four" category.
Accepting this, examination should be made of Aid to
Dependent Children funds to determine if there are
monies due the city under this program that it is not
receiving. Should this be so, then the city should

Form MA-11 (Rev. 5/66) (Face)

**APPLICATION FOR
MEDICAL ASSISTANCE**

NEW YORK STATE DEPARTMENT
OF SOCIAL WELFARE

Last Name of Head of Household	First Name	Initial

		LEAVE BLANK
		Case Number

Complete Address (Street or RFD, City, State, Zip)	Telephone Number

Date Applic. Rec'd.

Cross Refer. Number

If other families in the same household have made separate application, enter names of the heads of these other households.

Section A. Before completing, please read NOTE† below. Please answer every question for each person; if answer is none, write word NONE.

Line	Names of Persons applying for Medical Assistance (Indicate Family Name if different from name on line 1.)	Sex M-F	Relation-ship to Applicant	Date of Birth Mo-Day-Yr	Social Security Number	Relig-ion	Wages (See NOTE†)				
							Gross	Per	Deductions		
									Income Taxes	Health Insurance	
	2	3	4	5	6	7	8	9	10	11
1	Head of Household									
2										
3										
4										
5										
6										
7										
8										
9										
10										

Section B. Persons who Reside with Family who are NOT applying for Medical Assistance

	2	3	4	Room or Board Paid	
				Amount	Per
11					

†NOTE

Col. 9 "Per"—Indicate pay period, i.e., W=Weekly; M=Monthly; BW=Bi-Weekly; SM=Semi-Monthly; etc.
If Health Insurance is not deducted from wages, indicate in Item 1 below, the amount paid in cash.
All income from wages must be verified, see NOTICE below.

Figure 13 a. Form MA-11, Application for Medical Assistance (Obverse, Upper Half)

	Income other than wages must be reported in Section D on the other side of the form.		
	Other Deductible Payments	Amount	Per
12	1. Amount of Health Insurance premium paid if not deducted from wages		
13	2. Amount paid pursuant to Court Order		
14			

Section C. OTHER INFORMATION

1. Is applicant employed at least 35 hours per week or 5 days per week? ☐ YES ☐ NO

2. Does spouse of any person listed in lines 1-10, Section A, live outside the family? ☐ YES ☐ NO

3. Does parent(s) of any minor children listed in lines 1-10, Section A, live outside the family? ☐ YES ☐ NO

4. If answer to questions 2 or 3 is YES, give the name and address of absent spouse or parent(s):

To Be Signed When Applicant Applies Personally	To Be Signed When Representative Applies For Applicant
I hereby apply for Medical Assistance for the persons indicated in Section A of this form and certify that all of the information contained in this application is true and correct to the best of my knowledge and belief. I make this application with the understanding that I will furnish any additional information which may be required and that I will report immediately any changes in circumstances, including changes in financial resources, to the public welfare official to whom this application is submitted.	I hereby submit this application for Medical Assistance on behalf of the applicant named above, and furnish the information which is contained in the application based upon knowledge and information obtained from the applicant and other sources. The information furnished is true and correct to the best of my knowledge and belief. This application is submitted with the understanding that the certification of the applicant may be required and that such certification will be obtained if required.
Applicant: _____ Date Signed _____	Representative: _____ Date Signed _____

NOTICE: In order to insure prompt action on your application, you are requested to furnish proof of income from wages or business for all persons applying for Medical Assistance (those listed in Section A, lines 1 through 10). This proof may be the original documents or a photocopy; these documents will be returned promptly.

For wages, furnish paycheck stubs or pay envelopes for 8 weeks showing the total earned and deductions for income taxes and health insurance premiums, if any, for each pay period. If these are not available, please ask your employer for such a statement.

**PLEASE MAIL COMPLETED FORM AND REQUIRED STATEMENTS
IN THE RETURN ENVELOPE CONTAINED IN THIS BOOKLET**

Figure 13b. Form MA-11, Application for Medical Assistance (Obverse, Lower Half)

412

Form MA-11 (Rev. 5/66) (Reverse)

APPLICATION FOR MEDICAL ASSISTANCE

IMPORTANT INSTRUCTIONS:

1. Enter, in the NAME column, the name of the person whose income is described below (From Sec. A., Col. 2)
2. If more room is needed to answer any question, please use a blank sheet of paper and attach it to this application.

LEAVE BLANK

Section D. INCOME OTHER THAN WAGES

	Name	Type of Income (Specify: Social Security or Railroad Retirement, other Pensions, Workmen's Compensation, NYS Disability Benefits, Interest, Dividends, Rent, Etc.)	Period	Amount
INCOME OTHER THAN WAGES				

If none, check here ☐

NOTE: Indicate income taxes payable on this income, if any. $ _____   For PERIOD column, indicate whether payment is monthly, quarterly, annually, etc.

Section E. ASSETS OR BENEFITS

	Name	Name and Address of Bank	Account No.	Amount
BANK ACCOUNTS				

If none, check here ☐

	Name	Type of Assets	Name and Address of company, if any, or Other Identification	Face Value
OTHER LIQUID ASSETS (Stocks, Savings Bonds, etc.) Do Not Include Personal Property.				

If none, check here ☐

	Name	Name of Company	Policy Number	Face Value
LIFE INSURANCE				

If none, check here ☐

	Name	Owner	Location
REAL PROPERTY (Report			

Figure 13c. Form MA-11, Application for Medical Assistance (Reverse, Upper Half)

Rent Income in Section D.) If none, check here ☐

Section F. OTHER INFORMATION

VETERAN OR VETERAN'S RELATIVE — If none, check here ☐

Name	Specify Relationship to Veteran (Veteran, Widow(er), Child)	Armed Forces Serial Number	V. A. Claim Number

DISABILITY

Name	Describe Briefly

Describe Briefly

COMPLETE FOR PERSON IN HOSPITAL OR NURSING HOME — If none, check here ☐

Name	Name of Hospital or Nursing Home	Address	Admission Date

Section G. MEDICARE (Complete for each person 65 years of age or over.)

MEDICARE PARTS A AND B — If none, check here ☐

Name	Part A Enrolled or Applied (Check)	Part B Enrolled or Applied (Check)	Premium Ded. from Benefit (Check)	If YES is checked, indicate: Social Security Claim Number	Effective Date of Coverage
	YES NO	YES NO	YES NO		
	YES NO	YES NO	YES NO		

Section H. OTHER MEDICAL INSURANCE

OTHER MEDICAL INSURANCE — If none, check here ☐

Name	Name of Insurance Company	Group Insurance - Employer's Name	Policy Number

Figure 13d. Form MA-11, Application for Medical Assistance (Reverse, Lower Half)

consider staffing the hospitals and clinics with
enough people to obtain full information on each and
every individual who applied for aid.

The Health Services Administration has officially
suggested that state and federal authorities accept
an affidavit from Medicaid applicants stating that
they fall within certain income limits and that they
have certain dollars of net worth, thereby determining
entitlement by state and federal agencies for Medicaid.
This could be the only method that would be acceptable,
in view of the fact that the Welfare Department is apparently unable to obtain completed questionnaires in
the quantity required by the state and federal agencies
to substantiate claims upon those agencies.

The Bureau of Hospital Care Services of the
Department of Welfare has found that completed Medicaid questionnaires are quite difficult to obtain;
the majority are incomplete. In a sample of 95,000
Medicaid applications since November of 1966 (from
out-patient clinics), a very small percentage were
obtained in completed form by the Department of Welfare teams established at those clinic offices.

In some cases, questionnaire forms have been
given out with the request that they be completed and
mailed to the Bureau of Hospital Care Services for
processing. Of the 95,000 such cases, 44,000 were
never returned to the Bureau of Hospital Care Services.
Fourteen thousand were returned incomplete, and further study and work had to be carried out to justify
the claimants' eligibility. Also, examination of
forms completed at OPD's proved many to be erroneous
(wrong home address, etc.)

Many voluntary hospitals are assuming responsibility for obtaining information for the questionnaires.
Their performance in this regard has been better than
that of the city clinics. At these voluntary institutions, 72,000 applications were filled out of which
only 27,000 were returned incomplete (still a poor
showing in terms of needed accuracy).

The voluntary hospitals, therefore, have registered an average of 62% correct applications of those
applying for Medicaid. One hospital, Morrisania,
claims to have registered most of its out-patients.
Their claim is 100% of the emergency out-patients,
100% of the child OPD cases, and at least 70% of the

adult OPD.   (Note: All of these are not necessarily
considered complete applications.)

Figure 14 indicates that only 40% of the expected
eligible recipients of Medicaid have been correctly
registered in municipal clinics.   At the state-
promulgated rate of $8.23 per visit for early 1967,
the city could lose as much as $21 million and no less
than $14.8 million per year after July 1. (Visit rates
for voluntary hospitals have been between $7 and $11
per OPD visit.   Why city hospital rates should be less
than those for a visit to a voluntary hospital is unknown.   The city is losing a great deal of money by
assuming the costs of the difference.)

In the course of this study, an undesirable
practice was noted on the part of personnel from an
affiliate hospital working in a municipal OPD.   The
name of the affiliate hospital was entered on the
form as the recipient of money for the care.   It is
not known how extensive this practice is.

Medicaid Participation by Vendors

The transistion to participation in Title XIX by
vendors has not been, nor is it now, a smooth process.

With the intent of improving the quality of
health services and specifically to be assured that
the practitioner was meeting certain minimal standards,
the Health Services Administration asked private
physicians and dentists to register for the Medicaid
program.   Enrolling meant filling out a notarized
form for the city in return for which the doctors
received a control number that was the key to receiving
collections from the Department of Welfare.   Patients,
too, were to have a Medicaid number, on the theory
that the only newly automated system in the Department of Welfare would confirm the authorizing numbers
and send payment to the doctor.

A few doctors took advantage of the system and
submitted exorbitant bills.   Welfare officials felt
caution was in order and elected to pay, at most, only
50% of each submitted bill until verification was
complete.   A problem arose in that there was no adequate verification procedure nor people motivated to

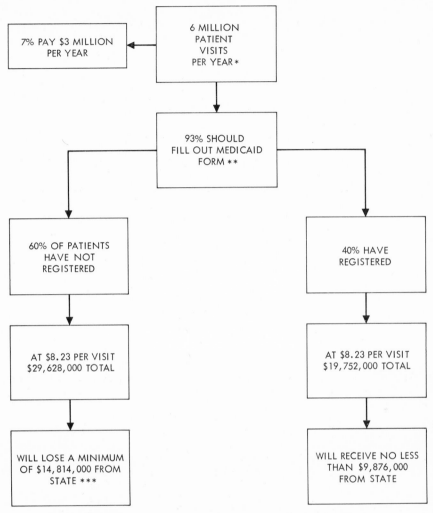

- * "SERVICE STATISTICS ON COMMUNITY HOSPITALS — 1965" OFFICE OF HEALTH ECONOMICS

- ** COLUMBIA UNIVERSITY — "OUT-PATIENT STUDY" 1965

- *** IF NOT PROPERLY REGISTERED FOR MEDICAID, THERE IS POTENTIAL OF AT LEAST $14.8 MILLION PER YEAR OF STATE SUPPORT TO BE LOST AFTER 1 JULY 1967

Figure 14. Reimbursement for OPD Visits at Fifteen Municipal Clinics and Two Health Department Ambulatory Treatment Centers

accomplish it. The results were that doctors continued to be 50% unpaid (and still were as of June 1.
1967). They remained unpaid for their December 1966
to March 1967 billings. The Welfare Department is in
the process of evolving a rapid reimbursement system.

In June 1967 the Commissioner of Health announced
that the city no longer would require physicians,
dentists, and optometrists to enroll in Medicaid to
qualify for payments under this program.

These problems focused controversy on the plan
and on the Health Services Administration. In reality
the trouble was caused by the absence of correlated
programs between HSA and the Welfare Department. Improper payment and collections by the Department of
Welfare assured defeat of the plan.

A Misinterpreted Law

The Blue Ribbon Panel Report to Governor
Rockefeller, May 1967, inadvertently contributed to
the belief that New York City would, by 1975, no
longer share health costs. The Panel's conclusions
have frequently been paraphrased as follows: "By
1975, New York City will not be paying a share of
health services delivery costs. It will be all state
and federal."

The part of the Report that stimulated the mis-
understanding was Paragraph 3.5, which states,

> Since the New York City Municipal
> hospital patients are almost all
> eligible for either Medicaid bene-
> fits or Medicare benefits or both,
> for the first time there is prospect
> that, when these programs have be-
> come fully implemented within the
> next three years, New York City
> will be paid for almost all of the
> costs of all hospital services
> which are now provided or will then
> be provided.

Various officials in fiscal capacities were contacted to clarify the meaning of this statement. No
one from the State Department of Social Welfare or
from the U.S. Department of Health, Education and
Welfare agreed with this interpretation.

Dr. Burney, Chairman of the Blue Ribbon Panel, and Dr. Phillip Bonnet, Panel Secretary, confirmed that the intent of the paragraph in question was not to hold out the promise that New York City would have no financial obligation after 1975.

In point of fact, when: (1) the Medicare and Medicaid programs are fully implemented; (2) claims for services delivered are properly qualified and submitted; (3) verification sampling is adequate; and (4) the collections machinery is running efficiently, then most of the costs of hospital services can be received from sources other than city taxes-- possibly in the order of 73%.

With its established traditions for public care, New York City is the least likely of all cities to deny financial responsibility for health care. Through increased efficiency, as well as by political and economic intent, it could lessen its burden--but not much below that existing today. Even so (considering the tremendous rise in costs of health care) future reductions in traditional burdens are not in prospect.

FUNDS-FLOW STATISTICS

New York State and California: Some Comparisons

Certain comparisons between New York and California may be helpful. Respective populations, based on the 1965 estimate of census, are very similar for the two states. There is nearly equal distribution of people within age brackets. They have similar percentages of population in urban areas. While it is expected that there will be a net change of some 100% between 1960 and 1985 in California and a net change of only 35% in the same period for New York, today the population figures are similar enough to facilitate comparison of medical and health care expense.

The amount of dollars received by the two states compares this way (based on federal grants-in-aid, social security, and public assistance payments): for health care, California ranks 47th in a total of 50 states. New York ranks 46th, just above California. For public assistance, California ranks 8th while New York State ranks 21st.

Hospital Use: Admissions and Patient Days

Hospital length-of-stay is of great financial significance. How do the two states and others compare in this regard? Does geographic location account for wide differences in length of stay in hospitals? Tables 16, 17, and 18 shed some light on these questions.

One of the most compelling questions raised in the course of the present study was, "Why do New York State and New York City experience a rate of patient days per 1000 population some 20% greater than that of the U.S. average?" This greater use of beds represents a substantial public cost.

This disparity between New York and the rest of the country is even greater in the case of patient days in psychiatric hospitals. There are 2,440 patient days spent in mental hospitals in New York State per 1000 population, the U.S. average being 1,325.7. With respect to the national average, New York State leads by 46%; it leads, as well, all individual states, yet the number of admissions to mental hospitals in New York State is 2.8 per 1000 population, very close to the U.S. average of 2.7. Table 18 lists fifteen other states in which the number of admissions to mental hospitals averages 2.6 to 3.0 per 1000 population. Vermont, Massachusetts, and Wyoming are the only other states with 2000 patient days per 1000 population spent in mental institutions; these states have admission rates of 3.1 and 4.0 respectively.

The purposes of the present inquiry do not include investigation of the reasons for this wide difference. Heavy public expenditures are being made for these hospital stays that other states seem to be avoiding. For financial and humanitarian reasons, this matter should receive careful study.

Hospital Statistics: New York City

In 1960 there were 1,047,184 admissions to hospitals in New York City, of which 25.1 per cent were to municipal hospitals, 60.3 per cent to voluntaries, and 14.6 per cent to proprietary hospitals. In 1965 there were 1,094,609 admissions, 23.8 per cent to municipal, 61.8 per cent to voluntary, and 14.4 per cent to proprietary hospitals.

Table 16. Hospital Use: Patient Days
(State Rankings)

(Rates per 1000 Population)

General & Special*			Mental**		
Rank	State	Annual Rate	State	Annual Rate	Rank
1.	Del.	1,788	N.Y.	2,441	1.
2.	Mass.	1,724	Mass.	2,180	2.
3.	N. Dak.	1,708	Vt.	2,093	3.
4.	N.Y.	1,674	Wyo.	2,083	4.
5.	R.I.	1,657	N.H.	1,844	5.
6.	Alaska	1,650	Maine	1,781	6.
7.	W. Va.	1,585	R.I.	1,773	7.
8.	Mo.	1,544	Conn.	1,664	8.
9.	Minn.	1,516	Ill.	1,619	9.
10.	Colo.	1,503	Mich.	1,577	10.
11.	Pa.	1,500	Pa.	1,546	11.
12.	Wisc.	1,464	Del.	1,517	12.
13.	Ill.	1,461	Nebr.	1,509	13.
14.	Hawaii	1,449	Minn.	1,506	14.
15.	S. Dak.	1,435	Md.	1,482	15.
16.	Mont.	1,431	Va.	1,393	16.
17.	Vt.	1,408	N.J.	1,341	17.
18.	Kans.	1,401	Ga.	1,325	18.
19.	Nebr.	1,385	Ala.	1,311	19.
20.	Iowa	1,341	Ind.	1,286	20.
21.	Md.	1,310	Ohio	1,278	21.
22.	Mich.	1,308	S.C.	1,247	22.
23.	Tenn.	1,304	S. Dak.	1,177	23.
24.	Conn.	1,284	Mo.	1,175	24.
25.	La.	1,261	Okla.	1,159	25.
26.	Calif.	1,253	Tenn.	1,111	26.
27.	Wyo.	1,249	Colo.	1,075	27.
28.	Ohio	1,243	Calif.	1,032	28.
	U.S.	1,327	U.S.	1,326	

Source: U.S. Dept. of Health, Education and Welfare; Public Health Service. Patient days are derived from data appearing in Part II of the August "Guide Issue" of the semi-monthly, Hospitals, official journal of the American Hospital Assoc. Rates per 1000 population are computed on the basis of Census Bureau population estimates excluding armed forces overseas, as of July 1 of the hospital year.

* Includes all types of hospitals other than mental and tuberculosis.
** Includes short-term.

Table 17. Hospital Use: Admissions and Patient Days, General and Special Hospitals*

	Admissions per 1000 Pop.	Patient Days per 1000 Pop.
New York	137.0	1,674.2
Hawaii	137.5	1,449.2
California	138.5	1,252.5
Ohio	135.0	1,242.9
Utah	138.1	1,134.8
Indiana	135.6	1,132.1
So. Carolina	135.9	1,127.6
Oklahoma	139.2	1,117.1
Maine	137.7	1,081.0
Alabama	138.6	1,020.5
U. S.	144.7	1,327.1

*Not including mental or T.B. hospitals.

Table 18. Hospital Use: Admissions and Patient Days,
Mental Hospitals*

	Admissions per 1000 Pop.	Patient Days per 1000 Pop.
New York	2.6	2,440.7
Rhode Island	3.0	1,772.6
Nebraska	3.0	1,508.9
New Jersey	2.6	1,341.3
Alabama	3.0	1,311.0
Ohio	2.6	1,278.3
Oklahoma	2.6	1,158.8
Tennessee	2.6	1,111.3
California	2.8	1,031.7
West Virginia	2.6	1,026.6
Mississippi	2.8	988.7
No. Carolina	3.0	988.0
Iowa	2.8	896.7
Arizona	2.8	436.8
New Mexico	2.8	405.4
U. S.	2.7	1,325.7

* Including short-term institutions.

In 1960 New York City hospitals provided
13,385,246 days of care, of which 43.4 per cent were
"public charge" days. In 1965 these hospitals provided 13,737,340 days of care, of which 45.2 per cent
were "public charge" days.

Omitting days of care rendered by proprietary
hospitals, which in New York City are not eligible
to receive public funds, the proportion of "public
charge" days is somewhat altered. In 1960, municipal
and voluntary hospitals together rendered 11,812,646
days of care, of which 49.2 per cent were "public
charge" days. In 1965 municipal and voluntary hospitals together rendered 12,409,733 days of care, of
which 50 per cent were "public charge" days.

In 1960 the total income of municipal and voluntary hospitals in New York City was $421,366.060, of
which 43 per cent (181,111,186) consisted of public
funds. In 1965 the total income of municipal and
voluntary hospitals in the city was $744.1 million,
of which 43 per cent ($322.8 million) consisted of
public funds. The above totals are limited to
hospitals receiving public funds.

Estimates of the proportion of public funds that
came from city tax levy are not available from the
data provided by state agencies. Using budgeted
allocations in the city expense budget to determine
the source of funds by level of government, it was
found that for the fiscal year 1960-1961, 82 per cent
of budgeted allocations for hospital care (Department
of Hospitals, plus Charitable Institutions Budget)
came from city tax levy, with state and federal funds
and collections from patients accounting for 18 per
cent of total appropriations. The comparable figure
for fiscal year 1964-1965 is 76.2 per cent.

In the year 1965, 64 per cent of all "public
charge" days were provided in municipal hospitals, and
36 per cent in voluntary hospitals.

The 36 per cent of "public charge" days provided
by voluntary hospitals accounted for 28.6 per cent of
all days of care rendered by voluntary hospitals.

Included in the roughly four million days of
care provided by the municipal hospitals in 1965 are
about 729,000 days of care provided in the public home
infirmary sections of homes for the aged.

The available information is far from complete.
What is known is that in 1960 the Department of
Welfare spent approximately $16,525,000 to provide
care in nursing homes for a monthly average of 7,400
persons.

Exactly comparable information is not available
for 1965. However, it is known that there was spent
in that year $34,371,000 for nursing home care in
voluntary and proprietary homes. It is also known
that a monthly average of approximately 8000 persons
were in nursing homes in New York City in 1965, of
whom 72 per cent were "public charge" patients.

Dr. Milton I. Roemer, Professor of Public Health,
UCLA, has compiled some statistics on hospital costs
today as compared to 35 years ago. There are 2.5
employees per patient in hospitals today compared
with 1.0 per patient in 1930, and the wages paid
those employees have multiplied many times. Hospitals
today provide many new services that were not available
in 1930, and these services require expensive new
equipment. Also, breakthroughs in technology often
make new equipment obsolete before it is paid for,
necessitating the purchase of newer and still more
expensive replacements.

New and increasingly sophisticated drugs and
widespread applications of these drugs mean steadily
increasing pharmaceutical expenses. Increased construction costs and improved standards of construction
make new care facilities far more expensive than the
obsolete structures they replace.

Cost of health care is rising faster than real
income. Health care now amounts to 6% of the gross
national product as compared with 4% in 1930; while
one-fifth of that 4% was used for hospitalization in
1930, almost one-half of the 6% today is expended for
hospitalization.

Eighty percent of care now involves third-party
payers--that is, group financing, private insurance,
or taxes. This percentage will probably rise.

No one knows what the average daily cost is per
patient in the municipal hospitals of New York City,
but certain facts are known:

- Annually, rates exceed those quoted by the
  Department of Hospitals by an unknown amount.

- There is no careful mechanism for computing precise costs.

- Rates vary for each hospital.

- Rates vary within hospitals.

- It _may_ cost the city more per patient day in a municipal hospital to maintain a patient than it would in certain other nonmunicipal institutions.

- Annual incremental cost increases are not well known; they are believed to be in the order of 12% to 15%.

- Rates for the present fiscal year for the entire system are pegged at over $80.00 per day. Officials believe the real average rate varies from somewhat higher to much higher.

- Annual rates published in federal studies are misleading and, with the lag in publication, tend to be grossly so.

Patient day costs are difficult to calculate even with good records and responsible accounting (both missing in New York's municipal hospitals). However, these costs are relatively sensitive measures of institutional efficiency. In recognizing this, the state government has sponsored a study of costs in many hospitals and written guidelines toward efficiencies and improved budgeting and record keeping. These, and more, are required in the city's hospitals in order to determine real costs and to budget responsibly for future needs.

The Commission staff had neither time nor resources to divert to the determination of costs (and cost-analysis system requirements) for the city hospitals.

In general, different hospitals provide different services and different intensities of care. Since the patients themselves have different needs it cannot be expected that the bill will necessarily match the average for any one institution, city, or state.

The American Hospital Association has published accounts stressing that hospitals are improving their accounting methods in an effort to achieve an across-the-board "cost plus" system of billing.

Proprietary Nursing Homes

The new federal laws provided for a relatively greater use of services alternative to hospital care, such as nursing home care service.

Although it was not the task of this study to determine whether the proprietary nursing homes should become part of the voluntary or public spheres, the matter was continually raised by those interviewed. There is some evidence that underlying controversy regarding this issue has brought some hardship to bear upon the proprietary nursing homes.

One can find good reason for supporting an argument for either voluntary or public care. If a satisfactory function is being performed by a nursing home, if the beds are needed and delivered at a cost appropriately below hospitals, if the rates paid are fairly set by state agencies, and if it meets applicable regulations and laws, then the nursing home should be considered part of, and treated in the same way as, any other health institution. Unfortunately, this is not usually the case, probably because so many of these homes are not capable of meeting existing standards.

The number of proprietary nursing homes is diminishing during a period of increased need. The number of nursing home beds should be increasing. The relative quality of nursing beds in the state as a whole as compared to other states is suggested by Table 19. Clearly, New York and New York City cannot take pride in this matter.

The codes are strict, as they should be. There are some proprietary nursing homes that could not pass the new building codes. However, they are protected by a "grandfather clause." Should those homes apply for resale, a change in owner-management, or even if they apply for a remodeling permit to meet present codes, they would risk losing their protection under the grandfather clause and would most likely lose their (temporary) license to operate. This anomaly

Table 19. Acceptable In-Patient Beds
(State Rankings)

Ratio of acceptable beds,* excluding those in Federal facilities, per 1000 population as of January 1, 1965.

| | | | | | | Long-Term Care** | | | | | |
| | General | | | Mental | | | Per 1000 Pop. | | | Per 1000 Pop. Aged 65 & Over | |
State Rank	State	Ratio	State Rank	State	Ratio	State Rank	State	Ratio	State Rank	State	Ratio
1.	Minn.	4.85	1.	R.I.	4.15	1.	Wash.	5.32	1.	Alaska	55.57
2.	N.Dak.	4.51	2.	N.Y.	3.73	2.	Minn.	5.04	2.	Wash.	54.17
3.	Wisc.	4.43	3.	Md.	3.68	3.	Okla.	5.00	3.	Okla.	46.45
4.	W.Va.	4.41	4.	Wisc.	3.22	4.	R.I.	4.17	4.	Minn.	46.02
5.	Kans.	4.30	5.	Mo.	3.14	5.	Nebr.	3.61	5.	Hawaii	40.37
6.	Nebr.	4.16	6.	Nebr.	3.10				6.	Tex.	38.63
7.	Okla.	4.06	7.	Calif.	3.07				7.	R.I.	37.65
8.	N.Y.	4.01	8.	N.J.	3.07	15.	Calif.	2.56	16.	Calif.	28.85
13.	Pa.	3.88	12.	Mich.	2.82	25.	Pa.	2.02	30.	Pa.	19.50
						26.	N.Y.	1.91	31.	N.Y.	18.53
20.	Mass.	3.71	16.	Pa.	2.64	30.	Mass.	1.79			
50.	Calif.	2.12	29.	Mass.	2.13	38.	Mich.	1.41	38.	Mass.	15.61
	U.S.	3.48		U.S.	2.53		U.S.	2.16		U.S.	22.53

Source: Division of Hosp. & Med. Facil., PHS, HEW. State inventory summaries (state plans for hospital construction) are contained in Hill-Burton State Plan Data (PHS Doc. No. 930-F-2).

*As classified by the State agencies.
**Includes chronic disease and skilled nursing home beds.

can result in only one direction for these homes;
unable to risk remodeling, they deteriorate even
further, to the detriment of the patients.

Funds Flow to Proprietary Homes

The Department of Welfare must validate charges
submitted by nursing homes before payment is made.
Then, on the first of the month, 45% is paid the home
and on the 15th of the month another 45% is paid. The
remainder is paid upon final approval.

There appears to be some "randomness" in the
selection of billings for disapproval. Names that
have appeared for several months on the rolls, and
that have received previous payments, can suddenly
be disapproved for a time. The claim usually is
that there had been improper billing on the part of
the home, thus causing delay in payment. These delays
are unfortunate for several reasons, not the least of
which is the costs that would have been shared by
federal and state funds.

A social security check is often the only source
of income for many persons in nursing homes. In the
case of a patient who must pay 20% (or some part) of
his bill to the home from his own funds, identification,
processing, and payment to the home is often so slow
that the patient will have already received and spent
his social security money. If this check was the
patient's only source of income, the nursing home costs
are probably unrecoverable from the patient. The Welfare Department must therefore compensate the home
owner--which it does, but only much later. Clearly
the greater the delay, the greater the expense to the
homes, to the Department of Welfare, and to the city.

The amounts outstanding and owed to nursing homes
since November do not appear to be large sums compared
to the total cost of delivery but could well amount
to the margin of survival for the individual owner.
Payment lags for April 1967 are shown in Table 20 .

Nursing Home Rates

On October 28, 1966, a report was completed by
a group at Columbia University describing the recommended principles of reimbursement for proprietary

Table 20. Lag in Welfare Dept. Reimbursements to
Nursing Homes - April 1967

Brooklyn

Name of Nursing Home	Bed Capacity	Dept. of Welfare Owes
Carlton	198	$10,251.32
Coronet	115	7,656.08
Esplanade	54	8,000.00
Farragut	70	21,351.32
Liberty	60	6,688.44
Ocean Parkway	76	8,000.00
Oxford	317	36,814.08
Park Haven	118	12,688.16
Parkway	40	7,307.02
Rugby	39	2,875.50
White	29	5,600.20
Willoughby	210	15,000.00

Queens

Clearview	179	20,882.06
Fairview	200	Nominal
Far Rockaway	60	22,379.06
Flushing Manor	60	3,500.00
Meadow Park	180	4,458.78
Oceanview	120	25,321:13
Park	280	38,903.00
St. Albans	35	11,044.97
Surfside	116	32,879.78

Manhattan

College View	233	43,386.42
East River	53	7,769.11
Mayflower	260	40,026.89
New York	120	11,117.64
Park Terrace	83	9,509.19
Riverside	50	5,085.49
Towers	310	39,000.00
Townview	150	14,000.00
Village	328	33,533.22

nursing homes in New York State. The committee,
chaired by Dr. Ray Trussel, was made up of Columbia
staff and private home owners.

A rate formula for payment to individual nursing
homes was drawn up for the January 1 to June 30 period
of 1967. Rates were all-inclusive with no extras
allowed. Rates were set on a per-home basis, and upon
a patient-day delivery cost as recommended by Dr. David
Schneider, health economist in the State Department of
Health, and endorsed by State Commissioner Ingraham.
They were subsequently approved by Dr. T. Norman Hurd,
Director of the State Budget. The new rate formula
is being discussed with interested parties and with
the association representing proprietary nursing homes
in New York City.

The formula for reimbursement, calculated on
1965 statistical and financial statements provided by
each nursing home, will essentially be as follows:

- Plus up to 3% of adjusted gross cost for
  repair.

- Plus 5% of adjusted gross cost for
  depreciation.

- Plus 2% of per-patient-day cost for
  contingencies.

- Plus 8% of 1965 costs to adjust for current
  cost level.

In State Hospital Memorandum Series 67-5, from
Dr. Robert Whalen, individual rates are given for
each home. They range from $12.82 to $17.50 per
patient day.

Existing data on past experience in the utilization of nursing home facilities are fragmentary.
It is very difficult to determine estimates of need
for these facilities but certainly the Health Services
Administration should firmly monitor any apparent
deterrent to expansion or improvement requests.

PROGRAM MANAGEMENT

The history of preparation for Medicare-Medicaid
in New York City has been unsatisfactory, as noted

earlier. This performance has been of particular
distress to officials of the Health Services Administration who often have been criticized for deficiencies
but who have not shared in the actual operating responsibility and authority.

During the past fiscal year, HSA officials
created a full-time post at the assistant-commissioner
level in the Health Department to improve the performance of the Medicaid program.

With the establishment of this office, it became
possible to develop a management program, involving
relevant elements of the Department of Welfare, which
appears to be most promising (proposed by R. S.
Alexander, Assistant Commissioner of Health, Medical
Insurance Program). It is as follows.

Purpose of Reorganization

1)   To centralize authority and responsibility
for the Medicaid program.

2)   To present a unified program to the
community.

3)   To apply appropriate management techniques
and skills in the solution of the many operating
problems.

Recommendations (Modified within Context of Present Inquiry)

1) Create a central Medicaid Administration
Agency to coordinate and direct all aspects of the
Medicaid program (see Figure 15). All bureaus,
divisions, sections, etc., working on Medicaid would
be structured into a Medicaid organization.

2) Hire, or reassign, a full-time staff to work
with Medicaid Administration. This staff, along with
the heads of the three operating divisions, would
form the executive group responsible for managing the
Medicaid program.

3) Centralize most Medicaid activities at the
34th Street location (with the exception of some

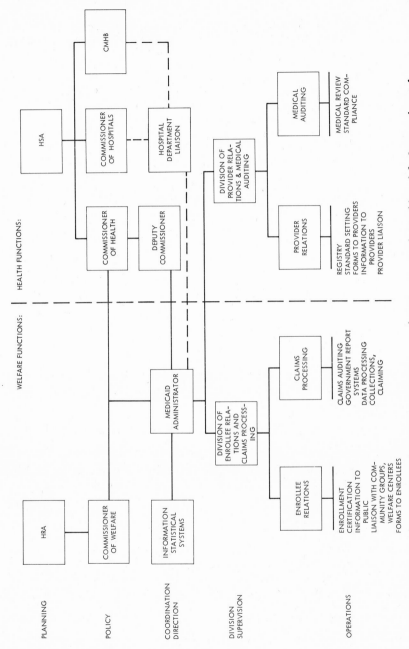

Figure 15. Commissioner Alexander's Proposed Medicaid Organizations

433

sections of the claims processing division). This centralization would facilitate administration, control, and communication.

4) Shift the operating responsibility for professional relations to the Medicaid Administration within the Hospitals Department.

5) Identify the total cost of running the Medicaid program (personnel, supplies, equipment). Establish an over-all budget, based on allocation of funds from the Departments of Hospitals, Health, and Welfare, with as much flexibility and authority as possible under present city regulations.

Programs for the Agency

1) Handle all on-going operational problems such as clinic enrollment, claiming procedures, provider payments, etc.

2) Codify all existing procedures. Rewrite into clear, intelligible language and ensure wide distribution among providers.

3) Set up a coordinated public relations program to explain benefits to both recipients and providers.

4) Review all forms and procedures and simplify where indicated.

5) Set up adequate vertical and horizontal communication systems among all personnel working on the program.

6) Centralize sources of information in one division for enrollees and the public and in another division for providers of service. Maintain this service seven days a week as necessary.

7) Centralize forms of distribution to providers of service. Provide for the widest possible dissemination of application and billing forms to providers of service.

8) Introduce affidavit sign-up procedures at the earliest possible time.

Staff Recommendations: Medicaid

While the staff study would endorse most of the
recommendations proposed by Commissioner Alexander,
including the concept of a single central agency for
Medicaid administration, it is the staff's finding
that the single agency envisioned should be implemented within the Health Services Administration, and
specifically within the Department of Hospitals. The
following recommendations incorporate this provision.

By Executive Order of The Mayor:

1) Form a single administrative Medicaid
Management Agency.

2) Place it under the Commissioner of Hospitals
within the Department of Hospitals.

3) Place the Bureau of Hospital Care Services
(Welfare Department) under the cognizant management
of the Medicaid Management Agency.

4) Establish a joint appointment in Hospitals
and Welfare for an Assistant Commissioner for Health
Insurance Programs to direct Medicaid administration
with the Department of Hospitals.

5) Place all Medicaid-relevant data processing
equipment, programs, and associated personnel now in
the Welfare Department under the cognizant management of the new Agency as necessary.

6) Establish a Board of Medicaid Administration
to conduct scheduled monthly meetings, and emergency
meetings, for the provision of policy guidance for
Medicaid administration. This membership is suggested:

- Commissioner of Hospitals (Chairman)

- HSA Administrator (ex officio)

- Commissioner of Health

- Chairman, CMHB

- HRA Administrator (ex officio)

- Commissioner of Welfare

- Assistant Commissioner, Insurance Programs

- Director of the Budget

- To be selected (local state official preferred)

7) Require a revision of case verification sampling policies and procedures now used by the Department of Welfare.

8) Form a 90-day Task Force to recommend the form and content of a workable affidavit instrument for quick sign-up processing of Medicaid applicants and renewals. The Task Force should take into account the present relevant efforts in the Welfare Department, related efforts in California and elsewhere, and the counsel of state and federal officials.

9) Appoint a second 90-day Task Force, working in conjunction with the first, to draw up recommended legislative changes to be directed both to the state legislature and to the Congress. Principal aims would be to permit local use of an affidavit for quick sign-up processing of Medicaid applicants, and to free health provision from welfare constraints.

10) Require each municipal hospital to undertake the minimum cost accounting efforts necessary in establishing accurate in-patient and OPD visit rates.

11) Formalize request to the state government that it forward 100% letters of credit quarterly to the Medicare Administration Agency.

12) As a temporary expedient applicable to non-institutional charges, require that the appointed Board of Medicaid Administration quickly establish an equitable "advisory rate schedule" for the services of physicians, surgeons and dentists, and for pharmaceutical items. (The procedure involved in developing such a rate schedule should be similar in principle to that used by the Veterans Administration hospitals within the city to determine their charge rates.)

13) When the advisory rate schedule is ready and appropriately coordinated (for most services and items, hopefully, within thirty days in its initial form) it should be widely publicized in the city with the advice to all institutions, physicians, dentists and pharmacists that, should they choose to accept the

advised rates, their properly detailed billings will
be met within 30 days or less, and existing backlogs
will be paid in a lump sum reimbursement; non-schedule
reimbursement claims would continue to take longer.

14)   Take all necessary action to assure that
state determined rates for OPD visits to municipal
hospitals are not at a rate lower than those for visits
to voluntary hospitals.

15)   Require that all Medicaid sign-ups in municipal hospitals record the municipal hospital as the
cognizant service agency rather than the associated
voluntary.

16)   Require the Medicaid Administration Agency to
prepare a detailed operational program for (a) the
future registration of all clients using publicly
financed health care facilities, (b) the routine,
rapid identification of all such clients, (c) an
interactively cooperative system between such agencies
for patient registration and identification, and (d)
a common unit-record system for all such clients and
all such agencies.

17)   Meet cash-flow problems of registered and
approved health care institutions by requiring the
Board of Medicaid Administration, in coordination
with state officials, to establish a mechanism whereby
such institutions can (a) advance 90% of proven average
charges by block number each day, weekly in advance
of anticipated admissions or clinic visits (subject
to special, full and/or random audit), and (b) receive
100% reimbursement upon acceptance of actual case
eligibility, together with quarterly return of funds
not used for valid reimbursements. Pending more
formal organization, within 90 days, the Medicaid
Management Agency should establish "eligibility certification field offices" within an appropriate number
and location of public health care offices of the
boroughs.

18)   Charge the Medicaid Management Agency, in
cooperation with state and city officials, and representatives of voluntary and other health institutions,
to establish standard forms and procedures for processing claims and related communications.

CHAPTER **8** STATUS AND
ROLE OF CENTRAL
ORGANIZATIONS

HSA AND THE OVERHEAD AGENCIES

The Health Services Administration

In May of 1966 the Health Services Administration
was established by executive order of the mayor.
Howard J. Brown, M.D., was appointed Health Services
Administrator. Subsequently, James G. Haughton, M.D.,
was appointed First Deputy Administrator, and
Paul M. Densen, D.Sc., was appointed Deputy Administrator. Mr. Jacob Levine was retained as special
consultant. A third post was restructured for Program
Planning.

According to the Official Directory of the City
of New York, "The Administrator shall have with respect
to the Departments of Health, Hospitals, and their
respective Boards, the Office of the Chief Medical
Examiner and the New York City Community Mental Health
Board, the power and duty to review, evaluate, initiate,
conduct and coordinate all programs and activities of
such agencies."

This simple statement is, at one time, a source of
great potential for improvement and a current controversy. Traditionally, the Commissioners of Health,
Hospitals, and Mental Health have functioned in autonomous roles. The Health Services Administration, like
other administrations created by the Mayor, is intended
to bring together into a functional whole those closely
related agencies--formerly autonomous--which, through
effective integration, can provide more efficient
administration in government.

In summing up a first year of history for the
HSA, it can be fairly observed that this so-called

438

"super agency," in the absence of authorizing legislation, has functioned more effectively than many
predicted but not nearly as well as some had hoped.
Several fundamental factors underly this record of
performance.

As of the time of this appraisal, legislation
had not been passed by the city council to empower the
Health Services Administration to perform fully its
designated role. Necessary legislation has been proposed, hearings have been held, and the matter remains
pending before the city council. Investigations within
the present study indicate that the legislation will
be a great benefit to the health services system of the
city and should be passed essentially as proposed.

A second factor leading to modest performance for
HSA is that implied above with respect to the formerly
chartered autonomous roles of departmental commissioners. Prior to the formation of the present administrations, commissioners of departments reported directly
to the Mayor. One of Mayor Lindsay's objectives in
the proposed city reorganization is to achieve workable
span of control with respect to administrative management. While, before, some 100 or more executives
reported to the Mayor's Office, now the number is in
prospect of being reduced to a workable span. In the
course of transition, however, there have been normal,
to-be-expected difficulties in the adjustment of commissioners to the structure of the new administrative
groupings. This matter has been of particular difficulty in the case of the Health and Hospitals Departments because the traditional roles of their commissioners involved vital relationship with the Mayor.

Another factor of importance has been the traditional roles of the Board of Health and the Board of
Hospitals--particularly the former. The Board of
Health is the health legislative body for the City of
New York. Its chairman is the Commissioner of Health.
The present form and function of the Board of Health
has a continuous history of over 100 years. The board
takes justifiable pride in its separation from politics
and the administrative structure of the city. By and
large, the board has been both effective and prestigious throughout its years. Its members assume tremendous responsibility and serve without pay.

Since the formation of the HSA, members of the Board of Health have expressed some reservations regarding the future role of the board with respect to the relationship between the Commissioner of Health (and his department) and that of HSA proper. The larger community of public health professionals has been similarly concerned. Attending fears have not been justified, however, because the relationships are becoming increasingly effective and mutually strengthening. Furthermore, the Mayor and other officials have expressed their intent that the Board of Health continue in its significant and effective role and that the Department of Health continue to fulfill its vital and traditional role. There remains only the reasonable requirement that programs, budgets, goals and activities in the field of public health in the city be coordinated with, and mutually supportive of, related programs in hospitals, mental health and medical welfare within HSA, as well as with respect to other programs of health significance, for example, air pollution and sanitation. It is the intent of the Mayor that the HSA Administrator and his immediate staff help to coordinate and develop these highly correlated programs--their manning, funding, and objectives.

An additional factor in the record of HSA has come about through the intent of the administrator to administratively join certain over-all programs that had previously been in the autonomous Health or Hospitals Departments. To this end, he has named several key officials in either of the two departments to joint appointments. An example occurs in the case of Dr. Mary McLaughlin, who holds an appointment as Assistant Commissioner in both the Department of Health and the Department of Hospitals for the area of ambulatory care program development. The effect of such joint appointments, and related actions, has been to raise concern on the part of both Health and Hospital Department personnel regarding the traditional functional separation between the two departments, namely that "integrative adjustments" might lead to a merging of the departments. This, however, has not been the intent of either the Mayor or the HSA Administrator, rather the intent being the development of common program planning and budgeting for areas that lay in both departments as well as elsewhere. This concern, too, is also subsiding.

Finally, there is the matter of competing expectations with respect to the capabilities of the first HSA Administrator. Public health personnel would have him oriented toward public health; hospital personnel would have him oriented toward clinical and institutional medicine; mental health personnel would have him oriented toward that field; groups of special interest throughout the communities would have him oriented toward special needs; the system of voluntary hospitals and agencies would have him oriented toward their laudable interests. Executive personnel, both in and outside local government, would have him a man of outstanding executive ability.

Months of search and evaluation were carried out prior to this first appointment.

In spite of all these factors, HSA is emerging as a key executive agency for health delivery in the City of New York. In the interests of improved health delivery it is vital that the agency be supported and strengthened. Its long-term evolution may be expected to experience many problems of growth and adjustment. Its ultimate character, though probably different from any other major public office in health delivery, may at least be likened to that of the Office of the Surgeon General at the federal level.

Part Three contains clearer specification of an anticipated evolution for HSA proper, the operating Departments of Health and Hospitals, and the Community Mental Health Board. Remaining present discussion will review the status and operational character of these Departments. First in order, however, is a brief appraisal of the role of the so-called "executive overhead agencies" with respect to their impact on the operation of HSA and its Departments.

The "Overhead Agencies"

Of first concern is the role of the Bureau of the Budget. Second only to the Office of the Mayor in its role as an executive agency, this bureau provides arms-length management of virtually all other executive agencies in the city through the mechanism of the executive expense budget. The deeply ingrained fiscal practice of line-item budgeting, coupled with bureau-centered regulation of budget preparation and subsequent budget change, places most monetary authority in

the hands of the Director of the Office of the Budget,
and more specifically, in the course of routine operation, within the hands of the budget examiners. Budget
examiners are, in fact, the delegates of the director.
They supervise the preparation of budgets for departments under their cognizance, and subsequently are
responsible for virtually all changes, however trivial,
at the line-item levels of the over-all budget. This
form of centralized authority means that very few
persons, regardless of level of position in the city
agencies, enjoy command of their own budget once
approved.

Equally disturbing to the operational arms of
government is the practice of imposing "accrual
savings." Accruals are imposed upon line organizations
by the Bureau of the Budget annually as deemed appropriate. Specifically, the practice of accruals is
that of imposing requirements on line organizations
for the nonimplementation of approved line-items of
expenditure in the original budget in order to enforce
levied "savings." This is the means, then, by which
the city, through the authority of the Bureau of the
Budget, cuts back expenses as a given fiscal period
matures. Imposed accruals may be very large. Their
imposition may mean sufficient cut-backs in operating
departments to materially change the expectation of
executives for their programs during a given fiscal
year. Subsequent discussion in Part Three, regarding
the flow and impact of public funds, will review the
present budget of the Health Services Administration
indicating that imposed accruals for the present
fiscal period, recently set, approximate $43 million.

Prior to taking office, and subsequently, Mayor
Lindsay has on numerous occasions stated his intent
to introduce program planning and budgeting into the
fiscal cycle of the city. Program planning and budgeting is an advanced and sophisticated style of budget
application. Shift from line-item budgeting to this
newer form will require a long term of transition,
itself requiring a carefully devised plan and implementation. Only limited progress toward that end can
be made each year with perhaps whole realization
achieved some four to seven years after the process
has begun. Fully realized, program planning and budgeting would achieve autonomous budget administration
within the line organizations of the city but on a
basis acceptable to central budget executives, to the
Office of the Mayor, to the Controller, and to other

responsible fiscal personnel, as well as providing
proper public accountability. Since it will not be
possible to achieve this state for a number of years,
the interim period will be characterized by a continuation of the ills of line-item budgeting and accruals.
It can be expected, therefore, that the many fundamental problems of administration now plaguing HSA and
its departments will continue for that period (in the
absence of the kind of innovations recommended in
Part Three. These limitations are sufficiently severe
that it would not be responsible to forecast anything
more than normative function for the Health Services
Administration during the time within which very great
expectations will be laid upon it. Recognizing this
basic fact, recommendations growing out of this study
will propose an entirely new approach to the whole
matter of health care administration.

The city's traditional budget practices would in
themselves, as noted, be quite enough to raise alarm
regarding the future effectiveness of the Health
Services Administration. Similar vexing constraints,
however, are applied from other quarters. Provision
of supplies is carried out independently by the
Department of Purchase. Authority for the provision
of personnel is fractionated in other hands, namely,
the Office of the Director of Personnel, the Civil
Service Union, and again, the Bureau of the Budget.
Provision of new construction and renovations is
handled by the Department of Public Works, which in
turn is severely crippled by a New York State law
requiring that public construction be undertaken by
multiple contractors in this city. This system induces
delays, redundancies, expenses, and obsolescence that
is incredible in terms of its impact on the health
system plant of the city.

Certainly, all of these circumstances collectively
are sufficient to make administration of HSA a very
difficult process. Unfortunately, a number of additional dimensions of complexity exist. There is the Office
of the Controller (a separately elected official) acting as an independent auditing agency for city expenses.
There is the city council, with legislative powers for
the city. Finally, there is the Board of Estimate
which, under the New York City Charter, must pass upon
all appropriations and expenditures in excess of $2,500.

Insofar as the efficacy of line administration is
concerned (HSA being a case in point), differences in

political party affiliation between the Mayor's office,
the Controller, the city council, and the Board of
Estimate, can be of real significance. In this arena,
one could expect at least modest administrative difficulty even if all officials were of the same party
persuasion. Ideally, the latter circumstance would
apply, as well as the existence of strong personal
regard between incumbents, in order for the problems
of line administrators of the city to be reasonable in
scope under present provisions of the city charter.

     There is little wonder that the HSA Administrator,
or the Commissioner of Hospitals, the Commissioner of
Health, or the Commissioner of Mental Health, must
spend a great deal of time (if not a majority) in
quasi-political activity, in trouble-shooting, in
"fire-fighting," and in the working-out of relatively
trivial matters which in an efficient organization
would be handled at a much lower level in the hierarchy.

     All matters considered, there is now a responsible
and promising working relationship between the Mayor,
the city council, the Board of Estimate, and HSA officials. In view of all the findings of the present
report regarding the needs of the health delivery system of the city, one can only anticipate the great
good that can be gained by increasingly strong relationships between these offices of government.

                    DEPARTMENT OF HEALTH

     The role, functions and problems of the Department
of Health are given extended discussion here (in contrast to the Department of Hospitals) inasmuch as it
is not considered elsewhere in this report in depth.
Its organization is depicted in Figure 16. These
discussions borrow heavily upon an earlier study sponsored by the Health Research Council.

     The New York City Department of Health is autho-
rized in Chapter 2 of the New York City Charter. In
general, the department's jurisdiction extends over
the city and the waters within quarantine limits of
the city. The areas of purview for the department
are those affecting health in the city, including the
enforcement of provisions of law affecting the preservation of life, and those sanitation conditions affecting health. So conceived, the department is the responsible agent for enforcing the Health Code of

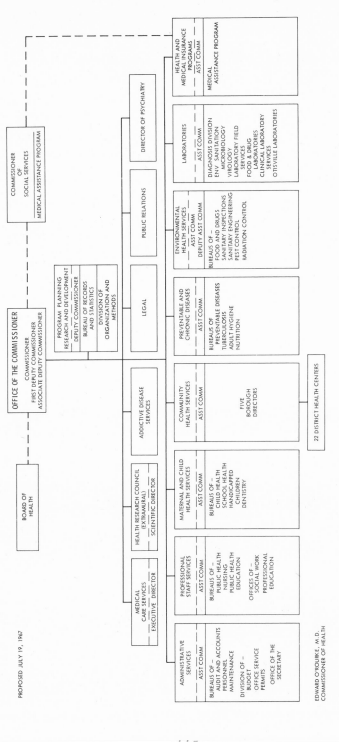

Figure 16. Organization of Department of Health

445

New York City, Public Health Law, Administrative Code, and other applicable law.

Although the implementation of the provisions of the New York City Health Code is the responsibility of the Department of Health, the Board of Health, within the department, is the legal agent in the promulgation of the code. The Board of Health is composed of the commissioner and four other members, two of whom must be physicians and two of whom are lay personnel. This body constitutes the legal authority to amend, repeal, or alter the health code, and sits as a board of judgment on appeals relative to decisions of the commissioner and/or the Department of Health. Additionally, the Board of Health is responsible for assuring that the code is compatible and consistent with federal and state legislation covering similar areas of concern.

The Health Code, which is a revision of the old Sanitation Code, is divided into five major titles, which are in general relation to the functional activity of the Department of Health. These are:

General provisions

Control of disease

Maternal, infant, child, and school health services

Environmental sanitation

Vital statistics

In addition to the provisions of the Health Code and other public law, which establish the scope of activity of the Department of Health, the commissioner has certain recourse to other implementation prerogatives. In general, these are:

Permits--He may grant, suspend, or revoke permits relative to any subject regulated by the Department.

Penalty--He can cause to be brought to a magistrate's court any instance of failure of compliance.

Imminent Peril--Under conditions which warrant
a declaration of peril, he may take measures even
beyond those provided for, such as barricading
neighborhoods and diverting traffic.

Suit--He may sue and be sued on all matters
affecting the department.

Right of Entry--Entry authorized without fee
or hindrance.

Thus, it would appear that the commissioner
has broad legal means at his disposal for his major
tasks of implementing provisions of public law and
keeping health matters under constant and continuing
surveillance.

The commissioner must decide what kinds of health
problems are in existence in the city and the ways in
which solutions can be approached. He must establish
a philosophy for the different kinds of programs and
determine whether the stress should be on the preventive or the therapeutic aspects. Research must be
planned and research results also must be applied
programmatically; this is an important facet of the
commissioner's activities. In general, therefore, the
commissioner has these duties:

- Normal administrative matters surrounding the
  Department of Health, including such problems
  as civil service, wages and compensation, and
  union matters.

- Assessment of population needs for the purposes
  of determining future areas of stress for
  assessing the effectiveness of programs under
  way.

- Planning and costing of new programs, including
  the trade-offs that might become necessary such
  as in determining the value of inoculation
  programs, etc.

- Accomplishment of the specific tasks as set
  forth in the chartering documents.

- Determination and establishment of the base-
  line philosophy of public medical care
  practice in the city as well as the fundamental
  basis of good public medical care.

- Interface with other departments of the city involved in medical care practices, as well as functioning as a member of the Mayor's staff.

- Interface with federal and state agencies on various public health and related programs.

- Effecting a relationship with the private medical sector to determine a complete public health picture of New York City.

- The presentation of services so that a maximum number of people will be motivated to use them or to comply with their use.

To aid the commissioner in the fulfillment of his statutory responsibility, line organizations and staff functions have evolved. In general, line organizations are responsible for the implementation of the various programs undertaken by the department. Staff organizations, which supply services to the rest of the department as well as to the commissioner, contain a number of functions, several of which are important in accomplishing the department mission.

Health Research Council

Tradition has allocated "$1 per year per citizen" to the Health Research Council to attack health problems of pressing relevance to New York. The council has developed a program of basic research, applied research, grant activity and laboratory development.

Laboratories

The Bureau of Laboratories, operating at a staff level, has three important functions.

- To serve, as necessary, the physicians in the city.

- To hold statutory responsibility regarding licensing and quality control of the 400 clinical laboratories throughout the city.

- To support departmental programs, such as epidemiological assessment.

To accomplish the first function it performs in excess of 1 million tests per year. A staff of 500 people, including 30 field station representatives, is involved in the performance of these tests.

The second function concerns the inspection and licensing of laboratories as they occur in hospitals, clinics, and independent settings--both profit and nonprofit. The procedures involved in this service require inspection to determine physical adequacy and soundness of procedures. Periodically, known specimens are sent to selected laboratories for diagnosis. Results are checked to determine accuracy. These efforts effect approvals, lead to revocation in some cases, and occasionally give rise to law suits of various kinds.

A third function, support to the Department of Health, involves normal laboratory practices directed to the specific needs of an investigation being undertaken.

The Bureau of Laboratories has identified a set of requirements which, if fulfilled, would allow it to provide services necessary for departmental support and its statutory functions in a more efficient manner. These requirements would lead to a system providing:

- Information on who is submitting specimens--to make certain the physician or agency is an authorized user.

- Formatted information with regard to patient, specimen, and test required.

- Rapid methodology for recording and reporting results.

- Data retrieval methods for source, requests of individual physicians, patient data, and correlation between clinical data and laboratory findings.

- Cost analysis for laboratory procedure.

- Surveys for a particular disease frequency in a given area in relation to type of patient.

- Follow-up procedures for findings of a pre-clinical nature.

- Records of data concerning licensed laboratories for Laboratory Field Services.

Line Functions

A number of assistant commissioners administer departmental programs in a line relationship to the Commissioner of Health. They function somewhat independently, usually in areas similar to the titles of the Health Code.

Medical Insurance Programs (See Chapter 7)

Administrative Services

Addictive Disease Services

Maternal and Child Health Services

Community Health Services

Preventable and Chronic Disease Services

Environmental Services

With the exception of Insurance Programs and Administrative Services, each of the commissioners administers programs which include prevention, diagnosis, therapy, and rehabilitation, and which vary in administrative implementation.

The city is divided into 30 health districts, each under the direction of a Public Health Officer. The work in health centers receives guidance and control from the Assistant Commissioner for Community Health Services through a borough director. Even though the programs of health implemented are generally administered through the local health officer, the specific authority for these programs is divided among the assistant commissioners.

Each health district is divided into smaller geographical segments referred to as health areas. These areas were not created relative to facilities or services but represent a statistical convenience for reporting disease incidence, treatment, and remission

as well as indigenous problems. Further, the districts
and areas, except for isolated instances, are not
common to the districting encountered in the Departments of Hospitals, Welfare, Education, Police, or
Fire, each being differently districted. Consequently,
programs are implemented by district health officers
only by circumventing or overcoming a variety of
coordination difficulties.

The Assistant Commissioner for Administrative
Services provides support for the remainder of the line
organizations, the staff, and the commissioner.

The administrative relationship relative to inter-
departmental budget problems is a function of HSA
initiative and agreement rather than legal requirement
(as yet), since each department remains statutorially
independent.

With respect to personnel matters, serious problems exist because of civil service salary specification. In general, public health salaries are well
below competitive levels.

The remainder of the Department of Health may be
divided into two broad functions: (1) Those services
associated with inspections, licensing, and pest control; and (2) those related to various health programs. In general, both functions are implemented
under the borough directors and district health officers who are responsible for administration. Technical
and/or medical supervision remains a function of an
assistant commissioner at the central office and, in
most instances, authority is further divided by bureau
chiefs, and division chiefs. As will be seen later,
both administrative control and technical/medical
control are divided over several levels of manage-
ment--not only between departments, but between the
assistant commissioners within a department.

The functions of inspections, licensing, and pest
control are concentrated under the Assistant Commissioner for Environmental Services. Technical supervision
is divided among bureaus, each of which functions
independently.

Food and Drug

Sanitary Engineering

Sanitary Inspections

Pest Control

The operational aspects of these functions are associated with the borough directors. The authority for their operation is Title IV of the New York City Health Code.

The largest single inspection service, concerned with licensing matters, is that provided by the Bureau of Food and Drugs operating in seven divisions:

Milk, Milk Products, and Frozen Desserts

Shellfish

Wholesale Foods (not under first two items)

Retail

Drugs (generally cosmetics)

Hospital and Institutional

Chemical and Poison Control

In general, these divisions are concerned with health aspects of food and drug processing and are not involved in detection of fraud or the degree to which products fulfill public expectations. The bureau cooperates with other departments, e.g., the Department of Markets, as well as other functions of the Department of Health such as epidemiological investigations in the areas of food handling. Bureau inspections occur through regularly scheduled visits, upon complaints from the central registry, by follow-up from previous discoveries, or as a team action in a more general investigation. A 24-hour poison control information center is maintained by the bureau to supply information pertaining to content of products which contain various types of poison.

The facilities used by the bureau to accomplish its investigations, aside from normal facilities of the department, are two types of unique laboratories. The first is used for chemical assessment and the second for bacteriological assessment. The results of the investigations are then used as the basic information through which the Bureau of Permits issues a permit for the purposes requested.

Both the Bureau of Sanitary Inspections and the Bureau of Sanitary Engineering operate in a similar manner, although their areas of purview relative to the broad function of inspections are somewhat different. The Bureau of Sanitary Engineering inspects both the public and private sectors for water pollution, waste disposal, water supply, sewage, and sewage plants. The Bureau of Sanitary Inspections, on the other hand, is specifically concerned with inspections of barber shops, beauty shops, theaters, laundries, and places of public assembly. In addition, it has a more generalized function of inspection for environmental nuisances, all other inspections not covered under Food and Drug, and areas where other departments maintain purview but where health complaints are forthcoming, e.g., rat bites, gas hazards, and plumbing.

As previously mentioned, the inspection functions are carried forth under borough directors but are related to sanitary districts. These districts are not coincident with health districts but are functionally related to concentrations of problems. Although the inspection services are treated similarly, here it must be remembered that the technical administration is functionally distinct with regard to the bureaus providing the control. Even though a discernible trend toward generalized inspection service does exist, such is not in fact the case.

The one direct service provided by the assistant commissioner has been assigned to the Bureau of Rodent Control. When rat-bite information is received from the Bureau of Sanitary Inspections, rodent control units are dispatched. Eradication service is provided whether the owner cooperates or not, and money is recovered from reluctant landlords through direct billing and courts when required. An important aspect of rodent control is education, and several impressive programs of this sort have been implemented in coordination with other Departments such as Police, Fire, and Buildings. Some of the more important of these are:

Weekend education programs

Block association programs

Junior high school programs

Teacher training programs

The complete cycle of rat infestation, discovery, and treatment involves an average of five or six reinspections, as well as the continued application of various rodenticides.

Other inspection services are performed within the areas managed by other assistant commissioners; by and large, these are not directed toward the public sector as in the case of environmental services. They are associated with programs of health, the second function to be described. The programs administered by the Assistant Commissioner of Preventable and Chronic Diseases are technically and medically controlled through several bureaus and divisions of bureaus. The first of these is the Bureau of Preventable Diseases, which is apportioned in four divisions:

Epidemiology

Tropical Medicine (Parasitology)

Social Hygiene

Veterinary Medicine

In most cases the services associated with these divisions are administered through several of the district health centers, which provide administrative control.

The Division of Epidemiology is concerned with all communicable disease with the exception of tuberculosis, venereal disease, and parasitic diseases, for which services are located in other bureaus. Through reporting of diseases and conditions, the division maintains surveillance of disease incidence and patterns, and significant variations are noted. It should be mentioned that the statistics thus reported are also utilized for base-line measurement to evaluate control procedures which have been taken in response to an outbreak. When an outbreak is discovered or reported, all relevant individuals are notified, pending an investigation to determine sources of infection and modes of transmission. The investigations are directed toward:

- Stopping the spread of disease and preventing recurrence

- Determining a causal relationship

Reaction time to reports is an extremely critical variable, since the ability to reach the two goals is directly related to the stage of the disease. That is, interpretation of the conditions is facilitated when the disease does not become too widespread or become intermingled with different modes or circumstances of transmission.

The reaction to outbreak generally involves preventive medication either through clinic service, direct service, or referral to the private sector. Further contacts are prohibited when such is indicated. When institutions such as hospitals are involved, the same procedures are utilized, but in conjunction with a hospital epidemiologist program. This program encourages the designation of a house physician as a part-time epidemiologist to:

- promote principles of control of infections,

- educate physicians and nurses to practice sound preventive measures,

- aid in investigation by the epidemiological teams during an outbreak.

The education involved in this program is provided by both central bureau and field epidemiologists.

The Division of Tropical Diseases provides both diagnostic and treatment services for the unique population of New York City. About 10 per cent of the individuals arriving in New York City from the South or Puerto Rico are infected with harmful parasites.

The next division to be considered is that of Social Hygiene, concerned with venereal disease. The implementation of both diagnosis and treatment occurs in various health districts. Administrative and technical supervision is provided by the Division Head for Social Hygiene. The clinics associated with Social Hygiene are responsible for Pap smears, inoculations of various sorts, and blood samples for a number of purposes.

The basic extra-clinic activity engaged in is education directed toward both the public and the medical professionals. Until recently there has been a decline in the incidence of venereal disease but increasing frequency has necessitated a reemphasis of the disease to medical schools, physicians, and the

public. Programs of education are required for the
private sector to understand the need for interviews
with those infected. Both the source of the infection
and the contacts must be determined to effect control.
Treatment of the individual in isolation does little
to prevent spread. Follow-up action required for the
prevention and spread of the disease has often been
held up because of the reluctance of private physicians to present the case to health officials.

Venereal diseases are in a category of reportable
diseases. Various methods of checking on private
physicians' reports are utilized. With these formal
and informal methods, most cases come under the surveillance of health officials. The U.S. Public Health
Service, which is closely related to the Department
of Health in these matters, performs follow-up inter-
viewing and other reactive programs, makes routine
visits to physicians and laboratories, and performs
contact activities. Diagnosis and treatment are
financed through city funds, while most of the other
programs are federally financed. Though venereal
disease is a reportable illness, physicians are not
legally obligated to submit their patients for
interview.

Another bureau under Preventable and Chronic
Diseases is that of Adult Hygiene. This bureau is
technically responsible for several programs aimed at
detection and research.

Cancer Prevention/Detection Centers

Diagnostic Services

Diabetes Control Program

Glaucoma Detection

Health Maintenance Service

Cancer Control and Research

Special Services

Most of these programs are preventive in nature
and referrals are made to the originating physicians.
Follow-up procedures are utilized between the department physicians and the originating physician to see
whether therapy has followed the diagnosis. Most of

the aspects of these programs are implemented at the operational level, although the research and research reporting are performed at the central bureau.

The remaining bureau under Preventable and Chronic Diseases is the Tuberculosis Bureau. In many respects the history of TB detection and treatment is similar to that of social hygiene, where a recent resurgence has followed a period of relative decline. In general, the bureau is responsible for:

- Treatment of nonhospitalized patients

- Coordination of case-finding activities

    - Routine X-ray examinations

    - Contacts and associates of known cases (two-year surveillance)

- Follow-up for ambulatory care patients (Public Health Nursing).

The next function to be discussed is that concerned with Addictive Disease Services.

Addictive Disease Services maintains a central registry of known addicts along with files and a tabulating unit. The central registry serves the following purposes:

- To compile a record of the extent of addiction incidence.

- To provide information for treatment, control, and detection of lapse or delinquency.

- To provide a tool for fiscal management, especially where local agencies are being reimbursed.

- To provide information for evaluation of results.

The staff is saturated with day-to-day problems. Professionals lament the necessity of the patients to "hit rock bottom" before coming to the attention of the department. They would like to devote much more attention to the preventive aspects of addiction but the fractionation of areas of responsibility at the state, federal, and municipal levels preempts this desirable course.

The Assistant Commissioner for Maternal and Child Health Services is responsible for direct and consultative services through four bureaus:

Child Health

School Health

Handicapped Children

Dentistry

These bureaus represent most of the direct services of the Department of Health and account for much of the complete services provided for children.

The Bureau of Child Health is responsible for children through school age and for the maternity and newborn services of the hospitals of New York City. It is organized in three divisions:

Maternity and Newborn

Infant and Preschool

Day Care, Day Camp, and Children's Institutions

The Maternity and Newborn Division is responsible for periodic inspection services to consult and set standards for those types of services. The division provides a consulting obstetrician, pediatrician, ·public health nurse, and social worker as a team for physical review, record reviews, and procedural reviews. In addition, the division is responsible for the operation of 15 premature baby centers and transportation of the premature baby to these centers from other hospitals when such is required. The division operates and pays for these services except in the case of handicapped children, where a means test and state and federal reimbursement apply. Further, a home delivery service is provided through the personnel of this division.

The Infant and Preschool Division provides direct service to all infants brought to the 93 child health stations. As such, some 40 per cent or more of all children born in the city each year are seen by the division. The child health stations, or well-baby clinics, provide diagnosis but not treatment. Most of the stations are heavily overcrowded because of the differential effects of population migration within the city since the clinics were established. The major problems of administering such child health stations are those associated with the several chan- nels of management referred to previously and the decline of the professional staff.

The Division of Day Care, Day Camp, and Children's Institutions is concerned with administration, licens- ing, standards, consultation, and inspections. It has a small, multidisciplined staff including consult- ing physicians, educators, nurses, and sociologists. They are responsible for setting standards for group day care service and licensing following a multidis- ciplinary inspection. For day camps, extensive con- sultation and recommendation services are performed, but no licensing.

The 58 children's institutions, in which children live full time in New York City, are an additional responsibility of this division. These institutions, involving some 22,000 children, are a major responsi- bility of the State Department of Welfare and the State Department of Health. These are operated by:

Department of Welfare

Public organizations

Not-for-profit organizations, both sectarian and nonsectarian.

The Bureau of Handicapped Children is responsible for eligible handicapped children under 21 years of age. The Bureau has three divisions which provide hospital consultation service, crippled children's programs, and direct service. These divisions are:

Medical Rehabilitation Service

School Programs for Handicapped

Direct Service

The Medical Rehabilitation Service surveys and consults with hospitals to approve the various

services required. To accomplish this they have
produced four guides to the 51 participating hospitals
and the 202 services involved. These are:

Financial and social eligibility

Procedures

Medical eligibility

Standards compendium

Since the budget of this division is 50 per cent
state reimburseable, medical and financial audits are
continuously undertaken for hospitals to be paid for
service. Definitions of handicapping and crippling
diseases are continuously reviewed and updated.

The second Division is the School Program for
the Handicapped. It is concerned with school placement services. Included is the screening and placement of the handicapped child in the proper setting,
along with follow-up and continuous consultation for
all participants. There are presently 21 schools
holding special classes for handicapped children.

The third Division is that of Direct Services,
which are consultative in general, with referrals
to proper agencies or the private sector as the result
of the consultations. The three types of services
provided, mainly in health centers, are eye, heart,
and orthopedics.

The broad basis of operation for the Bureau of
School Health is, first, to find the child in need of
help and, second, to assist him in getting help for
any kind of physical or emotional handicap which may
be holding him back from reaching his potential.

In the course of its multiple activities, the
Bureau of School Health is closely involved with many
other agencies outside of the Health Department. The
most important relationship to be considered is that
between the bureau, the district health centers, the
board of education, and the educational district
supervisors. The personnel of the district health
centers administer much of the work of the Bureau of
School Health with coordination between the District
Health Officer and the District Education Officer.
Since these districts do not have common boundaries,

considerable difficulty is often encountered in attempting to develop coordinated programs. The same is
the case for research activities which must be approved
by the Joint Coordinating Council on School Health.

     The last function to be described is that of the
Assistant Commissioner for Community Health Services.
It is this office that is responsible for the operation
of the 30 health districts. Historically, the operation of this part of the Department of Health has been
highly centralized, with separate groupings of professionals. Personnel have been trained in a number of
orientations in consonance with their use at the
community level. The city was divided into 30 districts and a health officer was placed in charge of
each district to determine local needs. The average
population served by a district is about 250,000.
Twenty-three of the districts have separate central
buildings, while the others are combined. The district health officers report to the borough director,
who in turn reports to the Assistant Commissioner for
Community Health Services.

     The Assistant Commissioner for Community Health
Services is responsible for two bureaus and several
offices, as well as the health centers. The bureaus
are:

     Public Health Nursing

     Public Health Education

The offices are:

     Social Work

     Civil Defense

     Professional Education

     The Bureau of Public Health Nursing represents
the largest nursing service in the country, capable
of dealing with a wide range of problems rather than
specialized services. The central bureau (as is the
case of other service programs provided by the department) does not provide direct services, but technically
supervises its staff who function at the district
level. In general, these activities and responsibilities include:

- Nursing service for all public, parochial, junior and senior high schools, and vocational high schools.

- Home care programs.

- Activities in support of departmental programs in the various districts and clinics.

- Recruiting, staffing and education.

In general, the most severe problems are occasioned by turnover and shortage of staff. Shortages have led to the creation of para-medical jobs such as Public Health Assistant and Public Health Aide. These new positions have helped but not solved the critical issues involved in obtaining and retaining staff nursing support. Some of the more important reasons for this state of affairs are as follows:

- Experienced nurses from outside the city must begin at the entry salary level.

- Many of the activities take place in substandard areas and in periods other than normal daylight working hours.

- Positions in other situations provide greater security and remuneration.

- The ever-increasing academic standards provide fewer graduates.

- Local universities are reluctant to accept transfer credits at the graduate level.

The second bureau under Community Health Services is that of Public Health Education. The mission of this bureau is to reach the out-of-school population in New York City by transmitting health information relating to sound health practices. The bureau hopes to bring new scientific knowledge to the public attention and thereby stimulate citizen action to achieve departmental health goals. The bureau functions similarly to other bureaus in the department by assigning public health educators to the health centers where their activities can be coordinated with other on-going health programs. The responsibility of the educator assigned to the district is that of assessing population needs and aggregating knowledge of how the population can best be influenced by the various educational techniques and materials.

Social workers under the technical supervision of the Office of Social Work have been trained to perform generalized services (as in the case of public health nursing). Their programs are implemented as parts of the other health programs at the district health level. The department has up to four social workers per district. Since between 15 to 30 cases per worker has been found to be an optimal load, and since the districts average 250,000 population, it is readily apparent that the department performs little direct social work.

The Office of Professional Education is concerned with recruiting, career planning, and various kinds of education programs for the Department of Health.

The salary structure for full-time physicians is a serious drawback to recruitment, career planning, and the fulfillment of other objectives. After gaining experience, the doctor can only gain a noncompetitive salary. At the possible levels, recruitment of strong people is nearly impossible, and as a result, an absence of adequate back-up full-time physicians is a chronic problem.

The Structure of the Services-Distribution Organization

For the purposes of provision of health services within the five boroughs of the city, the Department of Health divides the boroughs into 30 health districts. Twenty-two of these districts have within them a district health center. This is the hub of administration and distribution of health services within the area. The districts are formed to contain populations of residents varying from approximately 200,000 to 350,000 people. The district health center houses a number of clinics and services of various types. Some clinics are fairly standard and are found in each district health center. Others are centrally located at one or perhaps two district health centers within the borough. Six of the 22 districts which have district health centers are also provided with at least one facility, called a health center, which contains at least two or more clinics or services, often many. There may be one or more of these health centers within the district.

There are also child health stations, dental clinics,
and physician and nursing services provided to schools
throughout the districts.

Each health district is further broken down into
health areas. The health area, however, is not a
functionally oriented concept. Health district outlines were formed initially to enable use of census
data for comparative statistical analysis. (The major
source of comparative health data is still available
in the form of such comparisons.) A census tract
includes an area encompassing about 2,500 residents.
A health area was designed to envelop ten census tracts,
and a health district was a configuration of ten health
areas. The district bounded about 250,000 people and
was thus (geometrically) irregularly formed. The
health area, as a continuing concept, is employed more
for statistical or descriptive reasons than for practical or operational ones. That is, health stations
or centers are not set up or operated with any concern
for health area boundaries; sometimes they do coincide.
Only some nursing staff is assigned on a basis of
health area. The second major utility of the breakdown
of health districts into health areas is traceable to
the fact that the very size of the district tends to
obscure indications of health problems. Utilizing
the smaller areas, statistical data descriptive of a
problem were observable. If only district figures were
used, many indications of health problems would be
averaged out by data from larger trouble-free sections
of the district.

In terms of organization, the structure of the
field group runs as follows. At the head is the
Assistant Commissioner in charge of Community Health
Services. Responsible to him are the five borough
directors. They oversee the 22 district health centers, which are headed by district health officers.
There are six health officers in Manhattan, four in
the Bronx, eight in Brooklyn, three in Queens, one in
Richmond. The health officer is administratively
responsible for the programs, clinics, services, and
personnel staffing them within the district. These
personnel are physicians, public health nurses, public
health assistants, practical nurses, registered nurses,
lab technicians, X-ray technicians, social workers,
health educators, consultants from the Bureau of
Nutrition, clerical and administrative personnel, and
maintenance personnel. It should be noted that these
professional personnel are responsible to the health

officer under administrative rather than technical
lines of authority. Their technical leadership
resides within particular bureaus of the central
offices, according to their areas of specialization.
This presents a condition of dual administration
characteristic of--and troublesome to--the department.

Contact with the Department of Welfare is
extremely limited. There have been occasional,
sporadic attempts made to initiate and sustain a
formal contact and relationship with the Welfare
Department in terms of the health and medical requirements of its recipients who are also patients of the
Department of Health. These attempts have generally
been fraught with frustration and have led either to
a quick demise or to a general disenchantment, which
in turn led to a reduction in time and effort spent,
until the contact was eliminated. A typical description by a district health officer is as follows: "A
relationship would be attempted by scheduled meetings
with welfare-center workers on the medical problems
of their clients. These meetings would become less
frequent, then stop. Further attempts by bringing
welfare workers into the health center would also not
meet with success. Welfare workers appear to have too
many problems other than the health of their clients
to enable them to spend adequate time on these issues."
Further comments by one district health officer were
these: "There is now no formal contact; prior medical
conferences with medical social workers of the two
welfare districts which are within the Department of
Health district did not work out." This health officer
attributed the difficulties to too great a turnover in
the Department of Welfare and in excessively disparate
orientations of the two departments. The only continuing contact is in provision of vaccines to the
Department of Welfare physicians.

There is contact with the Department of Education
in each district, since the Department of Health
provides physicians and nurses to staff health clinics
within each school.

Generally, the only contact with the city's
private physicians or small, private clinics is in
terms of their referral of patients to Department of
Health clinics for testing, and in the provision to
private physicians of vaccines and other biologicals.
However, the Department of Health has also, in conjunction with the Public Health Service, been attempting

to provide educational materials to physicians on their
responsibilities in venereal disease follow-up.

The Department of Health and Public Health Service
often cooperate in programs of venereal disease reduction through investigation of contact sources and
treatment of these sources. The Public Health Service
often has its offices within a district health center.

Contacts with the Police Department are few.
There are usually a number of police districts (or
precincts) within each health district. The occasional
contacts are generally on T.B. forceable removal,
conferences on narcotics-control between the police and
the educational officer of the district center, or in
providing for parking and orderly use of a mobile
X-ray unit.

Contacts between the Department of Health and the
Community Mental Health Board are minimal. The usual
association of the Department of Health with mental
health problems is in terms of referral to various
centers or community mental health agencies. Occasionally, a mental health agency has been temporarily
housed within a Department of Health center.

Each district health center has a number of contacts with community groups through its staff, primarily in the person of the district health officer. The
number of these contacts, their permanence, and the
quality of their results is essentially a product of
the personality of the individual health officer. An
imaginative, energetic health officer may stimulate
many and varied contacts, all contributing to health
education within the community and the provision of
new and experimental groups and services. Health officers give lectures and sit on advisory boards for
many of these agencies. The education officers within
the district centers provide educational classes and
materials of various sorts.

The Problems of Health Services Distribution
in the Department of Health

There is inadequate information about the general
population, an apathy toward prevention of disease,
indecision in the face of many vague sources of apparently duplicated services, and difficulty by the

population in making use of services unless pressed
by emergency needs.

Also, there are large numbers of health and medical service agencies who do not communicate well with
one another. They appear as a series of isolated
groups generally characterized by (a) lack of adequate
funds; (b) inadequate personnel; and (c) an inability
to integrate their efforts with those of the many other
agencies involved in common services.

Staff within the department have dual loyalties.
The administrator is the district health director;
technical guidance comes from the worker's central
office bureau. The district health officer must spend
much time maintaining his technical/medical competence
to adequately recognize health needs of the community
(and of the individual as an indication of these) and
to be able to suggest programs to remedy his district's
health problems; but he is often not a technical manager and is frustrated by his lack of authority and by
the inadequate use of his knowledge and training in
medical-services program planning.

Programs may be suggested by the district personnel on the basis of needs in the community they serve,
but central office bureaus decide on what programs
will be instituted and plan the type and detail of
these programs. Districts must then execute the programs. District personnel feel that they are not
significantly involved in decisions on their programs.
Decisions are felt by at least some of the health
officers to be "blanket plans," with no district-
specific differences able to be taken into account.
Further, some district officers feel that the chain
of command is ill-defined, making additional difficulties for getting authorization for new programs or
modifications to existing ones.

The fact that special projects, such as Gouverneur
or Queensbridge, report directly to central office
bureaus may occasion resentment and frustration in the
regular districts. Special projects are not responsible to the borough director; nor in fact does there
appear to be much in the way of communication between
the project and other districts or health officers in
the borough. Resentment may occur not only from the
isolation, but from privileges of special status, such
as greater autonomy and authority within the project
area, in making decisions on its functioning, in

greater availability of funds and freedom in their use,
in publicity and plaudits for its work, prestige, etc.

Communication is a general problem. The categories above that suffer from dual administration, i.e.,
personnel, programs, and special projects, might not
be the problems they are if adequate communications
were employed. As it is, the regional offices are
not brought into program planning effectively, even
though the programs must be implemented by regional
personnel. It is not unexpected, then, that the district workers resent inadequacies in program planning
which do not take their particular district and its
problems into account.

There is also a communication problem between the
Department of Health and the community that it serves.
The population within the district does not generally
have a great understanding of the services provided
by the Department of Health, particularly, for instance,
of the preventive services. The child health stations
are known and used, but other clinics, while being
utilized, are not reaching as many of the areas as
they should to be used fully. Lack of knowledge of
them and, to some extent, rejection of public services
contribute to this. For example, even the polio-
immunization service is not fully utilized. Mothers
do not take their children in for adequate follow-up
services. The closest screening and follow-up is in
the schools with the younger children. The point is
often made that without adequate education concerning
health, the motivation is seldom present in lower
socio-economic groups to utilize preventive or health-
maintenance services. Most used are the emergency and
acute-symptom services.

District directors lack authority. They must
request authorization for financial outlays other than
those strictly budgeted (i.e., they have no flexibility
for unusual needs or occurrences):

- They cannot expand current programs or initiate
  new ones on their own initiative;

- They cannot buy or rent furniture or equipment;

- They cannot buy medical or office supplies;

- They are allocated a specific amount of supplies (monthly, or in similar intervals);

- They have no petty-cash fund;

- They cannot allocate their own funds to improve space utilization at the health centers;

- They cannot employ their own funds in innovations, where resistance is greatest at central bureau levels.

Health officers must request authorization for personnel modifications; they must request the numbers of people needed for service in district; they must request current personnel dismissal or transfer; they must request additional personnel on temporary basis (for one day, or for a longer temporary interval).

These bureaucratic hindrances lead to efforts to circumvent the chain of command.

Pay scales are low, and under state levels. Competition for personnel, especially nurses (who are in acute shortage), is great. The Department of Health cannot attract adequate numbers of competent personnel and loses even more to outbidding groups. Federal project pay levels, in particular, are a competing influence drawing the most highly qualified personnel away from the Department of Health.

The prestige of full-time Department of Health personnel is low. The district health officer may feel responsible for the welfare of as many as 350,000 residents of the district, but also feels that he is little trusted by the Health Department and that he is looked down upon as the lowest rung of the medical/ professional ladder by his colleagues in hospitals, private practice, etc., and also by the lay community. The medical profession would appear to appreciate the medical administrator only if he is in a hospital setting, or is a clinician (practicing or teaching) at the same time.

Full-time medical personnel on the physician level, such as health officers or borough directors, are paid so little that the younger ones are too often lured into other occupations where pay may be twice as high or greater, for positions of less work and responsibility.

Low pay of administrative and clerical personnel has often resulted in relatively untrained, inexperienced help. This leads to much wasted time of health

officers, physicians, nurses, and other professional
staff, and a lack of well-organized administrative
services.

DEPARTMENT OF HOSPITALS

In earlier chapters, this book has devoted heavy
emphasis to the municipal hospitals, all of which function under the Department of Hospitals. For the present discussion, there remains only need to discuss the
central functions of the department.

It should be noted that Commissioner Terenzio and
First Deputy Commissioner Derzon have taken vigorous
steps in planning for a reorganization of the department. Under discussion here is the long-standing
structure of the central department.

The care and treatment of patients in hospitals
has been established and defined in the Charter of the
City of New York. That document defines the role of
hospitals and other institutions as one primarily
devoted to the care and treatment of the medically
indigent and for the protection of public health.
The department may also handle other sick or injured
persons and even temporarily receive persons alleged
to be insane. In the event that patients in the latter
categories are able to pay for services and housing
received they are legally liable for such payments.

Local law provides for a Board of Hospitals com-
prised of five physicians and five laymen with the
Commissioner of Hospitals as chairman. In general,
the board resembles similar organizations in industry,
reviewing activities of the department and acting upon
policies and objectives. Among the broad powers of
the board are:

- development of long-range programs

- establishment of standards of care for the sick

- promotion of efficiency in the department

- approval of capital and expense budgets

- publication and enforcement of hospital and
  nursing home codes

   The central office is responsible for supportive
services and functions as represented in the Department
of Hospital organization chart depicted in Figure 17.
In broad functional terms the following represents a
listing and brief description of the traditional services performed.

   First Deputy Commissioner and Executive Officer

● Security Officer

● Counsel

● Labor Relations

   The programs carried forth under the first deputy
are disciplinary hearings and labor and legal matters.
The Security Division is responsible for assuring that
patients, visitors, and employees can function free
from risk and danger. In addition, this force is required to report all incidents related to violations of
criminal law which occur within the territory of the
institutions. The Labor Relations Division handles
disciplinary hearings of competitive civil service employees, collective bargaining certificates, grievance
procedures, and other related labor management functions.

   Deputy Commissioner for Supporting Services
               and Capital Budget

● Business Administration

● Engineering--Maintenance

● Personnel

   The Bureau of Business Administration is responsible for audits and accounts, budget control, elec-
tronic data processing, and administrative analysis.
The Bureau for Engineering and Maintenance is responsible for the capital program and the normal maintenance, repair, rehabilitation, and plant operation of
over 300 buildings. The organization to accomplish
this includes functions devoted to:

● Engineering and Design

● Contract and Fiscal

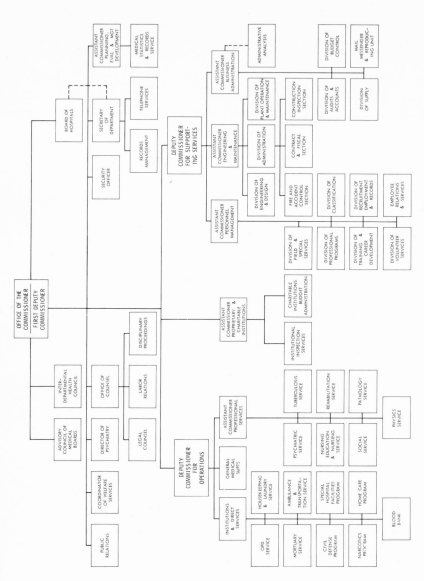

Figure 17. Organization of Department of Hospitals

472

- Contract Inspection

- Plant Operation and Maintenance

- Fire and Accident

- Automotive Equipment

The Bureau of Personnel Management is concerned
with immediate and long-term planning, integration of
the volunteer program within the bureau and participation in the city's antipoverty program. In addition,
the more highly routinized functions are likewise a
function of this bureau, including field services and
professional programs.

Deputy Commissioner for Operations

- Institutions and Direct Services

- Assistant Commissioner of Professional Services

- General Medical Superintendents

The Ambulance and Transportation Services are
operated by both municipal and voluntary hospitals
under Direct Services. Ambulances operate according
to geographic districts in the city. Radio monitors
have been placed in some hospitals and in the central
office for coordination of transportation activities.

The Housekeeping and Laundry Services, as the name
implies, is responsible to fulfill the departmental
standards relative to cleanliness. This system was
organized to operate within the clerical, inspection,
and supply needs and has emphasized the patient care
aspects of the service.

Also under Direct Services, the Mortuary Service
provides mortuary caretakers. Turnover has been
abnormally high because of the type of work and the
salary level involved. The complement of personnel is
adequate to provide minimal service, but insufficient
to meet emergencies (illness, vacation, attrition).
The inadequate staffing has resulted in an accumulation
of overtime, splitting of vacation, and difficulty in
providing proper schedules.

Assistant Commissioner, Professional Services

- Nursing Service

- Pathology Service

- Physics Service

- Psychiatric Service

- Rehabilitation Service

- Social Service

- Tuberculosis Service

The central office does not provide these services and indeed, for the most part, only deals with problems in these areas when such problems transcend the authority of individual hospitals. The central office counterparts to these services thus handle problems of coordination and those involving relationships to other departments.

Assistant Commissioner, Proprietary
and Charitable Institutions

- Institutional Inspection Service

- Budget Administration

On the basis of a proprietary hospital code, the Institutional Inspection Service imposes standards of conduct upon the various proprietary institutions.

Both proprietary hospitals and nursing homes are inspected and licensed on an annual basis and when a change occurs in ownership. In addition to the licensing of the institutions already in existence, the Institutional Inspection Service plans for new facilities. In this manner, code compliance is assured.

Planning, evaluation, and management development have generally been established to determine the best methods of organization and to determine how the department could function most effectively. This activity has been accomplished through the study of working programs and research in conjunction with other parts of the organization. Much of the hospital statistical

data on length of stay, improvement of care, and long-
term chronic care have been collected under the Assistant Commissioner.

Summary: Problem Areas

When compared to the nation as a whole, the
New York hospital system provides a population coverage
several times that in existence for other parts of the
country.   For example, the hospital use per person per
year is higher by 30%, OPD use by 350%, and emergency
room use by 230%.   Nevertheless, population trends,
rates of depreciation, lack of capital funding, shifting population, and rates of use per institution
indicate that certain problems now exist and other
problems will exist in the near future.

Historically, planning for hospitals has been
stimulated by studies of "demand" variables, such as
volume, location, and the ability of the institutions
to meet the health needs of a specific population.
More recently, however, basic changes in medicine and
hospital practices and community awareness of medical
problems have cast some doubt on the ability of present
institutions to adjust to demand.   In addition, spiraling costs of construction and operation, uneven distribution of buildings and equipment, variations in
quality, low utilization of certain facilities and
overcrowding in others have led to public criticism
and increases in popular demand for more efficient
service.

The present methods for providing new and replacement buildings are archaic and generally, after an
overlong interval, result in a less than optimal solution to the problem which stimulated the capital
expenditure.   It has been estimated that the time
interval between need and construction exceeds ten
years.   The lack of suitable design talent and flexibility to meet changing needs, even predictable ones,
is practically never accounted for.   In addition,
public and political pressures often cause institutions
to be built or replaced even when expert opinion is
in opposition.

The need for capital funds and hospital planning
in the context of community health needs goes beyond
replacement of unsuitable buildings.   The quality of
maintenance in all municipal hospitals is known to be
particularly poor.   Maintenance costs require

line-item approval and are therefore controlled by the Bureau of the Budget. Because of the insufficient maintenance budget, premature obsolescence of many buildings has occurred.

The problem of personnel, career and salary planning, and the retention of certain kinds of professional workers is a major problem in the municipal hospital system. These problems are similar to those discussed for the Department of Health, and essentially revolve around working conditions and civil service. Additional problems have been encountered in the municipal systems because they are now viewed as institutions with limited prestige, little research opportunity, and hazardous working conditions.

Since the costs of hospital care are extremely high, ways must be sought to involve other forms of institutions and to avoid the waste relative to duplication of services and resources. Recent demonstrations have indicated that countless acute bed space could be saved by utilizing other forms of continuing treatment, such as home care and half-way houses. In addition, these demonstrations have shown additional savings through the group prepaid practice concepts, where the costs per patient dropped appreciably relative to the fee-for-service methods. Some form of regionalization, together with the welding of other forms of institutional and noninstitutional care in the context of prepaid group practice, seems to offer potentially substantial relief.

The maintenance of a high quality of care has also been a major concern of state and city officials. To this end, all systems of hospitals are inspected periodically, although not from the viewpoint of community need. Voluntary hospitals are inspected by the State Department of Social Welfare to assure humane treatment and provisioning for safety. Approval is required for reimbursement by the state and federal government for the care of categories of public charge patients. As previously mentioned, the proprietary institutions are licensed and regularly supervised by the Department of Hospitals. For those hospitals to receive licenses, they must be in compliance with the Hospital Code. The license issued allows the proprietary hospital to receive payment from Blue Cross. The municipal hospitals, of course, are supervised directly through the department.

Many methods exist for attempting to assure high quality care in hospitals, other than inspection. Accreditation, approval for graduate training, inspections for specialized programs and--the one used most frequently--appraisal of available resources. Although there are inherent dangers in inferring performance from capability, this has been utilized extensively in past reviews. Every physician with hospital privileges has those privileges recorded with the Department of Hospitals. Thus, only those meeting minimum standards are allowed to practice accordingly. Much more research and evaluation must be performed, however, before uniform provision of high-quality care can be realized.

COMMUNITY MENTAL HEALTH BOARD

The History and Objectives of the Board

The New York City Community Mental Health Board was created as an independent agency of the city in 1954. It was set up in response to state legislation providing matching funds, through the State Department of Mental Hygiene, for five major categories of mental health services. Up to 50% reimbursement can be provided for support of expansion of mental health services through these funds.

Out-patient psychiatric clinics include mental hygiene clinics, child guidance clinics, and other facilities for out-patient care of mental or emotional disorders.

In-patient psychiatric services in general hospitals are regular departments of the general hospitals (voluntary or public) and services are provided under the direction of a psychiatrist.

In-patient psychiatric services in nonprofit institutions are provided if the institution is licensed by the Department of Mental Hygiene for in-patient care.

Psychiatric rehabilitation services provide medical treatment, social techniques, vocational training, and other measures directed at the handicapping effects of psychiatric disorders.

Consultation and education services are offered by mental health personnel to professional staffs of welfare agencies, schools, courts, Health Department facilities, and so forth.

The ultimate objective of the CMHB is to aid in the provision of adequate mental health services to the residents of New York City. This means support, encouragement, and guidance for municipal and voluntary agency efforts. The CMHB is interested in the latter, and along with the development of municipal facilities, would like to see expansion of the good voluntary-agency programs. The goal is to improve and increase their programs and to set higher standards. There is no idea of support of municipal and voluntary programs based on a preselected proportion of funding for each. There are 130 state-licensed clinics in the city. The board has contracts with 50 of these. There are also an unknown number of unlicensed clinics. The state sets minimum standards for licensing, which many of these cannot meet.

The CMHB does not feel that the goals or objectives of the municipal and voluntary hospitals and of the community clinics are incompatible. There are also few problems of overlap in their provision of services. Rather, the demands for mental health service in the city are too great. Conflicts between these organizations might appear only in the future, when the city finds itself in the enviable position of having enough services for competition to arise.

Structure of the Board

Though mental health boards are usually county organizations, there is one CMHB for all of New York City (five counties). This board is composed of nine members, two of whom (Commissioners of the Departments of Health and Welfare) are ex-officio. Reporting to the board is the Director of Community Mental Health Services, who heads the 130-man "line" agency of the board.

The term "board," however, is ambiguous, since it is used to refer to the board per se and also to the entire community mental health agency. The board functions as an executive agency rather than a "committee."

The CMHB line structure (referring to the agency) does not appear as firmly formed as would be the case if it were a department of the city. It rather seems to conform broadly to the two main functional areas of its concern, i.e., municipal and voluntary mental health activities. The Director has a Deputy Commissioner and Deputy Director, and various staff positions such as Assistant Director, Executive Assistant, State Representative for Planning, Public Relations Advisor, Mental Health Education Specialist, and a Counsel. There are also small fiscal and personnel groups, and a larger Research and Planning Division. However, the equivalent of line positions is seen in the positions of Directors of Psychiatry, of which there are six. There is a Director of Psychiatry for Voluntary Agencies, and one each for the Courts and the Departments of Correction, Health, Hospitals and Welfare. The organization ends abruptly here, since the Directors of Psychiatry have only one aide to assist them directly.

The Commissioner of Mental Health is appointed by the nine-man board. He is also Director of the Regional Mental Health Committee, a planning committee concerned with the development of mental health centers for future construction and utilization in New York City.

Functions of the Board

A fundamental premise determining development and implementation of CMHB programs in the past has been that the board does not participate in provision of services, but serves rather in management and advisory capacities. The CMHB aids in broadening mental health services through:

- Contracting. The board establishes contracts each year with voluntary groups maintaining psychiatric centers within the community and supports extension of their mental health services.

- Charitable institutions budget. Voluntary hospitals are evaluated by the CMHB, and their programs can be included in this budget.

- Affiliation contracts. These are contracts with voluntary hospitals and medical school hospitals.

The above methods are directed at the voluntary agency part of the program. That is, they provide support given to voluntary hospitals, medical schools, and independent voluntary institutions or clinics for mental health services within the community. Once a contract is written, the board sustains a general supervisory and monitoring role, making visits to, and reviewing monthly reports from, the agencies supported by these contracts.

The larger part of the service supported by the board is, however, through the municipal segment, i.e., support given to the programs of Education, Corrections, Courts, Hospitals, Health, and Welfare through those departments. Provision, therefore, is made to have those departments staffed with full-time mental health consultants.

The board also provides consultant services to the Departments of Health and Welfare additional to those of the Director of Psychiatry. In the welfare centers, for example, part-time services are contracted from local, private psychiatrists.

The board does not attempt to impose standards for agency functioning. It is, rather, very selective of agencies qualifying for support; it then aids these agencies to improve their services. The agencies, whether voluntary of municipal, are assisted individually and the aid to their programs is determined on a completely individual basis. Standards for professional personnel in terms of training and experience are set by civil service within the state for the municipal agencies. CMHB helped in setting these standards.

Research is the major internal board activity supporting policy formation, planning, and external implementation of mental health programs. The board has a staff division, Research and Planning, whose functions are fundamentally to provide support to state monitoring of funded activities and to develop statistical data to aid the board in accomplishing its program planning and fund allocation.

More specifically, the Research Division mission is to:

● Monitor reporting activities of all agencies funded by the CMHB.

- Provide consultation and support to all agencies in report requirements and methods of
  accumulating needed data.

- Acquire and analyze existing data on the mental
  health needs and services within New York City.

- Plan and execute studies providing new data
  on mental health needs and services.

- Improve the current system of acquisition,
  storage, and retrieval of mental health data
  used by the City of New York.

The board's major function is to be responsible
for psychiatric services in the city agencies. Here,
relationships are unique from one agency to another.
For example, in terms of functioning within the Department of Corrections, the Director of Psychiatry has
become responsible for management of all mental health
services and personnel. Prior to the board's assumption of this management function, mental health personnel in the Department of Corrections were part of a
very informal supervision by the Rehabilitation Division of the Department of Corrections. Now, however,
they are administratively responsible to the Commissioner of Corrections, but technically to the Director of
Community Mental Health Services.

The Director of Psychiatry in each of the other
departments is in a different relationship to the
commissioner of that department. Each of these is
handled individually and evolves as appears best for
the needs of the CMHB and the department involved.
The Director of Psychiatry with the Department of
Hospitals provides a degree of supervision over mental
health services within the department, but this is a
huge task. It is far from a one-man job. The Department of Health did not have a psychiatric service
before the Director of Psychiatry was appointed. His
job is to help in development of the psychiatric service for the Department of Health. Relationships with
the departments, then, are made by the personal effectiveness of the Directors of Psychiatry assigned and
the needs and personnel of the departments themselves.

This modus operandi is set in a framework of an
extremely complex set of interacting hospitals and
mental health philosophies and programs.

Approximately 1300 psychiatric beds are contained
in the municipal hospitals. There are plans for many
more in affiliated hospitals. Historically, the municipal hospitals have been receiving hospitals, or way-
stations between the community and the state hospitals
where patients were committed if they were not immediately returned to the community. Bellevue, which now
has over 500 psychiatric beds, was the first of these
receiving hospitals. Then Kings County Hospital in
Brooklyn was added. Kings County now has over 400 beds.

As treatment within the psychiatric wards pro-
gressed, drugs were used which enabled many patients to
be returned to, and treated within, the community. So
the receiving hospital became not a passageway but a
revolving door, with most patients coming out of the
community and being returned to the community on drugs.
Off drugs, the patients may present themselves again
at the hospitals.

In time, the over-65 age group has become an
increasing part of psychiatric admissions to city hospitals. This increase led to a need for a much greater
degree of processing through Bellevue. Therefore,
Bronx Municipal was built and the City Hospital in
Queens. These two, with Bellevue and Kings County,
then provided four receiving hospitals. At this point
the functions of the hospitals were able to be dichoto-
mized into receiving and treatment. All of the hospitals wanted to carry out treatment for reasons of
training and research. This was and still is a problem. Overcrowding in three of the four hospitals is
extreme, i.e., in Bellevue, Kings County, and City
Hospital. Differences in philosophy of these hospitals
have also developed, and there has been inadequate
communication between them. The differences in philosophy are reflected in the hospitals' differing decisions on whether the hospital should keep the patient
or send him to a state hospital. Bellevue has found
that after extended evaluation it sends more of its
patients home. So it treats its patients first (this
means drugs) while evaluating them for three weeks or
so, then makes the decision as to whether the patient
should be returned to the community or sent to the
state hospital. In Bellevue, however, this evaluation
process takes place in what has been characterized as
an "overcrowded, dehumanized environment." Differences
in patient-handling are revealed in a comparison of
admission rates and out-patient visits at Bellevue and
Bronx Municipal Hospital. (Bellevue has many more

admissions; Bronx Hospital has many more out-patient
visits.) Obviously, the CMHB Director of Psychiatry
cannot attempt to make arbitrary decisions in premature
support of one philosophy over another. Rather, he
has attempted to aid in improvement of each approach
so that better service to patients is provided now,
and research on the results of each method can lead to
scientific evaluation of these techniques in the future.

Planning is well advanced for the construction of
a number of mental-health centers under a combination
of federal and state support. Affiliation with a
hospital appears accepted as a guiding principle for
the management of each center.

The centers are expected to provide total psychiatric care for a specified area. This care would be all-
inclusive except in the case of persons needing hospitalization for more than a six-month period. These
chronic cases would be referred to state hospitals.
The Community Mental Health Board would probably limit
itself to the selection of the top personnel, and to
upper levels of management and program planning. Alternatively, they might hire some of their own staff for
parts of provision of these services. There is much to
be said, also, for contracting with a medical school
for the personnel with which to staff a center. The
centers may actually be administered in a variety of
ways. This will be determined in light of their individual needs. Another factor in this problem will be
the set of federal requirements put upon funds granted
for staffing of mental health facilities. These centers
are planned to serve as the primary mental health facility in the community. The center need not, however,
be a single facility. The concept of the center is
that of a group of functions, all of which need not
be made available in one building. Rather the set of
buildings or subcenters would be operationally connected.

Problems Facing CMHB

The question of whether the board should provide
services, or rather support and guide improvement of
services, has yet to be clearly answered. It should
be recalled that there is at this time direct provision
of services by the CMHB in the area of corrections.
That is, all personnel previously providing mental
health services under the Department of Corrections
have been transferred to the Community Mental Health

Board payroll and are fully responsible to the board.
This action, however, was an individual response to a
specific need. The question of trend, or policy,
arises again in the case of the planned mental health
centers with the problem of whether these should be
staffed by board-salaried personnel. The tentative
answer to this has so far been that it would be
determined on an individual need basis, and that several approaches might be utilized if different conditions
existed. Whether this degree of flexibility would lead
to larger problems of coordination of mental health
activities may need determination.

There appear to be not only benefits to affiliation of the voluntary and teaching hospitals with the
municipal hospitals and new mental health centers, but
also potential problems. The primary benefit to the
hospitals is financial; however, in addition to funding,
they also receive training and research opportunities
for their personnel. It enables them to expand the
size of their programs, and aids in the individual
development of their staff members. The potential
problem is one of primary missions. For example, the
primary mission of the teaching hospital is training.
The primary mission of other hospitals is treatment.
Therefore, admission criteria for the teaching-hospital-
oriented mental health centers may be too selective and
become detrimental to service to the patients. There
are also occasional problems with hospitals whose clinics are too research-oriented rather than treatment-
oriented. This is a similar process to the one that
occurs in the Health Department, accompanying affiliations of health centers to teaching and voluntary
hospitals. Once again, the question becomes, "Can
training and/or research be a significant detriment to
care?" Obviously, some gratification of the needs of
the hospital staffs for training and research must be
accepted, since the hospitals require some of this in
order to keep their own top-level staffs satisfied and
working efficiently. As noted earlier, the problem of
treatment as against research and training functions
is a major problem across all medical lines, not only
within the mental health area. It must, however, be
considered in the philosophy of program development
planned by each affiliating hospital connected with
a mental health center.

New medical legislation will increase the demand
for mental health services. This will mean more
neighborhood or community services, and more beds in

general hospitals and community mental health center
wards. The attendant problem of personnel to staff
the additional needs is easily foreseen, but is complicated by another issue. This is the problem of where
the elderly patient should be cared for if he is mildly
organic. At this time, most of these people are sent
to senile wards of the state hospitals. But many
psychiatrists believe that there is no real difference
in the populations at the senile wards as compared to
patients in nursing homes. It is rather a social and
financial decision as to where they should be sent.
Elderly people with mild organic symptoms can be managed
in nursing homes with adequate medication. The city
must face this issue.

There is legislation in effect in New York State,
as of September of 1965, which establishes the principle that psychiatric internment should be a medical
rather than a court decision. It provides definitions
of the criteria for forms of commitment (i.e., informal,
voluntary, involuntary) and requirements on committing
physicians. The law has been interpreted, however, in
different ways by court departments of the city. Consistent policy on this question would be advantageous,
and study beneficial. The legislation sets up a Mental
Health Information Service to inform prospective or
newly admitted patients of their rights concerning
admission status and subsequent release provisions.

Current needs for competent mental health staff
are great, and will be intensified by the addition of
the planned centers as they are put into operation.
The Mental Health Commissioner has expressed the opinion that the most reasonable method of providing
psychiatric consultation in the amounts necessary is
through contracts with private psychiatrists. He feels
that career plans should be developed for mental health
personnel who are willing to spend part-time as specialists for the city. That is, the board should develop people who would become specifically, for example,
Corrections Consultants or Hospital Consultants, and
so on. These people would spend part of their time in
their own practices, or in teaching, research, etc.
This principle is not yet as well established for
psychologists and social workers as it is for psychiatrists. Whether this approach is the best, or whether
others should be considered, the problem of providing
adequate numbers of well-trained mental health personnel
in New York City continues urgent.

Another possibility for attracting personnel that
could be utilized to supplement or even replace increases in civil service hiring is the hiring of mental
health staffs through affiliated hospitals. Being
attached to a recognized hospital staff could provide
added inducements of salary, prestige, supervision,
research, and training and might attract a total group
more competent than could be recruited through civil
service.

General Impressions

This discussion of the Community Mental Health
Board and mental health practices within New York
City has been brief. However, some issues, relationships, and problems have become clear. While the
needs for mental health services are huge (though
understandable, considering population size, population density, and the socioeconomic condition of
large numbers of the city's people), the municipal and
voluntary organizations providing service are in their
early development. This is true despite the age of
individual hospitals such as Bellevue, or of specific
voluntary groups. The total hospital, clinic, and
mental health center structure--the emerging philosophies of evaluation for commitment--the varying attempts at treatment (pshychotherapy, shock, and the new
psycho-pharmacologicals)--the 13-year-old CMHB and its
experiments with techniques of program stimulation,
support, and evaluation--the fledgling attempts at
research on basic mental health concepts--all bespeak
an emerging, unsophisticated but vitally necessary
area of service within the city. This implies an
opportunity for research, management evaluation, and
system analysis that can benefit the derivation and
evolution of the area, rather than the more difficult
and costly process of its reformation.

PART THREE

Toward a Successful System

CHAPTER **9** PROBLEMS,
CAUSES,
SOLUTIONS

PERSPECTIVE

New York City has pioneered among major U.S.
cities in its publicly financed commitment to traditional public health and to the provision of personal
health services for its people. The City's activities
in public health (environmental and preventive) and
in organizing, financing, and providing personal health
services are unmatched:

- Per capita expenditure for personal health
  care is 65% greater than the U.S. average--
  $227 vs. $146.

- Tax funds in New York provide 30% of this as
  compared to a national average of 18.5%.

- Only 20% of those receiving city medical care
  are on the general relief rolls.

Obviously, the city has not backed away from its
Charter stricture "to care for the emergent and indigent sick." But in recent years this responsibility
has been met primarily by pouring more dollars into
an increasingly archaic, fragmented, and inefficient
health care system. The city will be short-changed
for the $803 million budgeted for 1967-1968; and,
unless something is done, next year will be worse.

Despite the city's commitments, its enormous
expenditures, its dedicated efforts, the health care
system is in crisis. It fails to meet the health
needs of the people despite the efforts of local officials and employees; it is apparently incapable of
effectively combining the available material resources
with the richness in talent, skill, and knowledge represented by New York's unique medical community.

489

New York City is rich in terms of its resources for self-diagnosis and treatment. Therefore, in the spirit of tackling tough problems that urgently require solution, numerous study programs and demonstration activities have taken place over the decades. Initiative and resourcefulness have always been high and have produced significant contributions, often within the field of health care delivery.

This observation brings into question the role of the present Commission. Why have not earlier studies, programs, reforms, or demonstrations, met the problems with which this Commission has been charged?

Brief review of a few earlier efforts may be of value in searching out an answer.

In 1963, staff members of the School of Public Health, Columbia University, published an important study entitled, "Long-Stay Hospital Care." In considerable depth, it established the fact that the City of New York had a costly and expansive problem of long-stay patients in the hospitals. It documented an undeniable need for a program of chronic-care facility development. The effect of anticipated change due to this program would be that of "widening the back door of the hospital." Since 1963, the need for fulfilling the recommendations of that study has increased rather than lessened. But the City of New York still does not have such a program. The study also established that the city pays a high premium for operational inefficiency associated with the unnecessarily long stays of some patients, as a function of administrative factors. This problem also remains largely unsolved.

In the early 1960's, the Brookings Institute undertook a comprehensive study of professional and other personnel needs and reforms for civil service in the city. It is virtually a classic among such studies. Many of its most significant recommendations, if implemented, would have resolved fundamental problems before this Commission. None of those recommendations have in fact been met in any substantial form.

In this same period, Dr. H. E. Klarman published a fact book on a variety of studies that collectively diagnosed the professional staffing problems of the city's hospitals. By and large, circumstances that

brought about the need for his studies, and to which
he directed recommended solutions, are still inherent
difficulties before this Commission.

At the beginning of 1966, the Mayor's Advisory
Task Force on Medical Economics developed an integrated, rational set of recommendations for the improvement of the entire health care system. While
progress has been made in the last year in meeting
some of those recommendations, most are not fully met
because of continuing fundamental problems in the
areas of political "turf," administrative snarls,
and fractionated public authority.

It is possible here, but not desirable, to review
as many as 50 such special studies and reports completed since 1960--all of significance--having to do
with one or more of the many aspects of health care
delivery in the city. Very few have achieved their
avowed intent or have seen implementation; only two
or three have had basic influence on "business as
usual."

There has been great pressure on the present
Commission to focus solely upon the immediate controversy regarding affiliation contracting between
the municipal and voluntary hospitals. If the Commission's response to this great pressure were to
be exclusively that of the "quick fix," then the
duration and effectiveness of its recommendations
would suffer as did those of a predecessor, the Hyman
Commission. That Commission was charged to "do something about the hospital crisis" some years ago. The
thing that the Hyman Commission did was of landmark
significance, because it resulted in the development
of affiliation contracting. However, necessity for
the present Commission and its charge is adequate evidence that a "quick fix," however expediently necessary, can only work within the context of broader and
longer range planning. This does not oppose in any
way the need for or the appropriateness of expedient,
urgent measures; it argues only that those measures
be formulated in a larger framework so as to meet
the many inseparable problems of the system as a
whole.

In addition to reports (which often are regarded
merely as documents to be placed on shelves), New
York City has experienced very active campaigns to
bring about change for the better. Oftentimes, these

campaigns or projects have been described as "demonstration" programs (or "seed" programs, or "pilot"
programs). As confidence is lost in the efficacy of
"one more study," attention is turned to the need
for a "demonstration" program. And so the cycle has
alternated between "study" and "demonstration."

Demonstrations have had two effects. Either
they have fallen far short of the larger hopes of
their authors or, on a few occasions, they have been
so successful as to demonstrate what can happen when
a need is fulfilled, then subsequently denied. Several examples will suffice.

An expensive long-duration demonstration program
was undertaken to determine the feasibility of delivering comprehensive medical support to the family members
of an experimental segment of the welfare population.
The program proved the medical feasibility of doing
this, and also pointed up its economic infeasibility.
At the end of the long demonstration program, it was
necessary to withdraw the remarkably fine medical
services that had been provided these people.

Comprehensive (funded) affiliation began as a
demonstration program in the Gouverneur district.
Today, that contract remains the sole case of comprehensive affiliation. It worked as such and continues to work today--more successfully than most
other affiliations--yet all affiliations from that
time to this have followed a trend away from
comprehensiveness.

Finally, let us look at the dramatic case of a
demonstration program to undertake prevention and
early-detection dental examinations in Project Head-
start during summer months. This program was without
precedent in the city in that thousands of dentists
participated in an intensive program to discover the
dental needs of several hundred thousand children.
As a demonstration of cooperation and feasibility,
it was remarkably successful. However, its major
result was unforeseen: the need to continue it and
and to do something about the dental needs that were
uncovered. That is to say, no one at the federal
level who planned and instituted this demonstration
program had planned for its consequences in terms of
money, professional resources, community response,
and other factors. A tremendous demand was the only
product.

Again, it is well to raise the question, "What is it that this Commission should achieve?" It would seem--in view of the history of numerous pertinent and significant studies that have not brought solution to the problem, and in view of the long history of demonstration programs that added to our sense of reality but did not solve the problems--that this Commission will need to evolve a unique formula for blending short-term treatment with long-range system evolution.

Unevaluated Alternatives

The problem facing the Commission, like the proverbial iceberg, is about one-seventh above the surface. It is to that one-seventh that public controversy is pointed, and for which a viable quick treatment is needed. From much of the testimony given to the Commission, it is evident that the often-unseen six-sevenths of the problem must also be addressed-- in a creative framework of long-range recommendation and action.

But first things first. The visible portion of the iceberg has been the target of recommended "universal" solutions on the part of many people. It will be useful to note the diversity of these "final answers" which knowledgeable people throughout the health system are proposing and discussing. Each item in the following lists is an actual quotation (the lists themselves are representative rather than complete). The first group of these "answers" has to do with whether or not New York City should be "in the hospital business."

- "Give away all the municipal hospitals."

- "Give away some or most but not all of the hospitals."

- "Give away all the hospitals but keep ambulatory care."

- "Convert the municipal hospitals to nursing homes."

- "Have the city 'take back' the municipal hospitals but give them autonomy and authority so that they may be well run."

- "Replace all hospitals with new buildings."

- "Build 'halfway' houses for the aging."

There are other "final answers" that accept without question the city as a manager of hospitals but would alter how the hospital functions in health care delivery.

- "Make all community health care services fit into a pattern of satellites to a central hospital."

- "Extend hospital-based services by bringing them into the home."

- "Reconfigure hospital services (geographically and otherwise) so that selected hospitals are specialty centers."

- "Unify the hospital system."

And there are "final answers" that would seek solutions through administrative change or repair:

- "Increase hospital efficiency and reduce cost per patient day."

- "Get rid of central administration."

- "Clean up central administration."

- "Institute the presence of a local health service administrator in all districts of the city to integrate and supervise all local health services."

- "Institute widespread group practice."

- "Create a health services authority."

- "Recruit many more good people and get rid of the weak people."

- "Increase salaries."

- "Integrate authority."

- "Make all affiliations comprehensive."

- "Invent a new form of affiliation between the City Bureau of the Budget and the Health Services Administration so that, in effect, the H.S.A. can act as an 'Authority.'"

- "Establish a much broader H.S.A. so that it includes policy and planning responsibility for environmental health (e.g., air pollution, sanitation, etc."

- "Introduce program planning and budgeting."

These interpretations seem justified:

1) The diversity of "answers" implies that some of the knowledgeable persons involved are not using the same body of facts or are basing their opinions on selected aspects of the broad facts.

2) There are many special interests or points of view that some individuals or groups would emphasize at the expense of other interests or points of view.

3) There is a basic and widespread tendency to view the matter of personal health delivery as workable only when hospital-based.

4) There seems to be a greater concern with how to deliver health services than with what the need for those services might be.

5) A quick treatment which satisfies only one or a few of the above "answers" will--either early or in the long run--engender controversy and mismatch with respect to many of the others.

Factors Shaping System Evolution

There are evident certain trends and relationships in health care delivery that may be more basic and important to our deliberations than the "final answers" so readily available to inquiry. Some of these are:

1) The delivery of health services will increasingly involve greater relative numbers of paramedical personnel. This is a generic system problem.

Thus, the role of the physician is changing; the role of the nurse is changing; the role of recruitment and training is changing; and the nature of hospital services and personnel support functions is changing.

2) While severe health problems continue to be a function of "classic illness," they are also increasingly a function of the way in which we choose to live. Environmental health delivery is quite as significant a system problem for tomorrow as has been clinical health delivery in the past.

3) Cost of care is a basic system problem. It tends to increase inexorably as a function of many factors:

- Stage or severity of illness

- Increase in the technological sophistication of medicine and reduction in the time lag between research and application;

- Increasing availability of reimbursement payment (i.e., public funds versus private payment), requiring increasingly expensive fiscal mechanisms.

- Continuing treatment (as a new emphasis) versus traditional episodic treatment;

- Incremental increases in the general level of public education (people are seeking more care);

- The widening impact of federal medical legislation.

- The continuing ethic of medicine (responding to all who have need);

- The successes of medicine in prolonging life;

- The rapidity of system change;

- The obsolescence of plant (with reference to backlog, rate of change, and future need).

Clearly, one may do injustice by so grossly summarizing factors of cost in the face of the startling cost increases noted today. Nonetheless these would seem to be the basic factors that must be taken into account in devising an economically sound system of health care for the future.

4) The economic productivity and general utility of a citizen in our society is, in important part, a function of the intensity and duration of illness or incapacity that he may experience. While this statement remains to be well quantified, it is acceptable in principle. As such, it (and related face-valid generalizations) would dictate the need to invest delivery money on prevention and detection to every feasible extent, thus reducing long or otherwise costly illness.

5) As a whole, the practice of medicine is undergoing a subtle but significant change in orientation. Namely, from rather exclusive attention to individual clinical problems to an admixture of this emphasis with that of the "treatment" of populations or subcultures in their environments. As the concentration of ethnic groups increases in New York City, the health delivery system is forced more and more to deal with the characteristics of the community-defined population or subculture rather than to focus so exclusively upon individual clinical problems.

6) Practice-for-salary and group-practice are becoming increasingly evident forms of professional delivery in medicine. The traditional fee-for-service character of medicine will continue to <u>prevail</u> in most areas of the country for a long time while undergoing gradual modification. It will continue to <u>appear</u> to prevail in New York City for a long time. However, in this city, pressures and circumstances are such as inevitably to encourage the development of group practice and salaried practice; the trend is well underway.

7) When medical delivery is tied to Welfare, it is seen as inadequate or generally undesirable by the majority of persons in "welfare status" (and, in fact, it tends to be). The dehumanization and double-standard character of welfare-oriented medicine will continue to be a severe obstacle in the eyes of the community for the building of good community delivery programs; it is outmoded and in conflict with the larger social ethic.

8) The pace of modern system change in medical delivery is so great that one traditional means for

bringing about desired innovation, namely, the demonstration program, is losing its potential for impact.
In the one- to three-year period normally required for
"measuring the effectiveness" of a demonstration project, sufficient total system change now takes place
to require a new or altered demonstration.

9) There is a trend toward getting cities out
of the business of the direct management of hospitals.
Quality medicine continues to be based in institutions
in which outstanding physicians can find rewarding
identity, and in which administrative functions are
supportive rather than determinative.

An awareness of these trends is a first step
toward revising our conceptions of the city's health
delivery problems. From this altered viewpoint, then,
the following sections re-examine the nature of the
city's health crisis. What are its roots? What has
to be done? How?

THE HEALTH CARE DELIVERY PROBLEM

The staff looked at the manifold symptoms of
"system disease" primarily as a way to search out
causal factors. The staff members looked for trends
in the operation of the system as a means of identifying the forces with which the system was trying to
contend. They talked with hospital administrators in
each of the five hospital systems--municipal, voluntary, proprietary, state, and federal. They talked
with heads of services, with leaders in the nursing
field, and those delivering bedside care. They
talked with people in other city agencies. They analyzed reports and articles written about "the problem"
of the New York City health care system.

Some people were concerned about the unique problems created by the ethnic values and human foibles
of the populations they sought to serve. Others were
concerned about the impact of Medicare and Medicaid
on the financing of health services and upon the use
of municipal hospitals by patients who would now be
free to go to the hospital and the doctor of their
choice. Still others were concerned by the schisms
and special interests of the many groups that go into
the conducting of hospital operations. All or nearly
all were concerned about personnel shortages. And,
everyone, everywhere, was greatly concerned about the

overwhelming maze of red tape that almost paralyzes
the system with its interminable delays in acquiring
supplies, in undertaking renovations, and in performing services.

The staff found people who had simply given up
and were waiting only for retirement. They found
people who were "operators" and were expert at manip-
ulating the system, sometimes extralegally. Most
importantly, however, they found that most of the
system's battles are fought not against disease, its
real enemy, but against the administrative constraints
under which it now operates. When the system has a
chance it also fights disease.

The search for underlying causes of system problems began in the hospitals themselves. Part Two of
this book describes in some detail what was found
there. At a higher level of abstraction, the detailed
findings may be embraced in the following list of
serious deficiencies. (Cited here, with minor changes,
are the still applicable findings of the Mayor's Advisory Task Force on Medical Economics, 1966. The present
senior author was chairman of that Task Force.)

1. <u>Present organizational patterns and methods
of administering and distributing services are outmoded, result in inefficient use of the city's total
health resources, and are not always responsive to the
health needs of the population.</u>

For the most part, the pattern of health services
is characterized by uncoordinated effort; imbalance
in distribution or, in some instances, critical shortages; disparity of quality; inadequacies in financing;
and a variety of administrative and legal barriers to
the provisions of coordinated and comprehensive health
services.

Consequently, demands for services are not met
adequately. Of equal importance is the fact that large
numbers of people who should be getting care are not.

2. <u>There is wide variation in the quality of
medical care and related services.</u>

Among the essential characteristics of high-
quality medical care are professional competence, comprehensiveness, and continuity. Although residents

of New York City receive some of the finest medical
care available, too often one or more of these elements is lacking.

There is sufficient evidence to indicate that
in some instances physicians and other health professionals provide medical care and related services
which they are not professionally competent to offer.
Considerable variation also exists in the degree of
adequacy of hospitals and related health facilities
among all systems--voluntary, municipal, and
proprietary.

Fundamental deficiencies in the methods of organizing and distributing medical care also affect
quality of care.

3. There is probably a sufficient total number
of general care beds in New York City, but these beds
are poorly distributed.

Certain areas of the city have few or no facilities. Other areas have concentrations of small
hospitals with limited capability, which tends to
place undue burden on larger neighboring hospitals
having greater capacity to serve the needs of the
community. Availability of facilities is also limited
by inflexibility, which results from operating three
systems (municipal, voluntary, and proprietary), and
by the established practice of operating discrete
units within hospitals according to the patients' pay
status and clinical diagnosis.

4. There are serious deficiencies in facilities
and services for the care of long-term patients.

The need for additional nursing-home and extended
care facilities and programs is especially urgent in
the face of Medicare legislation. In March 1962, the
Hospital Council of Greater New York conservatively
estimated the need to construct 13,000 to 15,000 nursing home beds in New York City by 1970. About a third
of this number were beds in existing unsuitable facilities which needed replacement. Since then most of
the replacement beds have been built, but the total
number of available beds has not increased.

In addition to quantitative deficiencies, there
are wide variations in the quality of patient care
provided at existing nursing homes because of

deficiencies in programs which continued enforcement
of appropriate local codes is attempting to overcome,

The urgent need for suitable nursing home facilities and other appropriate alternatives to acute
general hospital care is highlighted by estimates
which indicate that perhaps 15 to 20 per cent of the
patients occupying wards of both voluntary and municipal general hospitals could be cared for by other
means, thus freeing hospital beds for patients who
need them.

5. There is a lack of suitable organized ambulatory medical care programs.

Existing facilities and services for the care of
ambulatory patients are inadequate to meet current
demands for services and potential needs of the
population.

Hospital emergency departments are being overwhelmed by constantly increasing numbers of patients,
and services are not geared to the qualitative and
quantitative changes in demand for care. Although
changes in the number of visits to hospital out-
patient clinics have not been as dramatic, clinic
services are organized in a manner which often results in fragmented medical care.

The municipal hospital system has also been
caring for an increasing proportion of the ambulatory
patient load over the years. This situation has also
made it increasingly difficult to provide adequate
services.

6. There are too few alternatives to institutional care--alternatives such as home care, day care,
foster home placement, and homemaker services.

Many patients currently cared for on an institutional basis could be cared for in their own homes
or in foster homes with the expansion of organized
programs of care and increased opportunity for foster
home placement.

There is a substantial deficiency in home care
programs especially in view of the potential need
resulting from Medicare legislation. There is a
disparity of available services on a geographic basis,
since most hospitals do not provide these services

and relatively few nursing homes have the organizational structure to do so. At the present time
the large majority of the home-care patient census
is cared for through programs operated by municipal
institutions.

In addition to financial barriers, the development of home care services has been limited by other
factors such as shortages of various categories of
health personnel (physicians, nurses, therapists)
essential to the provision of services in the home.

7. The inability or unwillingness of many institutions in the city to provide a broad range of community oriented health services constitutes a problem
of some magnitude.

The relatively large number of proprietary hospitals and small voluntary hospitals in certain areas
of the city, which either serve a limited segment of
the population or whose service program is devoted
almost exclusively to the care of in-patients, places
undue burden on larger neighboring voluntary and municipal hospitals.

Furthermore, the facilities and services of both
individual hospitals and groups of institutions serving a community are not organized to provide the type
of care appropriate to the patient's needs at any
given time in a manner which makes most effective use
of available facilities and health personnel.

8. There has been very little achievement, especially on the broad scale required in disadvantaged
areas of the city, in the provision of comprehensive
patient-centered medical care services at the local
community level.

The consequences have often been fragmented medical care delivered in a manner that has little regard
for the dignity of the individual and is wasteful of
professional time, effort, and public funds. Orderly
planning and provision of services is precluded by
uncoordinated districting and overlapping lines of
authority. Patients often receive ambulatory medical
care at the same time from more than one institution.
This may occur at the will of the patient or because
of multiple referrals by several different agencies

whose efforts on behalf of the patient are uncoordinated. Similarly, continuity of patient care is
often lacking as care shifts between ambulatory and
bed care.

9. Major and continuing problems are uneconomical utilization of health facilities and scarce
professional personnel which will become more pronounced with changes in demands for services.

These problems result from many factors, including, for example, unnecessary duplication of facilities
such as obstetrical departments; poor utilization of
medical manpower; utilization of certain laboratory,
radiology, and other services on five-day, eight-hour
basis.

10. Patterns of financing hospital and related
health services have been seriously inadequate.

A basic problem has been that the benefits of
financing have stressed, for the most part, services
applicable to in-patients in a general hospital.

Chronic underfinancing has been a major deterrent
to the development of organized ambulatory care services. Inadequate financing for both construction
and operation has been a major obstacle to the development of long-term care facilities, especially
under voluntary auspices. The insured and self-paying
patients have had to help subsidize the care of
the indigent patient. Most voluntary hospitals find
it difficult to finance major modernization needs.
Voluntary hospitals in deteriorating neighborhoods
have been handicapped because of increasing proportions of indigent patients, and inadequate reimbursement for the types of programs required to
provide an adequate level of care.

11. The program for the care of the mentally ill
residents of New York City is seriously inadequate.

Various statutory, administrative, and fiscal
problems have influenced the pattern of services for
the mentally ill. The traditional pattern has been
one of divided responsibility between the city and
the state, characterized for the most part by uncoordinated effort, excessive transferring of patients,
and patient care which is fragmented or not available

at all when needed.   Existing facilities are inadequate, poorly distributed, and overcrowded.

Throughout the city there is a tragic shortage
of mental health facilities that are capable of
providing comprehensive services, including in-
patient care (both short-term and medium-term) and
ambulatory care to residents on a local community
level.

The availability of facilities and services for
the mentally ill has also been limited by the relative
lack of participation of voluntary hospitals, largely
for financial reasons.

12.   The physical plants of both voluntary and
municipal hospitals require expenditures for replacement or extensive modernization.

This is necessary if they are to meet adequately
the increasing demands for services and needs resulting from rapid changes in medical technology.
Also of importance is the increased cost of operating an obsolete facility.   This can be a significant factor since expenditures for personnel exceed
two-thirds of the operating budget.

The Health and Hospital Planning Council of
Southern New York recently conducted a study of hospital facilities in New York City to determine modernization needs.   To correct deficiencies in existing
hospital facilities (voluntary, local government, and
proprietary) and make them adequate for their current
programs would require an expenditure of at least
$705 million.   In addition to being conservative, this
does not include the cost of necessary expansion of
nursing-home or psychiatric facilities, nor does it
include sums for such items as housing for staff,
research buildings, parking areas, site acquisition,
and funds for other purposes.

13.   There have been serious delays in the construction of hospitals and related facilities which
are costly and interfere with the effective provision
of services.

This problem applies both to voluntary and municipal institutions, but has been especially pronounced
in the replacement and modernization of municipal
facilities.

In general, delay is built into the entire planning and construction process, and it is not uncommon
for municipal projects to require as much as ten years
for completion. Such delays can result in newly constructed facilities which are obsolete in terms of the
program for which they were originally designed. They
also increase the length of time that inadequate facilities scheduled for replacement must be maintained in
operation, thereby causing additional capital expenditures which might be avoided.

Delays also impede the provision of medical care
services at individual institutions involved in construction and complicate the planning and provision
of services on an area-wide basis.

. . . .

At this level of generality, have the system problems been accurately specified? Unfortunately, the
answer is that they have not. Other Commissions and
other studies have gone this far. They have clearly
perceived and clearly stated some of these problems.
They have devised creative solutions, and some of those
solutions have been implemented. Yet the problems
stated have persisted and worsened.

Can we find some common thread--a clew winding
among all of these problems that will lead us to the
heart of the labyrinth?

The thread is there. It shows itself in terms
such as "uncoordinated," "unorganized," "fragmented,"
"divided responsibility."

A locus of responsibility, accountability, and
authority does not exist with respect to health services. Even if the Health Services Administration proposed as part of Mayor Lindsay's Charter reform plan
were a present reality, it would fail to reach the
diffusion and fragmentation above the HSA and, indeed,
above the Office of the Mayor itself.

This study has demonstrated very clearly that the
HSA proposal should be implemented, without change and
immediately. So imperative is a unification of the
health service functions in the city that it has been
almost impossible to address the issues covered in
this volume of the report--the central issues, at the

highest level of generality--without some "umbrella"
term by which to specify the many health service functions taken as a unit. In the pages that follow,
therefore, the reader will find that the proposed
Health Services Administration is referred to as an
existent agency. It is hoped that this usage will
serve to emphasize the necessity of HSA implementation.

But--to return to the main stream of the argu-
ment--even HSA would suffer from an absence of authority to meet its responsibilities: It is this that is
the central problem of health services delivery in
New York City.

THE ANALYSIS OF THE CAUSES

Current Authority and Public Accountability

In New York City, the authority to act is fractionated and dispersed among numerous "accountability
and services agencies" such as the Bureau of the Budget, the Comptroller's Office, the Board of Estimate,
the Personnel Department, the Department of Public
Works, the Welfare Department, and so forth.

Authority is further fractionated by the intent
and inherent character of federal, state, and city
legislation that affects construction, renovation,
reimbursements, personnel--in fact, virtually every
critical aspect of health delivery performance.

The accountability and services agencies, as such,
are not in the business of delivering personal health
services. They are in the business of assuring public accountability (as they understand this matter) and
delivering vital support or ancillary services. However, they can have little realistic appreciation of
the problems involved in spite of their beliefs to the
contrary and their good motivations. The sheer volume
of their work forces them into complex organizational
structures and procedures with consequences that are
often inimical to good health delivery performance.
The result is delay upon delay, to the great detriment
of health services delivery and the satisfactory
fulfillment of Health Services Administration responsibilities. Continued toleration of the impenetrable
snarl would be deplorable.

The staff finds: (1) that the current procedures for assuring public accountability and supplying services result in delays that make the delivery of quality health care virtually impossible; (2) under present charter provisions, it is possible to have public accountability without fractionation of authority; and (3) vital medical services cannot be delivered without undue delay.

Figure 18 illustrates how the present "system" of health care delivery functions, making clear the fundamental problems of fractionation of authority:

1) The Mayor, acting for the people, sets the executive policy for the operation of the Health Services Administration.

2) The health needs of the people are brought to the attention of the Health Services Administration by various means.

3) The Health Services Administration, under the guidance of the Mayor's policies, assesses these health needs and determines its. . .

4) Operational requirements to meet the health needs.

5) To meet the operational requirements, the Health Services Administration evolves a generalized budget request. (HSA has, in fact, only an advisory role in final formulation and in subsequent budget adjustments.)

6) To conduct operations the Health Services Administration issues "requisitions" (proposes expense requests of many kinds) against its established budget.

7) The review and evaluation of "requisitions" against the budget is conducted by the accountability and services agencies (primarily budget examiners of the Budget Director's Office).

8) The accountability and services agencies have their own ways of proceeding to assure what they believe will be a successful execution of their responsibilities; these ways are often incompatible in some

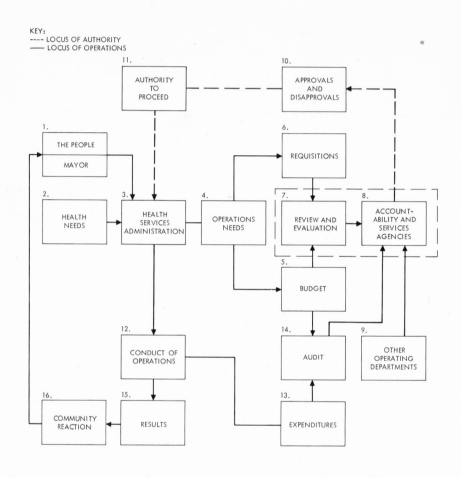

Figure 18.   The Present Health
             Care Delivery System:
             Fractionation of
             Authority

significant respects with the needs of operating health
care departments. Moreover, the needs of any given
operating department may vary from budgeted needs by
reason of unforeseen circumstances or by reason of
modifications of policy. The locus of judgment as to
whether to approve a desired change in expenditure
resides in agencies that are largely uninformed about
the operating department's needs and remote from them.

9) Many other city departments may be tangen-
tially involved but may be partially or wholly uncoordinated with HSA in their effects.

10) When the accountability and services agencies
have completed their reviews and evaluations of expense
requests, they issue approvals or disapprovals based
almost solely upon their own judgments. (In their
defense it must be observed that their responsibilities are too comprehensive, too detailed and too
centralized.)

11) The externally derived approvals constitute
authority to proceed (but only within the tightly controlled confines of the line-item budget procedure).

12) Having received authority to proceed, the
Health Services Administration can now "conduct" its
approved operations, subject to the imposition of
budgetary "accrual" constraints imposed by the Bureau
of the Budget.

13) In the conduct of operations, actual expenditures are made.

14) The expenditures are then audited by the
external accountability agencies.

15) Meanwhile, the conduct of operations in this
way achieves these results: patients wait in long
lines, walls go unpainted, toilets go without seats
or covers, corridors are filthy, vermin and rodents
proliferate, people may die waiting for a physician
to see them, and hundreds of administrative personnel
and thousands of professionals somehow "muddle through"
under constant frustration.

16) The consequence is pressure upon the Mayor
"to do something." (But what can he do? The manner

in which the city now assures itself of public accountability so fractionates authority that the Health
Services Administrator--or his Commissioners--cannot
give an order; he can only initiate a process in search
of authority. Can outstanding men be expected to remain long in such positions? Can the city expect to
recruit and motivate desirable replacements?)

Growth of the Fractionation of Authority

No one is to be blamed for the inability of the
Health Services Administration to deliver quality
health services. The Health Services Administration
is a victim of accreted governmental procedures for
assuring public accountability.

And no one is to be blamed for the current procedures for assuring public accountability. These
procedures were developed reactively in the wake of
public abuse (Figure 19). Checks and balances were
built into the governmental structure over many years
as ways of curbing abuses. Their cumulative impact,
however, has resulted not only in the curbing of
abuses but also in the curbing of efficiency--and, at
least in the case of the system for the delivery of
personal health services, their cumulative impact has
so hamstrung administration and delivery that, were
it not for the activities of many extremely dedicated
personnel--heroes of quiet determination--the "system"
would come to a complete breakdown.

This situation need not continue; it can be
altered effectively.

THE NATURE OF THE SOLUTION

Accountability Without Fractionation of Authority

Before presenting an organization chart of what
the staff envisions as a reorganized Health Services
Administration coupled to a Health Services Corporation, let us make clear how one may envision (1) that
even greater public and professional accountability
can be obtained than is now possible, (2) without the
need to fractionate authority, (3) through the redesign or reorganization of the total system.

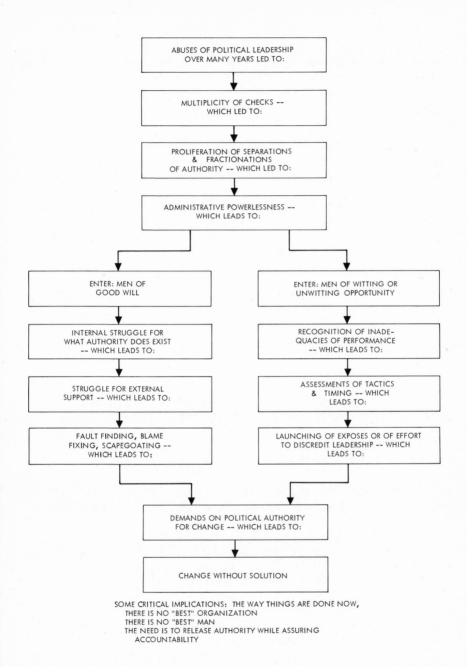

Figure 19.   How Authority Is Lost: A Capsule History

Figure 20 represents diagrammatically how governmental functioning could be realigned so as to provide
such a high degree of public accountability while
avoiding the pitfalls of the creation of a traditional
Authority. The following steps may be traced in
Figure 20:

1) The Mayor, acting for the people, sets the
executive policy for the operation of the Health Services Administration.

2) The Health Services Administration assesses
the. . .

3) Health needs of the community, and
establishes. . .

4) Broad program goals for the delivery of
health care.

5) Once established, these goals are turned
over to a Health Services Corporation, which then
devises. . .

6) A program plan to meet each established goal
and prepares operating budgets accordingly.

7) The Health Services Administration reviews
program plans and budgets and thereupon issues. . .

8) Authorization to proceed. (Note: all of the
above steps precede the applicable budget period.)

9) The Health Services Corporation thereupon
initiates its operations according to plan. (With approved budgets in hand, it would enjoy a high degree
of autonomous annual operation; the line-item accrual
system would have no place in this procedure.)

10) During the course of operations, the Corporation incurs expenditures, and. . .

11) Produces results.

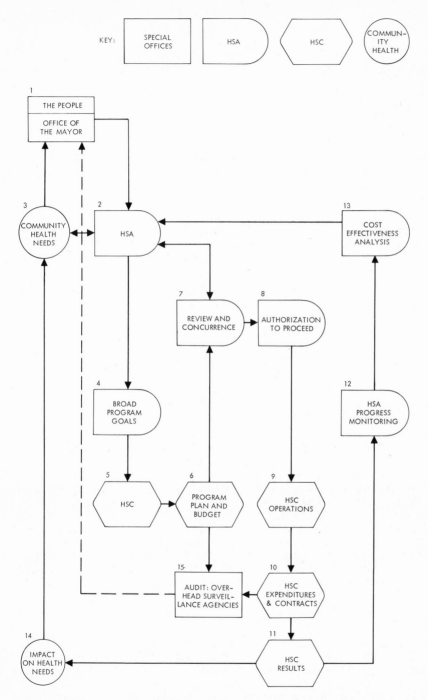

Figure 20. Proposed Health Care Delivery System:
Authority with Accountability

513

12) The Health Services Administration then assesses results against plans in order to produce a
continuing progress audit. (Such an audit might well
lead to modifications of program goals and changes in
contractual agreements).

13) Because the results of operations are being
carefully observed, it is possible to compare results
with expenditures and thus make cost-effectiveness
analyses.

14) The results of program execution produce
perceptible change in the health needs of the communities and, thereby, modification in program planning
for the next cycle of community effort.

15) The overhead surveillance agencies audit expenditures on a post-annual basis and participate in
original budget formulations and projections.

Solutions Considered

During the course of its studies the staff examined in depth a number of alternative courses of
action that had been proposed.

The first alternative considered was the possibility of solving the problem within the present governmental structure by such means as decentralization of
budget authority, or by shifting personnel to obtain
"strong administration," or by setting up a special
board of key city agency heads. These efforts were
reluctantly abandoned as fruitless as it became clear
that authority is so fractionated and dispersed
throughout the accountability and services agencies
that there is little meaningful authority to delegate
even to the strongest of administrators--short of
total reorganization of the city's enabling legislation and procedures.

A second course of action considered was the possibility that the city might turn over the responsibility of public personal health services to the private
sector (i.e., the voluntary system). While this
alternative would solve the dilemma of fractionated
authority, it may be tantamount to deserting large

blocks of the very poor, leaving them to variable and
uncertain acceptance by the private sector. Moreover,
one cannot be convinced that the city would find takers
for all of its facilities. This alternative was ruled
out as a full answer but retained in part as a desirable solution for certain functions and facilities.

A third possible course of action is the continuation of affiliation contracting as it now exists.
The staff finds the current practice of affiliation
contracting to be acceptable in principle but inadequate in practice. Contracts most recently written,
although improved over earlier forms, tend to be di-
rective and restrictive almost as though the affiliating
agencies were of ill will. The contracts do little to
specify goals to be achieved beyond the conduct of
"operations as usual." The contracts are seriously
lacking in the provision of public health care accountability as contrasted with fiscal accountability (which
has been improved). Finally and most significantly,
the contracts in no way improve on the city's frequent
inability to fulfill its part of the contractual
arrangement; indeed, they cannot do so under existing
circumstances.

That these conditions exist in the area of affiliation contracting should in no way be interpreted as
criticism of the personnel involved but as signs of
the health care delivery system's struggle to free itself from decades of outmoded administrative procedures.

There is no question but that affiliation contracting improved--and continues to improve--the quality of
medical services in the city's hospitals. Nevertheless, in its present state, it is an awkward, expedient,
and inefficient coupling of capability, authority,
and public accountability. However, under altered
circumstances, it could be made to work very well
indeed.

The potential for all affiliations becoming total
affiliations was also considered, i.e., to provide all
services including maintenance. While this would accomplish immediate release of authority, it presents
serious problems in securing accountability for both
the affiliate hospital and the city. At best, the
staff sees this alternative as an emergency solution

to which the city might have to resort. Again, under
altered circumstances, this procedure can be seen as
very attractive, viz., within a Health Services
Corporation.

Yet another course of action was considered.
Historically, when the city has found itself unable
to render services to the people through its existing
agencies, it has created an independent organization--
an autonomous "Authority"--to render those services.
In this sense, governments have often cut away major
segments of their public responsibility as a counter-
action to their inability to change themselves. For
the field of health care, the staff has labored to
find a workable alternative to this expedient.

The creation of an autonomous "Authority," while
successfully meeting the need for consolidation of
authority to act directly, does not permit satisfactory control and accountability to the people through
elected government officials, and therefore often constitutes an abrogation of governmental responsibility
particularly critical in the field of health care.
Additionally, an "Authority," once created, is extremely difficult to alter or terminate.

Therefore, examination was made of the possibility
of simply detaching the Health Services Administration
from the accountability and services agencies, with
provision of funds with which to operate and the authority to spend the funds while still reporting
directly to the Mayor; in effect an "Authority" within
the city (cf. The Burlage Report).

We believe that while such a course of action may
permit improvement, it simply does not go far enough
in resolving system problems and achieving adequate
public accountability. The vested interests in maintaining the status quo of centralized bureaucracy,
both within and outside the health agencies, would
constitute a formidable barrier to badly needed reorganization. There would be little or no incentive
for real change.

An entirely new alternative is needed.

During the course of its deliberation the staff established ten criteria for assessing alternative solutions. Commission members agreed that the alternative to be recommended should provide for:

- Consolidation of authority so that direct action can be taken;

- The highest possible degree of public accountability;

- Authority to administer an approved budget;

- Capacity to build buildings and conduct renovations;

- The ability to improve personnel circumstances (such as personnel shortages and the conduct of training);

- Decentralization of administrative authority to the community level;

- Initiation of program planning and budgeting as the central management tool;

- Systematic integration of health facilities into a service-oriented health delivery system;

- The ability to terminate the "solution" should it prove ineffective or unresponsive; and, above all,

- Improved health care delivery.

Utilizing this list of criteria, the staff examined various alternatives. It moved inexorably toward the recommendation of a much-reorganized and modified Health Services Administration, coupled through long-term contracts with a Health Services Corporation--a nonprofit corporation established to engage in the actual delivery of personal health services (Table 21). Of all the alternatives considered, this alternative appears to be the most manageable, the most accountable, and the most responsive to the changing scene in medicine today. It is believed that this alternative offers such an array of advantages as to make it possible for the city to become the world leader in the delivery of health care.

Table 21. Alternative Solutions vs. Criteria of
Acceptability and Effectiveness

Assure That Recommendations Encompass:	Comprehensive Affiliation (Fall Back)*	Independent Municipal Hospital Management**	Autonomous Authority***	Modified H.S.A. Plus Nonprofit Corporation****
Consolidation of Authority	Improvements Possible -- Limited	Meets Hospital Problem Only	Full	Less Review & Evaluation (H.S.A. Executive Agency)
Public Accountability	Improvements Possible -- Limited	Full (Applies to Municipal Hospitals Only)	Separated from Government	Full
Budget Authority	Improvements Possible -- Limited	Full (Applies to Municipal Hospitals Only)	Full	Full
Buildings and Renovations	Improvements Possible -- Limited	Full (Applies to Municipal Hospitals Only)	Full	Full
Personnel Deadlocks	Improvements Possible -- Limited	Possible Freedoms Over Time (Hospitals Only)	Possible Freedoms Over Time	Possible Freedoms Over Time
Decentralization to Regions	Not Probable	Not Applicable	Possible	Maximum

518

Program Planning	Improvements Possible -- Limited to Contract Provisions	H.S.A. & Corp. But Limited To Hosp. Operations	Within The Authority	Specified Responsibilities H.S.A. & Corp.
Systematic Integration	Not Probable	Possible But Probably Limited	Possible	Assured
Ability to Alter or Term.	Limited	May Be Specified (Municipal Hospitals Only)	Very Unlikely	May Be Specified
Improved Health Delivery	Limited	Highly Probable (Municipal Hospitals Only)	Highly Probable	Highly Probable

 * Full extension of present, partial affiliation practice.
 ** Each municipal hospital a nonprofit corporation.
 *** Bridge & Tunnel, Port, etc.
 **** Small, elite HSA; larger nonprofit Health Services Corporation.

THE EMBODIMENT OF THE SOLUTION

Proposed Organization

In implementing the principles discussed above, those charged with the reorganization for health care delivery must call for a clear separation between functions that are properly carried out by an executive agency (such as HEW or the Surgeon General's Office) and functions more properly carried out by an instrumentality (such as specialty contractors to the federal government) established for the purpose of engaging in the actual administration and delivery of health care.

Figure 21 illustrates the division of these two levels of functions. At the top, functions properly associated with public officials and their public offices are indicated. The lower portion of the figure displays the major functions to be undertaken by a new instrumentality, that is, the nonprofit Health Services Corporation (or HSC).

Functions to be conducted by a new or reoriented Health Services Administration are those having to do with the formulation of program goals, program review and evaluation, the preparation of long-range budgets, the conduct of cost-effectiveness analysis of programs to be carried out by the Health Services Corporation, the traditional functions having to do with health inspection and licensing, the development and promulgation of standards for health care, and of course, the major contracting efforts that would be undertaken with the Health Services Corporation. Finally, functions properly carried out by an executive public agency are those having to do with comprehensive city and regional health planning of a long-range nature. It is from such planning that both long-range and specific operational goals are derived. This function is illustrated in Figure 21 by the term "Comprehensive Planning Agency" in relationship to the Health Services Administration.

With these functions set for the Health Services Administration, it is evident that an entirely new, clear, and appropriate role is envisioned for HSA as a public agency. The reoriented HSA would then no longer need to engage in conflict-of-interest problems that are inherent in the current self-inspections of its own activities and facilities. It would be free

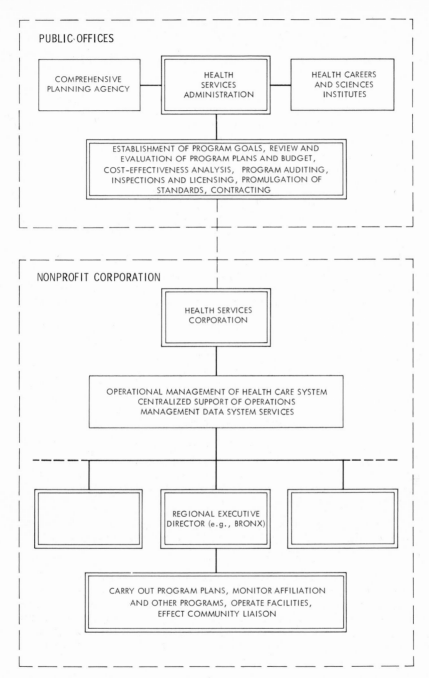

PUBLIC·OFFICES

COMPREHENSIVE
PLANNING AGENCY

HEALTH
SERVICES
ADMINISTRATION

HEALTH CAREERS
AND SCIENCES
INSTITUTES

ESTABLISHMENT OF PROGRAM GOALS, REVIEW AND
EVALUATION OF PROGRAM PLANS AND BUDGET,
COST-EFFECTIVENESS ANALYSIS, PROGRAM AUDITING,
INSPECTIONS AND LICENSING, PROMULGATION OF
STANDARDS, CONTRACTING

NONPROFIT CORPORATION

HEALTH SERVICES
CORPORATION

OPERATIONAL MANAGEMENT OF HEALTH CARE SYSTEM
CENTRALIZED SUPPORT OF OPERATIONS
MANAGEMENT DATA SYSTEM SERVICES

REGIONAL EXECUTIVE
DIRECTOR (e.g., BRONX)

CARRY OUT PROGRAM PLANS, MONITOR AFFILIATION
AND OTHER PROGRAMS, OPERATE FACILITIES,
EFFECT COMMUNITY LIAISON

Figure 21.   Executive and Administrative
Division of Functions, HSA and HSC

521

to guide and audit programs from the vantage point of public office.

It is clear that with this new orientation, the HSA would need personnel only in the order of hundreds (at most a few thousand) rather than the tens of thousands now employed in its various departments. The great share of operational employment and activity would henceforth take place within the Health Services Corporation. Community Mental Health Board functions as they are now structured would change little; their present function is compatible with the proposal. A great deal of change would occur in the functions of the Department of Hospitals. Here, most of the present employees would pass to the Health Services Corporation. Less impact would occur in the central bureaus of the Department of Health, where many employees would continue in their present capacities having to do with health standards, inspection, licensing, contracting, program development and audit, rat control, and the like. However, its present operations having to do with health care delivery at the community level (in terms of district health center activity) involving, for example, ambulatory care, X-ray screening, or school health, would be carried out by the Health Services Corporation. It is felt that this is mandatory if the city is to realize integrated systematic delivery at the community level.

Finally, all of those programs having to do with disease prevention and health maintenance within the classical province of public health would generally remain as they are today within the Department of Health within HSA.

There would be little if any change with respect to the functions and operations of the Office of the City Medical Examiner.

There would be more extensive change than may seem apparent with respect to those health-related activities now located in the Department of Welfare (case-finding, claims processing, reimbursement, and associated data processing). This matter is later discussed in conjunction with the flow and impact of public funds in health care.

Figure 22 provides a more detailed illustration of organizational alignment as well as the distribution of functions.

HEALTH SERVICES ADMINISTRATION

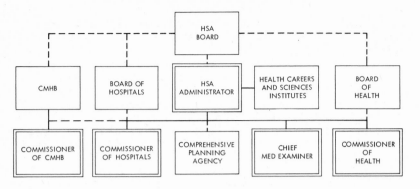

HEALTH SERVICES CORPORATION

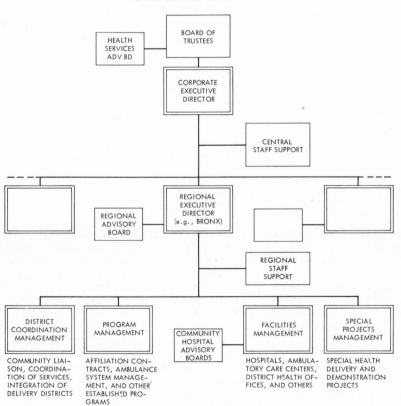

Figure 22. Organizational Alignment
and Functions, HSA and HSC

523

The Health Services Corporation would function
under a Board of Trustees, perhaps nine in number,
appointed by and serving at the pleasure of the Mayor.
It would be managed by a Corporate Executive Director
(or perhaps a President), appointed by the board, and
supported by necessary but minimum central staff. The
entire Corporation would be responsive--in terms of
the provisions of its corporate bylaws-- to the general
long-range planning, and to the applicable service
standards, of the Health Services Administration, its
cognizant executive agency.

Other than its necessary central staff support,
the Corporation as a whole would function through regional arms, each associated with a territory not larger than a borough of the city. Each arm would be managed by a Regional Executive Director having the
necessary local support staff for that particular area.
Four major functions are foreseen under the Regional
Executive Director.

First would be the administrators or directors
of actual health care facilities: hospitals and
ambulatory care centers. Each such facility manager
would be given relatively complete autonomy in administration, to include annual institutional budget
and personnel authority and program authority (comparable to a Veteran's Administration Hospital).

With respect to public hospitals, it is strongly
recommended that there be created for each a Community
Advisory Board manned by responsible spokesmen from
the local community to assure orderly and timely expressions of community needs relative to planning for
the given hospital. The chairman of each such local
advisory board would also be a voting member of the
Regional Advisory Board to function in relation to
the Regional Executive Director. In turn, the chairman of each regional advisory board of the city would
serve on the Health Services Advisory Board functioning in relation to the Board of Trustees of the Corporation as a whole. Thus, with respect to the major
public health facilities of the city, there is proposed not only the normal and necessary line of management passing from trustees to Corporate Director to
Regional Executive Director to facility administrator,
but "back-up" from the local community level through
the region, and finally to the level of the city as a
whole. This separate line of advisory bodies, properly
conceived and implemented, would assure appropriate
and timely consideration of actions and forces that

arise from the community and that must be taken into
account by all levels of management and delivery.

Remaining line functions under the Office of the
Regional Executive Director would be those having to
do with program management, special project management,
and district coordination management.

Program management, in contrast to the direct
line administration role of facility management, would
have to do with a variety of continuing administrative
responsibilities of the Corporation for that particular
area or borough. Evident examples are: contract management of those contractual relationships of either
partial or comprehensive nature between public institutions and voluntary institutions, and the coordination and direction of the local ambulance utilization
program.

The district coordination management function
would, in all probability, be served by a small central staff working out into the various subcommunities
of the region to effect appropriate planning and activity relative to the liaison between health agencies,
organizations, and projects. To coordinate the delivery of services in new and more effective ways and to
integrate the health delivery districts of an area, a
principal task of this office would be that of bringing
about common districting and optimum utilization of
special resources coordinated with such city-wide
efforts.

Finally, there are from time to time a wide variety of special projects in the field of health delivery.
These could be initiated, developed, and budgeted by
the HSA, then contracted for execution to the Health
Services Corporation. Special health delivery projects
might involve demonstration programs, mobile programs
(having to do, for example,with the feasibility of
diagnostic screening), or programs of health-need assessment. It would be difficult to specify the probable variety and extent of such programs. At any given
time, there may be a very large number and variety in
New York City.

Figure 23 outlines suggested general staff support
functions for the Corporate Executive Director in a
central office, as well as for each regional executive
director. Ultimately, central Corporate staff might
number in the order of several hundred personnel,

General principle: Assign and/or balance functions
at or between central and borough or area staffs
according to efficiency, economy, feasibility. In
this regard, detailed operational study must be
carried out; suggestions here should be taken as
illustrative.

```
┌──────────┐
│CORPORATE │
│EXECUTIVE │
│DIRECTOR  │
└──────────┘
    │
    ├── CLAIMS, COLLECTIONS, REIMBURSEMENTS ⎫
    │                                       ⎪
    ├── MANAGEMENT DATA SYSTEM CENTER        ⎪
    │                                       ⎪
    ├── AUDIT, BUDGET, & CONTRACTS           ⎪  Minimum
    │                                       ⎪  central
    ├── OPERATIONAL PLANNING & EVALUATION    ⎬  staff--
    │   SERVICES                            ⎪  in the
    │                                       ⎪  order of
    ├── MANPOWER REQUIREMENTS SERVICES       ⎪  hundreds
    │                                       ⎪
    ├── INTERNAL SUPPORT SERVICES            ⎪
    │                                       ⎪
    └── CENTRAL LABORATORY SERVICES          ⎭
```

```
┌────────────┐
│REGIONAL    │   (One per
│EXECUTIVE   │   borough
│DIRECTOR(S) │   or area)
└────────────┘
    │
    ├── REGIONAL EXECUTIVE STAFF          ⎫
    │                                     ⎪
    ├── REGIONAL COMPUTER DIVISION         ⎪
    │                                     ⎪
    ├── ACCOUNTS & DISBURSEMENTS DIVISION  ⎪
    │                                     ⎬
    ├── BUDGETING & CONTRACTS DIVISION     ⎪
    │                                     ⎪
    ├── PURCHASING & SUPPLIES DIVISION     ⎪
    │                                     ⎪
    ├── FACILITIES & SUPPORT DIVISION      ⎪
    │                                     ⎪
    └── PERSONNEL DIVISION                 ⎭
```

Support staff
varies in size
as a function
of scope of
regional re-
sponsibility;
in any case,
the bulk of
system sup-
port person-
nel are used
at this level
rather than
centrally for
the city as
a whole

Figure 23. Suggested General Staff
Support Functions

526

supplemented as necessary by special support personnel
elsewhere (laboratory, etc.). The central staff would
engage in the entire collection and reimbursement process, a responsibility now assigned to the Welfare
Department. They would operate a management data system center that would function to support the central
management of HSA and HSC as well as the various regional offices, administrators, and others. (Data
system principles and requirements are discussed in
Chapter 10.) Central staff would undertake certain
necessary internal auditing, budgeting, and contracting
responsibilities. They would carry out operational
planning as called for by the long-range planning
undertaken by HSA. They would specify and fulfill
manpower requirements for health care delivery, provide internal support services for HSA and HSC, and
undertake appropriate central laboratory and related
computer-based services.

Each regional executive director would need a
small executive staff. In addition, his office would
require a modest regional computer capability which
would be related to the central data system in the corporate offices, and would provide "central" store for
hospitals within the area. As necessary, regional
staffs would undertake accounting and disbursement, budgeting and contracting, purchasing and supplies, facility support, and borough-level personnel provisioning.

Health Careers and Sciences Institutes

Having clearly separated the proper functions of
public offices in health delivery from those proper
functions of an operating instrumentality, there remains one set of functions to be accounted for. These
have to do with education and with both applied and
basic research. These functions should be included
neither with the policy and audit functions of HSA as
an executive agency nor with the operational delivery
character of the Health Services Corporation. Therefore, all of the functions that have to do with education and research would be given special locus within
a new organization referred to here as the Health
Careers and Sciences Institutes (Figure 24). Under an
appropriate Board of Trustees and an Executive Director,
the Institutes would function as a wholly owned, non-
profit corporation attached to the Health Sciences
Administration proper.

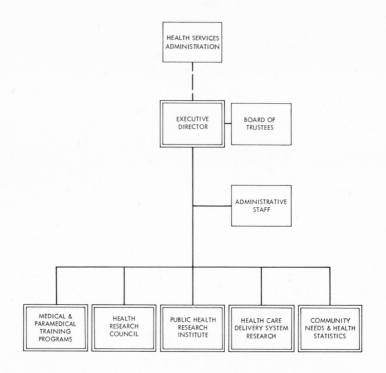

Figure 24.   Organization of Proposed Health
Careers and Sciences Institutes

(Dashed line indicates relationship to HSA.)

The Institutes would engage in manpower development programs, both directly and by contract, and
they would house the Health Research Council (which
presently exists within the Department of Health) as
well as the Public Health Research Institute (also
attached thereto). In addition to manpower development and training, two other new functions would be
organized and carried out within the Institutes: a
Program on Health Care Delivery to address the matter
of how to improve the actual delivery of techniques,
procedures, treatments, drugs, and the like in more
efficient ways; secondly, a new effort would be developed in the area of analyzing trends in medical
needs for the population. (This function has a predecessor in the work of Dr. Paul Densen and his staff
within present HSA.)

Management

It is evident that the aims of the new HSA, the
Health Services Corporation, and the Health Careers
and Sciences Institutes, would, for the first time,
permit a clear and workable assignment of role and
authority for the many functions within the total
health system.

The entire structure, however, would need to
have the benefit of fiscal control, of personnel control, and the freedom to develop management support
technologies. Also the Corporation would need to be
fiscally viable. This would require that it be (1)
budgeted properly by the city for the city's share of
expenses, (2) the central agency for the flow of public funds relative to health services, (3) firmly
budgeted by the city (short- and long-range) for
capital construction funds. (The staff anticipates
that the federal government will strongly enter the
field of health facility construction and renovation
in the years ahead, thus reducing that burden on
local government; also anticipated is the interim
possible need to raise such funds by loan and by
bond issue.)

To implement the proposed reorganization of the
Health Services Administration and to establish a
Health Services Corporation, extensive further planning
and detailing of the table of organization in line with

the new functions would be required. New job descriptions would need to be written. Enabling legislation would need to be prepared. The Corporate by-laws and the Corporate form would need careful specification. Qualifications of present personnel would need to be searched and decisions made as to new locations (including personnel in accountability and services agencies who presumably would need to be transferred to comparable functions in the Corporation). Career ladders for health services personnel would need to be devised, training programs composed, and training staff selected. Management support and patient-data information needs would need to be specified and computer needs determined. Finally, the fiscal operations of the Corporation would need to be established and appropriate enabling authority for such functions provided.

Presumably, the transfer of line operations from the Health Services Administration, and from other city agencies, to the Health Services Corporation would be an orderly step-by-step matter beginning early in the first year of corporate life and concluding by the end of the second; several subsequent years would see full corporate development. It seems reasonable to state that the ease of the transition would undoubtedly be a function of the care devoted to planning. The first major step could be that of assuming responsibility for the municipal hospital system.

The entire present process of claims and reimbursements involving public funds, principally Titles XVIII and XIX but also to include other budgets, would need to be managed within the HSA-HSC administrative structure. Among other matters, this would require changes in legislation and procedure as well as the development of appropriate computer and data handling capability within the Corporation.

Finally, it is desirable, if not necessary, for the city to undertake the training of nurses and paramedical personnel through the proposed Health Careers Institute.

CHAPTER 10 SOME RELATED RECOMMENDATIONS

SURVEY SUMMARY: DISPOSITION
OF THE MUNICIPAL HOSPITALS

Poorly defined goals are at the heart of the
recurring conflict between teaching, research, and
patient care. Each of these activities struggles
against the others in the city hospitals; each activity has its champions and its detractors. It has
been both stoutly asserted and stoutly denied that a
strong teaching program leads to effective patient
care; the staff cannot arbitrate this. Truly effective relationships among these activities must be
worked out and defined. It is not unlikely that in
the health services system of the future, these activities will be emphasized in different proportions in
each hospital.

A related matter is the duplication of facilities
among hospitals. A role for each institution must be
worked out within a planned and coherent framework.
A focus of purposes and resources will make of each
hospital a truly effective instrument for its system
role.

Well-defined performance standards must also be
established by which physicians and administrators
can gauge their successes or needs for improvement
and against which they can match their efforts. Further, there is no effective feedback mechanism that
is responsive to the needs of persons within the system or that allows them better to know what their
real needs are.

The waste of available resources is evident
throughout the city hospital system. One component
of this waste is the loss of Medicaid collections.
At one hospital the supervisor of investigators stated
that there is a backlog of 3,254 files for in-patients
that are unprocessed and that, in all likelihood, will

never be processed within the time limit set by law.
Most of the patients have already left the hospital.
It would take an enormous task force of field workers
to trace them in order to acquire needed information.
Additionally, investigators and clerks at the hospital
have all they can do to keep up with the new cases
which come in daily.

There are excessive duplications that are costly
in both time and dollars; these duplications occur
throughout the system. There are the innumerable
letters of requisition and approvals that are required
to get or do almost anything. This condition, together with the personnel required to maintain the function, produces an abnormally high cost, draining dollars
that are sorely needed elsewhere. With other factors
added, costs may increase as much as five times current
market for given expenses.

Operations are so retarded by fragmentation that
there is no way to avoid the phenomenon of "built-in
obsolescence." As currently constituted, often the
system is not capable of obtaining equipment or constructing a building while the needs which called for
them are still current. The result is that in a majority of instances buildings or equipment are in need of
modification or replacement on the day they are completed, delivered, or installed.

The compartmentalization of beds is a cause for
grave concern to doctors and administrators alike.
The procedures and facilities are so arranged as to be
inflexible. It is either difficult or impossible to
use an empty bed on one service to handle the overflow from another. The result is that on any given
day the municipal hospitals in New York City have approximately 3000 beds empty while patients are not
admitted, or are kept in hallways, or are doubled-up
in other wards.

The use of doctors and nurses as messengers and
housekeepers keeps them away from their patients and
is an inordinately costly and wasteful way of carrying
out these less-skilled functions. With the glaring
lack of guidelines establishing and governing the ratio of teaching and research to patient care, some
doctors who are patient-oriented feel that these other
activities dominate in the hospitals while other physicians who prefer teaching and research feel that their
interests are sorely neglected.

These circumstances often necessitate, as well as broadly encourage, doing business by devious methods. For administrators and doctors to get materials, personnel, repairs or, in short, almost anything, they must become skillful at beating the system. Once again, this relegates quality medical care to secondary status.

A need for new resources is clear in some areas; in other areas, new needs cannot be assessed until a maximum use of existing resources has been realized. Among the present troubles in the city hospital system is the shortage of nurses, which can be translated into a need for new training and recruiting programs. The nurse shortage is a problem of such magnitude that it has been treated in a separate section of this book.

The need also exists for a more responsive salary system--that is, a system with funds available to place the city hospitals in a posture matching that of the marketplace. Crisis response to salary problems is ineffective. As a result of last year's difficulty with nurses' salaries, the city hospitals leapfrogged the voluntaries and were leapfrogged in return. Had funds been available for competitive salary growth, this destructive bidding might have been avoided.

Additionally, the city might consider providing housing allowances for hard-to-obtain personnel. Since the city hospitals, as a class, are in undesirable neighborhoods, the city might further provide safe, low-cost transportation for its hospital employees. It is in terms of programs such as these that the need for new resources should be explored.

The main concern of this section is the manner in which management arrangements can be suited to each city hospital and to the community that is serves. It is doubtful that a single accommodation meets the needs of all hospitals. For instance, certain factors suggest that some must be managed independent of affiliate voluntaries (with partial affiliation contracts providing specified professional services as needed, similar to present practice). These factors include:

- The need to operate hospitals in impoverished neighborhoods not suited to the goals or needs of voluntary or proprietary institutions.

- The desirability of preserving for the city a
  brick-and-mortar hold in the delivery of health
  services where publicly funded health care is
  a dominant characteristic. The increase in
  federal and state funds make it important that
  the city maintain a tangible, firm role in
  health services if the city is to carry out its
  public responsibilities effectively.

On the other hand, for certain other of the municipal hospitals, different factors suggest that strong
voluntary hospitals manage them in the form of comprehensive affiliations. By the term "comprehensive affiliation" this document implies that the city would
retain "basic program control" over the relationship
in the form of contract negotiation and monitoring.
This arrangement is especially suited to the city hospitals that adjoin leading voluntaries. Among the
factors suggesting this arrangement are these:

- The need to reduce the management burden,
  wherever possible, and to make best use of
  existing resources and capabilities;

- The need to affirm the private sector's role
  in the delivery of health services;

- The need to minimize costly duplications of
  service.

Not all the city hospitals are suited to these
two management arrangements. Ownership of the two
cancer hospitals, Ewing and Delafield, should be re-
linquished to their affiliated institutions, Memorial
Hospital and Presbyterian Hospital. It is not in the
public interest for the city to maintain specialized,
limited-service hospitals with few beds.

At Columbia, there has arisen the question of
whether Delafield should not be converted to a general
hospital. This hinges on the role that city-wide planning envisions for Presbyterian Hospital. The Presbyterian staff fear that they could be called upon to
serve as the general hospital for the area, with no
privilege of selective admissions. They believe that
their institution should be devoted to teaching and
research, and that it must, therefore, be selective.
If city-wide planning calls for an open, general hospital in the area, it should be achieved by appropriate conversion of Delafield.

The out-patient statistics for Presbyterian suggest that one might also wish to assess Delafield as
a potential ambulatory care facility serving the full
OPD needs of the medical complex. This survey has
not fully explored either of these possible uses of
Delafield.

Further, the city should not maintain separate
chronic-care facilities, especially in isolated locations. The elderly are too easily forgotten at best;
their isolation should not be geographically emphasized. Certain chronic-care beds should be established
in connection with general hospitals. Special building
programs for voluntary and proprietary groups hold the
promise of providing the city with adequate extended-
care beds within the local community for persons who
do not require hospital services. Thus, the city
should consider converting Coler and Goldwater to different purposes.

Sea View should be "merged" under a comprehensive
affiliation with an existing voluntary on Staten
Island. The city should retain title to the 100-plus
acres now occupied by Sea View and anticipate a phased
rebuilding program.

Sydenham, because of its structure and its location, cannot be satisfactorily renovated in its laboratory and operating room areas. It is recommended
that this hospital be converted to an ambulatory care
satellite of Harlem Hospital. Satisfactory arrangements must be worked out with neighborhood physicians
who now use Sydenham for their private patients (a
use unique in the city).

These various management arrangements can be summarized in the following manner (see also Table 22):

    a.   Convert (assuming that chronic-care beds
        are provided through a new, special com-
        munity program)

        (1)   Coler
        (2)   Goldwater

    b.   Operate under a new administrative form (HSC)
        with partial affiliation as needed

        (1)   Fordham (relationships to be deter-
               mined; rebuild)

Table 22. Recommendations for Municipal Hospital Disposition

MUNICIPAL HOSPITALS	LEASE/SELL	PARTIAL AFFILIATION	TOTAL AFFILIATION	MERGE	N.P. CORP.	REBUILD/RENOVATE	CONTINGENCY REQUIREMENTS
*** BELLEVUE			NYU	FUNCTION AS "ONE PLANT"	PROGRAM CONTROL	BUILDING IN PROCESS	ACCELERATE CONSTRUCTION PROGRAM. FOUR BEDS PER "SIX BED WARD"
*** BRONX (JACOBI)			EINSTEIN	FUNCTION AS "ONE PLANT"	PROGRAM CONTROL		MASTER PLAN NEEDED. RENOVATE RADIOLOGY OPD, E.R.; MEET TRANSPORTATION PROBLEMS
* COLER					HDQ FOR HSA AND HSC****	BUILD COMMUNITY HOMES	NEED GOOD COMMUNITY CHRONIC-CARE FACILITY DEVELOPMENT PROGRAM, AND PHASE-OUT PLAN
* CONEY ISLAND	RELINQUISH						OWNERSHIP TO BE DETERMINED. RENOVATE E.R.
*** CUMBERLAND			BROOKLYN	FUNCTION AS "ONE PLANT"	PROGRAM CONTROL	BUILD	NEW BUILDING RENOVATE LABS, RAD., OPD

MUNICIPAL HOSPITALS	LEASE/ SELL	PARTIAL AFFILIATION	TOTAL AFFILIATION	MERGE	N.P. CORP.	REBUILD/ RENOVATE	CONTINGENCY REQUIREMENTS
* DELAFIELD	RELINQUISH TO PRESBYTERIAN						REVISE EITHER TO GENERAL CARE OR TO COMMUNITY AMBULATORY CARE
*** ELMHURST		TO BE DETERMINED	MOUNT SINAI		PROGRAM CONTROL	SOME NEW LABS NEEDED (HEM. & CYT.)	(BOROUGH SHOULD HAVE AFFILIATED MEDICAL COLLEGE)
* EWING	RELINQUISH TO MEMORIAL						THIS PROCESS NOW UNDERWAY
** FORDHAM		MISERI- CORDIA		NO	ADMINISTER	400 BEDS MOVE S.E. (NEED SITE)	PLAN FOR BUILD-UP TO INDEPENDENT STRENGTH
* GOLDWATER					HDQ FOR INSTITUTES	RENO- VATION TO BE PLANNED	NEED COMM. CHRONIC- CARE FACIL. DEVELOP- MENT PROGRAM WITH PHASE-OUT PLAN
** GOUVERNEUR		BETH ISRAEL			ADMINISTER		NEED LONG-RANGE EVALUATION FOR AD- DITIONAL SERVICES

(Continued)

Table 22 (Continued)

MUNICIPAL HOSPITALS	LEASE/ SELL	PARTIAL AFFILIATION	TOTAL AFFILIATION	MERGE	N.P. CORP.	REBUILD/ RENOVATE	CONTINGENCY REQUIREMENTS
** GREENPOINT		?			ADMINISTER	KAISER TYPE IN ORDER OF 600 BEDS	(CUT BACK BEDS AT KINGS CO.) E.R. RENOVATION, URGENT NEED FOR PLANNING, SURG. RENOVATION
** HARLEM		COLUMBIA	NO		ADMINISTER	(URGENT-- RENO- VATIONS IN PRESENT PLAN)	
*** KINGS COUNTY			DOWNSTATE		PROGRAM CONTROL	MODIFY & RENOVATE	CUT BACK ON BEDS. RENOVATE RAD., OPD, E.R.; SURG STAFF HOUSING NEEDED
** LINCOLN		EINSTEIN	NO		ADMINISTER	750 BEDS	REVISE BUILDING PLANNING; ACCELERATE DEVELOPMENT
** METROPOLITAN		N.Y. MEDICAL COLLEGE	(OR) MOUNT SINAI OR CORNELL MEDICAL		PROGRAM CONTROL		RENOVATE RAD., LABS., MED. RECORDS, BUILD PARKING & RESEARCH

MUNICIPAL HOSPITALS	LEASE/ SELL	PARTIAL AFFILIATION	TOTAL AFFILIATION	MERGE	N.P. CORP.	REBUILD/ RENOVATE	CONTINGENCY REQUIREMENTS
** OLD MORRISANIA *** NEW MORRISANIA		MONTEFIORE (OLD)	MONTEFIORE (NEW)	FUNCTION AS "ONE PLANT" (NEW)	OLD: ADMINISTER NEW: PROGRAM CONTROL	RENOVATE & REBUILD OLD; BUILD NEW	ADD: AMB. CARE, ACUTE CARE, EXTENDED CARE FACILITIES, REVISE PRESENT PLANS
*** QUEENS		TO BE DETERMINED	TO BE DETERMINED		PROGRAM CONTROL	RENOVATE	MODERNIZATION NEEDED
*** SEA VIEW			STATEN ISLAND HOSPITAL	FUNCTION AS "ONE PLANT"	PROGRAM CONTROL	REBUILDING PROGRAM NEEDED	MOVE STATEN ISLAND HOSPITAL TO SEA VIEW GROUNDS
SYDENHAM				SATELLITE TO HARLEM		ELECTRIC & OTHER RENOVATIONS	AMBULATORY CARE CENTER
ADDED FACILITIES							
RIKER'S ISLAND		WITH BELLEVUE-NYU			ADMINISTER	250 BED WING OR NEW 500 BED UNIT	FOR BEST SECURITY, PLACE ON RIKER'S ISLAND; FOR BEST STAFFING, PLACE AT ELMHURST

(Continued)

Table 22 (Continued)

MUNICIPAL HOSPITALS	LEASE/ SELL	PARTIAL AFFILIATION	TOTAL AFFILIATION	MERGE	N.P. CORP.	REBUILD/ RENOVATE	CONTINGENCY REQUIREMENTS
ST. FRANCIS				SATELLITE TO LINCOLN		RENOVATE	AMBULATORY CARE CENTER

* ELIMINATE FROM THE PUBLIC SYSTEM

** FULL ADMINISTRATION BY H.S.C. USING PARTIAL AFFILIATION AS APPROPRIATE

*** ADMINISTERED BY AFFILIATE UNDER COMPREHENSIVE CONTRACT

**** NEED FIRM CAPITAL PROGRAM OF TRANSPORTATION ACCESS FROM MANHATTAN

   (2)   Gouverneur (Beth Israel)
   (3)   Greenpoint (relationships to be
         determined; rebuild)
   (4)   Harlem (relationships to be deter-
         mined; under reconstruction)
   (5)   Lincoln (Einstein)
   (6)   Metropolitan (N.Y. Med. Coll., Mt. Sinai
         or Cornell)
   (7)   Present Morrisania (rebuild and
         renovate; relationships to be determined)

c.   Maintain Program Control (with affiliate
     operating hospital and providing medical
     and other services under comprehensive
     affiliation)

   (1)   Bellevue (New York University)
   (2)   Bronx (Einstein)
   (3)   Cumberland (Brooklyn)
   (4)   Elmhurst (Mt. Sinai)
   (5)   Kings County (Downstate)
   (6)   "New" Morrisania (Montefiore)
   (7)   Queens (relationships to be deter-
         mined)
   (8)   Sea View (Staten Island Hospital)

d.   Relinquish City Ownership

   (1)   Delafield (to Columbia)
   (2)   Ewing (to Memorial)
   (3)   Coney Island (to be determined)

e.   Operate as Ambulatory Care Satellites

   (1)   St. Francis (to Lincoln)
   (2)   Sydenham (to Harlem, or otherwise
         merge).

A great deal of construction and renovation, com-
mited in earlier years, is still in process (or in-
definitely delayed, as is often the case). In addition, new commitments totaling some $60 million
appear in the present executive budget. Beyond past
and current commitments, the present study recommends
an additional schedule of construction and renovation.
With no attempt at definitive specifications, this
new schedule is presented in Table 23.

Table 23. Tentative Capital Program: Hospital Construction and Renovation

	TOTAL COST	REPLACES PRESENT PLANS ESTIMATED AT:	68-69	69-70	70-71	71-72	72-73
BELLEVUE NEW OPD WING WHEN PRESENT CONSTRUCTION IS FINISHED. COST ESTIMATE SAME AS AMBULATORY CARE FACILITIES.	$ 2,000	$	$	$	$ 100	$ 1,900	$
BRONX TOWER OF ACUTE BEDS, PLUS RECONSTRUCTION OF PRESENT BUILDING FOR TEACHING, RESEARCH, & OFFICE SPACE. ESTIMATE BASED ON KAISER CONCEPT.	16,000 (NEW)		600	3,400	12,000		
	4,000 (RENOVATION)	4,000 (EST.)			1,000	3,000	
COLER CONVERT COLER TO A HEADQUARTERS FOR HEALTH SERVICES ADMINISTRATION. (THIS DEPENDS ON THE DEVELOPMENT OF GOOD COMMUNITY CHRONIC-CARE PROGRAMS.) DESIGN & RENOVATION COSTS ARE SHOWN.	2,000				100	1,900	
CUMBERLAND BUILD TOWER OF ACUTE BEDS ADJACENT TO BROOKLYN HOSPITAL; CONVERT CUMBERLAND TO EXTENDED CARE AND AMBULATORY CARE. THIS REPLACES PRESENT PLAN TO BUILD PHIC FACILITY ADJACENT TO BROOKLYN HOSPITAL.	16,000 (NEW)	11,172 (PHIC)	600	3,400	12,000		
	4,000 (RENOVATION)	4,040			1,000	3,000	

542

	TOTAL COST	REPLACES PRESENT PLANS ESTIMATED AT:	68-69	69-70	70-71	71-72	72-73
DELAFIELD — CONVERT HOSPITAL EITHER TO GENERAL CARE OR TO AMBULATORY CARE.	$ 4,000	$	$100	$3,900	$	$	$
ELMHURST — SUPPORT DEVELOPMENT OF MEDICAL SCHOOL IN QUEENS. RANGE OF CITY SUPPORT ESTIMATED AT $30 TO $50 MILLION.	40,000					1,000	5,000
ALSO: TOWER OF ACUTE BEDS PLUS RECONSTRUCTION OF PRESENT BUILDING FOR TEACHING, RESEARCH, AND OFFICE SPACE.	16,000 (NEW)	12,724	600	3,400	12,000		
	4,000 (RENOVATION)				1,000	3,000	
GOLDWATER — CONVERT TO HEADQUARTERS FOR HEALTH SCIENCES INSTITUTES. AS WITH COLER, THIS DEPENDS ON THE DEVELOPMENT OF GOOD COMMUNITY CHRONIC-CARE PROGRAMS. (ESTIMATED DESIGN AND RENOVATION COSTS, INCLUDING EQUIPMENT, ARE SHOWN.)	4,000	2,000 (ALT. & RENOVATION)			100	3,900	
KINGS COUNTY — TOWERS OF ACUTE BEDS, CONVERTING PRESENT PLANT FOR TEACHING, RESEARCH OFFICES, AMBULATORY CARE AND STAFF HOUSING.	16,000 (NEW)	93,160 (RECON-STRUCTION)	600	3,400	12,000		
	6,000 (RENOVATION)				1,000	5,000	

(Continued)

543

Table 23 (Continued)

	TOTAL COST	REPLACES PRESENT PLANS ESTIMATED AT:	68-69	69-70	70-71	71-72	72-73
MORRISANIA (NEW) TOWER OF ACUTE BEDS ON MONTEFIORE GROUNDS.	$ 16,000	$ 32,292	$600	$3,400	$12,000	$	$
MORRISANIA (PRESENT) CONVERT PRESENT PLANT TO AMBULATORY CARE & EXTENDED CARE.	6,000				1,000	5,000	
QUEENS TOWER OF ACUTE BEDS PLUS RENOVATION OF EXISTING PLANT FOR TEACHING, RESEARCH, AMBULATORY CARE, AND EXTENDED CARE.	16,000 (NEW) 4,000 (RENOVATION)	26,115 (PHIC)	600	3,400	12,000 1,000	3,000	
SEA VIEW ASSIST IN MOVING STATEN ISLAND HOSPITAL TO SEA VIEW GROUNDS.	10,000 (EST.)				500	4,500	5,000
SYDENHAM CONVERT SYDENHAM TO AMBULATORY CARE	1,000	1,090	100	900			

	TOTAL COST	REPLACES PRESENT PLANS ESTIMATED AT:	68-69	69-70	70-71	71-72	72-73
ST. FRANCIS CONVERT TO AMBULATORY CARE.	$ 1,000 (ALSO $ FOR PURCHASE?)	$	$100	$ 900	$	$	$

OTHER FACILITIES

	TOTAL COST		68-69	69-70	70-71
RIKER'S ISLAND ADD APPROXIMATELY 250 BEDS TO PRESENT ADULT FACILITY, OR BUILD NEW 500-BED SECURITY HOSPITAL ELSEWHERE.	25,000 (RIKER'S) 50,000 (ELSEWHERE)	$186,593	500	5,000	44,500

*$213,000
**$238,000

* WITH 250-BED SECURITY ADDITION ON RIKER'S ISLAND.
** WITH 500-BED SECURITY HOSPITAL (NEW).

PUBLIC FUNDING: FINANCING THE CORPORATION

Funds Flow Based on New Legislation

The acceptance of the Medicaid plan by New York
State in May of 1966 caused a significant increase of
funds flow into New York City. In the single example
of public hospital care, the collections by the city
in fiscal 1966 increased 60% over fiscal 1965.
So far in fiscal 1967, the collections for public
hospital care indicate that the year's total will be
270% of the fiscal 1965 collections. It is clear
that the collection machinery and the management of
the flow must be appropriately enlarged and increased
in efficiency.

Because the demand for public health services
has increased so greatly, the city share of the
delivery costs is now greater than the entire health
delivery costs were a few years ago.

Based on the history of funds flow, there have
been requests from the city to the state to obtain
settlements of claims over periods of time during
which claims had not yet been substantiated. These
requests have all been partially successful in that
some payment has been made by the state. Testimony
indicates, however, that payment has been no more
than 80% of the amount that could have been realized
under good claiming procedures.

If the Department of Welfare continues to follow
its own established procedures after July 1, 1967,
state and federal criteria will continue to be unmet
and partial settlements will be the rule; the city
will undoubtedly suffer a substantial loss in reimbursements as a result.

A close look should be taken at what could or
can now be collected and current capability evaluated
against what is needed to accomplish a maximum return.

Table 24 summarizes gross approximate reimbursement by formula.

Investigations show that it is not likely that
the Department of Welfare will be geared up in time
to obtain full possible reimbursement in this fiscal
year. Indeed, it will probably be July 1969 before

Table 24. Portion of Health Services Delivery
Costs Eligible for Federal and
State Grants

(Mental health services and health facility
construction funds not included)

(millions of dollars)

	Gross*	Federal	State	Local
Actual for FY 1965-66	$308.4	$ 52.4	$ 75.7	$180.3
Percent of gross	100.0%	17.0%	24.5%	58.5%
Estimated for FY 1966-67	$329.1	$125.1	$102.0	$102.0
Percent of gross	100.0%	38.0%	31.0%	31.0%
Estimated for FY 1967-68	$414.1	$150.0	$132.0	$132.0
Percent of gross	100.0%	36.3%	31.8%	31.8%
Under Medicaid formula	100.0%	46.6%**	26.7%***	26.7%****

*Not to be confused with total public health
expenditure. This is clarified in later
discussion.

**Maximum federal reimbursement to New York, unless
eligibility standards are lowered (even a lower
percentage if standards are raised).

***State continues to match city percentage of costs
in any event. (In practice, full amounts have
never been reimbursed to the city because full
claim substantiation by the city was lacking.)

****Minimum city requirement under existing laws
and eligibility rules. (To the extent that
claiming procedures remain faulty, the city will
pay an increased percentage.)

the city approaches a high percentage of the full
potential income under the prescribed formula of
reimbursement requirements. In the long run, reasonable fulfillment of this potential will reduce the
percentage amount of public funding to be budgeted
from the city tax base; however, the latter will remain substantial--in the order of 28 per cent of the
total. Since over-all costs continue to increase,
eventually the city's actual dollar contribution
will, in all probability, continue slowly to increase.

The administration of health services delivery,
as well as the agency rendering claims for payment,
should be a single operational entity, as already indicated. There is presently not enough administrative
cohesiveness to cover this single-purpose task successfully. A preferred role for such a single agency,
with respect to the flow of funds, is illustrated in
Figure 25.

The checking of a Medicaid patient's control
number in the present data system is grossly inefficient, often resulting in a loss of reimbursement.
A quick-access numbering system should be provided
to facilitate each patient's admission request. The
patient can then be advised to register for Medicaid
or pay (already established as policy effective
July 1, 1967, and enforceable by the Administration).
This desirable process would fare best when implemented by the Health Services Corporation.

A Columbia study showed 93% of the patients at
out-patient clinics to be medically indigent. The
present recommendation is to accept an affidavit
from those claiming to be medically indigent rather
than cause all patients to fill out a detailed eligibility form, the latter being a practice which proves
to be correctly carried out in less than 30% of cases.
Investigation costs of this great number of faulty
cases (compared to the possible losses within the remaining 7%) would certainly be excessive. This proposal must have acceptance by federal and state offices. Our investigation shows federal and state
offices to be favorably disposed toward some form of
affidavit.

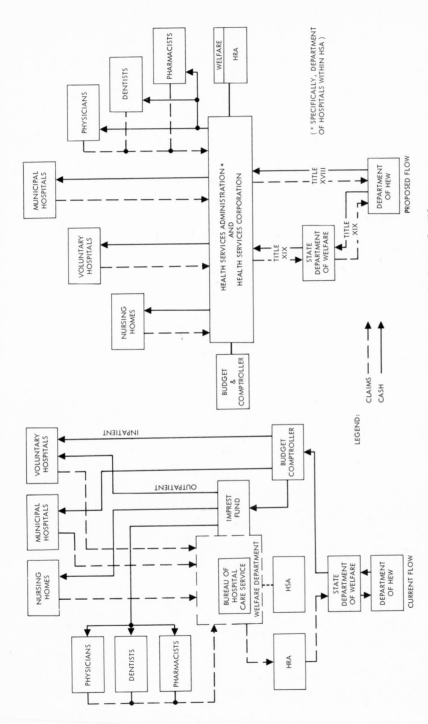

Figure 25.   Current and Recommended Cash Flow

549

Cash Flow Cycle

Present cash flow for health services is based on quarterly estimates going from city, to state, to federal agencies (Figure 26).

The federal fiscal offices advance 100% of the adjusted quarterly estimate by letter of credit to the New York State Department of Social Welfare. (Adjustments are made according to the previous quarter's actual claims.)

Presently the state advances only 80% of the city's estimate to the city (and only one-third of that 80% each month), then adjusts the quarterly claim, and later provides varying amounts of the final 20% share.

It is recommended that the state forward 100% of the quarterly estimate to the Health Services Corporation directly and adjust on the previous quarter, as the federal government now does with the state. (It is assumed that the cash flow cushion presently used by the Welfare Department, the Imprest Fund, would be transferred to the Health Services Administration.) Letter of credit sums would be adjusted on the basis of certified claims (or acceptance of affidavits) backed by investigation of a 5% random sample of cases. (It is recommended that the present sampling technique be altered to provide a true 5% random sampling of cases--a "must" for satisfactory reimbursement practice.)

As a proposed alternative, the federal portion of funding could flow directly to the Corporation instead of to the State Department of Social Welfare.

In either case, this would mean the burden of proof for valid claiming would be upon the Corporation and, for appropriate response, the Corporation would necessarily have to possess the full range of operational responsibility from delivery to collections under the policies and guidance of HSA.

Other sources of funds available to health services collectively are significant in the total picture. The OEO is sponsoring neighborhood health clinics for services not covered by other health programs. HUD will have a significant impact on health facilities. Other HEW grants and private contributions

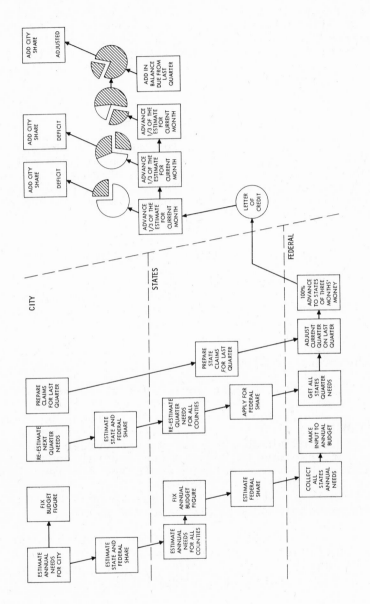

Figure 26.   Cash Flow Cycle

will affect the health services delivery picture.
Though all collections cannot be controlled by the
proposed HSA-HSC configuration, an office of the
Corporation could regularly engage in obtaining
grants and gifts to fit in with total health program
planning and budgeting.

The Larger Financial Structure

Mayor Lindsay's executive budget for fiscal year
1967-68 calls for expense allocation of $803 million
and an allocation of $67.1 million for capital con-
struction and renovation. Table 25 illustrates the
major relationship of the expense budget to state and
federal reimbursement.

Financing a Health Services Corporation

If the proposed Corporation were in full operation for the next fiscal period, its expense budget
would be presumed to be that projected for HSA as now
constituted, less the amount necessary to fund the
new, much smaller HSA operation, plus budgeting for
claims collection and processing. The total would be
in the order of $700 million.

The capital budget would, for the time being,
consist of that projected at present by the city. In
time, it would show a significant increase based upon
expanded planning for construction and renovations,
an era during which the city's cost burden would probably decrease due to anticipated federal construction
funding. However, that era would see continuation of
state and federal construction funding as provided by
existing legislative acts, to be expended by the Corporation according to duly approved plans.

It is desirable that the Corporation be chartered
to raise funds for construction and renovation, beyond
those available from the city, with the agreement of
the city and according to long-range plan.

A MANAGEMENT DATA SYSTEM

The Problem Domain

The staff finds that present or future health
care system management cannot do its job properly

Table 25. Estimated Expense Budget, HSA, FY 67/68

(millions of dollars)

Funding direct to City General Fund: $20 million not included here. (Blue Cross, Blue Shield, Workman's Compensation, miscellaneous fees.)

(NOTE: Original budget of $803.4 million was published with error due to inclusion of $19 million in Welfare fringes in Medicaid line.)

	Tax Levy	State	Federal	Other	Total
Medicaid (Welfare)	$ 43.3	$ 43.3	$ 43.3	$ --	$130.0
Charitable Institutions (Also spends $8 million entered below in Mental Health)	31.0	30.0	29.0	--	90.0
Hospitals* (and Mental Health in Hospitals) ($72 per diem rate)	246.0 (-19)**	45.0	132.0(a)	19.0	461.0 [less 32. less 5. less 37.]
	19.0	19.0	--	--	

(Continued)

553

Table 25 (Continued)

	Tax Levy	State	Federal	Other	Total
Health*	$ 33.0 [less 3.0] (c)	$ 22.0 (d) [less 3.0]	$ --	$ 1.0	$ 56.0
Mental Health** (excludes general hospitals)	12.0	21.0	1.5	11.5	46.0 [less .15] (e)
Chief Medical Examiner	1.4	--	--	--	1.4 [less .12] (e)
	$385.7	$180.3	$205.8	$31.5	$784.4
		\$386.1			

(a) Includes Title XVIII.
(b) Required accrual: 32.0; required return on affiliations: 5.0
(c) (d) Required accrual: 3.0 + 3.0, or 6.0
(e) Required accruals: 0.27

*Both hospital and health totals include debt service & fringes.

**(-19) is 3rd party reimbursement other than government; recovered in "Other."

***Mental Health expenditures in hospitals included in Hospital Budget Line.

Adjusted Gross Total:	$784.40
Less Required Accruals:	43.27
Estimated Net Actual:	741.13

554

until a sound capability for information and data
handling exists; needs occur in three general areas.

Patient Data Needs

Medical science and technology are revolution-
izing the delivery of health care both in terms of
the quality of medicine and the ability to provide
more of it. The demands for information have risen
astronomically, but the keeping and utilization of
records has fallen behind alarmingly. This dilemma
has seriously eroded the time and efficiency of physicians, nurses, and others. Of central concern
must be the harnessing of the computer to save the
professional's time and to bring efficiency to institutional management.

Under wide development (and in certain instances
now available) are computer equipment and programs
which interrogate patients and take histories in the
fields of cardiology, allergy, gynecology, neurology,
psychiatry, endocrinology, gastroenterology, as well
as general screening programs fashioned after the
Kaiser Multiphasic Screening technique. There are
also available computer programs which permit the
physician to "dictate" his record directly to the
computer. The saving of physician-time can be
significant.

While current capabilities represent early starts
in state-of-art improvement, it is our anticipation
that some lines of technological development will be
rapid in leading to practical utilization. It is
imperative that the city's health delivery system
plan now to take advantage of these advances.

Support Services Needs

Availability of computer services to handle such
activities as payroll, inventory, ambulance dispatch-
ing and routing, accounting, and other internal support activities, will speed system response and, in
the long run, save considerable public money.

Management Control Needs

As envisioned, the Health Services Administration
will become an _executive agency_ engaged heavily in

assessing health needs, establishing long-range
program goals, monitoring program progress, and
conducting cost-effectiveness analyses so as to establish rationally the most effective and least
costly ways of delivering health care (Figure 27).
The data base for a major health information system
would include health data on the entire population.
Thus, such a data system would play a prime role in
support of HSA, while providing as well an operational management information capability for HSC. Its
scope requires extensive computer facilitation.

Elaboration of the Information System Concept

To a significant degree, the delivery of health
care is inherently based on timely, accurate, and
useful information from many sources to support many
functions. Because these many functions are all
interrelated in the delivery of health care, there
is no way of solving the problems of orderly and
timely integration of operations without solving the
information-handling problem. No amount of opti-
mization nor improvement in facilities, patient
handling, personnel training, etc., will prove ultimately satisfactory if the basic underlying information system is not developed in parallel with other
such improvements. Today, and for many years, our
public health institutions have experienced a range
of information-handling difficulties running from
simple inefficiency to chaos (particularly in the
area of medical records).

Fortunately, automated information-processing
systems have undergone far-reaching advances in design and management control during the past few
years. Inputs may be processed from many sources
without the need for extensive, time-consuming, in-
accurate, laborious copying and transcribing of information. Outputs as information can be prepared
selectively for different purposes at the same time.
However, the capabilities of automated information-
processing systems cannot be realistically attained
without integrating the design and management controls
into the system concept. For example, if each institution (or even each borough!) has an independently
designed ADP system, there may be no way to eliminate
extensive manual and automated efforts in reporting
to higher levels for ambulance assignment, regional

LEVEL OF PRIMARY OPERATIONS	GENERAL INFORMATION SYSTEM FUNCTIONS	SPECIFIC INFORMATION SYSTEM FUNCTIONS		
HSA/INSTITUTES	CONCEPTS AND POLICY PLANNING & GOALS AUDIT & EVALUATION STANDARDS & CODES LICENSING & INSPECTIONS	PROGRESS REVIEW NEED ANALYSIS PROCEDURES SPECIFICATION		
HSC	INFORMATION SYSTEM DESIGN, STANDARDIZATION, AND INTEGRATION EQUIPMENT SPECIFICATIONS ADP PROGRAMS PROCEDURES FORMS CONTROL	MANAGEMENT CONTROL REIMBURSEMENTS FISCAL ANALYSIS CENTRAL LABORATORY SUPPORT		
REGIONAL OPERATIONS	MANAGEMENT CONTROL OF INFORMATION SYSTEM COMPONENTS LOCAL MANAGEMENT DATA & CONTROL SYSTEM COLLECTIONS & REIMBURSEMENTS MEDICAL RECORDS AMBULANCE RESOURCE CONTROLS		PATIENT ID NO. CENTRAL MEDICAL RECORDS STORE AMBULANCE ASSIGNMENT PER SESSION STAFF COORDINATION	
LOCAL INSTITUTIONS & PROGRAMS (HOSPITALS, AMB. CARE CENTERS ETC.)	INFORMATION FLOW--I/O REPORTING LOCAL PROCESSING (MASSIVE)			CURRENT MEDICAL RECORDS INSTITUTIONAL MANAGEMENT PHYS. INFORMATION STORE

Figure 27.   Information System Function Hierarchy

557

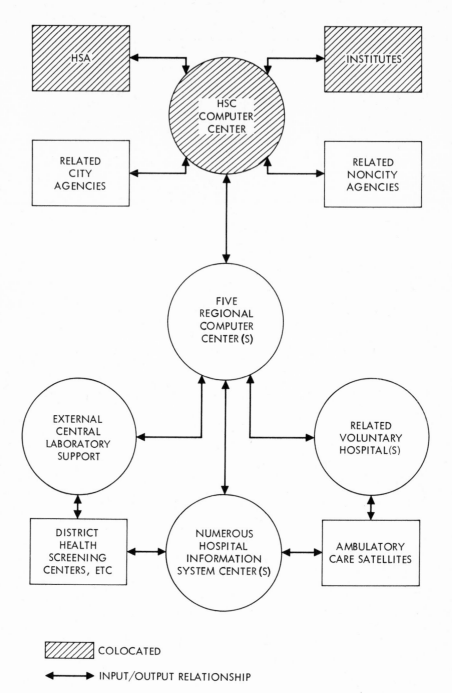

COLOCATED

INPUT/OUTPUT RELATIONSHIP

Figure 28.   Information System Concepts

resource control, central statistical analysis, reimbursement processing, etc. Briefly, long-range
planning for improved, evolutionary, and efficient
information systems can only be developed with integrated design and management controls. Figure 28
depicts the system concept and the functional hierarchy presently proposed.

CHAPTER **11** POLICIES FOR HSA

GUIDELINES FOR THE DEVELOPMENT OF HEALTH SCIENCES

The future goal for health services in New York City must be the development of a system--

- that is rationally financed as a coordinated network of facilities and services

- in which services are organized and available to meet the varying needs of all residents of a local community

- capable of maintaining high standards of medical excellence and the dignity of the individual

- sufficiently flexible to permit effective and economical utilization of available resources (facilities, manpower, and funds) as changes occur in demands for services.

With these goals in mind, it is also important to recognize that tremendous changes in the health field have occurred in the last 15 years and equally dramatic changes can be expected in the next 15 years, which will influence the future organization and financing of health services.

Greater emphasis will be placed on early diagnosis and health education activities and less emphasis on definitive medical treatment.

The average patient will be older and chronic illnesses will increase. Population increases in the under-15 age group will also dictate greater emphasis on comprehensive ambulatory care services.

In short, the hospital will become a medical
health service center, strongly oriented to providing
various levels of care needed especially by patients
with chronic illness, and caring to a much greater
extent than presently for patients who are up and
about and not admitted to bed-care facilities.

Changes in the types of patients and changes in
the role of the hospital in their care will also be
accompanied by changes in the methods of payment for
services, with increasingly greater proportions of
the service being financed through prepayment plans
and government (as adapted from the report of Mayor
Lindsay's Advisory Task Force on Medical Economics).

Progress toward these goals can be realized if
effective means are found to implement the following
recommendations.

Guideline No. 1

Taking advantage of the fiscal relief that will
be available from new state and federal legislation,
the city must move rapidly to coordinate existing
services, fill serious deficiencies that presently
exist, and generally strengthen and shape medical
care resources into a systematic network of services
that will meet the needs of the people, especially
in low-income neighborhoods. A substantial portion
of additional funds coming into the city should be
used to provide higher salaries for scarce professional, technical, and administrative personnel who
are essential to developing and carrying out health
programs.

Guideline No. 2

City policy should be aimed at strengthening the
partnership between municipal and voluntary hospitals
and medical schools in order to achieve systematic
and coordinated resources and to spread throughout
the entire hospital system the best medical talent
in the city.

Guideline No. 3

It is unwise to save money by arbitrary reductions in the operating budgets of agencies responsible for providing health services, although certain limited savings are possible from time to time. It is important to be aware that in the health field arbitrary budgetary cutbacks in any one year may actually increase the volume of service required and its costliness in subsequent years.

Guideline No. 4

Future opportunities to reduce expenditures can probably best be realized directly and indirectly through a carefully planned reduction of general hospital beds contemplated in the city's capital program. It is essential that the need for beds for short-term patients be conservatively estimated in the light of the following developments: the effect of a better coordinated hospital system; the expansion and improvement of ambulatory care, extended care and various non-institutional services; and the impact of new federal and state legislation.

Guideline No. 5

It will be necessary for the city, in its current review of the administrative and fiscal structure of government, to modify outmoded budgetary and personnel policies, practices, and procedures so that an adequate corps of health professionals, technicians, and middle management can be developed, and so that greater flexibility can be afforded to management at the operating level. (This guideline is necessary even with the provision of a Health Services Corporation.)

Guideline No. 6

High priority should be given to the completion of capital projects which are needed to replace existing obsolete facilities and which will provide comprehensive community mental health services and urgently needed additional beds and services for the care of long-term patients.

Guideline No. 7

Immediate steps must be taken to avoid future
costly delays in capital programs for hospitals and
related facilities, through appropriate changes in
the methods and procedures employed by the Department
of Public Works and other municipal agencies involved
in the planning and construction process. The possibility of making required changes in the legislation
governing this process must be explored.

Guideline No. 8

The city government, in cooperation with voluntary organizations concerned with the provision of
health services, should develop basic standards applicable to health services, which providers of services must meet to be eligible for payment with public funds.

Guideline No. 9

The city must plan continued support of the
broad application of the principle of cost reimbursement as the basis for payment for hospital and related
health services.

MAJOR RECOMMENDATIONS FOR ACTION

Recommendation No. 1

Steps should be taken to achieve the goal of a
coordinated hospital system in which every hospital
and related health facility serves all elements of
the population regardless of source of payment for
care and in accordance with community need.

At the present time, hospital and related health
services in New York City are provided by three major
types of institutions which serve different segments
of the population: voluntary institutions, which
generally serve all segments of the population; municipal facilities, which primarily serve the indigent;
the proprietary institutions, which treat patients who
pay for their care directly or through third-party
payers.

The fact that the beds and related services of
an institution are not equally available to all socio-
economic levels of the population results in inefficient utilization of facilities and scarce health
personnel and creates problems in the availability
of services. Selective admission practices of certain
voluntary and municipal hospitals which place primary
emphasis on "interesting teaching cases" also tend to
limit somewhat the institutions' availability to serve
all patients in the community.

Present and anticipated demands for services and
the relatively high utilization of voluntary hospitals
necessitate the continued operation of municipal facilities which have sufficient flexibility, administratively and otherwise, to serve all elements of the
population in accordance with community need.

Various approaches for achieving this objective
are available to the city. They will require the
development of new policies and, in some instances,
the extension or modification of policies for which
there is precedent. In any event, it is clear that
the city cannot abdicate its basic responsibility for
maintaining high standards of care in all institutions
which are the recipients of tax funds.

Long-range planning assumes that the City of
New York will (a) contract with strong voluntary
teaching hospitals or medical schools for the total
operation of certain municipal institutions; (b) turn
certain of the municipal facilities over to, or lease
them to, voluntary nonprofit institutions for the care
of patients of all economic groups; (c) open the municipal institutions to patients of all socio-economic
levels in accordance with community need, using every
precaution to maintain professional standards and safeguard quality of care; (d) develop new administrative
structure for the operation of those remaining hospitals and other health facilities which would continue to be the direct management responsibility of
the city; and (3) devise an over-all system of public
control applicable to all health institutions.

Recommendation No. 2

The general hospital should be the core facility
for medical and related health services for a community, and services should be increasingly hospital

related. Most hospitals should be capable of providing a broad range of high-quality services, including ambulatory care and extended care, either
within their own walls or through formal affiliation
or close working relationship with other institutions.

It is not always feasible or desirable for every
hospital to provide a complete range of services. However, to the extent possible "medical service centers"
should be developed providing a broad spectrum of ser-
vices--to be progressive patient care hospitals.

This coordinated pattern of facilities and services should care for both bed patients and ambulatory
patients. Included should be a hospital offering
varying levels of care for the short-term patient--
an intensive care unit for the critically ill patients,
a self-care unit for the ambulatory patient who can
walk to the cafeteria or X-ray department, and an
intermediate care unit--as well as out-patient and
emergency care units. The facilities should also include an extended care unit for patients who can be
moved to less costly accommodations after a few days
of hospitalization, a long-term care unit (on- or
off-site) for the patient requiring prolonged institutional care, and organized home care services.

Additional units should include a health service
center containing offices for both official and voluntary agencies, a community mental health program,
and facilities for private physicians' offices, including group practice.

The development of such "medical service centers"
would result in better utilization of scarce professional and technical personnel and provide services
appropriate to the patient's need at any given time.

In order to carry out this recommendation:

(1) Existing free-standing municipal long-term
care facilities should be affiliated with an institution that can provide strong medical supervision.

(2) Any long-term care facility which the city
constructs should be an integral part of a general
hospital complex or affiliated therewith.

(3) All municipal hospitals should have extended
care units to reduce the need for general hospital beds.

(4) Home care programs based at municipal general
hospitals should be expanded to the extent possible
without sacrificing the scope or quality of services
provided.

(5) The city should develop and enforce policies
and procedures designed to assure early planning for
the discharge or transfer of patients from acute hospital beds to other appropriate and available facilities
and services.

Recommendation No. 3

Certain highly specialized health services and
health related activities should be centralized in a
limited number of hospitals which are capable of providing high volume and quality care.

Those services which could be provided on a regional basis include open-heart surgery, neurosurgery,
radiation therapy, burn centers, premature newborn
centers, and amputee services.

Certain specialty training programs should also
be limited to a select number of institutions. There
should also be centralization of certain other service activities which can benefit from economies of
scale and computerized techniques.

In order to carry out this recommendation:

(1) The city should develop methods and procedures for continuing review of its programs in relation to those of affiliated voluntary hospitals to
assure that highly specialized services which often
require expensive equipment and specially trained
personnel are used to capacity and not unnecessarily
duplicated. Arrangements should be made for referral
or transfer of patients to institutions having appropriate services which meet acceptable standards.

(2) Careful consideration should be given to
ways of having certain laboratory procedures performed
on a centralized basis for all municipal hospitals in

a borough or the city as a whole, with services available on a seven-day-a-week basis. Voluntary hospitals
should also be permitted to purchase these centralized
services.

Recommendation No. 4

Every general hospital should ultimately have a
capacity of at least 350 beds.

A system having hospitals of this minimum size is
required to achieve high quality services at a reasonable cost to the community.

In order to carry out this recommendation, the
city should give high priority to the replacement,
conversion, movement, or closing of hospitals which
are below this desired size.

Recommendation No. 5

Facilities should be designed to permit flexibility
of use to meet continuing change which can be expected
in the medical care field.

The large-scale modernization and replacement
needs of hospitals in New York City offer the opportunity to incorporate maximum flexibility in the design of facilities.

General hospital nursing units should be sufficiently flexible to permit their conversion for the
care of long-term patients, if necessary to meet the
demand for such services. This means, for example,
that no patient rooms should be constructed to accommodate more than four beds or without toilet facilities. The initial location of supporting services
and out-patient services should be such that they can
be readily altered if necessary to meet changes in
demand.

Recommendation No. 6

High priority should be placed on the development
of hospital-based or hospital-related diagnostic
screening and ambulatory care centers, providing appropriate services at the local community level.

The program should emphasize patient-centered
medical care and related health services concerned
with the promotion of the physical and mental health
of the individual, and the early detection, diagnosis,
and treatment of disease. Programs must be related
to institutional services in a manner which will assure availability of in-patient services when required, continuity of care, and highly specialized
diagnostic and treatment services as needed.

Diagnostic screening and ambulatory care centers
should be conveniently available to the populations
served, with priority given to local communities
having large concentrations of economically disadvantaged persons. Such centers offer the potential for
reducing utilization of more costly general hospital
in-patient services.

In order to carry out this recommendation:

(1) There should be gradual integration at the
local community level (hopefully within the structure
of the Health Services Corporation) of the services,
staffs, and facilities of the Department of Hospitals,
Health, Mental Health, and medical welfare to avoid
the continued proliferation of specialized clinic
services, which is wasteful of resources and results
in uncoordinated delivery of medical and related services.

(2) Ambulatory care centers should be established
at all municipal and voluntary hospitals. Consideration should also be given to establishing free-
standing ambulatory care centers conveniently located to the population served and providing comprehensive family-centered care. These should be instituted on a selective basis, in certain economically
depressed areas, as dictated by demand and need. Such
centers should be related to municipal and to strong
voluntary hospitals which are community oriented.
Patients should be referred to the hospital for certain specialized services and in-patient care as
required.

The city should accordingly designate certain
existing suitable health centers in which to develop
comprehensive ambulatory care programs.

Recommendation No. 7

There should be centralized capability in the
Health Services Administration to achieve improved
coordination of the efforts of various city agencies
and voluntary institutions in economic analysis and
planning and programming.

The need to establish a strong mechanism to
achieve this end is highlighted by the magnitude
of the projected capital program for hospital and
related health facilities. The development of these
projects not only involves the various municipal
agencies but also the affiliated voluntary institutions. The need to avoid costly delays in program
planning and design and eventual construction of
facilities is evident.

Effective policy and decision making at a centralized level is also necessary to help assure coordinated delivery of services in the community.

There should also be improved coordination of
planning of all health services at the community
level (presumably, via the Health Services Corporation).

RECOMMENDED POLICIES

Based upon the findings and recommendations of
the present study, upon the findings of the Mayor's
Task Force on Medical Economics, upon HSA's internal
planning efforts, and upon other formal recommendations as provided by various commissions and study
groups, the following operational policies are suggested for the HSA. These recommendations are offered in response to the Mayor's charge to the present Commission. It will be evident that each policy
implies a subset of long-range objectives. The latter
will be set forth in subsequent discussion.

Policy No. 1

(1) For planning and development purposes, it
should be a policy of the HSA to visualize, formulate,
and promulgate a full-spectrum system of medical delivery for the citizens of New York City.

The hospital is an established, familiar element
of American institutional form. It is now and has been
for decades a center of localized medical practice,
recognized as such by both medical professionals and
citizens at large. Clearly, this established image
and role of the hospital will continue, though ab-
sorbing evolutionary change. On the other hand, it
is increasingly evident that the traditional hospital
as a single institutional form cannot be all things
to all people in the complex urban communities of the
decades before us. Additional institutional forms
are rapidly evolving for specialized aspects of the
delivery of medical care. Within one or two decades
these additional forms will range alongside that of
the traditional hospital and will work with the latter to form a more complete array of specialized delivery facilities for the comprehensive care of the
population.

While these forms may evolve with considerable
variation, it will be sufficient here to group them
into four categories. First, those that have to do
with prevention, diagnostic screening and early detection, health education, and medical referral.
Included in this group will be the traditional forms
of public health including school health, environmental health, and community health. In short, the
emphasis in such programs and facilities will be upon
the maintenance of health, the prevention of disease,
and the alleviation of social-environmental factors
leading to disease, rather than upon the treatment
of disease.

A second major category may be characterized as
that of ambulatory care. Here the established locale
of effort has been in the familiar hospital setting
in the forms of the out-patient departments and the
emergency rooms. While it is anticipated that all
general hospitals could and should continue improved
forms of the traditional OPD and emergency room activities, it is also anticipated and planned that
there be free-standing ambulatory care centers located
at strategic places in large, dense urban communities.
Here medical delivery will take place in the form of
routine and specialized clinic functions which together and in an integrated fashion will bring comprehensive treatment to the community where it is needed.

There is every reason to believe that the ambulatory
care center of the near future will be quite as significant in the array of medical delivery facilities
as has been the traditional hospital historically.
Organized, localized ambulatory care will not only
raise the general health of the community but will
cut down on the number of patients entering a general
hospital for clinic care.

The third institutional category is, of course,
the general hospital. Even here, however, evolutionary change is already evident and will be planned
more particularly for realization in the near future.
In this regard, it is now evident that each general
hospital should have, in addition to its intensive
care wards, units, and clinics, an extended care unit
into which patients are moved and where they are cared
for once they have passed through a phase of intensive
care in traditional hospital functions. Also, it will
be increasingly desirable that each hospital develop
or expand home care (and foster-home care) programs
in which long-term care patients needing minimal medical attention may return to the community and be seen
only occasionally by members of the hospital staff.

Finally, a fourth institutional category is directed to chronic, long-term care. For this category
of facility, comprehensive programs are needed for
facilities development, project development, staff
development, and standards development so that we may
be assured of uniformly high standards of medical
care delivery to those who require chronic, long-term
care. These facilities should be affiliated with
general hospitals.

In summary, the full-spectrum system of medical
care delivery visualized builds upon this basic lin-
ear model of: prevention, ambulatory treatment,
in-patient treatment, chronic long-term care. These
institutional forms must, of course, be properly related to other specialized institutions, independent
medical practice, and the activities of the allied
health professions and agencies in the community.
Further, it will not be necessary to view them as
geographically separate since they may, in a given
instance, occur all in a single health center complex,
or in part, in a community service center.

Policy No. 2

It should be the policy of the HSA to integrate
and consolidate in reasonable and productive ways the
historically separate, if not sometimes competitive,
urban systems of health care delivery in the City of
New York.

These systems have been typified by the administrative separation of the Department of Hospitals,
the Department of Health, the Community Mental Health
Board, medical welfare, the reimbursement mechanisms
within the Welfare Department, and finally the Office
of the City Medical Examiner.

The new Health Services Administration has been
chartered and directed to bring about appropriate and
effective integration and consolidation of these traditionally separate functions so as to end duplication,
overlapping, competitive programs, and sometimes the
effect of little or no attention to programs for which
responsibility has been poorly defined.

It will be appropriate, however, to continue the
vital roles of the three official boards involved in
health delivery: first of all, the Board of Health,
for its indispensable services as the health legislation body for the City of New York; secondly, the
Board of Hospitals with respect to its key function
in the promulgation of standards in our health institutions; and finally, the Community Mental Health
Board for its vital role in policy guidance and performance standards in the field of mental health.

It is anticipated that there will be gradual
and necessary change in the evolutionary roles of
the Commissioners of Health, Hospitals, and Mental
Health. These changes will come about as the over-
all system of health care delivery becomes
operational.

It is clear that in the case of the Commissioner
of Hospitals this office will become increasingly
concerned with the tremendous responsibilities and
complexities of health facilities administration
throughout the City of New York. On the other hand,
it is equally clear that the Commissioner of Health

will become increasingly concerned with, and specialized in the development and promulgation of, city-wide
programs in environmental health, prevention, and
professional standards.

Policy No. 3

It should be the policy of the HSA gradually but
effectively to disengage the City of New York from its
historical but unnecessary and inappropriate role in
the direct management of health care delivery support
activities, particularly those that are concerned with
construction, renovation, supply, institutional administration, and operational budgeting.

Far more effective administrational forms and
vehicles are possible and proven for the conduct of
such responsibilities. Once city officials and departments with responsibility for health care delivery
are freed from the traditional problems associated
with the above support responsibilities, it will be
possible for these officials and departments to exercise far more effective attention in the area of long-
range program planning and public accountability.

Policy No. 4

It should be the policy of the HSA to make functional throughout the city an objectives-oriented
system of health care delivery operations for the entire health system.

This policy makes evident recognition of a system-
wide need for the development and pursuit of health
objectives of the kind that are established in the
course of comprehensive program planning and program
budgeting. In the early years of this planning period,
the HSA will be heavily engaged in the development,
definition, clarification, and application of long-
range program planning of health activities throughout
the communities of the city. Necessarily, these objectives will cut across all traditional lines of outmoded organization, whether official (that is, part
of the government), voluntary, or proprietary. The
purpose of program planning is to achieve a rational,

integrated, comprehensive, and priority-ordered assignment of resources against similarly derived objectives. As program planning begins to take concrete
form, it will be possible to translate the health budgets of the city into appropriate program format so
that no longer will health administration be subject
to outmoded line-item budgeting.

Policy No. 5

It follows from policies cited above that the
HSA should develop and promulgate major planned programs having to do with prevention, early detection
and treatment, ambulatory care, intensive clinical
care, extended care, and chronic care, each comparable in emphasis to the present long-standing traditional institutional practices of the general
hospital.

Here a major function will be that of relating
the capabilities and resources and goals of all the
health institutions of the city.

Policy No. 6

It should be the policy of the HSA to encourage
the decline and ultimate removal of the impeding effects of professional schisms in health sciences and
delivery as seen in the separate, sometimes unrelat-
able approaches of subdisciplines in the health sciences and allied health disciplines.

Fresh approaches should be encouraged to bring
about the teaming of disciplines so that comprehensive
care can in fact be delivered both in the hospital and
in the community. Through joint program planning and
implementation, encouragement should be given to more
effective teaming of the physician, the psychiatrist,
the nurse, the social worker, the various social
scientists, technicians, and others, all of whom are
engaged in the ultimate delivery of health care to
our citizens.

Policy No. 7

It should be the policy of the HSA to bring about a sound, effective, and accountable system of control and operation for all public funds in health care operations.

It is evident that the cost of medical care will continue to rise and equally evident that the role of government--federal, state and local--will become increasingly prominent in providing funds to meet this increasing cost. Significant new health legislation has already brought about large increases in funds available for health care. The HSA is fully aware of mounting need to build effective capabilities for control and public accountability so that there will be realized on behalf of the citizens a full measure of health care delivery for public funds expended.

Policy No. 8

It should be the policy of the HSA to bring about the regionalization of public health care delivery through localized administration and activity.

This concept calls for reduction in the role of central administration, historic to the city's health activities, and the development of locally planned, administered, and implemented care within the community.

Under this policy, the HSA should seek to integrate delivery services within the given communities. Localized planning and implementation should seek to identify the reasonable and workable goals for existing institutions and activities as well as to bring about new institutional forms and activities not now present in such communities.

This policy calls for a balance of service distribution in the community, so that duplication and overlap is minimized and optimum utilization of resources available to the community is realized.

Where necessary, diagnostic screening and ambulatory care facilities should be developed geographically separate from hospitals, though in each instance they will be affiliated with appropriate hospital centers. In those regions of the city where community service centers are to be developed, the diagnostic screening and ambulatory care facilities should be planned and installed as part of those centers.

When a point is reached where each borough of the city contains virtually all the necessary prevention and treatment facilities necessary to its citizens, a system of patient registration, identification, and referral should be established. (This vital system of patient flow control may be initiated in one, two, or three boroughs at the outset, rather than city-wide.)

At the minimum, each borough of the city should be associated with one or more major medical schools, one or more major teaching hospitals, one or more voluntary hospitals, community health centers and satellites, various voluntary and proprietary hospitals and nursing homes, and other appropriate municipal health facilities. Within the communities of the borough, there should be located diagnostic screening centers (whether fixed or mobile), ambulatory care facilities, and facilities for intensive in-patient clinical treatment, extended care, home care, and chronic care, together with appropriate child health and mental health facilities. Also, there should be appropriate, planned coordination with special services such as the visiting nursing function and with special city-wide programs of which narcotics and venereal disease control are examples.

Each borough should be directed by a regional executive director with appropriate responsibilities, authorities, support functions, and staff. These organizations would constitute the line "arms" of the Health Services Corporation.

Policy No. 9

It should be the policy of the HSA to develop an "optimum formula" for the development, change in, and application of, health care services at the regional level and within the communities of the city.

This optimum formula must, itself, be developed through study, planning, and adjustment over a period

of years. Among other factors it must reflect those
of geographical distribution, of demography, of resource location, and of health need patterns, so
that realistic decisions may be made as required for
the development, renovation, or other treatment of
facilities and for programs in these communities, as
well as for their evolutionary control.

This policy calls for the development of predic-
tive measures that have to do with the need for given
numbers of general care medical beds per unit of population, as well as beds for extended care and chronic
care. It calls for determination of the number and
size of general hospitals and their composition and
function in each community. It will require determination of the number and distribution of both hospital-
attached and satellite ambulatory care facilities, and
for the number and distribution of diagnostic screening
capabilities. It will require determination of the
number and kinds of health workers per unit of population required in each community.

The proposed Health Careers and Sciences Institutes, under HSA, will be a natural future locus of such
effort.

Much progress has already been made by the HSA
in developing appropriate data base information for
the determination of factors such as those indicated
above. Until such improved determinations are available, and until an optimum formula for health care
service application is perfected, the HSA must continue to follow the base of current planning guidance.

Policy No. 10

It should be the policy of the HSA to assure an
effective linkage between research advances and improved patient care by establishing a continuing relationship among the research and teaching environments of the medical centers, the patient care activities involving the community hospital, and practicing physicians.

The impact of research advances on the development of high-quality patient care has typically been
most direct in the university medical centers or other
medical centers which combine extensive research,

teaching, and patient care activities. The primary
benefits of this interrelationship, however, have
often been confined to the medical center itself and
its affiliated hospitals. A basic premise of this
policy is the desirability of extending this productive interrelationship to additional hospitals and
to practicing physicians and affiliated institutions
through the establishment of cooperative arrangements.

Policy No. 11

It should be the policy of HSA to formulate,
stimulate, and (if necessary) itself carry out innovative training programs to overcome the fundamental
problems of personnel shortage in the professional,
semi-professional, and support categories of health
manpower.

In most categories of health manpower, the City
of New York has labored under the constraints of
severe shortages for decades. It is evident, for
example, that presently existing programs for the
training and supply of nurses have failed to produce
the necessary number in the city. It is evident, as
well, that the mounting needs of medical specialization and health care delivery will require ever-
increasing concentrations of health support manpower
per unit of population. Even in the presence of a
reasonable achievement of current objectives to improve the physical and other working circumstances
of health professionals and support personnel, it is
clear that the normal means of training and provision
will fall short of manpower requirements.

Policy No. 12

It should be the policy of the HSA to effect the
use of support technologies to every reasonable and
feasible extent in realizing its objectives for improved health care delivery.

In this regard the HSA should seek to develop
regionally oriented but city-wide information processing capability which will ultimately make available
to salaried staff or private physicians, as appropriate,
medical records and other patient information. (In

turn, this capability will require development of a
patient registration system.) As possible, the HSA
should also bring about regionally centralized or
city centralized laboratory support for public health
care functions.

Policy No. 13

It should be the policy of HSA to provide comprehensive strengthening of traditional programs of
environmental health.

To do so will require: (a) improved operational
and long-range planning involving city, region, state,
and federal agencies; (b) specified working relationships and programs involving (lateral) city agencies
(air pollution, sanitation, etc.); (c) improved
funding; and (d) improved and expanded professional
manning. While this improved effort should be planned,
developed, and led by the Department of Health, HSA
per se becomes a prime vehicle for its coordination
and execution.

Policy No. 14

Finally, it should be the operating policy of
the HSA to bring about realization of sufficiently
improved health care delivery that New York City will
not only achieve appropriate delivery for funds
expended but will achieve an outstanding rank in the
nation and in the world for the delivery of health
care to its citizens.

APPENDIXES

APPENDIX A

Persons Interviewed

Again, the staff wishes to acknowledge its
deep indebtedness to the hundreds of persons
contributing their personal and professional
time to this study. It is our regret that
all cannot be cited here; only the names of
those persons participating in extensive
scheduled interviews are shown.

Abeles, Hans, M.D., Medical Director, Department of
        Corrections
Accettola, Albert B., M.D., President, Physicians
        Guild
Achs, Ruth, M.D., Director, Pediatrics, OPD, Kings
        County Hospital
Adamek, Kenneth F., Administrator, Misericordia
        Hospital
Adams, Freda, Pediatric Unit Manager, Lincoln Hospital
Adams, Grant, Executive Director, United Hospital Fund
Adelman, William, Executive Director, Beth Abraham
        Hospital
Adler, Sam, Director of Purchase, New York City
Alexander, Raymond, Assistant Commissioner of Health,
        Department of Health
Altman, Robert, Health Careers Center, City University
        of New York
Anderson, George, M.D., Director of OPD, Cumberland
        Hospital
Baehr, George, M.D., Vice President, HIP
Baglio, Peter, Administrator, Maimonides Hospital
Bard, John, M.D., Director of ER, Cumberland Hospital
Baron, Carl, M.D., President of the Board of Directors,
        Lefferts General Hospital
Benson, Murray, M.D., Home Care Medical Coordinator,
        Lincoln Hospital
Benza, Louis C., Coordinator of Community Services,
        Borough of the Bronx
Bergen, Stanley S., M.D., Director of Medicine,
        Cumberland Hospital
Bernstein, Leslie, M.D., OPD, Lincoln Hospital

Binkert, Alvin J., Executive Vice President,
        Presbyterian Hospital
Blatt, Sylvia, Bureau of Labs., Riverside Health
        Center, Manhattan
Brady, John J., Assistant Commissioner, Department
        of Hospitals
Brayton, Robert, M.D., Night Administrator, Bellevue
        Hospital
Brightman, Jay, M.D., Director of Medicaid, State
        Dept. of Health
Brooks, Oretha, Director, Community Planning Boards,
        Manhattan
Brown, Howard, J., M.D., Administrator, Health
        Services Administration
Brudno, Joseph J., Affiliation Administrator, Director,
        OPD/ER, Elmhurst Hospital
Buckingham, Mr., Liaison Administrator, University
        Hospital
Burkley, John, Office of Public Information, HEW
Burnett, Graham, Administrative Assistant, Harlem
        Hospital
Butzel, John E., Administrative Resident, Brooklyn
        Hospital
Bykofsky, Irving R., Asst. to the Borough President,
        Brooklyn
Carver, Mrs. Gerald, Community Planning Area Chairman,
        Richmond County
Cattell, Stuart, Director Health Res., Community Coun-
        cil of Greater New York
Cerbone, Ermelinda R., R. N., Executive Director,
        Bronx Eye & Ear Infirmary
Cherkasky, Martin, M.D., Director, Montifiore Medical
        Center
Cohen, Wilbur, Under Secretary, HEW
Collica, Carl, Head of the Radioisotope Laboratory,
        Fordham Hospital
Cooper, Valerie, Staff Associate, Hospital Visiting
        Committee, U.H.F.
Corn, R., Director of Data Processing, Downstate
        Medical Center
Corrigan, John, Assistant Dep. Dir., New York State
        Budget Department
Costa, Marjorie, Public Health Ed. Dir., Bedford
        Health Center
Costello, Timothy, Ph.D., Deputy Mayor, City
        Administrator
Craig, Maude, Mrs., Director of Research, New York
        City Youth Board
Crowley, Miss, National League for Nursing

Cugliani, Anne, Research, Health Population Survey
Daily, Mrs., Director of Nursing Services and Director
        of School of Nursing, Harlem Hospital
Danel, John J., M.D., Assistant Visiting Physician,
        Queens General Hospital
Deliyanidis, T., M.D., Assistant Hospital Administrator,
        Metropolitan Hospital
Densen, Paul, D. Sc., Deputy Administrator, HSA,
        Deputy Commissioner, Dept. of Health
Derzon, Robert, First Deputy Commissioner, Dept. of
        Hospitals
Diamond, Oscar K., M.D., Director, Manhattan State
        Hospital
DiGiacomo, Roberta, R.N., Supervisor, OPD, Bellevue
        Hospital
Dimendberg, David, Administrator, Morrisania Hospital
Dixon, Alan, Bureau of Health Economics, State Dept.
        of Soc. Welfare
Dormstader, Henry, External Auditor, Flower & Fifth
        Avenue Hospital
Dryer, John, Head X-ray Technician, Lincoln Hospital
Dunphy, George J., Acting Commissioner, Bellevue
        Hospital
Durrel, Martin J., Senior Administrative Assistant,
        Elmhurst Hospital
Eagle, J. Frederick, M.D., Dean, New York Medical
        College
Einhorn, Arnold, M.D., Chief of Pediatrics, Lincoln
        Hospital
Elinson, Jack, Ph.D., School of Pub. Health & Adm.,
        Columbia University
Elliott, Donald, Chairman, City Planning Commission
Enoch, Grace, Personnel Officer, Ewing Hospital
Erhardt, Karl, M.D., Director, Records and Statistics,
        Dept. of Health
Fahey, Pauline, Nursing Services, American Nurses
        Association
Feinstein, Arnold, Administrator, Interborough Gen.
        Osteopathic Hosp. & Nursing Home
Feldman, Carolyn, Director OPD, Greenpoint Hospital
Finnis, Mary, R.N., Assistant Director, New York
        State Nursing Association
Fischer, Alex, Controller, Coney Island Hospital
Fitzpatrick, Monsignor, Director, Health Services,
        Catholic Archdiocese of Brooklyn
Flynn, Arthur, Attorney, Metro. New York Nursing
        Homes Association
Ford, Joanne, R.N., St. Vincent's Hospital

Frank, Marjorie H., Ass't.to the Commissioner, Comm.
        Ment. Health Board
Freeman, M., M.D., Medical Director, Gouverneur
        Ambulatory Care District
Freeney, Arthur, Administrative Assistant, ER, Queens
        Hospital Center
Freilich, Herbert, M.D., Administrator, Elmhurst
        Hospital
Freiwirth, Martin, Hospital Administrator, Parkway
        Hospital
Gabor, George, M.D., Emergency Room, Lincoln Hospital
Galaid, Ruth, Editor of "Welfare in Review," HEW
Gambuti, Gary, Assistant Vice President, Roosevelt
        Hospital
Garfield, Sidney, M.D., Vice President, Kaiser Klan
Gaynor, Florence, R.N., Pediatric Nursing Coordinator,
        Lincoln Hospital
Gentile, Lupe, R.N., Nursing Supervisor, Metropolitan
        Hospital
Gibson, Charles R., Comptroller, Interborough Gen.
        Osteopathic Hosp. & Nursing Home
Glazier, Roy, Statistics, Com. Council of Greater
        New York
Goldberg, M.J., M.D., Director of Physical Medicine,
        Cumberland Hospital
Goldstein, Arnold H., Affiliation Administrator,
        Morrisania Hospital
Goldstein, M.D., New York Medical College
Gollance, Harvey, M.D., Deputy Commissioner, Depart-
        ment of Hospitals
Goodkin, Rhonda, Consultant, City Planning Commission
Gottfried, Oscar, Executive Secretary, Association of
        Private Hospitals, Inc.
Granger, Carroll R., Controller, Brooklyn Hospital
Gristina, J., M.D., Head of Physical Medicine, Fordham
        Hospital
Grogan, Miss, Secretary to Head of Services Bureau, HUD
Grossman, David A., Assistant Director of the Budget,
        Bureau of the Budget
Grun, Gerta, R.N., Director of Nurses, Aron Manor
        Nursing Home
Gutstein, Sidney, M.D., Screening, OPD, Lincoln
        Hospital
Haldeman, Jack C., M.D., President, Hospital Review
        and Planning Council of Southern New York
Hancock, Millicent, R.N., Director of Nursing, Flower
        & Fifth Avenue Hospital
Hankin, Henrietta, Executive Director, Queensboro
        Council for Social Welfare

Harmon, Alexander, Executive Vice President, Brooklyn
        Hospital
Harris, Robert, Director, Bureau of Nursing Homes
        Companies, State Dept. of Health
Harrison, Norman B., Assistant Administrator,
        Cumberland Hospital
Hastall, Frank, Jr., Community Mental Health Board
Haughton, James, M.D., First Deputy Administrator,
        Health Services Administration
Hayes, Frederick O'R., Director of the Budget, City
        of New York
Hayes, John, Associate Director of Public Relations,
        Interfaith Hospital
Heard, Gordon, Acting Administrator, Manhattan Veterans
        Administration Hospital
Henroit, Sara, Welfare Administration Documents, HEW
Hernandez, Miss, Director of Nursing, Gouverneur
        Ambulatory Care District
Heroy, Charles, R.N., Director of Nursing, Ewing
        Hospital
Herter, Frederic P., M.D., Director of Surgery,
        Delafield Hospital
Hoberman, Soloman, Personnel Director, City of New
        York
Holmes, Margaret, Prof., Director, School of Nursing,
        Hunter College
Horowitz, Jacob, M.D., Director, Ambulatory Unit,
        Harlem Hospital
Howe, Suzanne, M.D., Assistant Director, OPD/ER,
        Queens Hospital Center
Hult, Eugene E., Commissioner Public Works, New York
        City
Ianconi, Anthony, Admin. Ass't., Admitting and Emer-
        gency, Kings County Hospital
Igoe, Margaret, R.N., Director of Nursing, Bronx
        Municipal Hospital
Jacob, Eloise, Clerical, Delafield Hospital
Jenkins, Alva, M.D., Director of Home Care, Harlem
        Hospital
Johnson, David, Medical Care Planning, Regional
        Planning Association
Jorgensen, Lawrence R., Assistant Administrator,
        Harlem Hospital
Kafka, Malcom, Assistant Administrator, Clinical
        Services, Elmhurst Hospital
Kahan, Philip, J., M.D., Administrator, Queens Hos-
        pital Center
Kahn, Ivan, M.D., OPD, Lincoln Hospital

Kail, David, D.D.S., Assistant Hospital Administrator,
        Kings County Hospital
Kanof, Abram, M.D., Acting Chairman, Ped. Div.,
        Downstate Medical Center
Kapald, Harry, Fiscal Branch, Department of Welfare
Kaplan, Francis, Information Officer, Bureau of
        Family Services, HEW
Kara, Evelyn, R.N., Director of Nurses, Beth Abraham
        Hospital
Karabaich, Nicholas, Assistant Hospital Administrator,
        Metropolitan Hospital
Karassik, Irwin, Exec. Dir., Met. New York Nursing
        Home Association
Katzell, Kitty, Evaluation Services, National League
        for Nursing
Kaufman, William, M.D., State Department of Health
Kavaler, Florence, M.D., Narcotics Directory
Kelsky, Morris, Assistant Hospital Administrator,
        Kings County Hospital
Kerst, Richard N., Ass't. V.P., Ass't. Secr.-Treas.,
        Presbyterian Hospital
Kesner, Bernard, Hospital Administrator, Morrisania
        Hospital
Kinoy, Susan, Research, Com. Council of Greater
        New York
Kinsella, Cynthia, Ed.D., Director of Nursing, Dir.
        of Sch. of Nursing, Bellevue Hospital
Klein, Irving F., M.D., Administrator, Sea View
        Hospital and Home
Klem, Margaret, (former) Coordinator, Union Health
        Centers
Koblenz, Stuart, M.D., Ass't. Hosp. Administrator
        Bronx Municipal Hospital
Koretsky, Jack, Administrator OPD and ER, Mt. Sinai
        Hospital
Kramer, Edward, Attorney, Metro. New York Nursing
        Home Association
Krause, Mr., Welfare Department, Bellevue Hospital
Krauss, E. M., Director of Medical Records, Bellevue
        Hospital
Kreiger, Lewis, Personnel Director, Bellevue Hospital
Kresky, Beatrice G., M.D., Hosp. Rev. & Plng. Council
Kuo, Nicetas, M.D., Health Officer, Queens County
Kuo, Richard, Research Analyst, Urb. Med. Econ. Res.
        Project
Kushnereff, Tatjana, M.D., Director, OPD, Lincoln
        Hospital
Lamattina, Silvio R., Hospital Administrator,
        Westchester Square Hospital

Lamb, Edmund, Comptroller, Flower & Fifth Avenue
        Hospital & New York Medical College
LeCaille, Rupert, M.D., Assistant Director, ER,
        Greenpoint Hospital
Lerner, Ray, Senior Research Associate, Hosp. Review
        and Planning Council
Levine, Jacob, Special Consultant, HSA (Vice President,
        Yeshiva University)
Leviss, Sidney, Deputy President, Borough of Queens
Leiman, Joan, Bureau of the Budget
Lieberman, Bernard, Administrator, Aron Manor Nursing
        Home
Light, Harold, Administrator, Gouverneur Ambulatory
        Care District
Lindsay, John V., Mayor
Liu, Judy, R.N., Cornell Medical Center
Louchleim, Joseph, Deputy Commissioner, State Dept.
        of Social Welfare
Lowenthal, Milton, M.D., Dir., Center for Chronic
        Disease, Coler Hospital
Lukashode, Herbert, Spec. Ass't. to the Director,
        Montifiore Hospital Center
Lyden, G. Collins, Ass't. Director, Narcotics Ed.,
        State Narcotics Commission
Malet, Sidney, M.D., Medical Dir., Interborough Gen.
        Osteopathic Hosp. & Nursing Home
Mann, Joseph B., Administrator, Deputy Ass't. Commis-
        sioner, Cumberland Hospital
Marchi, Ferdinand C., Director, Community Plng. Boards,
        Richmond
Marion, Charles G., Administrator, Jamaica Hospital
Markowitz, Robert, Assistant Director, Brooklyn Hospital
Marley, William, Assistant Director, Brownsville
        Community Council
Marner, Sol, State Auditor, State Dept. of Social
        Welfare
Martin, Charles, Assistant Administrator, Bellevue
        Hospital
Mason, Dennis, Assistant Administrator, OPD, Queens
        Hospital Center
Matthew, Carol, Director of Social Services, Inter-
        faith Hospital
Matthew, Thomas W., M.D., Executive Director, Inter-
        faith Hospital
Maynard, Edwin P., Ph.D., Director of Development,
        Brooklyn Hospital
McCarthy, Frank J., Liaison and Affiliation Adminis-
        trator, Coney Island Hospital

McFadden, Grace, Director of Public Health Nursing,
          Department of Health
McGlove, William, State Department of OEO
MacInnes, Helen, R.N., Supervisor Nursing, Ped. & OPD,
          Morrisania Hospital
McLaughlin, Mary, M.D., Assistant Commissioner, Dept.
          of Health
McLemore, Louise, Ass't. Dir., Ambulatory Care Services,
          Harlem Hospital
Meehan, Patricia, R.N., New York University Hospital
Mereny, L., M.D., Queens Hospital Center
Merritt, H. Houston, M.D., Dean, Faculty of Medicine,
          College of P & S, Columbia
Messeloff, Charles, M.D., Medical Director, Beth
          Abraham Hospital
Meyer, Harry, Director of Institutional Facilities, HSA
Michelen, Nasry, M.D., Administrator, Assistant
          Commissioner, Lincoln Hospital
Minges, Irma, Com. on Aging, Com. Council of Greater
          New York
Moore, Doris E., Chief Medical Records Librarian,
          Harlem Hospital
Morgan, F. Hayden, Research Admin. Vice Pres., Flower
          & Fifth Avenue Hospital
Morris, Norman, M.D., Director, ER, Greenpoint Hospital
Morton, Annette F., Director, Community Planning Boards,
          Bronx
Mueller, John F., M.D., Chief of Medicine, Brooklyn
          Hospital
Mugge, M.D., Social Statistics, Bureau of Family
          Services, HEW
Muller, M.D., New York Medical College
Murtha, Rena, R.N., Nurse in Charge of ER, Elmhurst
          Hospital
Muscatine, Mrs., Director, School of Nursing, Beth
          Israel Hospital
Nadell, Bernard B., M.D., Hospital Administrator-
          Medical, Coler Hospital
Nauen, Richard, M.D., Assoc. Dir., Cntr. for Chronic
          Diseases, Ch., Community Med., Coler Hospital
Nealy, Miss, Director of Nursing, Director of School
          of Nursing, Harlem Hospital
Nelson, Frieda, Records and Statistics, Department of
          Health
Nieto, Eugene J., Administrator, Mary Immaculate,
          Queens Hospital Center
Nogan, Herbert, M.D., Dir., Physical Med. & Rehab.,
          Sea View Hospital & Home
Notter, Lucile, Ph.D., American Nursing Association

O'Connel, Kathy, R.N., New York University Hospital
O'Connor, Joseph, Emergency Room Director, Morrisania
        Hospital
O'Meara, Edward S., M.D., Director, OPD/ER, Queens
        Hospital Center
Oppenheim, Adolph, Statistics, City Planning Commission
O'Rourke, Edward, M.D., Commissioner, Dept. of Health
O'Toole, Rosemary, Director, Bur. of Hosp. Care Serv-
        ices, Dept. of Welfare
Padilla, Elena, Ph.D., Chief, Research, Comm. Mental
        Health Board
Pako, Albert, Administrator, Sydenham Hospital
Peach, Walter, OPD Director, Morrisania Hospital
Pennington, Constance, R.N., Supervisor Nursing, OPD,
        Morrisania Hospital
Perkins, Ellen, Bureau of Family Services, HEW
Perry, Charles, Bureau of Nursing Rates, State Dept.
        of Health
Perry, Mary F., R.N., Superintendent, Midtown Hospital
Piazza, Ferdinand, M.D., Executive Administrator,
        Metropolitan Hospital
Piccoli, Leonard R., Administrator, Assistant Commis-
        sioner, Fordham Hospital
Piore, Nora, Adjunct Assoc. Prof., Hunter College, Dir.,
        Urb. Med. Econ. Res. Proj.
Pitchford, Helen, Exec. Housekeeper, Bellevue Hospital
Porter, Milton R., M.D., V.P. of the Medical Board,
        Presbyterian Hospital
Posman, Harry, M.D., Director, Off. Soc. Res. and
        Stat., State Dept. of Soc. Welfare
Potter, Kincey, Social Security Administration, HEW
Pruitt, Alton, Acting Administrator, Bronx Veterans
        Administration Hospital
Purmont, Mr., Head Record Librarian, Metropolitan
        Hospital
Rabinow, Barney, Local Area Planning, City Planning
        Commission
Rankin, J. Lee, Corporation Council, City of New York
Rappleye, Willard C., M.D., Board of Hospitals,
        New York City
Rauch, Hugo, D.D.S., Analyst, Medical & Health
        Research Association
Raynor, M., Head Record Librarian, Queens Hospital
        Center
Reese, Eva, Exec. Director, Visiting Nurse Service
Reid, Seymour, Administrator, Lefferts General Hospital
Ried, Maude, R.N., P.H.N., Jamaica Health Center,
        Queens County
Riess, Wallace, Pharmacist, Lincoln Hospital

Rizer, Donald C., Assoc. Administrator, Maimonides
        Hospital
Roberts, T. W., M.D., Director of Pathology, Harlem
        Hospital
Robertson, Alexander, M.D., Executive Director,
        Milbank Memorial Fund
Robitzek, Edward H., M.D., Director of Medical
        Services, Sea View Hospital & Home
Roemer, Milton I., M.D., Prof. of Public Health, UCLA
Rosen, Albert J., Administrator, Fairview Nursing Home
Rosen, James H., M.D., Medical Director, Fairview
        Nursing Home
Rosenberg, Marvin, Community Organizer, Gouverneur
        Ambulatory Care District
Rosenthal, Edward, M.D., V.P., Board of Directors,
        Lefferts General Hospital
Rosman, Sophie, Dir., Bureau of Special Services,
        Department of Welfare
Rosner, Henry, Assistant Commissioner, Dept. of Welfare
Roth, Marvin, Research Analyst, Hospital Rev. &
        Planning Council
Rubenstein, Vicki, R.N., Bellevue Hospital
Runge, Vernon, Chief of State Grants Branch Dept., HEW
Rusk, Howard A., M.D., Board of Hospitals, New York
        City
Russell, Maurice, M.D., Director of Social Service,
        Harlem Hospital
Saunders, Sally, R.N., Cornell Medical Center
Sawokin, Martha C., R.N., Administrator, Delafield
        Hospital
Scaglione, Peter R., M.D., Chief of Pediatrics,
        Brooklyn Hospital
Schmid, Joan, R.N., Cornell Medical Center
Schorr, Elizabeth, Assistant to the Dir., USOEO
Schwartz, Arthur, Liaison, Bronx Board of Education
Selbst, Paul L., Assistant Hospital Administrator,
        Bronx Municipal Hospital
Sheps, Cecil, M.D., Director, Beth Israel Hospital
Sheridan, Frances, R.N., Ass't. Dir., Nursing Services,
        Delafield Hospital
Sherwood, Edward, Mary Immaculate Coordinator, Queens
        Hospital Center
Silberman, Carolyn, M.D., Administrator, Ewing Hospital
Silberstein, Richard, M.D., Director, Staten Island
        Mental Health Soc.
Silverberg, Abe, Affiliation Administrator, Lincoln
        Hospital

Skelly, Marion, R.N., Nurse in Charge of OPD, Elmhurst
        Hospital
Slack, Warner V., M.D., School of Medicine, University
        of Wisconsin
Sloan, Allan K., Planning Prog. Coord., City Planning
        Commission
Slobody, Lawrence, M.D., Acting Dean, Vice President,
        New York Medical College
Smith, Lawrence L., Hospital Administrator, Flower &
        Fifth Avenue Hospital
Smith, Sander V., M.D., Administrator, Kings County
        Hospital
Soberano, O., Head Record Librarian, Elmhurst Hospital
Sokoal, Sonia, Research Analyst, Urb. Med. Econ. Res.
        Project
Spinelli, Frank Z., Assistant Administrator, Cumberland
        Hospital
St. Lawrence, Edith, R.N., Supervisor, OPD, Delafield
        Hospital
Starin, M.D., Einstein College of Medicine
Stattel, Florence, Coordinator, Rehabilitation Centers
Stern, Edward A., M.D., Chief, OPD, Metropolitan
        Hospital
Stix, Regine, M.D., Consultant, Department of Health
Stone, M.D., New York Medical College
Strauss, Kathryn W., Research Scientist, New York
        University
Streator, Mrs. Ella, Dir. of Education, Boro. Pres.
        Off., Queens County
Sullivan, Dorothy, Welfare Administration, HEW
Sullivan, James, Ass't. Dir. of the Budget, State of
        New York
Sweitzer, John, Plant Engineer, Sydenham Hospital
Taite, Barbara, Ph.D., Research and Studies Unit,
        Nat'l. League for Nursing
Talbert, Mr., State Department of Social Welfare
Terenzio, Joseph V., Commissioner, Department of
        Hospitals
Terenzio, Peter B., Executive Vice President,
        Roosevelt Hospital
Tinkler, Ivy, R.N., Director of Nursing, Lincoln
        Hospital
Toan, Arthur, Executive, Price-Waterhouse
Tobier, Emanuel, Chief Economist, Regional Plan
        Association
Trussel, Ray E., M.D., Chairman, Dept. of Prev. &
        Adm. Med., P & S, Columbia
Ultmann, J., M.D., Visiting Physician-Medicine,
        Delafield Hospital

Unger, Moses, Administrator, Surfside Nursing Home
Vandow, Eva S., M.D., Hospital Administrator, Bronx
        Municipal Hospital
Vidao, Raphael, M.D., Head of Medical Clinic, Lincoln
        Hospital
Walsh, Thomas, State Department of Social Welfare
Warschavski, Joseph, Ass't. Director, Brooklyn Board
        of Education
Wasserman, M.D., New York Medical College
Wechsler, George, D.D.S., Richmond County Dental
        Society
Weddige, Dorothy, Director of Nursing Education and
        Nursing Services, Dept. of Hospitals
Weinberg, Howard, Administrator, Greenpoint Hospital
Weindorf, Herbert T., General Manager, House of
        St. Giles the Cripple
Weinstein, Bernard, Affil. Coord., Admin. of Mt. Sinai
        Services, Elmhurst Hospital
Weiss, Elizabeth, R.N., Superintendent of Nurses,
        Morrisania Hospital
Weiss, Milton, Assistant Hospital Administrator,
        Sydenham Hospital
Westbrook, Sadie, R.N., Director of Nursing,
        Interfaith Hospital
Weston, Jerry, R.N., Nursing Research, Urb. Med.
        Econ. Research Project
White, Alex, Librarian (Medical), University of the
        State of New York
Wilmot, Mr., Administrator, University Hospital, NYU
Wise, Carl R., M.D., Assistant Vice President,
        Presbyterian Hospital
Wolkwitz, Robert E., M.D., (former) Pres., Phys.
        Guild, Richmond County
Wyman, Randolph A., M.D., Administrator, Bellevue
        Hospital
Yarnell, Ruth, R.N., Nursing Supervisor, OPD, Queens
        Hospital Center
Zelmanowics, Chaim M., Administrator, Eastchester
        Park Nursing Home
Zimmerman, Fred, M.D., Director, OPD and Home Care,
        Bellevue Hospital
Zwilling, Mrs. V., Chief Pharmacist, Harlem Hospital

APPENDIX B

Bibliography

In the course of its studies in support of
the Commission, the staff has assembled,
examined, and referenced the 367 entries
listed herein. Entries in this bibliography have been placed in 22 broad subject
classifications. Within each classification and subclassification, entries have
been listed alphabetically by author (in
the case of books) or by title (in the
case of periodical articles, reports,
technical papers, letters, etc.). Late
additions are separately numbered at the
end of the categorical bibliography. Each
entry appears only once.

Ambulance Services

1. "Ambulance Service in New York City," a report
by the Committee on Public Health, New York
Academy of Medicine. Reprinted from Bulletin
of the New York Academy of Medicine, 2nd
series, vol. 43, no. 4, pp. 336-345
(April 1967).

2. "Data Collected on Ambulance Service," a report
by TECHNOMICS, Inc., (June 4-16, 1967).

3. "Emergency Ambulance Services," a report by the
Hospital Review and Planning Council, New
York City (June 1964).

Comprehensive Health Planning

4. Weinerman, E. R., "Anchor Points Underlying the
Planning for Tomorrow's Health Care" in
Bulletin of the New York Academy of
Medicine, vol. 41, no. 12 (December 1965).

5. Pollack, Jr., "Community Decision Process as an Aspect of Planning for Health," a paper presented at the National Health Forum of the National Health Council (Chicago, March 20-22, 1967).

6. Stewart, W. H., "Comprehensive Health Planning," a paper presented at the National Health Forum of the National Health Council (Chicago, March 21, 1967).

7. "Comprehensive Health Planning and Public Health Services, Amendments of 1966," HEW document PL 89-749.

8. Densen, P., "Comprehensive Plan Report Outline," a proposed document for the Comprehensive Planning Agency, New York City (June 7, 1967).

9. "Environmental Health Planning Guide," an HEW publication (1962).

10. Sigmond, R. M., "Health Planning," a paper prepared for the Seminar on Health Policy, Institute for Policy Studies (Washington, D. C., March 8, 1966).

11. "New Directions in Public Policy for Health Care," a collection of articles reprinted from Bulletin of the New York Academy of Medicine, 2nd series, vol. 42, no. 12 (December 1966).

12. Stewart, W. H., "Partnership for Planning," an extension of remarks made by Dr. Stewart, U. S. Surgeon General, on November 27 and 28 and December 6, 1966.

13. Blumberg, M. S., "Performance Measures as an Aspect of Health Planning," a paper presented at the National Health Forum of the National Health Council (Chicago, March 20-22, 1967).

14. Hauser, P. M., "Social Goals as an Aspect of Planning," a paper presented at the National Health Forum of the National Health Council (Chicago, March 20-22, 1967).

15. Wagner, C. J., "A Systems Approach to Health Planning," a paper presented at the National Health Forum of the National Health Council (Chicago, March 20-22, 1967).

16.   Parks, R., "Systems Development as a Part of
      Planning for Health Enterprises," a paper
      presented at the National Health Forum of
      the National Health Council (Chicago,
      March 20-22, 1967).

                  Drug Addiction and Alcoholism

17.   Ramirez, E., A Comprehensive Plan for the
      Management of the Addiction Problem in
      New York City. New York: February 1, 1967.

18.   "First Report," by the Task Force on Addictions,
      to the New York State Planning Committee on
      Mental Health (February 1965).

19.   "The Narcotics Register Project," data collected
      by TECHNOMICS, Inc., including a description
      of the project and a directory of narcotics
      addiction service agenices (1965), users
      (1963-64), and other data (1965-66) obtained
      through the New York City Health Office of
      Research.

20.   "Proceedings of the White House Conference on
      Narcotic and Drug Abuse" (Washington, D. C.,
      September 27 and 28, 1962).

21.   A report on the New York State Narcotic Addiction
      Control Commission and its agencies (1967).

22.   "Specialized Alcoholism Treatment Resources in the
      New York Alcoholism Program," a report by
      the Community Council of Greater New York
      (October 1966).

            Family Planning and Prenatal-Maternal Care

23.   Jaffee, F. S., Programming for Community Needs:
      A Strategy for Implementing Family Planning
      Services in the U. S., prepared for the
      Region II Family Planning Conference of HEW
      (December 14, 1966).

24.   ____, Welfare's Role in Maternal Health and
      Family Planning Services, prepared for the
      Advisory Council on Public Welfare, HEW, and
      the Welfare Department (February 19, 1965).

25. "Conference on Prenatal Clinic Care in New York City," a report by the Maternity Center Association, New York (May 9, 1963).

26. Deschin, C. and Smith, J. J., "Evaluative Study of Lincoln Hospital's Obstetrical Home Care Program," submitted to the Albert Einstein College of Medicine, Lincoln Hospital, New York.

27. "Family Planning and Infant Mortality--An Analysis of Priorities," a report by the Department of Program Planning and Department of Research, New York (June 1967).

28. "Guidelines and Recommendations for the Planning and Use of Obstetrical Facilities in Southern New York," a report by the Hospital Review and Planning Council of New York State (January 1966).

29. Smith, J. J. and Romney, S. L., "A Neighborhood Maternity Clinic (NMC)," proposed and submitted to the Albert Einstein College of Medicine, Lincoln Hospital, New York.

30. "Prenatal Satellite Project: Maternal and Infant Care," a report by the Department of Health, New York City (1967).

31. "Therapeutic Abortion," a statement by the New York Academy of Medicine, reprinted from Bulletin of the New York Academy of Medicine (April 1965).

Health, General

32. Tunley, R., The American Health Scandal, New York: Harper & Row, 1966.

33. Linder, F. E., "The Health of the American People" in Scientific American, vol. 214, no. 6 (June 1966).

34. James, G., "Health Challenges Today" in The American Review of Respiratory Diseases, vol. 90, no. 3 (September 1964).

Health Insurance

35. Somers, H. M. and A. R., <u>Doctors, Patients, and
    Health Insurance</u>. Washington, D. C.:
    Brookings Institute, May 1961.

36. <u>Source Book of Health Insurance</u>, 1966. Health
    Insurance Institute: 1965.

37. "Comparison of the Governor's Bill and Speaker
    Travia's Bill to Implement Title XIX of
    Medicare," a report by Speaker Travia (1966).

38. "Comparison of the Governor's Bill with Objectives
    of Ad Hoc Committee on Title XIX of Medicare,"
    a report (March 17, 1966).

39. "Conditions for Coverage of Services of Independ-
    ent Laboratories," a report on Health
    Insurance for the Aged, HEW document HIM-4
    (December 1966).

40. "Conditions of Participation for Extended Care
    Facilities," a report on Health Insurance
    for the Aged, HEW document HIM-3 (March
    1966).

41. "Conditions of Participation for Home Health
    Agencies," a report on Health Insurance for
    the Aged, HEW document HIM-22 (March 1966).

42. "Conditions of Participation for Hospitals," a
    report on Health Insurance for the Aged,
    HEW document HIM-1 (February 1966).

43. "Cost Settlement in Lieu of Full Claim," from a
    letter to State Health Deputy Commissioner
    Lauchheim from H. Rosner (December 6, 1966).

44. "Extended Care Facility Manual," a report on
    Health Insurance for the Aged, HEW document
    HIM-12 (January 1967).

45. "For Physicians: A Reference Guide to Health
    Insurance Under Social Security," an HEW
    document (June 1966).

46. "Health Insurance Coverage in New York City," a
     Population Health Survey Report, New York
     City Department of Health (May 24, 1965).

47. "Health Insurance Plan Statistical Report," a
     summary of services provided by the 31
     medical groups affiliated with the Health
     Insurance Plan of Greater New York (1964-65).

48. "Health Insurance Under Social Security--Your
     Medicare Handbook," an HEW document (1966).

49. "Home Health Agency Manual," a report on Health
     Insurance for the Aged, HEW document HIM-11
     (June 1966).

50. "Hospital Manual," a report on Health Insurance
     for the Aged, HEW document HIM-10 (June 1966).

51. "Insurance Findings of Population Health Survey,"
     attachment on hospital insurance plan from
     a letter of P. Densen, deputy commissioner,
     to G. James, commissioner of health (June
     1964).

52. "Medicare and Medicaid in New York City," a study
     by System Development Corporation, document
     no. TM-LO-2036 (July 22, 1966).

53. Densen, P., "Notes on Medicare Meeting--Titles
     XVIII and XIX," (June 7, 1966).

54. "Principles of Reimbursement for Provider Costs,"
     a report on Health Insurance for the Aged,
     HEW document HIM-5 (revised January 1967).

55. "Principles of Reimbursement for Services by
     Hospital-Based Physicians," a report on
     Health Insurance for the Aged, HEW document
     HIM-6 (February 1967).

56. Alexander, R., "Proposal for Medicaid Reorganiza-
     tion," a paper by the New York City Depart-
     ment of Health (February 15, 1967).

Health Legislation

57. "Declaration of Policy and Statement of Purpose,
     As Well As of Approval of Construction,"
     New York State legislation of June 3, 1965,
     Art. 28, Hospital Sections 2800 and 2802.

58. "Proprietary Nursing Home Operation," chap. 5 of
     State Hospital Code, Public Health Law,
     New York State.

59. "Public Law HR 5710--Social Security Amendments
     of 1967," sections of Limitation on Federal
     Participation in Medical Assistance, docu-
     ment no. 74-99930 (February 20, 1967).

60. "Public Law 89-97, HR 6675--State Plans for Medi-
     cal Assistance," (July 30, 1965).

61. Clark, H. T., "Some Background Considerations
     and Recommendations for the Implementation
     of the Regional Medical Programs Legislation
     (PL 89-239)," an interim report (December 30,
     1965).

62. "Summary of Health Legislation," a memo from
     Peter Eccles to Mr. Gottlieb on New York
     legislation (May 9, 1967).   .

Health Personnel

63. Silver, G., New Types of Personnel and Changing
     Roles of Health Professionals. New York:
     1966.

64. Kissick, W. L., "Health Manpower in Transition,"
     a report prepared for the Seminar on Health
     Policy, Institute for Policy Studies,
     Washington, D. C. (February 22, 1966).

65. Peck, H. B., Levin, T., and Roman, M., "Training
     Manpower for Health and Mental Health
     Services in New York City," a preliminary-
     draft report (May 9, 1967).

66. "Physicians in New York City," a preliminary re-
    report on their number, type of practice,
    and specialties as reported to the AMA in
    1959 and 1966, prepared by the Urban Medical
    Economics Research Project at Hunter College
    (March 10, 1966).

67. "Salaries and Related Personnel Practices of
    Voluntary Social and Health Agencies in
    New York City," a report prepared by the
    Community Council of Greater New York
    (September 1966).

          Health Programs and Public Health

68. James, G., Emerging Trends in Public Health and
    Possible Reactions. New York: 1965.

69. "Closing the Gaps in the Availability and Access-
    ibility of Health Services" in Bulletin of
    New York Academy of Medicine, vol. 41, no. 12
    (December 1965).

70. "The Commission on the Delivery of Personal
    Health Service," an interim statement in
    brief (working draft) (March 30, 1967).

71. "Comprehensive Health Care: A Challenge to
    American Communities," a report by the Task
    Force on Comprehensive Personal Health
    Services, National Task Forces Project,
    National Commission on Community Health
    Service (1966).

72. Terris, M., "The Comprehensive Health Center" in
    Public Health Reports, vol. 78, no. 10
    (October 1963).

73. Baehr, G., "Comprehensive Health Service Centers,"
    a paper presented before the Committee on
    Social Policy for Health Care (June 16, 1967).

74. Peterson, O. L., "Medical Care in the U. S." in
    Scientific American, vol. 209, no. 2 (August
    1963).

75. Baehr, G., "Medical Care: Old Goals and New
    Horizons" in American Journal of Public Health,
    vol. 55, no. 12 (December 1965).

76. Bureau of Family Services, "Program Facts," an
     HEW document (August 1965).

77. "Proposals for Better Delivery of Health Services,"
     a report by the Citizens' Committee for
     Children of New York City (October 1965).

78. Terris, M., "The Role of the Public Health Depart-
     ment" in Bulletin of the New York Academy of
     Medicine, vol. 41, no. 1 (January 1965).

Community Programs

79. "Comprehensive Care Services in Your Community,"
     an HEW document (September 1966).

80. "Comprehensive Community Health Action Report,"
     prepared by Tufts University (June 23, 1966).

81. "Comprehensive Neighborhood Health Services
     Programs--Guidelines," a document of the
     Office of Economic Opportunity (February
     1967).

82. Terris, M., "The Future of Community Health
     Services" in Public Health Reports, vol. 77
     no. 10 (October 1962).

83. "Guidelines for Evaluating Proposals for Neigh-
     borhood Clinics and Health Centers," a
     report by the New York Hospital Review and
     Planning Council.

84. "Health Is A Community Affair," a report by the
     National Commission on Community Health
     Services (Harvard University Press, 1966).

85. "Health Needs of the Bedford Health District,"
     a memo to Dr. Fannie I. Tomson, assistant
     commissioner, from Dr. Dorothy L. Trice,
     district health officer (June 9, 1967).

86. "HHC Patient Care and Program Evaluation Project,"
     a report on the Harlem Project by Columbia
     University (1966).

87. "Hunts Point Neighborhood Multi-Service Center,"
     a program development demonstration.

88. "Local Health Organization and Staffing Within Standard Metropolitan Areas," HEW documents (1961-63).

89. "Manhattan Community Mental Health Center," an architectural plan by Caudill, Rowlett, Scott (1967).

90. "The Need for a General Health Facility in the Neighborhood Surrounding Howard Park Hospital" February 14, 1967.

91. "The Neighborhood Health Center," a document of the Office of Economic Opportunity (1967).

92. Wise, H. B., "Neighborhood Medical Care Demonstration," a report (May 1967).

93. McLaughlin, M. C., "Public Health and Medical Aspects of Neighborhood Ambulatory Health Services," a revised report by the associate deputy commissioner of the New York Public Health Department (April 24, 1967).

94. "Renovations of Various Health Department Facilities for Neighborhood Family Care Services," a report prepared by a Meridian architect-engineer as an effort to define the problem adequately enough to serve as a program for design.

Regional Programs

95. Issue Papers for the Conference on Regional Medical Programs (Washington, D. C., January 15-17, 1967).

96. James, G., "New York City's Health," a report of the New York City Department of Health (1961-62).

97. "Progress in Medical, Hospital, and Related Health Services in New York City," a report to Mayor Wagner by the Task Force on Organization of Medical Services (April 1963).

98. "Report of the Commission on Health Services of the City of New York" (July 20, 1960).

99.   "Selected Characteristics of State Medical Assis-
          tance Programs Under Title XIX of the Social
          Security Act Approved and in Operation as of
          December 31, 1966," an HEW document (May
          1967).

Federal Programs and Assistance

100.   "A Policy Statement on the Role of Government
           Tax Funds in Problems of Health Care,"
           reprinted from Bulletin of New York Academy
           of Medicine, vol. 41, no. 7 (July 1965).

101.   Burns, E. M., "The Role of Government in Health
           Services" in Bulletin of New York Academy
           of Medicine, vol. 41, no. 7 (July 1965).

Planning and Policy

102.   "Areawide Planning of Facilities for Long-Term
           Treatment and Care," a report of the Joint
           Committee of the American Hospital Associ-
           ation, Public Health Department, HEW and
           Welfare Public Health Service (February
           1963).

103.   "New Direction in Public Policy for Health Care"
           in Bulletin of New York Academy of Medicine,
           vol. 42, no. 12 (December 1966).

104.   "Planning Data for the Proposed Affiliation
           Between Memorial Mission Hospital and the
           Bowman Gray School of Medicine," a report
           by the Planning Staff of the Association
           for the North Carolina Regional Medical
           Program.

105.   Somers, A. R., "Some Basic Determinants of
           Medical Care and Health Policy: Trends
           and Issues," a report prepared for the
           Seminar on Health Policy, Institute for
           Policy Studies (Washington, D. C.,
           January 25, 1966).

106.   Parks, R. B. and Adelman, H., "Systems Analysis
           and Planning for Public Health Care in the
           City of New York" (March 25, 1966).

Preventive and Home-Care Programs

107.   "Homes Aides for the Sick and Aged in Queens,"
       a final report on Community Health Project
       Grant No. CH 34-21 C-65, Visiting Nurse
       Service of New York (September 30, 1966).

108.   "Preventive Home Care and Health Maintenance
       Programs," an interim report by the Citizens'
       Committee on Aging, Subcommittee on Health
       (March 1963).

109.   "Report of the Special Committee on Home Care
       and Extended Care Services," Hospital Review
       and Planning Council (February 1966).

110.   "The Status of Homemaker and Home Aide Service
       for the Marginal-Income, Chronically Ill
       Adult," an overview prepared by the Citizens'
       Committee on Aging of the Community Council
       of Greater New York (March 1964).

Health Research

111.   Slack, W. V., et al., "A Computer-Based Medical-
       History System," a special article from the
       Department of Medicine, University of Wis-
       consin Medical School, reprinted from the
       New England Journal of Medicine, no. 274,
       pp. 194-198 (January 27, 1966).

112.   Slack, W. V., et al., "A Computer-Based Physical
       Examination System," reprinted from The
       Journal of the American Medical Association,
       vol. 200, pp. 224-228 (April 17, 1967).

113.   Gardner, J. W., "The Government, The University,
       and Biomedical Research" in Science, vol. 153,
       no. 3744 (September 30, 1966).

114.   "Health Services Research I," a series of papers
       commissioned by the Health Services Research
       Study Section of the U. S. Public Health
       Service, discussed in conference (Chicago,
       October 15 and 16, 1965).

115.   "Health Services Research II," discussed in
       conference (New York City, May 6 and 7, 1966).

116. "Research and the Public Health," a report by
     the Medical and Health Research Association
     of New York City (1966).

117. McDermott, W., "The Role of Biomedical Research
     in International Development," reprinted from
     The Journal of Medical Education, vol. 39,
     no. 7 (July 1964).

118. Hicks, G. P., et al., "Routine Use of a Small
     Digital Computer in the Clinical Laboratory,"
     reprinted from The Journal of the American
     Medical Association, vol. 196, pp. 973-978
     (June 13, 1966).

Health Statistics

119. Health Resource Statistics, Public Health Service
     National Center for Health Statistics, HEW
     (1965).

120. HEW Division of Research and Office of Special
     Services, "Advance Release of Statistics
     on Public Assistance" (January 1967).

121. Brady and Gollance, "Average Daily Patient Cost,"
     a report of statistical data for the year
     ended December 31, 1961, Department of
     Hospitals, New York City.

122. Alexander, R., "Basic Statistical Table Required
     on Medicaid Programs," published by the
     Office of Programmed Planning, Research, and
     Evaluation, New York City Department of
     Health.

123. Elinson, Jr. and Loewenstein, R., "Community
     Fact Book for Washington Heights, New York
     City," a report by the School of Public
     Health and Administrative Medicine, Columbia
     University (1960-61 and 1963).

124. Posman, H., "Expenditures During State Fiscal
     Year 1967-1968," a report on the Medical
     Assistance Program in New York State, pub-
     lished by the Department of Social Welfare.

125. "General Care Hospital Statistics," a report by the Hospital Review and Planning Council (1964).

126. "Health and Welfare Trends--1965 Edition," a selection of charts on state data and rankings in HEW, document no. 254-185/10.

127. "Hospital Discharges and Length of Stay," a New York City Population Health Survey, report #H-1, New York Department of Health (1964).

128. "Hospital Statistics of Southern New York for the Years 1964 and 1965," a report by the Hospital Review and Planning Council of Southern New York.

129. "Hospital Use:　Patient Days, State Rankings," a chart reprinted from The Journal of the American Hospital Association (August 1966).

130. "Maps and Statistics for Health Institutions, New York City," a reference volume by TECHNOMICS, Inc. (March 10, 1967).

131. "Medical 'D' Schedule," New York State Department of Health and Department of Social Welfare (July 1, 1966).

132. "National Trends--1965 Edition," a table and chart of in-patient bids, acceptable bids, and state rankings--a portion of the State Inventory Summaries, HEW Division of Hospital and Medical Facilities.

133. "Population and Statistics Charts," a report by the Special Committee of the Hospital Review and Planning Council of Southern New York, Inc. (February 1966).

134. Posman, H., "Public Assistance and Medical Assistance Statistics," from a monthly summary of social statistics (February 27, 1967).

135. Schneider, D., "Recent Public Assistance Data," from a memorandum from the New York State Department of Health (April 19, 1967).

136. Klarman, H. E., "Reflections on Hospital Use in New York City by Age of Population, Ownership of Facility, Availability of Funds, and in Relation to the U. S.," a report (November 14, 1963).

137. "Source of Funds Expended for Public Assistance for Payments," an HEW document (March 28, 1967).

138. Bureau of Family Services, "Source of Funds Expended for Public Assistance," an HEW document (March 2, 1967).

Hospitals

139. James, G., "Adapting Today's Hospital to Meet Tomorrow's Health Needs," one of a series in the Stuart M. Crocker Lectures, Roosevelt Hospital, New York City (May 5, 1964).

140. "Annual Report to Mayor Lindsay of Department of Hospitals" (1965).

141. "Appraisal of Hospital Obsolescence," methods and findings of a study of hospitals in New York, 1963-65, special report #4, by the Hospital Review and Planning Council (1965).

142. "The Brooklyn-Cumberland Medical Center Affiliation Report," prepared for the United Hospital Fund and Hospital Review and Planning Council of Southern New York, Inc. (February 20, 1967).

143. "The Brooklyn Hospital--A Comprehensive Family Health Care Program," application for a comprehensive health service program under section 211-2 of the Economic Opportunity Act.

144. "Columbia-Presbyterian Medical Center," New York City, 8th annual report (1966).

145. "Fordham in Crisis--Emergency Crash Program," a
     report on the Fordham Hospital, New York
     City, by the Misericordia Task Force to the
     Commissioner of Hospitals (May 1967).

146. Baehr, G., "The Hospital as the Center of Com-
     munity Medical Care: Fact and Fiction,"
     in American Journal of Public Health, vol. 54,
     no. 10 (October 1964).

147. "Hospital Costs," a report by the Governor's
     Committee on Hospital Costs, New York State
     (December 1965).

148. McGibbon, J. R., "Hospital Medical Records--A
     Criteria for Administrative Evaluation,"
     Intramural Research Division, Public Health
     Service, HEW document no. 930-C-5.

149. "Hospital Profiles, A Decade of Change, 1953-
     1962," a report on non federal, short-term,
     general hospitals, Public Health Service,
     HEW document.

150. "Hospitals and Related Health Facilities in the
     Bronx," a report by the Hospital Review and
     Planning Council (1965).

151. "Hospitals and Related Facilities in Southern
     New York," a report by the Hospital Review
     and Planning Council (1966).

152. "Midtown Hospital," New York City, 1965 annual
     report.

153. "Municipal Hospitals," a report by the City
     Hospital Visiting Committee, United Hospital
     Fund of New York (1965-66).

154. "Municipal Hospitals of New York City," a report
     by the Blue Ribbon Panel to Governor
     Rockefeller (April 1967).

155. "The Municipal Hospitals of New York City," a
     report by the Committee on Public Health,
     New York Academy of Medicine (February 6,
     1967).

156. "New York City and Its Hospitals--Study of the
      Roles of the Municipal and Voluntary Hos-
      pitals Serving New York City," a report by
      the Hospital Council of Greater New York
      (December 1960).

157. "New York Medical College Center for Chronic
      Diseases," a report from Bird S. Coler
      Hospital (General Programs), Department of
      Community Medicine's Activities and Programs
      (October 1966).

158. "1966 Budget," The Roosevelt Hospital, New York
      City.

159. "Preamble to the Statement of Scope for the New
      Lincoln Hospital."

160. "Present Hospital Facilities on Staten Island,"
      a report to the Community Planning Board
      No. 3 (1967).

161. "Report to Mayor John V. Lindsay by the Task
      Force on Hospitals," New York City (June 10,
      1966).

162. "The Roosevelt Hospital," 1964 annual report.

163. "The Roosevelt Hospital," 1965 annual report.

164. Terenzio, J. V., "Statement by the Commissioner
      of Hospitals to the New York State Civil
      Service Commission" (May 4, 1967).

165. "Statement from Brooklyn-Cumberland Medical
      Center" (1966).

166. "Toward a Healthier Community--A Pioneering Con-
      cept of The Brooklyn Hospital at the
      Brooklyn-Cumberland Medical Center," a re-
      port (1967).

Administration

167. Terenzio, J. V. and Brown, H. J., Health Services
      Administration Annual Report. City of New
      York Department of Hospitals: 1966.

168. Yerby, A. S., <u>Annual Report for the Years 1964,
     1965, and 1966</u>. City of New York Department
     of Hospitals.

Fiscal, Budgetary, and Contractual Matters

169. Van Dyke, F. and Brown, V., "Charitable Institu-
     tions Budget--Hospital Medical Care, New
     York City, 1961-1964," a report by the
     School of Public Health and Administrative
     Medicine of Columbia University (1965).

170. Thompson, J. D., "Consumer and Community Costs
     of Hospital Services," a report prepared
     for the Seminar on Health Policy, Institute
     for Policy Studies (Washington, D. C.,
     January 1966).

171. Terenzio, J. V., "Expense Budget Estimate of
     Department of Hospitals for Fiscal Year
     1967-1968" (December 22, 1966).

172. "Hospital Affiliation Contracts," a confidential
     reference manual on New York City Hospitals,
     vol. 2, prepared by TECHNOMICS, Inc.
     (March 10, 1967).

173. "Income to Hospitals for 1967," a letter from
     F. Hayes, director of the budget, to
     M. Ginsberg, commissioner of welfare,
     New York.

174. Terenzio, J. V., "New Affiliation Contracts,"
     a memo (May 9, 1967).

175. "Report of the Committee on Health Care
     Financing," Hospital Review and Planning
     Council of Southern New York, Inc. (April 11,
     1967).

176. "Statement of the Cost of Maintaining and Oper-
     ating the Department of Hospitals, New York
     City," for the year ended December 31, 1965.

177. Meyer, R. S. and Reichbart, R. H., "Toward
        Rational Purchasing for the Hospital Serv-
        ices Administration of the City of New
        York," a study with recommendations, writ-
        ten at the request of the HSA Administrator
        in conjunction with the Legal-Administrative
        Workshop of Yale Law School.

178. "United Hospital Fund of New York," the 86th
        annual report (1965-66).

Policy and Planning

179. "Areawide Planning for Hospitals and Related
        Health Facilities," a report by the Joint
        Committee of the American Hospital Associ-
        ation and Public Health Service, Public
        Health Service, HEW (1961).

180. Roth, M., "Computer Graphics for Hospital
        Planning," a reprint from Hospital Adminis-
        tration in Canada (1961).

181. "Evaluating Need for Hospital Construction,"
        criteria to guide the Hospital Review and
        Planning Council (November 1963).

182. "The General Hospital Needs of Brooklyn," a
        report by the Hospital Review and Planning
        Council of Southern New York, Inc. (May
        1966).

183. "General Hospital Planning and Design," selected
        references, Public Health Service, HEW
        (January 1963).

184. "Guide and Suggested Procedures for Use by a
        Hospital Long-Range Planning and Development
        Committee," a report by the Hospital Review
        and Planning Council of Southern New York,
        Inc. (1964).

185. "Guidelines and Criteria for Planning Hospital
        and Related Health Services in New York City,"
        a report by the Hospital Review and Planning
        Council (June 1966).

186. Young, W. R., "Hospital of the Future?" in
        Reader's Digest, reprinted from Life
        (December 2, 1966).

187. "Hospital Planning for the People of Southern
      New York--A Study of Hospital Use, 1950-
      1962," special report #2 of the Hospital
      Review and Planning Council (1964).

188. "Hospital Planning for the People of Southern
      New York--A Study of Population Trends,"
      special report #1 of the Hospital Review
      and Planning Council (1963).

189. "Hospital Planning for the People of Southern
      New York--The Hill-Burton Program, 1948-
      1963," special report #3 of the Hospital
      Review and Planning Council (1964).

190. "Hospital Review and Planning Council of Southern
      New York, Inc.," the 28th Annual Report
      (1965-66).

191. "New York City's Municipal Hospitals, A Policy
      Review," prepared by the Institute for
      Policy Studies, Washington, D. C., in 3
      parts, 2 vol. (1967).

192. "Pharmacy Department: Planning and Equipping
      for 50-, 100-, and 200-Bed General Hospital,"
      a report by the Public Health Service, HEW
      (1951; reprinted 1963).

193. "Planning the Laboratory for the General Hospi-
      tal," a report by the Public Health Service,
      HEW (March 1963).

194. Terenzio, J. V., "Reorganization of Department
      of Hospitals, City of New York" (February 1,
      1967).

195. "The Roosevelt Hospital Master Plan," a report
      on the major conclusions of a three-year
      planning effort (April 1967).

Personnel

196. "Brief in Support of Establishing Noncompetitive
      Titles for the Following Executive Positions
      in the Department of Hospitals: Assistant
      Commissioner, Deputy Assistant Commissioner,
      Superintendent of Buildings and Grounds, and
      Manager of Building Services" (March 15,
      1967).

197. "A Survey of Personnel Management Activities for the Department of Hospitals," a report by the New York City Department of Personnel (September 1962).

Patient Care

198. American Medical Association Department of Hospitals and Medical Facilities, Emergency Departments: A Handbook for the Medical Staff (1966).

199. W. K. Kellogg Foundation, The Complete Gamut of Progressive Patient Care in a Community Hospital, An Experience Brochure. Battle Creek, Mich.: 1966.

200. Klarman, H. E., Hospital Care in New York City. New York: Columbia University Press, 1963.

201. Esselstyn, C. B., "The Ambulant Patient and the Teaching Hospital," a study by the Community Health Association, Detroit, Mich. (January 26, 1967).

202. Weinerman, E. R. and Edwards, H. R., "Changing Patterns in Hospital Emergency Service," Yale Studies in Ambulatory Medical Care, no. 1 of a series, reprinted from Hospitals, vol. 38 (November 16, 1964).

203. Weinerman, E. R., "Changing Patterns in Medical Care: Their Implications for Ambulatory Services," reprinted from Hospitals, vol. 39 (December 16, 1965).

204. Snoke, P. S. and Weinerman, E. R., "Comprehensive Care Programs in University Medical Centers" in The Journal of Medical Education, vol. 40 no. 7 (July 1965).

205. Weinerman, E. R., et al., "Determinants of Use of Hospital Emergency Services," Yale Studies in Ambulatory Medical Care, no. 5 of a series reprinted from American Journal of Public Health, vol. 56, no. 7 (July 1966).

206. "The Expanding Role of Ambulatory Services in
     Hospitals and Health Departments" in
     Bulletin of the New York Academy of Medicine,
     vol. 41, no. 1 (January 1965).

207. "Hospital Out-patient Services, a Guide to Sur-
     veying Clinic Procedures," Public Health
     Service, HEW (1964).

208. Terenzio, J. V., "Improved Care in Troubled
     1966," a study by the City of New York De-
     partment of Hospitals (April 1967).

209. "Kaiser Foundation Medical Care Program--1964."

210. Van Dyke, F., Brown, V., and Thom, A., " 'Long-
     Stay' Hospital Care," a study by the School
     of Public Health and Administrative Medicine
     of Columbia University for the Department of
     Hospitals of the City of New York (1963).

211. "Organized Ambulatory Medical Care Services--
     Fundamental Problems and Goals and Guidelines
     for Planning and Programming," a study by
     the Hospital Review and Planning Council of
     Southern New York (November 1965).

212. "Out-patient Application Processing Requirements,"
     from a letter to State Health Commissioner
     Ginsburg from Deputy Commissioner Lauchheim
     (January 27, 1967).

213. Weinerman, E. R., "Out-patient-Clinic Services
     in the Teaching Hospital," Yale Studies in
     Ambulatory Medical Care, No. 4 of a series,
     reprinted form New England Journal of
     Medicine, no. 272, pp. 947-954 (May 6, 1965).

214. "Patient Waiting Time," a study by the Hospital
     Review and Planning Council (October 20,
     1966).

215. "The Quality of Hospital Care Secured by a
     Sample of Teamster Family Members in New
     York City," a study by the School of Public
     Health and Administrative Medicine of
     Columbia University (1964).

Medical Economics

216. Harris, S. E., _The Economics of American Medicine_. New York: Macmillan Co., 1964.

217. Klarman, H. E., _The Economics of Health_. New York: Columbia University Press, 1965.

218. Schneider, D., "Average Expense per In-patient Day in General Hospitals," a report on health economics (April 14, 1967).

219. "The Basis for Municipal Capital Outlay on Health Care Facilities in New York City," a study by the Urban Research Center of Hunter College (April 1964).

220. "Changes in Public Expenditures for Personal Health Care of New York City Residents...," a report by the Office of Research, Urban Medical Economics Research Project.

221. "Discussion of the Columbia University Study on Social and Economic Characteristics of Out-patients," from a letter to State Health Commissioner Ginsburg from R. Learner (October 18, 1966).

222. Nicol, H. O., "Guaranteed Income Maintenance, Another Look at the Debate" in _Welfare in Review_, vol. 5, no. 6, pp. 1-13 (June-July 1967).

223. "Local Neighborhood Studies: Gouveneur Medical Service Area Population Statistics," an effort by the Urban Medical Economics Research Project, no. 1 (1960).

224. New York City Department of Welfare, "Medical Assistance Program" (1966).

225. "Medical Care Prices," a report to the President by HEW (February 1967).

226. Piore, N. K., "Metropolitan Medical Economics" in _Scientific American_ (January 1965).

227. "A Preliminary Classification of Tax-Supported
     Personal Health Care Services Administered
     by New York City Departments and Available
     to New York City Residents--1965," an ef-
     fort by the Urban Medical Economics Research
     Project (June 1966).

228. "Preliminary Inventory of Existing Tax-Supported
     Health Services for Children in New York City,"
     a report by the Office of Research, Urban
     Medical Economics Research Project.

229. Piore, N., Snyder, E., and Sohn, S., "Public,
     Private, and Philanthropic Expenditures for
     Dental Care in New York City," reported from
     The Journal of Public Health Dentistry,
     vol. 27, no. 1, pp. 7-20 (Winter 1967).

230. Piore, N., "Rationalizing the Mix of Public and
     Private Expenditures in Health," a paper
     for a CUNY seminar (April 19, 1966).

231. "Report of the Mayor's Task Force on Medical
     Economics, Part I" (February 14, 1966).

232. Weinerman, E. R., "Trends in the Economics and
     Organization of Medical Care" in The Yale
     Journal of Biology and Medicine, vol. 36,
     no. 1 (August 1963).

233. "Vendor Payments, Contracts, and Other Disburse-
     ments by the City of New York to Private
     Vendors and Voluntary Institutions, for
     Health Services Rendered to New York City
     Residents," an effort by the Urban Medical
     Economics Research Project (June 1964).

Medical Education

234. American Medical Association, Directory of Ap-
     proved Internships and Residencies, 1966.

235. Kaiser Foundation Hospitals' Educational Programs
     (April 1967).

236. "Background Data Book of the DOL-HEW Conference
     on Job Development and Training for Workers
     in Health Services" (Washington, D. C.,
     February 14-17, 1966).

237. Smith, J. J., et. al., "Health Education for
         Living Program (HELP)," a proposal from
         the Albert Einstein College of Medicine
         at Lincoln Hospital, New York.

238. Pollack, J., "Health Services and the Role of
         the Medical School," a report prepared by
         the Seminar on Health Policy, Institute
         for Policy Studies (Washington, D. C.,
         April 5, 1966).

239. "Internship and Residency Program, Maimonides
         Medical Center" (1967).

240. "Manpower for the World's Health," a report of
         the 1966 Institute on International Medical
         Education, Association of American Medical
         Colleges, ed. by H. van Zile Hyde, in The
         Journal of Medical Education, vol. 41, no. 9
         part 2 (September 1966).

241. Sheps, C. G., "The Medical School--Community
         Expectations," advance section of a book,
         Trends in the Foundation of New Medical
         Schools (November 1966).

242. Smith, J. J., "Obstetrical Technicians' Program,
         Lincoln Hospital," New York City.

243. "Organizing Comprehensive State Health Career
         Councils," a program developed by the
         National Health Council, an HEW document
         (November 1966).

244. Levin, T., "Proposal for an Albert Einstein
         College of Medicine--Lincoln Hospital Health
         Careers Program," a draft report (May 9,
         1967).

245. "Training Health Service Workers: The Critical
         Challenge," proceedings of the DOL/HEW Con-
         ference on Job Development and Training for
         Workers in Health Services (Washington, D. C.,
         February 14-17, 1966).

246. "A World Program for Health Manpower," report
     of a study of medical education in the de-
     veloping countries, by the Association for
     American Medical Colleges for the Agency of
     International Development (October 15, 1965).

Medical Practice

247. Weinerman, E. R., "Patients' Perceptions of
     Group Medical Care" in American Journal of
     Public Health, vol. 54, no. 6 (June 1964).

248. Baehr, G., "Prepaid Group Practice: Its
     Strength and Weaknesses, and Its Future"
     in American Journal of Public Health,
     vol. 56, no. 11 (November 1966).

249. Glaser, W. A., "Socialized Medicine in Practice"
     in The Public Interest, no. 3 (Spring 1966).

Mental Health

250. Hollingshead, A. B. and Redlick, F. C., Social
     Class and Mental Illness. New York: John
     Wiley, 1958.

251. Joint Information Service of the American Psy-
     chiatric Association and the National Assoc-
     iation for Mental Health, The Community
     Mental Health Center--An Analysis of Existing
     Models. Washington, D. C.: 1964.

252. Peck, H. B., Riessman, F., and Hallowitz, E.,
     The Neighborhood Service Center: A Proposal
     to Implement a Community Mental Health
     Network. New York: Albert Einstein College
     of Medicine, 1964.

253. Perkins, M. E. and Padilla, E., Area Planning
     for Comprehensive Mental Health Care in
     New York City. New York: 1967.

254. ____, and Elinson, J., Public Image of Mental
     Health Services. New York: 1967.

255. "Bedford Mental Health Clinic," the annual re-
     port to the Board of Directors (September 14,
     1966).

256. Pines, M., "The Coming Upheaval in Psychiatry,"
      in Harper's Magazine, pp. 54-60 (October
      1965).

257. Bernard, V., "Education for Community Psychiatry
      in a University Medical Center" in Handbook
      of Community Psychiatry and Community Mental
      Health, ed. by L. Ballak. New York: Grune
      and Stratton, 1964.

258. "Inventory of Operating Psychiatric Clinics in
      New York City," New York City Community
      Mental Health Board Reports (November 1966).

259. "Lincoln Hospital Community Mental Health Center,"
      a preliminary draft (May 26, 1967).

260. "Lincoln Hospital Mental Health Services," the
      annual report (July 1, 1965 to June 30, 1966).

261. "A Master Plan for Comprehensive Mental Health
      and Mental Retardation Services in New York
      City," a report by the New York City Commun-
      ity Mental Health Board (1967).

262. "National Institute of Mental Health Study:
      Cost Analysis in Community Mental Health
      Centers," prepared by the Committee on
      Special Studies, New York Academy of Medi-
      cine (June 25, 1965).

263. Holt, R. R., "New Directions in the Training of
      Psychotherapists" in Journal of Nervous and
      Mental Diseases, vol. 137, no. 5 (November
      1963).

264. Rioch, M. J., "Pilot Project in Training Mental
      Health Counselors," a study for the National
      Institute of Mental Health, PHS document
      1254 (1965).

265. Lieberman, M., "Public Expenditures for the
      Mentally Ill in New York City" in Public
      Health Reports, vol. 79, no. 10 (October
      1964.

266.   "Queensboro Council for Social Welfare Institute
       on Mental Retardation," the proceedings and
       a progress report (June 1966).

267.   "Report of Special Advisory Committee on Psychi-
       atric Services to the Commissioner of Hos-
       pitals," New York City (September 21, 1961).

268.   "Report of the Department of Hospitals Committee
       on Psychiatric Services for Children to the
       Commissioner of Hospitals in New York City"
       (March 1963).

269.   "The Scope and Role of Public Expenditures for
       Mental Illness Services in New York City,"
       an Urban Medical Economics Research Project
       (1960-61).

270.   Pines, M., "Training Housewives as Psychothera-
       pists," in Harper's Magazine.   (April 1962).

Nonmedical Source Material

271.   The City of New York Executive Capital Budget
       for 1967-1968.

272.   Community Information Manual, Central Brooklyn
       edition (December 1966).

273.   Total Population for New York City by Ethnic
       Group and Borough, 1920-1965.

274.   Vital and Service Statistics, by health center
       districts, New York City (1965).

275.   "Age and Ethnic Group by Health Area in the
       Washington Heights Health District," a
       study by Columbia University (February
       1967).

276.   "Biennial Report of the Department of Welfare,
       New York City" (January 1, 1963 to
       December 31, 1964).

277.   "Borough of Brooklyn, New York City," the
       annual report (1966-67).

278. "Borough President's Report to Bronx Community
     Organizations on the 1967-1968 Capital Budg-
     et as Adopted by the Board of Estimate and
     the City Council" (July 28, 1967).

279. Parks, R., et. al., "A Brief Survey of Selected
     Departments and Functions, City of New York"
     (December 1965).

280. "Budget Message of the Mayor to the Board of
     Estimate and the City Council for the Fis-
     cal Year 1967-1968," by Mayor John Lindsay
     (April 15, 1967).

281. "Bulletin 182 of the New York State Department
     of Social Welfare--Federal Provision of
     Title XIX of the Social Security Act
     (April 28, 1967).

282. "Community Master Sample Survey in the Washington
     Heights Health District," a study by Columbia
     University (January 1966).

283. "December 1965 Graphic Presentation of Public
     Assistance," a report by the Bureau of
     Family Services, HEW document no. GPO
     910-655 (May 1966).

284. "Delinquency Rates, 7-20 Years," a study by the
     New York City Youth Board (1962-66).

285. "Directory of Offices of the Department of
     Welfare" (June 1966).

286. "Financing Government in New York City," a
     report by the Graduate School of Public
     Administration, NYU (June 1966).

287. "Looking for Skilled Workers? Manpower Develop-
     ment and Training Act," a report by the
     State of New York Department of Labor,
     Division of Employment (February 1965).

288. "The Mayor's Task Force on Reorganization of
     New York City Government," a report and
     proposed local law (December 1966).

289. Snyder, E., "Measures of the Dimensions of
      Poverty in New York City," a study for the
      Urban Research Center (June 15, 1965).

290. "Model Neighborhoods under the Demonstration
      Cities Act," a document of the U. S. Depart-
      ment of Housing and Urban Development (1966).

291. "More Socioeconomic Indices," a study by the
      New York City Youth Board Research Department
      (May 1965).

292. "New York City's Renewal Strategy--1965," a
      report by the Community Renewal Program,
      New York City Planning Commission (1965).

293. "Older Population of New York City--An Analysis
      of 1960 Census Facts," a report by the
      Community Council of Greater New York,
      Research Department (June 1964).

294. "Population by Ethnic Group," a report of New
      York City Health areas taken from the U. S.
      1960 Census, by the New York City Youth
      Board Research Department (April 1967).

295. "Population Characteristics," report #8-1 by
      the Department of Health, New York City
      Population Health Survey (1964).

296. "Population Characteristics," a study by the
      New York City Youth Board from the 1960
      Census.

297. "President's Proposals for Revision in the
      Social Security System," from a hearing
      before the Committee on Ways and Means,
      U. S. House of Representatives, on Bill
      #HR 5710, parts 1-4, first session.

298. "The Region's Growth," a report by the New York
      Regional Planning Association (May 1967).

299. "Statistical Data for Health Areas 56, 57, 58.29,
      59, and 60 in Brownsville, Brooklyn, New York"
      a report by the New York City Youth Board
      Research Department (February 1966).

300. Shiffman, R., "Strategy for a Coordinated Social
          and Physical Renewal Program: Bedford-
          Stuyvesant," a report in draft (1966).

301. "Summary of Vital Statistics, 1964," a document
          of the New York City Department of Health
          (1964).

302. Office of the Mayor, "Supplemental Budget Items
          for the 1967-1968 Budget of New York City."

303. "Urban and Rural Poverty," a message from the
          President to the 90th Congress, House of
          Representatives document no. 88 (March 15,
          1967).

Nursing

304. American Nurses' Association, Facts About
          Nursing (a statistical summary) (1966).

305. Haughton, J. G., "The Nursing Dilemma: More
          Training or More Trainees or Both?"
          presented to the New York State Senate
          Committee on Public Health and Medicare
          (September 26, 1966).

306. "Nursing Education and Nursing Service," from
          a collection of television projects known
          as "Nursing Today," Prepared by the New
          York City Department of Hospitals (1963-
          66).

307. New York City Department of Hospitals, "Nursing
          Education and Nursing Service," 1966 pre-
          liminary annual report.

308. "Utilization of Nursing Services by Residents
          of the Gouverneur Hospital District," a
          report by the Gouverneur Economic Research
          Project Team (1967).

Nursing Homes

309. New York State Department of Health, Selected
          Characteristics of Proprietary Nursing
          Homes in New York State, and Their Patients
          (1964).

310. "Ad Hoc Committee on Nursing Home Bed Needs,"
     a memo from Mr. Jack Haldeman (1967).

311. Wyman, G., "Application to Proprietary Nursing
     Homes," a report on Medical assistance, by
     the New York State Department of Social
     Welfare (October 14, 1966).

312. "Guidelines for Nursing Home Mortgage Loans,"
     a report by the State of New York Department
     of Health (July 29, 1966).

313. Haughton, J. C., "Medical Care in a Private
     Nursing Home: The Use of Physicians in
     the Community as a Resource," a report
     (October 1964).

314. "Nursing Home Manual, The City of New York,"
     prepared by the Department of Welfare,
     Bureau of Special Services (May 1966).

315. "Nursing Home Project of United Hospital Fund
     Nearing Completion," a report by the
     Community Council's Citizens' Committee
     on Aging (May 1967).

316. Haughton, J. C., "Organization of Medical Ser-
     vices in a Private Nursing Home--Three New
     Approaches," reprinted from The New England
     Journal of Medicine (May 1965).

317. Learner, R., "Recommended Principals of Reim-
     bursement for Nursing Homes in New York
     State," a report published by the Columbia
     University School of Public Health, sections
     A-1 through A-15 (October 28, 1966).

                Nursing Home/Hospital Affiliation

318. Wood, C. B., "Beth Israel Hospital/Riverview
     Nursing Home Affiliation--One Year's Experi-
     ence in Operation" (April 1966).

319. Haughton, J. G., "Experience in a Hospital/
     Private Nursing Home Affiliation" (February
     1964).

320. Wood, C. B., "Lenox Hill Hospital/Peter Cooper
        Nursing Home Affiliation--One Year's Experi-
        ence in Operation" (April 1966).

Rehabilitation

321. "Guideposts and Roadblocks to Areawide Rehabili-
        tation in New York City," a report by the
        New York Regional Interdepartmental Rehabili-
        tation Committee (March 4, 1965).

322. "Manpower Utilization in Rehabilitation in New
        York City," a report by the New York Regional
        Interdepartmental Rehabilitation Committee
        (September 1966).

323. "Rehabilitation Centers in New York City," a col-
        lection of data by TECHNOMICS, Inc. (1967).

324. "Selection, Training and Utilization of Supportive
        Personnel in Rehabilitation Facilities," a
        report by the Arkansas Rehabilitation Re-
        search and Training Center and The Association
        of Rehabilitation Centers, Inc. (1966).

Subsets of the Population:
Their Special Health Needs

Union Groups

325. "Census of Union Medical Groups in New York City"
        (August 15, 1964).

The Aged

326. Klarman, H. E., "Background Issues, and Policies
        in Health Services for the Aged in New York
        City," a report (March 1962).

327. "The Community Reaches Out to the Elderly Home-
        bound," a conference summary, prepared by
        the Citizens' Committee on Aging of the
        Community Council of Greater New York and
        the New York Association of Senior Centers
        (June 18, 1963).

328. "Homemaker/Home Health Services for New York
        City's Aging: Background Information,
        Goals, and Tentative Plan," a first-draft
        report by the Community Council of Greater
        New York (May 11, 1967).

329. "The Place of the Aging in the 'Great Society':
        Present Position, Future Prognosis," sum-
        mary of the annual meeting of the Citizens'
        Committee on Aging (June 10, 1965).

330. "Queensbridge Health Maintenance Service"
        (statistics) (May 31, 1964).

331. "Queensbridge Health Maintenance Service for
        the Elderly--An Evaluation" (1965).

332. Starin, I., Kuo, N., and McLaughlin, M.,
        "Queensbridge Health Maintenance Service
        for the Elderly," a report.

333. "Queensbridge Health Maintenance Service for
        the Elderly," the 2nd annual report
        (October 31, 1963).

The Young

334. "The Administration of Services to Children and
        Youth in New York City," a report by the
        Institute of Public Administration (1963).

335. O'Rourke, J. A., "The Economics of Child Health
        Care in the Gouverneur Area in New York City:
        An Empirical Analysis," a report prepared
        for the Gouverneur Economic Research Project
        (June 1, 1967).

336. Lukashok, H., "First Report to the Citizens'
        Committee for Children," a health and
        hospital survey (January 25, 1967).

The Poor

337. Brown, H. J., "The Delivery of Personal Health
        Services and Medical Services for the Poor:
        Concessions or Prerogatives?" a paper pre-
        pared for the Seminar on Health Policy, In-
        stitute for Policy Studies (Washington, D. C.,
        May 17, 1966).

338. Yerby, A. S., "The Disadvantaged and Health
     Care," a paper presented at the White House
     Conference on Health (November 3, 1965).

339. Bernstein, B. J., "Examination of Health Aspects
     in Early Planning of the Poverty Program in
     New York City," a speech delivered on
     October 19, 1965).

340. "Medical Assistance for Needy Persons in New
     York State" (April 30, 1966).

341. "Poverty and Health in the U. S.," a report
     by the Medical and Health Research Associ-
     ation of New York City (1967).

342. "Providing for the Medically Indigent: A Re-
     statement of Principles," a report by the
     Ad Hoc Committee on Medical Indigency,
     Health Division, Community Council of
     Greater New York (May 10, 1967).

                    Miscellaneous

343. American College of Radiology, X-Ray, The
     Inside Story.

344. Bryant, J. H., The Application of Modern
     Managerial Concepts to Health Problems.

345. Freeman, H. E., Levine, S., and Reeder, L. G.
     (eds.), Handbook of Medical Sociology.
     New York: Prentice-Hall, 1963.

346. "Biomedical Science and Its Administration," a
     study by the NIH, report to the President
     (February 1965).

347. "Cities--A Closer Look," reprinted from
     Scientific American (September 1965).

348. "Closing the Gap in Social Work Manpower," a
     report of the Departmental Task Force on
     Social Work Education and Manpower, a HEW
     document (November 1965).

340. "Data on Laboratories," a collection of data for
     June 4-16, 1967, by TECHNOMICS, Inc.

350. "Data on TB," a collection of data for June 5-16, 1967, by TECHNOMICS, Inc.

351. Randal, J., "Lack of Wealth Often Spells Lack of Health," reprinted from the Newhouse National News Service (December 1966).

352. Robertson, A., "Medical Care: Its Social and Organizational Aspects; Role of the Private Foundations in Medicine," reprinted from the New England Journal of Medicine, vol. 270, pp. 398-401 (February 20, 1964).

353. McDermott, W., "Modern Medicine and the Demographic Disease Pattern of Overly Traditional Societies--A Technological Misfit," a paper presented at the Institute on International Medical Education/Association of American Medical Colleges (Washington, D. C., March 28, 1966).

354. Rappleye, W., "The New Era of American Medicine," a report (April 30, 1966).

355. Terris, M., "On the Distinction Between Individual and Social Medicine" in The Lancet (September 26, 1964).

356. Elling, R. H., "The Shifting Power Structure in Health," a paper prepared for the Seminar on Health Policy, Institute for Policy Studies (Washington, D. C., March 22, 1966).

257. "The U. S. City--Its Greatness Is At Stake," a special issue of Life Magazine, vol. 59, no. 26 (December 24, 1965).

358. Welfare in Review, issues dated December 1966- April 1967.

The following entries were received
too late to be included within
categories:

1. National Commission on Community Health Services,
   Health Is a Community Affair. Cambridge:
   Harvard University Press, 1966.

2. Tentative By-Laws for the Board of Governors of
   the Catholic Medical Center, Diocese of
   Brooklyn.

3. Anderson, O. W., "Health Services and Well-Being:
   Problems and Prospects," a paper prepared
   for the American Institute of Planners.

4. Davis, M., "Health Work Paper I: Suggested
   Approach to Health Facility Planning for
   the Department of City Planning," (February 1966).

5. Anderson, O. W., "Influence of Social and Economic Research on Public Policy in the
   Health Field," reprinted from the Milbank
   Memorial Fund Quarterly, vol. 44, no. 3,
   part 2 (July 1966).

6. ____, "The Medical Profession and the Public:
   An Examination of Interrelationships," a
   paper presented at the Michigan State
   Medical Society meeting on March 7, 1966.

7. Wise, H. B., "Neighborhood Medical Care Demonstration," a report of the organization founded
   in August 1966 by the Office of Economic
   Opportunity (January 12, 1967).

8. "Physicians, Patients, and the General Hospital:
   Professional Judgment," an unsigned article
   in Progress in Health Services, bimonthly
   publication of the Health Information
   Foundation, vol. 14, no. 4 (September-
   October 1965).

9.   Lerner, R. C., and Kirchner, C., "Social and
        Economic Characteristics of Patients in
        New York City Outpatient Departments, 1965:
        Financial Eligibility Under Medicaid and
        Potential Reimbursement to the City,"
        report no. 1 of a Municipal General Hospital
        Outpatient Population Study by the School
        of Public Health and Administrative Medicine
        at Columbia University (June 1967).

APPENDIX C

Testimony And Proposal:
District Council 37, AFSCME

(Reproduced verbatim as provided to the Commission.)

Mr. Gerard Piel, Chairman
The Commission on the Delivery
of Personal Health Services
420 Madison Avenue
New York City 10017

Dear Mr. Piel:

Following our discussion with the Commission,
you requested that we amplify in writing our ideas
about how a Hospitals Authority might be structured,
and what its functions should be. Here is our response to that request.

Let me repeat our statement before the Commission that we support the principle of a strong authority with broad powers over many aspects of health
service. Its scope should include the metropolitan
area. It must have a professional and technical staff,
and the funds to function. Its responsibilities should
include these areas:

1. Planning and approval of hospital construction and
design.

It should develop a master plan for the construction, expansion, and closing down of hospitals in the
metropolitan area, on the basis of population projections over ten and twenty-year periods. It should
require the coordinated use of central facilities--
open-heart surgery, radiological therapy, biochemistry
laboratories, computer diagnostic centers, etc. It
should identify sub-sectors of need among the classes
of hospitals and hospital beds--general care, long-
term care, psychiatric care, and other specialties

633

such as tuberculosis, etc. Each of these needs integration into the master plan; the authority must have
the technical staff to do this, and the power to see
that its plans are carried out.

2. Dissemination of technical advances in medical
    care.

The authority should be equipped to identify
and provide full information on new technical advances,
and to provide guidelines under which institutions
are expected to incorporate these advances. Here,
control of certain fund flows provides incentive to
compliance. Though we often assume that good communication takes place between hospitals within the
metropolitan area, this is often not the case, and
institutions may differ markedly in their responsiveness to new technical opportunities, particularly
when it is expensive to purchase or operate them.

3. Supervision of standards for hospital staff.

There should be open access to appointment for
qualified physicians to hospital staffs; denial of
such appointment should be only for valid professional
reasons. At the same time, standards for appointment
should be high and uniform. The powers to formulate
and apply these standards belong to the authority.

4. Development of auxiliary and supportive health
    facilities.

Hospitals are one element, though the major one,
in a system of health care. Other facilities which
are needed include neighborhood health stations, well-
baby clinics, nursing and recuperative centers, laboratories, research facilities, roving immunization,
x-ray, and diagnostic facilities, etc. Planning by
the authority should include all of these elements
and their integration.

The foregoing are only illustrative of the major
areas we believe important. Let me stress that we
are not experts in the delivery of health care, and
we rely on the insights of the experts in these and
other areas. Our chief concern is that the authority
should hold a broad mandate covering all the major
determinants of a successful, dynamic, and acceptable
system of health care, and that its mandate should
embrace and govern those of existing private and,

indeed public institutions now authorized to make
these decisions. Its focus must be precise and its
authority unquestioned.

But even more important is the concept of ac-
acountability. We do not propose the creation of a
new Port of New York Authority or Triborough Bridge
and Tunnel Authority, so powerful and impregnable
that it can function virtually without check or control by elected officials or by the community it is
intended to serve. We strongly urge that a health
services authority be broadly representative, truly
responsive to the needs and desires of the community,
and clearly accountable to the people. Let me highlight each of these elements:

Representative: We do not think that pro forma appointment of representatives of certain broadly based
groups in the community meets the criterion. Rather,
we would want members selected who have an active and
continuing interest in the problems of health. Certainly, representatives of the unions belong on such
an authority, and we would be happy to serve. The
professional organizations of doctors, nurses, and
other personnel who operate within the system also
belong. The community must have a voice as well.

The way we would recommend achieving the latter
objective is through a decentralization of the structure of the authority. We think that there must be a
solid rooting of the authority's functions in the communities which it serves, particularly in the low-
income areas where the clients of publicly supported
health services are concentrated. There can be no
meaningful representation without this. We recommend
neighborhood health councils, affiliated with the
authority, with members either elected or chosen by
community groups. These councils should operate
grievance clinics for the neighborhood, with the help
of professional staff and others from the hospitals
and health facilities where they are located. They
should also engage in certain planning functions,
again with the help of professionals, identifying
the health needs of the community as they see them,
and the services which are either lacking or in short
supply.

Out of these neighborhood health councils can
be elected representatives to serve on the authority.
Ideally, there should be one from each neighborhood.

If this number is too large, there can be borough-wide committees, each with a representative. Alternatively, neighborhoods can alternate in selecting representatives, just as nations and areas alternate in selecting members of the Security Council.

Union members from the hospitals and health facilities would be available to serve as members of the neighborhood health councils.

Responsive: Responsiveness will come from the frequency of meetings with the community and other interest groups, and from the feedback arising out of the decentralized structure. Regular public meetings are a necessary feature. It is important at such meetings that the resources be available to answer questions which are raised and to provide information. Otherwise, a cumulative process of frustration and alienation can take hold. Regular dissemination of information through newsletters and other media in the neighborhood, and distribution of health literature, should be a normal part of the operations of neighborhood councils, working through community organizations as well as in hospitals, health stations, etc. Here again, union facilities will be available and union members will be glad to take part.

Accountable: We mean more than fiscal accountability, the matching of expenditures to vouchers and adherence to established budgetary guidelines. Accountability for the quality of the services rendered, and for the awareness which those who manage health services have of the needs and desires of the community, are the values which need to be built into the structure. Specifying this in detail is difficult, but we are convinced that it is essential. Accountability also means that those to whom the specialist or administrator are accountable have the power to discipline or remove those who do not meet their responsibilities. We believe in this principle, though we would surround it with suitable procedural safeguards, the right of representation and--where penalties are proposed-- impartial arbitration for those in subordinate positions. Such procedures derive directly from collective bargaining, and are adaptable to this area as well. It is difficult to be more precise in terms of structural arrangements, though we would be glad to see and discuss any tentative proposals which your commission may develop along these lines.

Let me conclude with this note. We have spent
enormous time and energy developing a system of collective bargaining for City employees. The arrangements now in force in New York City must apply to
all who are paid in part from City funds, or through
City fiscal mechanisms. We would not cede to any
authority the power to negotiate with us under other
rules or arrangements, and I am sure that you understand why this is so. I say this simply to protect
you from erring in the field of labor relations,
where we have both the expertise and the jurisdiction.
I think the record will show that our union is in
favor of a more effective hospital system, better
standards of personnel administration, more opportunities for employees to serve the sick, and all the
other objectives which are encompassed in the charge
to your commission. Good labor relations practices
will further these goals.

We very much appreciated the opportunity to speak
before the commission, and look forward to your report. To the degree that it meets the standards
which are articulated in our testimony and in this
letter, we will give it full public support.

                              Sincerely,

                              /s/Victor Gotbaum,
                              Executive Director

VG:1s

June 30, 1967

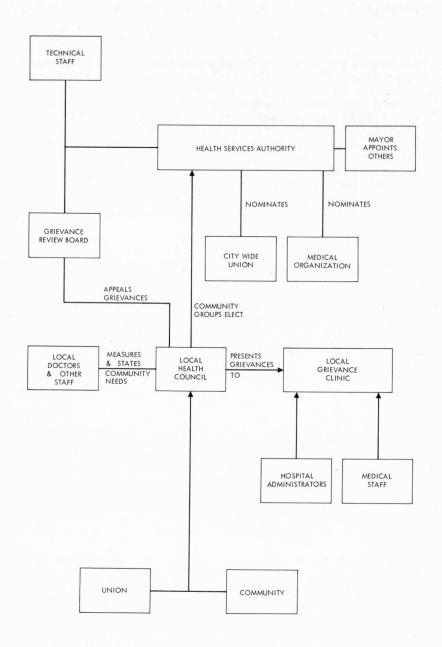

TECHNICAL
STAFF

HEALTH SERVICES AUTHORITY

MAYOR
APPOINTS
OTHERS

NOMINATES

NOMINATES

GRIEVANCE
REVIEW BOARD

CITY WIDE
UNION

MEDICAL
ORGANIZATION

APPEALS
GRIEVANCES

COMMUNITY
GROUPS ELECT

LOCAL
DOCTORS
& OTHER
STAFF

MEASURES
& STATES
COMMUNITY
NEEDS

LOCAL
HEALTH
COUNCIL

PRESENTS
GRIEVANCES
TO

LOCAL
GRIEVANCE
CLINIC

HOSPITAL
ADMINISTRATORS

MEDICAL
STAFF

UNION

COMMUNITY

New York's Hospitals--A Union View

(Testimony before the Commission on
the Delivery of Personal Health Services, District Council 37, AFSCME,
June 7, 1967.)

Preface

Those who man the city's hospitals have a special
obligation to participate in decisions which will determine their future. Their many years of devoted
service have played a major part in achieving and
maintaining standards of care. Their long struggle
for recognition, for decent standards of pay and working conditions, for status and dignity, has been and
is being waged so that they can render the services to
which they are dedicated. They want to be part of a
team which includes and which recognizes the contribution of everyone who works in hospitals, from aides
and orderlies to doctors and administrators. Hospital
workers are also an integral part of that portion of
the community which depends for medical care on the
municipal hospitals, free clinics, and other health
facilities. When these institutions fail to meet
their responsibilities, workers, their families and
friends suffer the consequences.

This is a time of crisis. It is also a time of
transition and hope. The crisis, now widely discussed,
is the result of neglect and mismanagement over decades. No quick solutions are possible; none should
be embraced. At the same time, a new era has begun
with the passage of the Medicare and Medicaid laws.
For the first time, the principle has been accepted
that decent standards of health care must be provided,
as a matter of right, to all who need them.

The crisis has been known to us, the workers, for
many years. We recall the bitter strikes in New York
to secure recognition of the right to organize for
hospital workers, won many years ago by other workers.
The views and considerations of the employees should
be part of any meaningful discussion. Decisions which
will determine the future of health and hospital care
for many years to come should not be made without the
full participation and involvement of all concerned.

The hope we see is that new ideas and new commitments can ensure a single standard of care for

everyone. Let the traditional dichotomy between the
"private"--i.e., voluntary and proprietary--and the
"public" sectors disappear. It has been outmoded for
many years; in the future, the vast preponderance of
funds for construction and operation of hospitals will
by publicly provided. Private philanthropy no longer
represents a significant source of financing for hospital construction and operation. Under these circumstances, we call for equality of care and equality of
access to care, coupled with decent wages, hours, and
working conditions for everyone who works in hospitals. This can best be provided through a single
hospital system, which combines the virtues of the
best independent voluntary hospitals with the system-
wide potential of the municipal hospital system. Such
a single system must combine high levels of professional management with effective control by the community which this system serves. The time is now to
end a class system of care, under which hospitals for
the poor are poor hospitals, just as housing for the
poor is poor housing and schools for the poor are
poor schools.

Outmoded Ideas Which Are Barriers to Progress

Old ideas die hard. If we are to make progress,
myths which have lost their validity must be chal-
lenged, examined, discarded. Here are some of these:

1) Public-Private: In some discussions, one
hears that the voluntary hospitals are models of efficiency, effective control and progressive management, while the municipal hospitals are hopelessly
inefficient, backward, doomed to ineffectiveness.
From this one draws the conclusion: turn the public
hospitals over to "private enterprise" and all will
be well.

This is contrary to the facts. Voluntary hospitals vary enormously in quality, as do municipal
hospitals. What determines the level of quality is
the adequacy of funds, the ability of administrators,
the vision and dedication of those who direct the
hospital. None of these qualities is inherent in
either the "private" or the "public" sector; they
must be sought, cultivated, rewarded. For many aspects of medical care, the publicly owned veterans
hospitals are models which leave others far behind;
in other cases, voluntary hospitals have pioneered;

in still others the municipal hospital has been in the
forefront. Many forget, for example, that for many
years Bellevue Hospital was considered one of the
world's great hospitals. These are artificial distinctions which are now outmoded.

2) Professional-Nonprofessional: The affiliation of municipal to teaching or voluntary hospitals,
undertaken on a large scale beginning in 1962, was
based on the myth that the quality of medical and
nursing personnel--and that alone--determines the
quality of patient care. Accordingly, the affiliating
institutions were given virtual carte-blanche, provided only that they assumed the responsibility for
medical services in the municipal hospitals. Recent
months have demonstrated both the fallacious nature
of this myth, and the abuses which inevitably occur
when public officials abandon their obligation to
scrutinize, audit, and evaluate the performance of
others, even the most prestigious medical staffs of
the most prestigious institutions. After five years
of affiliation, the hospital crisis is worse than ever.

All employees who work in a hospital have a responsibility and a role to play in the provision of
decent standards of medical care. We know that the
obligations of hospital administrators to their employees have been scandalously neglected for decades;
it was only in response to the efforts of our unions
that, for the first time, the basic rights of hospital workers began to be recognized. But this is not
enough. The contribution of the "nonprofessional"--
the nurse's aide, dietary aide, laundry worker, ward
clerk, messenger, elevator operator, and many others--
must be recognized. Who has assumed the burden of
nursing care in the face of an acute and continuing
shortage of professionals? Official reports of the
New York City Department of Hospitals show that as
many as 40 percent of the unfilled positions for professional and licensed practical nurses are filled by
nurse's aides. But these workers do not receive the
recognition due them for a magnificent job done under
enormous hardships. Neither do they receive the
training, motivation, opportunity for advancement
which would enable them to play an even more important role in patient care. Until the provision of
hospital care is defined as a group responsibility,
and everyone who plays a part is given the opportunity

and the challenge to play his part fully, decent standards of hospital care will continue to elude us.

3) <u>High Costs-High Wages</u>: Alarmists point to
rising costs of hospital care as an argument against
giving decent wages to hospital workers. As unionists,
we know that this argument has been used against <u>every</u>
group of workers who ever tried to help themselves
through organization and collective action. It is
threadbare, worthless in this case as in all the
others. We insist that hospital workers need and deserve decent wages, hours, and working conditions.
We know from history that the pressure of rising wages
has been, in industry after industry, the major stimulus to technical progress, better management, and
more efficient use of labor. There is in principle
no reason why this sequence does not apply to the
hospital industry, despite the fact that hospital care
is, and will remain, labor-intensive. We see the
source of rising costs in other areas. One is the
simple fact that most hospitals are poorly managed.
Hospital administrators are usually chosen for reasons
with little or nothing to do with their managerial
abilities. The art of hospital management has been
neglected, and has yet to be developed to anything
comparable to management in most of industry.

A second reason is the resistance of professional associations and organizations to any innovations in the training or deployment of health manpower.
Ancient guild-like restrictions govern the training
and use of doctors, nurses, and certain other key
groups. They bestow virtual autonomy on these people,
even in areas where they have no special competence.
As a result, hospitals must be run to accommodate the
traditions and self-interests of these groups, no matter how obsolete or inappropriate. We know, for example, that nurse's aides can in many cases do far
more for patient care than the rules and regulations
permit them to, and that with some further training,
they could do even more. They are not permitted to
take on additional responsibilities. Until the deployment of manpower, the assignment of tasks, and
the allocation of training resources is completely
restudied, these problems will remain unsolved.

A third reason is the anarchy of hospital construction. There is no effective mechanism for determining what the needs are, and for directing resources

to meet these needs. Instead, each group with a stake
in hospitals, or with a desire to take part, makes its
own plans, raises its own funds, builds its own hospitals, and then competes for a place in the sun. Examples of duplication of facilities have been abundantly documented, but nothing is done to stop it.
Prestige and status are more important than rational-
ity. Some kinds of facilities are in oversupply;
others are chronically short. Hospitals build complete plants, and seldom plan to share expensive facilities. Both an oversupply and a shortage of
facilities escalate costs, in the one case because of
heavy overhead costs, and in the other because the
shortage, like any shortage, forces prices upward.
Until there is real authority to plan the network of
hospital facilities needed in this metropolitan area,
and to ensure that the plan is adhered to, this chaos
will continue with all its consequences.

Affiliation--A Critique

Affiliation was hailed as a panacea. It has
failed totally to meet expectations. We have already
said that affiliation grew from certain widely held
myths which tend to dominate discussion of hospital
problems. Affiliation, in fact, was a makeshift.
Given the widely-held belief that the municipal hospitals faced a crisis which needed quick action, and the
refusal of the City of New York to recognize the full
magnitude of that crisis, affiliation could be justified as a temporary holding operation, a time-buyer
to permit other, fuller solutions to be brought to
bear. But it has not been so treated. Once it began,
those in authority simply washed their hands of the
problem, and went on to other things. A time bomb was
left ticking, until it exploded in 1966. Incredibly,
there were no audits, no analyses, no measures of performance, despite the expenditure of hundreds of millions of dollars in public funds over the 1962-1966
period.

This is now well-known. Less well-known is the
fact that in many cases the affiliating institutions
were given freedom to enlarge their operations outside
of the primary medical area, until they were exerting
authority in virtually every aspect of hospital operations. Not only did this swell the costs; it threatened the integrity of the jobs of every city employee,

of whom there are some 36,000 in the municipal hospitals. Repeated efforts to call attention to this
process, with its demoralization of employees, went
unheeded--under every Commissioner including the present one--until the union brought its members to the
very verge of direct action. Only then did these
abuses receive the recognition and the correction
which had been demanded for years. When an employer
has so little faith in his employees as the City of
New York has shown over the years, those employees
will understandably show the effects of their demoralization. Until the rights of employees are honored,
the obligations of employees--invoked by the pundits
and the pontificators--will have no meaning. Both go
together. That is why decent procedures, full recognition of union rights and responsibilities, and
honorable compliance with labor-management agreements
are essential parts of any solution to the hospital
crisis in New York.

What Is To Be Done?

We call for fundamental solutions to the problems
which beset the hospital system in New York. Let us
begin with what we consider to be the standards which
any solution must meet:

1) Hospital and medical care of high quality
equally accessible to all citizens, regardless of
where they live or what they earn.

2) Hospitals uniformly utilizing the most progressive standards of care and treatment, with joint
use of facilities and equipment not present in every
institution.

3) Hospital management under competent professional direction, philosophically free of any medical
or other bias or obligation.

4) Access to hospital staff appointments open to
all doctors on merit; requirement that all medical
staff meet standards of qualification in their
specialty.

5) Systems-based utilization of all manpower.

6) Training, up-grading, and promotional opportunities available at all levels, adequately funded and staffed, and related to the total occupational ladder; career opportunities for all who seek them.

7) Area-wide control of investment resources used to build, enlarge, modernize, or modify hospital plant and equipment, such control relating investment decisions to long-range plans defining needs.

8) Accountability to the community for the quality of care, the cost of care, and the utilization of manpower by all hospitals.

A Mechanism for Results

We can see no other way to meet these standards than the creation of a metropolitan hospital and health care authority, broadly representative, with real power and authority in the areas cited in the previous section. We assert that labor belongs on such an authority. We believe such an authority must take precedence in its dealings with hospital boards, professional associations, accrediting agencies, medical and nursing schools, and others. We believe consumers of medical care must be represented along with the purveyors. We believe such an authority has an urgent short-run job to do, in bringing some order out of the present chaos; its major role is in laying and carrying out long-term plans which will assure this metropolitan population an adequate supply of doctors and nurses, hospital facilities of all categories, preventive care facilities, medical care workers of various kinds, and whatever else is needed, at costs which are truly reflective of the necessary balance between needs and what it takes to meet them.

We see such an authority planning--in cooperation with the educational resources of this area--medical schools, nursing schools, and other schools and institutes to train health workers at all levels. We see it sponsoring innovations in systems for delivering health care economically and readily, particularly to the low-income population. We see it making sure that all institutions conform to standards of practice which are, or should be, widely applicable, so that the lag between what is developed in one place and its over-all application is minimized.

To fulfill these and other function, such an authority must have a broad mandate and the power to
carry it out.   The New York metropolitan area is precisely the place, in our view, where such an authority must be promptly brought into being and given life.
What we do here in the years to come can set the pattern for the entire nation.   There is, in our judgment,
no time to lose.   That is why we make this statement,
and invite all those who care to respond.

We welcome the comments and the cooperation of
all groups in the community.

APPENDIX D

Review of Applicable Health Legislation

A memorandum prepared by Mr. Peter Eccles of the firm
of Cleary, Gottlieb, Steen and Hamilton reviewing
applicable city, state, and federal legislation.

MEMORANDUM TO THE COMMISSION

The delivery of health services in the City
of New York is governed by the legislation of the
City of New York, New York State and the Federal
government.

NEW YORK CITY LEGISLATION

The relevant New York City legislation is contained primarily in the City Charter and the Administrative Code. At present this legislation provides
for the Departments of Hospitals and Health, the Community Mental Health Board and the Office of the
Chief Medical Examiner. Although special provisions
contained in the City Charter establish the health-
related Departments, the rules, regulations and procedures by which they must operate are very largely
the same rules, regulations and procedures applicable
to other City departments. For example, the procedures to be followed with respect to adopting and
amending the budgets of the health-related departments, the letting of their contracts, the purchasing
of their equipment and the employment of their personnel are in large measure identical with the procedures established for other City departments.

Health Department, Commissioner, Board of Health

Presently existing legislation[1] establishes a Department of Health headed by a Commissioner who must be either a doctor of medicine or holder of a degree in public health with at least eight years of relevant experience.[2] Since the Department has "jurisdiction to regulate all matters affecting health in the (C)ity"[3] and its geographical area of responsibility includes the City and waters within and adjacent to the City,[4] its powers and duties are extensive.

For example, the Health Department is charged with the duty "to enforce all provisions of law applicable in the area under its jurisdiction for the preservation of human life, for the care, promotion and protection of health and relative to the necessary sanitary supervision of the purity and wholesomeness of the water supply and the sources thereof."[5]

In carrying out these activities, the Health Department is required to operate and maintain in addition to a main office, other offices, health centers and health stations in each Borough of the City and designate an office in each Borough in which records of births, still births and deaths are to be maintained.[6] The Department of Health is made amenable to suit and, concomitantly, officers and agents of the Department are relieved of all personal liability for any acts they might do or omit to do in good faith on behalf of the Department, or pursuant to its regulations.[7] The Department is barred from the acceptance of private funds unless approved by the Commissioner and the Board of Health.[8]

The Commissioner of Health has all the powers and duties of the Health Department except those vested by law in the Board of Health.[9] He and his agents are authorized without fee or hindrance to enter, examine and inspect all vessels and premises and all underground passages of every sort in the City to determine whether the provisions of law enforced by the Department and its rules and regulations are being complied with.[10] Moreover, since December 1963, the Commissioner has been authorized, subject to Board of Estimate approval, to enter into affiliation contracts on behalf of the City.[11]

The Board of Health is composed of the Commissioner and four other members, at least two of whom
must be doctors of medicine with a minimum of ten
years' relevant experience.[12] The four members other
than the Commissioner are appointed by the Mayor for
eight-year terms without compensation and may be removed for cause, after an opportunity for a hearing.[13]
The primary duties of the Board of Health revolve about
the enactment and enforcement of a health code "for
the security of life and health in the City."[14] The
Board may include in the health code all matters and
subjects to which the broad power and authority of the
Health Department extends, without limiting the application of the code to the subject of health only. The
provisions of the health code have the force and effect
of State law within the City of New York. In re Bakers
Mut. Ins. Co. of New York, 301 N.Y. 21, 92 N.E. 2d 49
(1950).

Apart from its quasi-legislative power to enact
a health code for New York City, the Board of Health
is authorized to grant, suspend or revoke permits for
businesses or other matters in respect of any subject
regulated by the Department of Health;[15] and, in the
event of an epidemic, take possession of any building
in the City for use as a temporary hospital, paying
just compensation therefor.[16] In addition, with the
written consent of the Mayor, the Board of Health may
designate any hospital operated by the Department of
Hospitals as a hospital for the care and treatment of
communicable diseases and may, in its discretion,
direct the removal to any such hospital of any person
suffering from a communicable disease or any carrier
of a communicable disease.[17]

Finally, the Board of Health is authorized, with
the written approval of the Mayor, to declare an
emergency "in the presence of great and imminent peril
to the public health" of the City. After such a
"declaration", pursuant to Section 563 of the City
Charter and subject to the availability of funds in
the City budget, the Board of Health is empowered to
take all such measures and order the Health Department to perform all such acts, as it deems appropriate,
for the preservation of the public health of the City,
including the taking of possession and occupancy of
any building in the City as a hospital.

Hospital Department, Commissioner, Hospital Board

Under presently existing legislation Chapter 23 of the City Charter establishes the Department of Hospitals. It is generally charged with: (i) the operation and maintenance of all hospitals, sanitoria, almshouses or other institutions of the City for the care of sick, injured, aged or infirm persons; (ii) control of the City's ambulance service and any psycho- pathic service for the examination, observation and treatment of persons, except as otherwise provided by law; and (iii) any other service maintained by the City for the care of the sick or aged as may be as- signed to the Department or the Commissioner by law.[18]

In addition, the Hospitals Department has the duty to visit, inspect and license all private pro- prietary institutions where human beings receive medi- cal attention, nursing care or custodial supervision, including, with specifically stated exceptions, private proprietary hospitals, sanitoria, nursing home, con- valescent homes, homes for the aged or for chronic patients.[19]

The Department of Hospitals is headed by a Com- missioner of Hospitals[20] who possesses all the powers of the Hospitals Department except those vested in the Hospital Board.[21]

Chapter 23 also establishes the Board of Hospitals which is composed of the Commissioner of Hospitals who acts as Chairman and ten other members, five of whom must be medical doctors with broad experience and five of whom must be laymen distinguished in community or business affairs. The members of the Board of Hospitals serve five-year terms without compensation and must, pursuant to the Charter, meet at least once each month.[22]

The powers and duties of the Board of Hospitals[23] include the following: (i) developing and maintaining long-range programs of hospital service for the care of sick, injured, aged and infirm persons who are the responsibility of the Department; (ii) establishing and promoting the highest possible standards for care of sick, injured, aged and infirm persons to be com- plied with by all institutions under the jurisdiction of or subject to licensing by the Department of Hos- pitals and by institutions which care for any such

persons at the expense of the City; (iii) developing,
establishing and promoting standards and methods for
increasing the efficiency of operation, maintenance
and management of facilities for the care of sick,
injured, aged and infirm persons in institutions
"under the jurisdiction" of the Department;[24] (iv)
approving the capital and expense budget estimates
of the Department of Hospitals before submission
thereof to the appropriate City agencies; and (v)
reviewing, within its discretion, any action of the
Commissioner of Hospitals with respect to the revocation of a license.

In addition to the foregoing, the Board of Hospitals is authorized to enact and amend a hospital
code consisting of such rules and regulations, consistent with the City Charter and the constitution
and laws of the State of New York, as may be necessary
to carry out the powers and duties vested by law in
the Department of Hospitals and the Board of Hospitals.
Violations of the hospital code are made misdemeanors
punishable by fine or imprisonment. Similarly, failure
to observe any order of the Department of Hospitals or
Board of Hospitals may result in fine or imprisonment.[25]

Removal of members of the Board of Hospitals may
be obtained by procedures similar to those applicable
to the members of the Board of Health described above.[26]

In addition to the Department and Board of Hospitals, the City Charter provides for the establishment of an Advisory Council consisting of one representative from the medical board of each hospital or
other institution "under the jurisdiction" of the
Hospitals Department and seven members appointed by
the Mayor who may or may not be physicians.[27] The
members of the Advisory Council, serving without
compensation, advise the Commissioner of Hospitals in
respect of all matters submitted by him. In addition,
the Advisory Council may on its own initiative recommend to the Commissioner such changes of administration
in the Hospitals Department or in any hospital or institution or service "under the jurisdiction" of the
Hospitals Department as may seem to it advisable. In
carrying out its duties, the Advisory Council is given
access to all records and other documents of the
Department of Hospitals.[28]

Finally, Chapter 23 of the City Charter provides that there shall be a medical staff for each hospital or institution "under the jurisdiction" of the Hospitals Department and sets forth its composition, powers and duties.[29]

The medical staff of each hospital or institution organizes and appoints a medical board for such hospital or institution "under the jurisdiction" of the Hospital Department, which in turn in conjunction with the superintendent, proposes regulations to govern the medical procedure in said hospital or institution.[30] Medical staff appointments may be terminated at any time by the Hospital Commissioner after consultation with the relevant medical board and a vacancy may be filled by the Commissioner after like consultation.[31]

Section 585c of the City Charter provides that a physician who serves in a hospital without compensation shall nevertheless be authorized to charge medical fees for services rendered to patients under the provisions of the workmen's compensation law or to patients who carry sickness or accident insurance which covers physicians' fees or to patients who recover damages in tort. Section 587 states that the hospitals or other institutions "under the jurisdiction of the (D)epartment" shall be primarily for the care and treatment of the indigent poor of the City and for the protection of the public health, "but the (D)epartment may receive for care and treatment in any hospital or other institution other sick or injured persons and temporarily may receive therein persons alleged to be insane under regulations made by the Commissioner." A patient in a hospital or other institution "under the jurisdiction" of the Department who is able to pay, in whole or in part, for his care and maintenance shall be liable for and shall pay to the extent of his ability for such care and maintenance.[32] It would appear that, though indigent patients would have priority to space in a municipal hospital, the Charter provisions are already broad enough to permit treatment of non-indigent patients.

Finally, Section 588 of the City Charter provides that no grant, gift, devise, legacy or bequest and no work or research paid for from private sources shall be accepted or carried on by the Department except with the approval of the Hospital Commissioner.

Chief Medical Examiner

Chapter 39 of the City Charter establishes the Office of Chief Medical Examiner, the head of which is appointed by the Mayor from the classified civil service. The Office of the Chief Medical Examiner is charged with the duty to investigate suspicious deaths, keep records thereon, and report to the appropriate district attorney any indication of criminality, such records not being open to public inspection.

Community Mental Health Board

Chapter 43 of the City Charter provides for the City Community Mental Health Board which is composed of the Commissioner of Health, ex-officio, the Commissioner of Welfare, ex-officio, and seven (7) other members appointed by the Mayor. Of the appointive members, at least two (2) must be physicians actively engaged in private practice, the others being representatives of interested groups in the community. The term of each appointed member is four (4) years, though the Mayor has power to remove any appointed member for cause after giving a written statement of charges and affording him an opportunity to be heard.

Section 910 of the City Charter sets forth the powers and duties of the Mental Health Board which are keyed to the State Mental Hygiene Law to assure maximum reimbursement by the State. The Board appoints a psychiatrist to serve as Director of the Community Mental Health Service and to serve as chief executive officer of the Mental Health Board.

Since the State Mental Hygiene Law is to remain unchanged, the provisions for the Community Mental Health Board and the Director of Community Mental Health Services are unmodified in the legislative proposals now before the City Council.

Overhead Agencies

Examples of provisions of the City Charter which affect the health-oriented departments in much the same way as other departments include those setting forth the functions and responsibilities of the Comptroller, the Bureau of the Budget, and the Department of Purchase and Personnel.

Comptroller

Chapter 5 of the City Charter provides for the election of a Comptroller and sets forth his powers and duties which include "inspection and acceptance or rejection of all deliveries of supplies, materials and equipment."[33] The Comptroller issues warrants for payment of invoices only after this inspection is completed. In addition to the foregoing, the Comptroller is charged with auditing all vouchers before payment is made by the City and establishing a substantially uniform system of accounts for City agencies.

Department of Purchase

In order to ensure the ideal of central purchasing in the City and thus, purportedly, to obtain the advantages of lower costs, the Charter draftsman vested in the Commissioner of Purchase virtually all power to purchase and store supplies, materials and equipment. Section 782(a) provides:

> "The Commissioner shall, except as otherwise provided by law, have sole power to purchase, store and distribute all supplies, materials or equipment required by any department, office, board, body or commission of the city, or by any office of any county wholly included in the city for which supplies, materials or equipment are required, payment for which is made from the city treasury."

Section 342(b) confirms and supplements this authority in the following terms:

> "All . . . supplies, materials and equipment (other than those incident to a contract for work or labor done under Section 342(a)) shall be purchased or procured by the department of purchase, except as otherwise provided by law."

In spite of this general power, the Commissioner of Purchase may, in his discretion, authorize a City agency to make purchases of supplies, materials and

equipment directly up to an amount not to exceed
$2,500 per agency per calendar month, provided that
the Board of Estimate may by regulation fix a lesser
aggregate expenditure in any one calendar month or a
greater aggregate expenditure not in excess of $5,000
in any one calendar month.[34] The Board of Estimate
has in fact authorized this redelegation of purchasing
authority to a monthly departmental expenditure not
exceeding $5,000 ("in the case of very large agencies")
and an individual transaction limit of $25. More-
over, no City department may issue such purchases to
any one vendor in excess of $100 in a calendar month
or in excess of $2,500 in a calendar quarter.[35] Any
purchases beyond the monthly or quarterly limit even
for sums less than $25 must go through the regular
channel via the Department of Purchase.[36]

While a substantial proportion of all transactions
of the Department of Health are of a petty cash variety,
the petty cash authority described above is of limited
value to the Department of Hospitals which spends the
bulk of money in the Health Services Administration.

Pursuant to the Charter, virtually all purchases
must be by some form of competitive bidding, although
there are exceptions for emergency situations. Section 342(e) of the City Charter provides:

"In the event of an emergency requiring
an immediate purchase involving an expenditure of not more than $500, the
agency for whose use such supplies,
materials or equipment are necessary
may purchase them directly under rules
and regulations adopted by the Board
of Estimate."

In fact the Board of Estimate has promulgated emergency purchase regulations covering amounts greater
than $500 as well. The definition of an emergency
as stated in the Board of Estimate regulations is
extremely narrow: "a breakdown in service ...during
a period when the office of the Department of Purchase
is not open for business and it is vitally necessary
that materials, supplies or equipment be obtained
for immediate use in order to restore operation of
service."

The Board of Estimate rules for procurement in an emergency vary, as do the normal competitive bidding rules to be described below, as the total amounts of money involved increase. For example, for amounts up to $500, purchases may be made from the "most practicable source." For purchases involving amounts greater than $500 if the items needed can be construed as "of an emergency character that must be furnished to meet the therapeutic or surgical needs" of a patient, purchase may be made on the open market from the only available source of supply.37

As regards the usual bidding procedures established by the Charter, formal bidding based upon public advertisement is required for amounts in excess of $2,500; the public advertisement requirement is dispensed with for amounts in excess of $100 but less than $2,500,38 and the need for bidding is entirely dispensed with for amounts below $100.39

The Charter goes on to provide that the Board of Estimate may issue rules and regulations governing the exact procedures for competitive bidding, which authority was employed by the Board of Estimate in passing a detailed regulatory resolution in 1949.40 This regulation recognizes the need for speed in medical care and consequently provides for a shorter advertisement period for "medical, surgical, dental, laboratory, supplies and implements, and food supplies involving an expenditure in excess of $2,500." While purchases totaling between $100 and $2,500 need not be advertised, the Board of Estimate regulations require that whenever possible, contracts for such "open market" orders be offered to at least three vendors.41

Finally, in spite of the underlying aim of central purchasing to avoid corruption through requiring competitive bidding for most transactions, the Board of Estimate regulations recognize the possibility that some vendors may be superior to others regardless of equal pricing policies and permits a department to restrict bidding to a limited number of vendors by certifying particular brands as being superior.42

Bureau of the Budget

Chapter 6 of the City Charter sets forth the functions of the Bureau of the Budget, the head of which is appointed by the Mayor, along with the

procedures by which the line budget estimates are to
be approved and modified. Budget modifications between separate lines in the budget of a single agency
require the Mayor's approval, while modifications involving the shifting of funds between agencies require, in addition to the Mayor's favorable recommendation, approval by the Board of Estimate and the
City Council.43

Department of Personnel

Chapter 35 establishes the Department of Personnel
headed by a Personnel Director who serves as Chairman
of the City Civil Service Commission. This Chapter
sets forth some terms and conditions for appointment
of City personnel. Section 816 provides that no compensation may be paid to an unauthorized employee and
that all appointments, promotions and changes in status
of persons in the City government be made in accordance
with the Civil Service Law, the State Constitution and
the City Charter.

STATE LEGISLATION

State, like Federal, legislation tends to exert
a more subtle influence on health delivery in New York
City.

Many of the relevant provisions take the form of
conditioning grants of funds to the City upon satisfactory compliance with State procedures and standards.
For example, the recently enacted provisions relating
to Medical Assistance for Needy Persons (Medicaid)44
follow this pattern. These statutes set up the
machinery for establishing State standards and eligibility requirements which mesh with the intent of
Title 19 of Federal law. A pre-eminent role is given
thereunder to the State Department of Welfare as well
as the various local Departments of Welfare. Compliance with the standards prescribed by the State provisions is a prerequisite to receiving State reimbursement of expenditures.

Similarly, reimbursement of one-half the cost of
medical services rendered by the City to handicapped
children and certain victims of poliomyelitis and
tuberculosis is, under relevant provisions of New York
State law, made subject to compliance with procedures

and standards enacted by the State legislature.[45]   In addition to the foregoing, as already observed in the section dealing with the New York City Community Mental Health Board, State law exerts its influence on the City in this field by establishing the format and prescribing the essential organization of the City Community Mental Health Board.

Apart from these various State arrangements hinging on reimbursement, several areas of concurrent State and City interest are dealt with in the State statutes by delegating authority to the City Departments of Health and Hospitals and declaring compliance with the standards established by these Departments as a condition to compliance with State law. For example, the new provisions of State law dealing with operating certificates for hospitals[46] and permits for ambulance services within the City of New York[47] delegate authority to the City's Department of Hospitals and Health respectively as an integral part of the State scheme.

Other revised provisions of New York State law which affect the City picture became effective, with amendments, on February 1, 1966.[48] These provide for the creation of a State Hospital Review and Planning Council within the State Department of Health, composed of 31 persons appointed by the Governor. The Council's powers include adopting standards for the recognition of Regional Hospital Planning Councils. Failure of a Regional Council to meet such standards within a stipulated period of time would result in automatic withdrawal of recognition. The Hospital Review and Planning Council, in cooperation with the various Regional Councils, consider and advise on applications for the incorporation or establishment of new institutions in accordance with the Social Welfare Law[49] and all "construction" of hospitals in New York State. For this purpose, "construction" is broadly defined in Section 2801(3) of the Public Health Law to include among other more usual things: "substantial acquisition, alteration, reconstruction, improvement, extension or modification of a hospital, including its equipment." Before taking any action contrary to the advice of a Regional Council which might be substantially affected by such an application, the State Hospital Council is required to afford them an opportunity to request a public hearing where each such council and the applicant may be heard.[50]

Finally, as regards the operation of the City departments concerned with the delivery of health services, as mentioned above, the State civil service rules are applicable to such New York City departments.

FEDERAL LEGISLATION

As already indicated, the bulk of Federal legislation takes the form of conditional grants-in-aid. For example, Medicare legislation for the aged financed under social security and contained in Title 18 as well as the Federal legislation related to health assistance for the needy contained in Title 19 establish federal standards, compliance with which is a prerequisite to obtaining federal grants or reimbursement. The State legislative provisions regarding Medicaid described in the preceding Section is closely keyed to the procedures and standards established under Title 19. The State thus adopts the federal standards and then imposes them on the City of New York along with other welfare districts in the State. Some of these federal standards have posed particular problems in New York City. An example of this is the federal requirement under Title 19 that need be certified by the Department of Welfare if federal reimbursement is to be obtained.

Title 42 provides for grants to states to cover costs of medical care rendered in accordance with plans approved by the Secretary of Health, Education and Welfare for (i) the aged; (ii) certain mothers and children; (iii) crippled children and (iv) the permanently and totally disabled. Federal legislation also provides for reimbursement to States of the costs incurred in connection with certain research projects approved by the Secretary of Health, Education and Welfare.

Other Federal legislation of more peripheral significance to the delivery of health services in New York City exist and make available additional funds in the form of grants for (i) the training of teachers of handicapped children; (ii) research and demonstration projects in the education of handicapped children; (iii) immunization programs for children; (iv) migratory workers' health services, including hospital care; (v) health services to the chronically ill; (vi) "killer disease" research; and (vii) education of health professors and the staffing of community mental health centers.

Thus, as a general matter, the delivery of health services in New York City is indirectly influenced by the requirements of Federal law, much as observed in connection with the summary of State provisions-- through the mechanism of conditional grants.

May 9, 1967   Peter W. Eccles

NOTES TO APPENDIX D

1. Proposed amendments to the New York City Charter are currently under consideration by the City Council. The amendments in the health field provide for the consolidation of the great bulk of the health-related activities of the municipal government (apart from environmental health matters) into a single Health Services Administration headed by a Health Services Administrator.

2. City Charter, Par. 551.

3. City Charter, Par. 556a.

4. City Charter, Par. 556b.

5. City Charter, Par. 557.

6. City Charter, Par. 557.

7. City Charter, Par. 564, 565.

8. City Charter, Par. 568.

9. City Charter, Par. 555.

10. City Charter, Par. 566.

11. City Charter, Par. 556d.

12. City Charter, Par. 553.

13. City Charter, Par. 554.

14. City Charter, Par. 558.

15. City Charter, Par. 561.

16.   City Charter, Par. 560b.

17.   City Charter, Par. 560a.

18.   City Charter, Par. 583-a-1.

19.   City Charter, Par. 583-a-2.

20.   City Charter, Par. 581.

21.   City Charter, Par. 583.

22.   City Charter, Par. 582-a.

23.   These are set forth in the City Charter, Par. 583-b.

24.   The words "under the jurisdiction of the (Hospitals) (D)epartment" occur in several places in the statute, sometimes contrasting it with institutions "subject to licensing by the (D)epartment." Section 583-a titled "Jurisdiction of (D)epartment" actually embraces both the institutions which the Department must maintain and operate and those it merely visits, inspects and licenses. Despite this, it appears that when the statute refers to institutions "under the jurisdiction" of the Department, it means the former, not including the latter.

25.   City Charter, Par. 583-d; 583-a.

26.   City Charter, Par. 583-c.

27.   City Charter, Par. 584.

28.   Ibid.

29.   City Charter, Par. 585.

30.   City Charter, Par. 585e.

31.   City Charter, Par. 585b.

32.   City Charter, Par. 587-b.

33.   City Charter, Par. 346.

34.   City Charter, Par. 342c.

35. Cal. No. 318-A, Par. 8, June 30, 1949, as amended Dec. 3, 1964.

36. Ibid. at Par. 8(b)

37. Cal. No. 318-A, Par. 12(g) and Par. 10(d).

38. City Charter, Par. 344.

39. City Charter, Par. 344(a).

40. Cal. No. 318-A.

41. Cal. No. 318-A, Par. 7.

42. Cal. No. 318-A, Par. 12.

43. City Charter, Par. 124.

44. Sections 363-369, McKinney's Social Welfare Law.

45. See, e.g., Section 600, McKinney's Public Health Law.

46. Section 2805, McKinney's Public Health Law.

47. Section 3002, McKinney's Public Health Law.

48. Section 2904, McKinney's Public Health Law.

49. Par. 35, Par. 35a, McKinney's Social Welfare Law.

50. Section 2904, McKinney's Public Health Law.

APPENDIX E

Report of the Subcommittee on Affiliation Contracts
of the Medical Advisory Committee to the
Commission on the Delivery of Personal Health Services

(Reproduced verbatim as provided to the Commission.)

The following recommendations are based on a
series of discussions held by the members of the
Subcommittee. They are based solely on both personal
knowledge of the affiliation programs and the experience of individual members of the Subcommittee with
one or more specific affiliated municipal hospitals.
Attempts were not made to secure detailed fiscal or
statistical data or to make field studies.

The City's affiliation contracts with voluntary
teaching hospitals for the professional staffing of
municipal hospitals were recommended five years ago
by a study commission appointed by Mayor Wagner and
the recommendation was subsequently carried out by
Commissioner Ray Trussell during the Mayor's administration. In almost all instances, the affiliations
have been successful in raising the professional
standards of the City's hospitals through the employment of competent full-time and part-time professional
personnel operating under the supervision of chairmen
of the various clinical and laboratory divisions of
teaching hospitals. Those municipal hospitals which
were affiliated with strong voluntary institutions
have become teaching hospitals and, as a result, have
been able to recruit increasing numbers of interns by
the intern-matching plan and have significantly increased the number and quality of residents in residencies approved by the American Medical Association.

Although firm criteria for assessing improvement
in the effectiveness of health care as a result of
the affiliations are lacking, it is appreciated that
a modest increase in the size or quality of professional training of the professional staff of a hospital

663

service does not in itself insure improved services. However, as happened at Lincoln Hospital between 1958 and 1967, when the staffing of a pediatric service containing eighty in-patient beds and a very large ambulatory service is increased from a house staff of two foreign-trained interns and three part-time attendings to a house staff of twenty-five interns and residents including ten graduates of American schools, a full-time staff of ten university faculty members and an additional staff of twenty-five attendings and consultant pediatricians, there can be little question concerning the improvement in medical care. Striking improvement in staffing at all professional levels also followed the affiliation of Morrisania Hospital in 1962, Greenpoint Hospital in 1962, at City Hospital at Elmhurst in 1964, and at Harlem.

Although the quality of in-hospital patient care depends largely upon the quality and adequacy of the house staff and the time devoted to their supervisory duties by a well-qualified attending staff, it also depends upon the availability of up-to-date clinical, laboratory, and x-ray equipment and upon an adequate staff of nurses and ancillary personnel. In many of the City hospitals replacement of obsolete equipment has been long delayed by red tape and, when acquired, delays in installation have been frustrating. Nurse manpower is still in grave short supply. As a result, the full benefits of the affiliations have not as yet been achieved.

In a few instances, affiliation contracts were made with weak voluntary hospitals because the number of strong voluntary hospitals with superior standards and full-time professional leadership has been exhausted. In such instances, the benefits of affiliation have been less than satisfactory. These should be critically reexamined.

The funds available under the contracts may have materially benefited the small voluntary hospitals professionally and this has tended to improve the care of city-pay patients hospitalized in the parent institution, although this was not the primary purpose of the affiliation. The strong voluntary hospitals have benefited less in this way, although the affiliations have provided them with additional opportunities for good clinical teaching of medical

students, residents, attending staff, and neighborhood physicians, as well as additional full-time'
clinical and laboratory professions required for
this purpose.

Your advisory subcommittee recognizes that the
crisis faced by the City's Department of Hospitals
five or six years ago required that it give priority
to the affiliations consummated since that time. As
a result, the older medical school hospital affili-
ations--Bellevue, Bronx Municipal Center, Kings
County, and perhaps Metropolitan--have been neglected.
They now deserve the same assistance provided hereto-
fore to the previously unaffiliated City hospitals.

s/   s/
George Baehr, M.D.   Henry L. Barnett, M.D.

s/
E. Hugh Luckey, M.D.   April 25, 1967

ADDENDUM

In addition to the formal report the Subcommittee
has considered some of the matters which appear to have
limited the services of the affiliation program. The
following addendum sets down some of our considerations
which may be of interest to the Commission.

Your advisory subcommittee is convinced that the
prevailing red tape is due to centralization in a
variety of separate City departments of virtually all
authority for structural alteration of facilities,
plant maintenance, purchasing and installation of
essential equipment, and control by the budget director
over the filling of all line personnel positions. The
situation calls most urgently for decentralization of
administrative responsibility, at least among the larger
municipal centers such as Bellevue, Kings County, Bronx
Municipal, Presbyterian-Harlem, Mount Sinai-Elmhurst,
Brooklyn-Cumberland, and Maimonides-Coney Island. In
all large hospital centers, the present line budget
should be replaced by an annual performance budget,
which is the operational pattern in all voluntary hospitals of the Veterans Administration, the U.S. Public
Health Service, the State Health Department, and the
State Department of Mental Hygiene. Control over the
use of the annual budgeting appropriations of such

institutions can be efficiently exercised by adequate central department surveillance and cost accounting.

The recent enactment of federal, state, and local legislation concerned with payment for the medical care of the indigent and medically indigent makes possible the consideration of the progressive transformation of all City hospitals from charity institutions to community hospitals serving all economic levels of the population. Each such community hospital would be governed by a Board of Directors. They would differ from the voluntary hospitals only in that they would not provide luxury accommodations.

All licensed physicians who do not hold appointments in voluntary hospitals could be invited to become staff members of an affiliated community hospital in their borough, provided they agree to the following requirements:

1. Restrict their practice within the limitation of their training and experience as recorded in the directory of the State Medical Society and the regulations of the Departments of Health and Hospitals.

2. Abide by the regulations of the hospital's medical board and accept supervision of their professional conduct and in-hospital practice by the chairman of their respective clinical department or his designated representative.

3. Attend at least 50 per cent of the teaching rounds, the clinical pathological conferences, and other educational exercises of their department.

4. In recognition of the fact that in-hospital practice differs from solo practice in that it involves the collaboration of many other staff physicians and hospital services, pool all in-patient income from private patients with all other professional income of the medical staff of their respective department (except official salaries) and accept in return an adequate monthly payment from their department based on rank, hours of attendance, and other regulations of the medical board.

Your advisory subcommittee recommends that for purposes of gaining experience with the above suggestion the operation and general administration of one or more affiliated City hospitals be transferred wholly to the parent voluntary hospital under a long-term contract whereby it will receive all income from patients and third-party payers and, with this income, operate the affiliated City hospital as it does its own. Third-party payments are now based upon cost reimbursement plus an allowance for depreciation. Out of the cost reimbursement formula and the depreciation allowance the parent hospital should be able to assume the cost of future structural alterations of the existing facility and equipment and all personnel salaries.

The advantage to the City would be:

1. Elimination from the operating budget of the Hospital Department of financial responsibility for the operation and maintenance of the hospital;

2. Elimination from the capital outlay budget of the Hospital Department of most of the future responsibility for maintenance and physical alterations of existing buildings and for new equipment. The cost of construction for new buildings required by the City's increasing needs should continue to be included in the City's capital budget if recommended by the Department of Hospitals and approved by the Council on Health and Hospitals.

3. Although the City would assign all income for patient care under Medicaid, Medicare, and other private or governmental programs to the affiliated hospital, most of this income will come hereafter from the Federal and State governments, and much of the remainder from Social Security, insurance carriers, and supplementary payments by patients for deductible and coinsurance.

The advantage to the voluntary hospitals would be:

1. Freedom to administer the affiliated City hospital without red tape;

2. The cost reimbursement formula plus the allowance for depreciation should enable it to operate the City institution without a deficit while maintaining a high standard of patient care.

To safeguard the public, it is essential that such a contract include the following requirements:

1. All patients needing hospital care shall be admitted within the limitations of the combined

capacity of the voluntary and its affiliated community hospital.

2. There shall be no dumping of unwanted patients from one hospital to the other.

3. The professional quality of the medical and ancillary staffs of two hospitals shall be identical.

4. Within two years, the voluntary hospital and its affiliate shall acquire and operate a long-term care facility and provide medical services to one or more nursing homes.

5. The voluntary hospital and its affiliate shall operate an ambulatory care service and shall also agree to provide prepaid comprehensive health services for persons and families who choose to enroll for prepaid continuing comprehensive services in preference to fee-for-service episodic care in the conventional pattern of hospital out-patient departments.

s/
George Baehr, M.D.

s/
Henry L. Barnett, M.D.

April 25, 1967

s/
E. Hugh Luckey, M.D.

APPENDIX F

Report of the Subcommittee on Integration of Private
Practitioners of the Medical Advisory Committee to
the Commission on the Delivery of Personal Health
Services

(Reproduced verbatim as provided to the Commission.)

Gentlemen:

In your charge to our subcommittee, you asked
us "to help the Commission develop a program that
will increase the interest and cooperation of the private practitioner in the evolving health system in
the City" . . . and to "make any suggestions as to
how these private practitioners, many of whom have no
hospital associations, can be integrated into these
facilities." One member of our Committee, Dr. C.
Joseph Delaney, is president of the New York County
Medical Society, and because of his long involvement
in that society's affairs, has considerable famil-
iarity with the problems of delivery of health care
from the point of view of the practicing physician.
Another, Dr. Louis M. Hellman, as professor and
chairman of the Department of Obstetrics and Gynecology, State University, Downstate Medical Center,
has had long experience and special interest in the
problems of providing obstetrical care to the population served by Kings County Hospital. The third,
Dr. Edwin P. Maynard, Jr. has been intimately involved
in staffing the Brooklyn-Cumberland Medical Center,
a project that has included the integration of general
practitioners who were members of the staff of the
Cumberland Hospital before the affiliation into the
out-patient department of the combined institution.

In the charge to our subcommittee, mention is
made of private practitioners as distinguished from
those in full-time salaried positions. A majority

669

of these private practitioners are board-certified
or board-eligible specialists, who are on the staffs
of our voluntary and municipal hospitals. A large
number of these already serve in our new municipal-
voluntary hospital affiliations. Your Committee feels
that these specialists present no unusual problem and
can and are being recruited in the normal manner.

The real problem concerns the general practitioner
who at present is ineligible, in most instances, for
appointment to the staffs of voluntary and municipal
hospitals. These institutions, in order to retain
approval for their intern and residency training programs require that physicians on their staffs be
board-eligible or board-certified specialists. As a
result, general practitioners, with rare exceptions,
have been excluded from these institutions.

In order to find out approximately how many
general practitioners there are in the City of New
York, your Committee contacted the directors of five
county medical societies and, where necessary, the
presidents of the county subdivisions of the American
Academy of General Practice. The following table
presents the findings, which are an approximation,
especially in the case of those physicians who are
neither members of their county societies, nor of the
American Academy of General Practice.

	MEMBERS OF COUNTY SOCIETY	NOT MEMBERS OF COUNTY SOCIETY
Bronx	400	200
Kings	700	500
New York	450	1,057
Queens	300	400
Staten Island	130	
Totals	1,980	2,157
Grand Total	4,137	

The approximate total manpower pool we are considering, therefore, is 4,137. Because a high percentage of these men are in the older age group and
because very few young men are entering general
practice, this pool gradually will disappear. The
problem of training and motivating medical students
to practice family medicine is a tremendous one
concerning medical educators throughout this country
and abroad.

Because it is necessary to utilize as many
physicians as possible to meet the manpower shortage,
the Committee next addressed itself to the problem of
how to get the general practitioners connected in
some way with the municipal-voluntary hospital affiliations. The members were unanimous in agreeing that
this should not be attempted by any method involving
compulsion. At this point, Dr. Torrens' experience
at St. Luke's Hospital proved very enlightening. It
becomes apparent that there is a significant number
of general practitioners who are perfectly satisfied
with solo office and home practice and who have no
desire to become attached to the hospital in their
neighborhood other than to use it as a place to send
their patients requiring in-hospital care. These,
we cannot expect to influence very much. There are
others, nevertheless, who are or can be motivated to
establish connections with teaching hospitals.

The members of your Committee are convinced that
for the foreseeable future there always will be a
need for physicians practicing in neighborhoods,
either singly or preferably in groups, who will be in
the front line of attack in bringing health care, including the prevention of disease, to all the people.
One of the best ways to keep these men abreast of the
advances in medicine, your Committee feels, is to
expose them to the environment of teaching hospitals.
How to do this for general practitioners is the
problem. The Commission on Medical Education of the
A.M.A. is already studying this matter.

From the opinions expressed and the experience
gained so far, it appears that much more needs to be
learned. The members of the Committee are of the
opinion that the municipal-voluntary hospital affiliations that are willing and qualified to do so should
set up pilot projects designed to discover the best
means to accomplish these ends. These studies will
be expensive and must be adequately financed.

The methods used and the experience gained at
St. Luke's Hospital may be cited as examples. The
first step at that institution was to establish a
department of community medicine with Dr. Paul Torrens
as director. One of the major functions of that
department is to bring as many of the general practitioners as possible in the area served by St. Luke's
into a closer relationship with the hospital. To this

end, Dr. Torrens recruited a full-time physician and a secretary to implement the program.

The second step was to find the names and addresses of those physicians who had been referring their patients to St. Luke's. These men were contacted by letter and called upon by the physician-in-charge, a procedure indicating that the hospital was interested and anxious to do a better job for the physicians and their patients.

Good referral forms were devised. They provide space in which the physician can enter important data about his patient and in which the house officer at St. Luke's can return a summary of the patient's course in the hospital, the treatments carried out, important laboratory and x-ray data, the final diagnosis and recommendations as to future treatment. This step has been very successful and has been received so well by the physicians that many more doctors in the area are referring patients for admission to the hospital. The Office of Community Medicine has become the point of contact in handling referrals and all inquiries from neighborhood physicians about their hospital patients.

The next step in integrating physicians in the area was to develop a diagnostic clinic for ambulatory patients in the out-patient department. Consultations in all the required specialties are available here. At the end of the study, the physician receives a complete report with recommendations. It is important to stress that all patients, whether treated in the hospital or in the diagnostic clinic, are returned to the family physician for his care. Because laboratory tests, especially the unusual ones, are so expensive, the laboratory facilities of St. Luke's have been made available to these physicians and their patients at moderate costs.

Next comes the problem of continuing education of the general practitioner who has no hospital connections. It is safe to say that up to the present no one knows the best way to accomplish this, in spite of the fact that educators have been and are studying the problem in depth. One of the major difficulties arises from the fact that the medical training of many of these men is seriously deficient in modern methods of diagnosis and treatment.

The simplest and most obvious remedy is to give lecture courses, but unless credits of some sort are obtained, the attendance is usually poor. When St. Luke's Hospital announced that its course had been approved by the American Academy of General Practice for credit and by Dr. James G. Haughton, first deputy health services administrator of New York City, as a qualifying course in the treatment of Medicaid patients, there were 200 applicants. It was soon discovered that the content of the lectures had to be simplified, because the physicians wanted them presented at a practical and useful level and because their background was lacking in the appreciation of modern medical concepts. The inadequacy of their basic medical training and the long interval between their schooling and the present results in a formidable problem in re-education, the solution for which has not been found.

Because it is recognized that direct involvement with patients is one of the best methods of teaching, St. Luke's has invited a small number of physicians to attend specialty clinics in the out-patient department. Here the student, either alone or with two or three colleagues, observes the workup and treatment of patients at first hand by a specialist. Only the most promising and most highly motivated men are admitted to this course, and the results so far have been encouraging.

All these methods -- lecture courses, referral diagnostic clinics and work directly with patients under specialist supervisors -- must be evaluated in some manner before final conclusions can be drawn. How much does the physician remember one month after the course and six months later? Even more important, how much of what he has learned does he apply to the care of his patients?

The next and probably the most difficult problem is how to provide for the admission of general practitioners to the staffs of the municipal-voluntary hospital affiliations. These institutions and the City of New York are legally liable for the performance of the members of their staffs. No one, therefore, can be permitted to carry out treatments or procedures for which he is not properly qualified. At present, all the municipal-voluntary hospital affiliations require special board eligibility or certification for admission to their staffs, thus

automatically excluding general practitioners. The
medical schools, therefore, cannot use these physicians at present in the teaching of undergraduate
students, interns or residents. Yet, it seems clear
that some sort of reward be given to those general
practitioners who do well in their re-education
program.

One way out of this dilemma might be for the
hospitals to provide a category of staff membership
that would permit these physicians to practice in the
hospital out-patient departments under the supervision
of qualified specialists. This plan would be similar
to the program in use for interns, residents and
fellows. After a time, if this proves successful, a
more formal division of family practice -- where the
skills of the best qualified general practitioners
might be put to use -- could be created.

Summary

1. There are approximately 4,137 general
practitioners in the City of New York; 1,980 of these
are members of their respective county medical societies and fellows of the American Academy of General
Practice; 2,157 are not members of either of these
organizations. A sizable percentage of the total
have no desire to become attached to a hospital in
their neighborhood.

2. Your Committee believes that for the for-
seeable future, there will be a need for physicians
to practice in neighborhoods in order to bring modern
health services to the people and to link our hospital
centers to the communities.

3. The municipal-voluntary hospital affiliations
that are willing and qualified to do so should set up
pilot projects designed to integrate properly qualified
general practitioners with the hospitals' professional
staffs. Some of the steps necessary are as follows:

Professional Services:

a) Set up a department of community medicine
with a budget adequate to support a full-time staff
of one physician, or other qualified personnel, a
secretary and an office.

b)   Establish good rapport with the general
practitioners in the area by personal contact and by
rendering good service to the patients they refer to
the hospital.

c)   Offer a diagnostic clinic designed especially
to take care of patients re-referred by the area
physicians.

d)   Offer a laboratory service with charges set
at moderate levels.

Continuing Education:

a)   Arrange lecture courses fulfilling the requirements of the American Academy of General Practice
for Fellowship and of the Health Services Administration for qualification to treat Medicaid patients.

b)   Furnish opportunities for the best qualified
to observe the work of specialists in the out-patient
clinics, either alone or in a small group.

c)   Devise methods of evaluating the results of
the educational program as to how much is retained
and how much is applied in actual patient care.

Hospital Staff Privileges:

Devise methods by which hospitals can legally
and properly admit general practitioners to their
staffs with permission to care for patients within
their areas of competence and under adequate professional supervision.

Respectfully submitted,

s/_____   s/_____
C. Joseph Delaney, M.D.   Louis M. Hellman, M.D.

s/_____
Edwin P. Maynard, Jr., M.D.   July 12, 1967
Chairman